C0-AUT-859

Man-Made Fibers

Science and Technology

POLYMER ENGINEERING AND TECHNOLOGY

Executive Editor: D. V. Rosato

Editors: R. B. Akin, H. F. Mark, J. J. Scavuzzo, S. S. Stivala, L. J. Zukor

---

SYNTHETIC FIBERS IN PAPERMAKING

Edited by O. A. Battista

FILAMENT WINDING: Its Development, Manufacture, Applications, and Design

D. V. Rosato and C. S. Grove, Jr.

REINFORCEMENT OF ELASTOMERS

Edited by Gerard Kraus

ENVIRONMENTAL EFFECTS ON POLYMERIC MATERIALS (2 volumes)

Edited by D. V. Rosato and R. T. Schwartz

FUNDAMENTAL ASPECTS OF FIBER REINFORCED PLASTIC COMPOSITES

Edited by R. T. Schwartz and H. S. Schwartz

MAN-MADE FIBERS: Science and Technology (3 volumes)

Edited by H. F. Mark, E. Cernia, and S. M. Atlas

THE SCIENCE AND TECHNOLOGY OF POLYMER FILMS (2 volumes)

Edited by Orville J. Sweeting

PLASTICS FOR ELECTRICAL INSULATION

Edited by Paul F. Bruins

EPOXY RESIN TECHNOLOGY

Edited by Paul F. Bruins

ADDITIONAL VOLUMES IN PREPARATION

Man-Made Fibers

Science and Technology

VOLUME 2

Edited by

H. F. Mark
Polytechnic Institute of Brooklyn, New York

S. M. Atlas
Bronx Community College of The City University of New York, New York

E. Cernia
ABCD, Rome, Italy

Interscience Publishers

a division of John Wiley & Sons

New York • London • Sydney

Library of Congress Catalog Card Number: 67-13954

Printed in the United States of America

Foreword

In 1953 there appeared in Elsevier's Polymer Series a volume on *Fibers from Synthetic Polymers,* which was edited by Dr. Rowland Hill of ICI and which contained chapters written by the most prominent experts in the field.

When 13 years later—in 1966—the Editors of the Interscience High Polymer Series felt that a new book on the same subject matter would be timely and justifiable, they approached, as a matter of course, Dr. Hill and asked him whether he had planned a new edition of his classic book. Dr. Hill indicated that he did not plan to issue another edition of his book and, it was therefore decided that a new treatise on *Man-Made Fibers: Science and Technology* should be prepared incorporating the substantial progress in science and technology since the appearance of Rowland Hill's classical work. Some of these developments have been covered in other books.

One is the book of R. Meredith and J. W. S. Hearle on *Physical Methods of Investigating Textiles* which was published by Interscience Publishers, Inc. in 1959. It gives an excellent review of virtually all techniques which are used in studying and testing fibers and fabrics. Although many properties of specific fibers are described in this monograph it does not intend to present the entire field of man-made fibers in a complete and comprehensive manner.

Another important book is that of R. W. Moncrieff—published in England in 1963. It gives a brief and lucid exposition of the principles of fiber formation and then enumerates and describes in considerable detail practically all commercial fibers which existed at that time. The emphasis is on technology, individual operations, and economic aspects. Moncrieff's book is a very complete and dependable source of information on man-made fibers.

In view of Hill's original treatise and Moncrieff's book, the planning for the present volume followed the following considerations:

1. The synthesis of fiber-forming polymers was, as such, eliminated because since 1953 several comprehensive treatises on the synthesis of polymers have appeared which give such complete and authoritative presentations that any duplication would have been a waste of time and effort. Whenever new methods of synthesis and production are involved in certain special cases, they are included in the appropriate chapters or in the appendices to these chapters.

2. It was felt that cellulosic fibers should be included because of their close relation to natural fibers and because of the spectacular progress made in this field during the last 15 years.

3. In 1953 most knowledgable experts in the field of synthetic fibers worked in England, the United States, and Western Europe. Today, important work in the science and technology of man-made fibers is carried out all over the world and it was, therefore, decided to engage expert authors of all countries in which substantial efforts in this field are being made. Although a world-wide team of contributors increases the complexity and responsibility of the editors' activities, it was felt that these difficulties would have to be shouldered in order to give the new volume the necessary international competence and flavor.

4. In view of the different aspects of authors working in such different environments as the U.S.S.R., Japan, Eastern Europe, Western Europe, and the United States, the editors felt that it would be desirable to add to certain chapters an appendix of essentially editorial character, which would—if necessary—bring up to date the literature references, explain overlapping between different chapters, and fill in special data and recent information.

S. M. Atlas
E. Cernia
H. Mark

May, 1967

Authors of Volume 2

D. G. H. Ballard
Petrochemical and Polymer Laboratory, Imperial Chemical Industries, Ltd., Cheshire, England

W. B. Black
Chemstrand Research Center, Inc., Durham, North Carolina

H. Peter von Bucher
Chemtex Inc., New York

J. Chambion
Rhodiaceta, Lyon, France

John L. Hathaway
Beaunit Fibers, Beaunit Corp., Elizabethton, Tennessee

H. Hopff
Department of Industrial and Engineering Chemistry, Swiss Federal Institute of Technology, Zurich, Switzerland

Yu. A. Kostrov
Textile Institute, Moscow, U.S.S.R.

H. Krässig
Director, Research and Development, Chemiefaser Lenzing AG, Lenzing, Austria

K. C. Laughlin
Department of Consumer Sciences, University of California, Davis, California

W. J. McGarry
Courtaulds Ltd., Coventry, England

J. Preston
Chemstrand Research Center, Inc., Durham, North Carolina

M. H. Priest
Courtaulds Ltd., Coventry, England

Z. A. Rogovin
Textile Institute, Moscow, U.S.S.R.

Walter Sbrolli
Bombrini Parodi-Delfino, Rome, Italy

Contents—VOLUME 2

Contents—VOLUME 1

Contents—VOLUME 3

Cellulosic Fibers Made from Cuprammonium

John L. Hathaway
Beaunit Fibers, Beaunit Corporation, Elizabethton, Tennessee

CONTENTS

I. HISTORY OF CUPRAMMONIUM

Known commercially since the turn of the century, the cuprammonium process still provides rayon yarn for the textile markets in which such qualities as smoothness, luster, and novelty are important to consumers.

Bemberg is the trade name for cuprammonium rayon yarn in the United States, and all current production is in the hands of Beaunit Fibers, Division of Beaunit Corporation, at Elizabethton, Tennessee.

The cuprammonium process was introduced to the textile trade at the end of the nineteenth century by M. Fremery and J. Urban of the German firm, Glanzstoff-Fabriken. Filaments were made by forcing spinning solutions through fine-holed spinnerets into a caustic soda coagulating bath. Subsequently, the yarn was acidified, washed, and dried. A high-luster product (Glanzstoff) resulted. Several years later, Glanzstoff-Fabriken abandoned the process in favor of the viscose method.

In 1919, the cuprammonium process was revived in a modified form by Dr. Edmund Thiele. He replaced the coagulation in caustic soda by a mild coagulation in water. Simultaneous stretching of the newly formed thread was also achieved as it passed through the spinning funnel. That same year, the revived spinning method, called the cuprammonium stretch-spinning process, was started on a commercial scale by the J. P. Bemberg Company. Guided by the company's Dr. Elsaesser, it was expanded in a few years to large-scale production. In 1926, other cuprammonium plants emerged. An additional one was erected in Germany by

I. G. Farbenindustrie, and single plants were constructed in the United States, England, Italy, and Japan.

American Bemberg Company began production in the United States in 1926 at Elizabethton, Tennessee. Beaunit Corporation acquired the Elizabethton plant in 1948 and has been making Bemberg there since that time.

II. SKEIN SPINNING PROCESS

Raw material for the cuprammonium process can be either purified cotton linters or purified wood pulp of high α-cellulose content. Linters produce a whiter yarn than pulp, but they also cost more. In the early years, cotton linters were used exclusively; in recent times, wood pulp containing at least 95% α-cellulose has proved to be very satisfactory because of its high reactivity with cuprammonium solvent.

Spinning solutions are prepared by mixing moist disintegrated linters or wood pulp with a slurry of basic copper sulfate and ammonia at low temperature. Subsequent addition of caustic soda and stabilizing agents complete formation of the ammoniacal copper solution (solubility of cellulose in ammoniacal copper solution or "Schweitzer's Reagent" was discovered in the mid-nineteenth century). Ratio of solvents to cellulose is maintained within given limits, as is the cellulose content of the spinning solution. Impurities are removed by filtration through several sets of filter presses containing fine-mesh nickel screen. The solution is then deaerated for 8 to 16 hr at about a 24-in. vacuum, and can be stored for weeks or months prior to spinning if kept at low temperatures.

The spinning process consists of pumping a metered amount of solution through large-holed spinnerets into conically shaped spinning funnels filled with water. Water flows concurrently, with the solution extracting most of the ammonia and about a third of the copper. This extraction causes a mild coagulation of the extruded solution into the form of filaments. Water flow in the funnel and a pulling action from the take-off reel cause stretching of these newly formed filaments in the funnel.

The extent of this stretching can be visualized by comparing the diameter and cross-sectional area of the spinneret holes with that of the filaments. The diameter ratio is 1:72, and the area ratio is 1:5184.

The individual filaments converge at the apex of the funnel, and after they leave it they are separated from the aqueous extractant by a bending action around stainless steel rods. Dilute sulfuric acid next completes hardening of the threads by converting the remaining ammonia and copper salts to their respective sulfates. The yarn is then collected on reels in skein form.

After completion of the spinning cycle, the length of which depends on yarn denier, reels are taken out of the spinning machines and skeins are laced with lacing strips to prevent entanglement in subsequent washing and drying operations. Lacing strips are dyed in various colors to identify yarn denier.

A first washing next removes copper and ammonium sulfates and excess acid, and provides softening of the yarn with suitable lubricants prior to drying. Drying is achieved by passing skeins on wooden sticks through chain dryers. A second washing takes place in a soap and oil emulsion or in a soaking bath which can contain tints for identification purposes. The yarn is then dried a second time.

III. CONTINUOUS SPINNING PROCESS

After a few days' conditioning at controlled humidity, skein-spun yarn is ready for shipment or converting. Some of it is sold as untwisted skein; the remainder is converted to cones, beams, or tubes, in the twisted or untwisted state. Unlike viscose, Bemberg continuous-spun rayon yarn can be used in the untwisted state for certain purposes. The filaments in Bemberg are not separated as in viscose yarn. They become separated only if subjected to relatively high friction.

In 1944, a continuous process was introduced. It is described in U. S. Patent 2,587,619, issued to Dr. Hugo Hofmann. Since that time, production by the continuous system has gradually replaced that by the batch process. The majority of Bemberg rayon today is made continuously.

The continuous system comprises 120 spinning funnels and two thread layers of 60 threads each running side by side. As filaments exit from the funnels, they enter a pretreatment pan (closed system) containing hot dilute sulfuric acid. In this acid bath, the threads contract to one-third their original size. Unaligned cellulose adhering to the outside of the filaments is removed by outflow from the pan. From the pretreatment pan, thread passes through another acid bath for further removal of copper, and then is washed in a water trough. Next, the thread goes over a preparation roll for application of lubricants or sizing. The yarn is then dried, treated with coning oil, and wound on flangeless spools. Manufacturing time from spinneret to spool is about 18 sec.

Since the continuous process requires no handling of the yarn until it is taken from the spools, imperfections are reduced to a minimum. Continuous-process yarn costs less than batch yarn, and has better physical properties for certain end uses. It shows excellent running qualities in textile converting, weaving, and knitting.

TABLE I. Physical Properties of Bemberg Novelty Yarns

Yarn type[a]	Denier	Twist	Slub description
Cupioni	70, 100, 150, 285, 450, 600, 900, 940	$2^1/_2$, $3^1/_2$, 7	Slubs are entangled and have different dimensions to imitate Douppioni Silk
Multi-Cupioni	100, 200	$2^1/_2$, $3^1/_2$, 10	Cupioni-type slubs, but more frequent than those contained in Cupioni yarn
Dull Cupioni	150, 285	$2^1/_2$	Cupioni-type slubs in dull luster
Ondelette	150, 285, 450	$2^1/_2$, 5	Slubs have a flakelike shape
Nublite	200, 315, 410, 860	$2^1/_2$, 5, 10	Short, entangled slubs; irregular size and frequency
Dream Slub	2500, 5200	$1^1/_2$, $2^1/_2$	Large slubs (7.5, 15.5 in. long) spaced 17–18 in. apart
Strata	275, 450	$2^1/_2$, $3^1/_2$	Large torpedo-shaped slubs (4.8–6.4 in. long) very widely spaced (210–387 in.); slub length and spacing vary with denier
Stratella	100, 150, 450	$2^1/_2$, $8^1/_2$, 12	Slubs are similar to but more frequent than those in Strata; they are smaller in length and size
Cuprel	265–2625		A textured yarn usually produced with one or two ends of natural or skein-dyed Bemberg, or combinations thereof. The ends are usually selected from the above listed novelty yarns.

[a] All of the yarn names are registered trademarks of Beaunit Corporation.

Bemberg yarn has been spun in a wide denier range, but weavers and knitters use mostly 50, 65, 75, and 100 deniers.

The Farbenfabriken Bayer produce in the Dormagen plant a Cuoxam rayon under the name of Cupresal. They use the "Continue Process" (cf. *Ullmanns Encyclopedia*, 3rd ed., Vol. 11, page 270) in which 230 double spinning funnels are arranged in seven rows in such a manner that a strand of 460 parallel threads is formed which are led through the various baths at a distance of 4 mm. The time from the emergence of the filament from the spinneret to the windup is about 50 sec.

The normal deniers range from 40 to 300 and the quality from bright to dull; the product is characterized by a very high degree of uniformity, soft hand, and pleasant drape.

IV. UTILIZATION AND CONSUMER EVALUATION

Meeting the demand of the textile market for novelty products, American Bemberg developed a series of specialty yarns containing slubs and showing a boucle effect. The slubs are thick irregularities in the otherwise uniform yarn and have a three-dimensional character. This effect is achieved in some yarns by entangling the filament in a single thread. In others, the effect is obtained by spinning two threads side by side. One thread is looped or otherwise distorted as it leaves the spinning funnel and attaches itself to the second thread before both are completely hardened.

Bemberg novelty yarns are available in a variety of deniers, colors, and slub stylings. A description of the yarns in contained in Table I. These novelty yarns are used mainly for filling, but some warp applications exist, particularly for the Stratella class.

The fine deniers (30 to 300) are used in such items as dress goods, blouses, neckwear, sportwear, curtains, etc.; heavy deniers (300–5000) find application in such markets as drapery, upholstery, bedspreads, and men's suits. These novelty yarns are preshrunk and are delivered mostly in cone and tub form.

APPENDIX:

1. General Information

Makeup and chemical formula: cuproxide ammonia fiber $(C_6H_{10}O_5)_n$

Method of production: solution of linters cellulose in copper ammonia and successive wet spinning

Commercial form: continuous filament

Appearance: spun bright and dull, silken luster and hand

Titers of single filaments: den 1.3

Titers of normal production in density: 25, 40, 50, 60, 80, 100, 120, 150, 200, 300
luster: 100/2c, 180, 230/2c, 450/2c

2. Main Characteristics
    - Appearance under microscope:
        - longitudinal: without striations
        - transversal: almost round section
    - Tensile strength in g/den:
        - dry: 1.8–2.3
        - wet: 1.1–1.4
    - Loop strength
        - dry: 1.4–1.8
    - Knot strength
        - dry: 1.3–1.7
    - Tensile strength in kg/mm^2: 25–31
    - Length of break in km: 16–21
    - Elongation to break:
        - dry: 16–18%
        - wet: 27–29%
    - Elastic recovery from 5% strain: 45%
    - Specific gravity: 1.54
    - Rate of recovery: 13%
    - Moisture regain at 21°C and 65% RH: 11%
    - Absorption of water when immersed: 90–110%
    - Softening range: does not soften
    - Melting point: does not melt
    - Behavior in fire: burns
    - Effect of sunlight: good resistance
    - Effect of atmospheric agents: loss of strength through prolonged exposure
    - Effect of concentrated mineral acids: when cold, they degrade the fiber
    - Effect of diluted acids: when hot, they degrade the fiber
    - Effect of organic acids: good resistance
    - Effect of strong alkalis: serious swelling if concentrated until the fiber is destroyed
    - Effect of weak alkalis: fiber swelling
    - Effect of oxidizers: good resistance to the oxidizing agents normally used for *bleaching;* strong oxidizing agents degrade the fiber
    - Effect of organic solvents: unchanged
    - Resistance to moths: good, like cotton
    - Resistance to moulds and bacteria: like cotton
    - Electric properties: does not generate electrostatic charges
3. Dyeability
    - Good with direct dyes, vat dyes, and acid dyes
4. Identification
    - Typical reactions for purposes of recognition and differentiation in the presence of other textile fibers
    - Soluble in Cuoxam and Cuene
    - Distinguishable from other cellulosic fibers by differential dyeing with Detex (CIBA)

Viscose Rayon Textile Fibers

H. Peter von Bucher
Chemtex, Inc., New York City

CONTENTS

I. INTRODUCTION

Many "viscose" solutions were prepared during the second half of the nineteenth century from which artificial silk could be formed by drawing or, later, by extrusion from orifices. Audemars, in 1855, was probably the first to do so, by nitrating cellulose and dissolving it in a mixture of alcohol and ether. Filaments drawn from this solution solidified in air and could be wound on spools. Chardonnet's silk, prepared from nitrocellulose in the 1880's, was the first product to arouse commercial interest. At the turn of the century, there were three viscose solutions of cellulose which seemed to hold the most promise for spinning: sodium xanthate, which was found to be soluble in dilute sodium hydroxide;

acetone-soluble diacetate; and a solution of cellulose in aqueous ammonia with copper complexes. The cellulose sodium xanthate solutions were the first to achieve full commercial usage and thus received the descriptive name used at the time for all spinning dopes; they are still referred to as viscose rayons, in contrast to acetate rayon or cuprammonium rayon.

Viscose rayon is not only the oldest commercial man-made fiber, but it is also still the most important man-made textile fiber. The rapid growth and popularity of viscose rayon is due to the fact that cellulose

TABLE I. World Man-Made Fiber Production, 1000 T/yr

Year	Viscose rayon			Total synthetics
	Filament	Staple[a]	Total	
1900	0.9	—	0.9	—
1910	5.5	—	5.5	—
1920	14.5	—	14.5	—
1930	205	3.2	208.2	—
1940	543	587	1130	5.5
1950	873	738	1611	70
1955	1050	1240	2290	265
1960	1140	1470	2610	710
1964	1330	1965	3295	1695
1965	1370	1980	3350	2020

[a] Including acetate. In 1964, the total acetate was 339,000 T, or roughly one-tenth of the viscose rayon production.

TABLE II. United States Man-Made Fiber Production, 1000 T/yr

Year	Viscose rayon			Synthetics		
	Filament[a]	Staple	Total	Filament	Staple	Total
1950	145	86	231	46	10	56
1955	92	153	245	124	48	172
1960	67	142	209	198	108	306
1965	77	295	372	453	352	805

[a] Excluding tire cord.

is still the cheapest polymer and possesses the inherent advantages of cellulosic fibers, such as high moisture adsorption and excellent dyeing characteristics.

Staple fiber has contributed primarily to the continuing growth of viscose rayon, and it is expected that it will retain its position as the largest-volume man-made fiber for some time, with the introduction of such improvements as the high-wet-modulus fibers. Tables I and II illustrate the development of man-made fiber production in the world and in the United States, respectively.

Economical plant sizes for continuous filament are considerably smaller than for staple. Depending on the country, the minimum economical size of a continuous-filament plant may range from 2.5 T/day to 20 T/day, while rayon staple plants generally range from 10 T/day to 100 T/day or more. Accordingly, viscose preparation for continuous filament is generally done in batch operation equipment, while continuous processes are generally used in staple plants. Most filament yarn is spun by batches, while all staple is spun continuously. The respective processes will be described briefly in the following chapters.

II. CHEMISTRY OF THE VISCOSE RAYON PROCESS

Although chemistry of the viscose rayon process is basically simple, the succession of chemical reactions is actually quite complex, and much of the viscose rayon process is therefore still considered an art.

Cellulose is present in practically all plants; however, certain trees (pine, gum, beech, etc.) constitute the most economical supply of "desolving pulp, either because of their yield of cellulose per unit of land, or their growth in areas which are not required for food supply, or because of the chemical accessibility and relative purity of the cellulose. Other plants, such as bamboo, wheat straw, and esparto grass, are being considered; the converting costs, however, are generally much higher.

After the cellulose has been made more reactive, than it is in its original form by digestion and purification it is called pulp; it has a macromolecule content of 87–98%. Only the macromolecules contribute to the desired characteristics in the regenerated fiber, and the pulps of higher purity are used for high-performance fibers. Each type of the various viscose rayon end products has its optimum degree of polymerization or average cellulose chain length, ranging from about one-fourth the original chain length for regular rayon fibers to one-half for certain high-performance fibers. This optimum degree of polymerization is generally established by effecting a compromise between process economics and desired end product properties.

Pulp in bulk or sheet form is treated with sodium hydroxide to form alkali cellulose (see Figs. 1 and 2). Since this reaction is not possible in practice on a stoichiometric basis, excess solution is pressed out, carrying along soluble parts of the pulp, hemicellulose and resinous impurities. If properly conducted, the process of alkalization, generally referred to as *steeping* or mercerization, can be used to further refine the pulp.

For batch operations, hydraulic presses are used, holding several hundred kilograms of pulp, with the pulp sheets carefully arranged vertically in a tank holding the steeping sodium hydroxide solution. After an immersion time of approximately 30 min., the excess steeping liquor is pressed off and the alkali cellulose is dumped directly into the shredder.

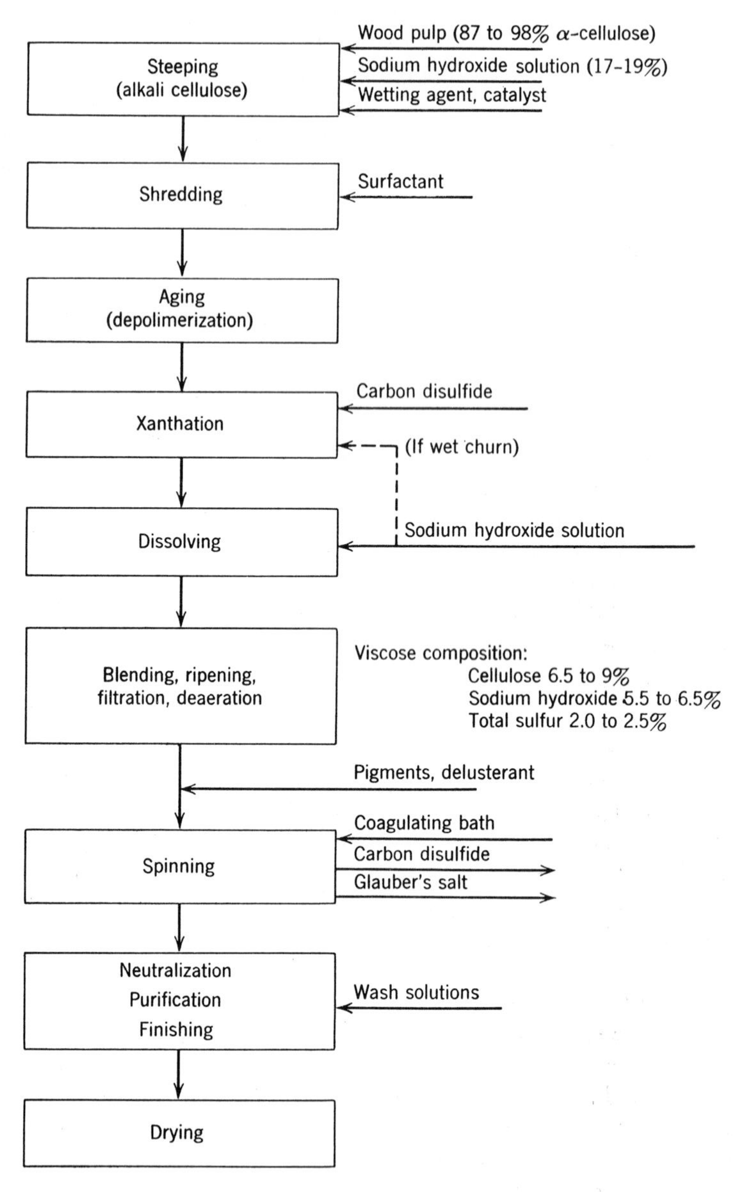

Fig. 1. Viscose rayon process.

For continuous operations, the most widely used machinery is based on using a slurry of 4–5% cellulose in steeping soda and pressing off the excess liquor between two perforated rolls. This process was originally developed by du Pont.

The alkali cellulose (30–35% cellulose, 15–17% alkali) is now *shredded* into fluffy crumbs and *aged* under carefully controlled conditions to the desired degree of polymerization. Oxidative depolymerization takes place, and the rate can be varied with temperature changes and catalysts. The oxygen available from the air within the fluffy crumbs is sufficient, and exposure of the alkali cellulose to excessive amounts of air is avoided; otherwise, the crumbs dry out and carbonates are formed with the carbon dioxide in air, causing difficulties in filtration and spinning. Catalysts used to accelerate aging are heavy metal salts, such as manganese or cobalt. Sensitivity to catalytic reactions in this step of the process indicates the importance of pure, or at least uniformly impure, raw materials. Iron introduced into the process with the sodium hydroxide can make control of the process difficult. Electrolytic sodium hydroxide is therefore preferred.

Aging may take anywhere from a few minutes to more than 30 hr, depending on the temperature and catalysts used, for practical reasons conditions are generally selected to allow for a holdup time of several hours.

In batch operations, aging is done preferably in large cans, holding several 100 kg, equal to one batch and handled by lift trucks. Several methods are in use for continuous operations, such as horizontal storage on an endless belt, or vertical storage in a silo-type tower.

Properly aged alkali cellulose is ready for *xanthation*. In a batch process, this is done by simply dumping it into the xanthator, which is called either (*1*) a dry churn or baratte when the reaction product is transferred to the next process step in the form of orange crumbs or (*2*) a wet churn, when sodium hydroxide solution is used to flush the xanthate into the dissolver. Barattes are airtight, rotating drums. Wet churns have rotating blades for low-speed mixing during the reaction with carbon disulfide and high-speed agitation for rapid dispersion after addition of sodium hydroxide. Both types of reactors are generally evacuated before introducing the carbon disulfide. The total cycle time required is approximately two hours.

The dry-churn process is somewhat easier to operate and control. Wet churns were introduced primarily to avoid possible exposure of the operator to noxious fumes during emptying.

In continuous operations alkali cellulose may be treated with carbon disulfide on an endless belt, in an inert atmosphere.

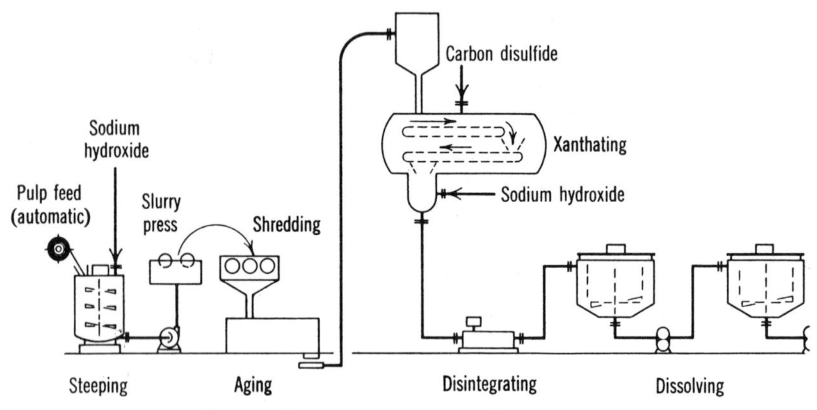

Fig. 2. Continuous viscose making process.

Approximately 65% of the carbon disulfide reacts with cellulose, while the remainder forms sodium carbonate and certain sulfur compounds, giving the crumbs a deep yellow-orange color. The ratio of total sulfur to the xanthate sulfur is an important variable during the ensuing coagulation and regeneration reaction.

Dissolving the xanthate crumbs is a delicate operation because the xanthate crumbs are sensitive to mechanical handling; if they are handled improperly initial absorption of the dissolving lye may be nonuniform, resulting in viscose of various degrees of solvation and thus causing poor filterability and spinnability.

In a batch process the dry crumbs are dumped directly from the barатte into the dissolver containing dilute sodium hydroxide solution. Rapid mixing, using a draft-tube, impeller, and screen, gives a uniform dispersion of the sodium cellulose xanthate in approximately two hours. The dissolving lye is preferably precooled to close to 0°C, and cooling is provided to absorb the mixing energy input, with the temperature held below 18°C at the end of the mixing cycle.

The slurry from the wet churn is usually passed through a disintegrator into the dissolver.

Continuous operations utilize essentially the same principle of dissolving, with the difference being that the mixer has several sections and the slurry, or later the dispersion, is forced from one section to the next until a clear, honeylike "viscous" liquid is obtained.

Whether a continuous or batch system, the viscose is now pumped into a large vessel with slow agitation for *blending*. Nonuniformities of processing are evened out, thereby helping to obtain a uniform end product. Uniformity is particularly important for continuous filaments; however, high-performance staple fibers also require viscose of utmost uni-

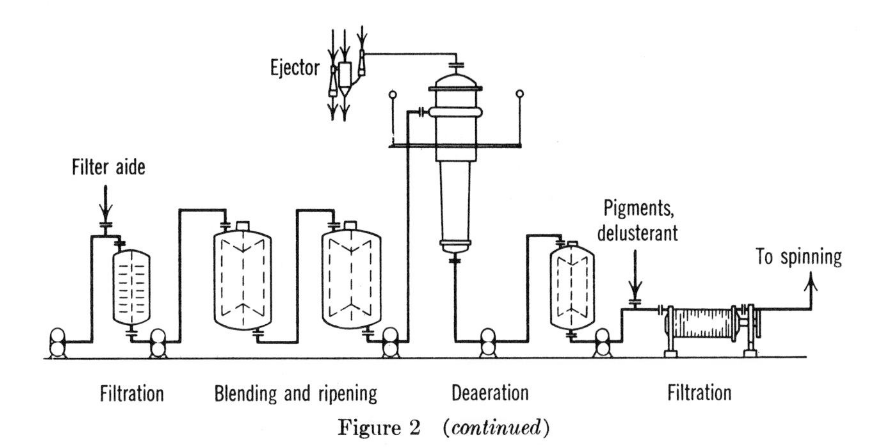

Figure 2 (*continued*)

formity, since optimum process conditions, and indeed, even the range of operability are generally within narrow limits.

The viscose is *filtered* to remove dirt and undissolved cellulose either through filter-cloth or with the help of filter-aids. For economic reasons, filtration is done in several steps, with the last filtration as close as possible to the spinnerets.

During dissolving, a considerable amount of air is usually whipped into the solution which has to be completely removed, since hollow or broken filaments would result every time a bubble squeezes with the viscose through a spinneret orifice. *Deaeration* is achieved by evacuation, either in storage tanks or thin-film continuous-flow equipment. In the latter case the vacuum is high enough so that a certain amount of water evaporates, which helps removal of the air within a few seconds.

One problem of viscose rayon is the instability of the viscose. Viscose held at room temperature, or above, eventually gels. Below 10°C it is quite stable and it can be preserved for a long time in frozen form. The changes which take place in the viscose at elevated temperatures are known as *ripening*. The chemical mechanism behind ripening is dexanthation, coupled with rearrangement and improved distribution of the xanthate groups, agglomeration of cellulose molecules, and development of a structure, gradually reducing the solubility. The progress of ripening can be followed by the determination of the readiness to coagulate in standard salt solutions (ammonium chloride–Hottenroth number; sodium chloride–Salt Index). The viscosity decreases initially until the optimum degree of dispersion is reached, increasing later until the viscose gels. Furthermore, the degree of xanthation (gamma number) decreases.

Each type of viscose requires a certain time of ripening to make it spinnable. Among the many process variables influencing ripening, temperature is the most convenient for obtaining the proper degree of ripeness within the desired time, and means are provided to control temperature accurately. Total ripening time is usually measured from the beginning of dissolving. Storage requirements and process flexibility determine the length of the overall ripening time; eight to ten hours is probably the lower practical limit.

Viscose ready for *spinning* is pumped to the spinning machine. At this point pigments can be added for spun-dyed fibers, dulling agents for controlling the luster, or other chemicals for specialty yarns. Adding

Fig. 3. Spinnerets (courtesy Engelhard Industries, Inc.).

these materials at this point facilitates switching from one product to another.

At the spinning machine the viscose stream is accurately metered to each spinning position.

The spinnerets (Fig. 3) are made of alkali- and acid-resistant materials, primarily precious metal alloys; some tantalum and glass spinnerets are in use. Much depends on the design, manufacture, and maintenance of the spinnerets.

The diameters of textile fibers range from 0.01 to 0.1 mm. Variations of up to about $\pm 5\%$ can be tolerated, which is an indication of the high degree of precision required.

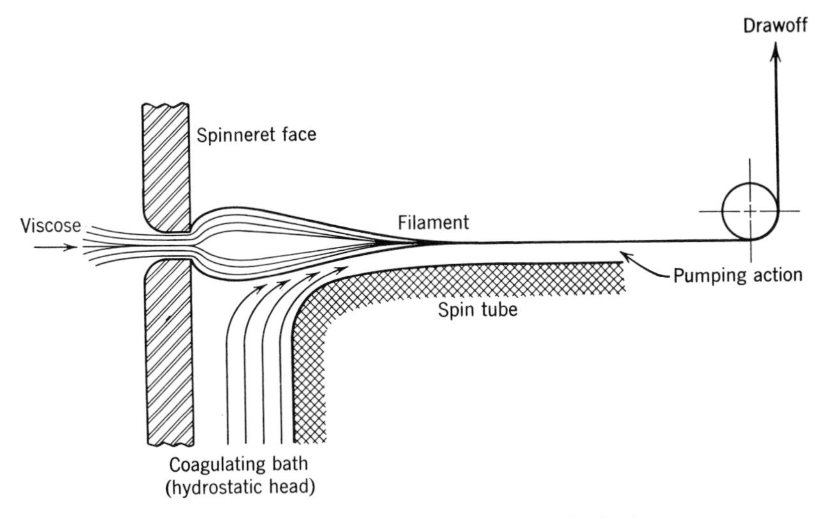

Fig. 4. Formation of filament (tube spinning).

Viscose entering the spinbath coagulates gradually, first forming a skin. A minimum viscosity is required to resist the surface forces of the viscose extruding in the shape of a cylinder to form a drop, equalizing diameter and length, and also to provide sufficient flow orientation and thus structural strength for the skin. Depending on the nature of this structure, the final fiber will have a smooth surface or lengthwise striations. The skin is attached to the edge of the spinneret orifice and bulges under the pressure of the extruding viscose (Fig. 4); it serves as a membrane, regulating the rate of dehydration and the reaction between the viscose and the bath. Thus, as the filaments are drawn off from the face of the spinneret, coagulation and regeneration proceed. The rate at which the various reactions proceed can be regulated by modifying the permeability of the membrane, by changing the stability of the cellulose xanthate, varying temperatures and concentrations. Many different properties can thus be built into the nascent fiber. For example, strong fibers require that as many as possible of the molecules are oriented parallel to the longitudinal fiber axis. For further explanation of the spinning process, see the Chapter on high-performance staple and tire cord.

Figure 5 shows three cross sections through filaments of (*1*) regular, (*2*) high-performance, and (*3*) high-crimp rayon. Conditions of the process to produce regular rayon are such that relatively rapid regeneration occurs; the outer regions have become rigid before the completion of dehydration and folding (serration) occurs, as the fiber shrinks in di-

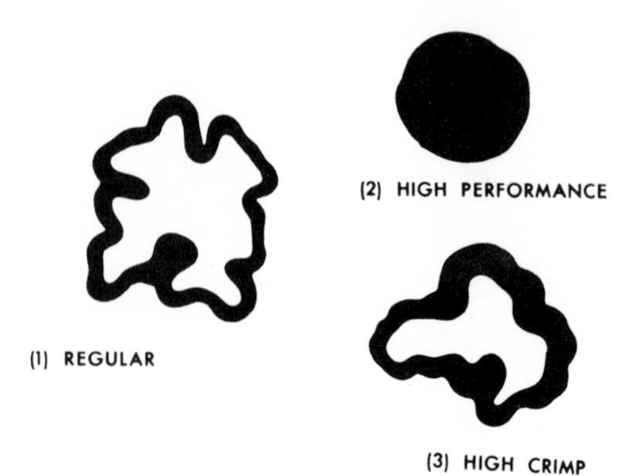

Fig. 5. Cross sections through filaments of (*1*) regular, (*2*) high-performance, and (*3*) high-crimp rayon.

ameter. The serration of the filaments increases its surface considerably over round cross-sectional fibers, increasing covering power and the capillary or wicking effect.

The high-performance fiber (*2*) under the conditions outlined above, remains uniformly unregenerated over the entire cross section until all water is squeezed out, under pressure of osmosis and drawing. The fiber does not shrink any more over the cross section after completed regeneration, and a round fiber results.

The third type of fiber (*3*) is produced with an uneven skin. If allowed to relax, thick-skinned sections will contract differently than others, and a "chemical" crimp develops.

Only a few of the many variables determining the properties of the end product have been mentioned; a consideration of these, together with the complexity of viscose preparation suggests that the viscose rayon process is the most intricate of all man-made fiber processes, and particularly more so than synthetic fiber processes. As it is the oldest and the most widely used commercial process, much research has been done over a period of more than 40 years, investigating all phases of the process. However, new discoveries are being made constantly, improving existing fibers or introducing new types, thus firmly maintaining viscose rayon's position as one of the basic man-made fibers.

III. CONTINUOUS FILAMENT

A. Manufacturing

The fiber, as formed in the coagulating bath, is pulled away from the spinneret by a wheel made from glass or plastic generally called a godet wheel. For each spinning system there exists a definite and critical relationship between the rate of flow of the viscose through the spinneret orifice (jet velocity) and the rate at which the fiber is pulled away (drawoff velocity); it must be determined experimentally. The proper drawoff speed can be readily recognized by observing the filaments at the jet. At a given jet velocity and low drawoff speed the filaments form waves; as the speed is increased these waves disappear at a definite speed and further increase does not cause any obvious changes until the skin of individual filament starts to be pulled away from the edge of the spinneret orifice; viscose flows through the break, coagulates, and forms an uneven section in the filament. Crimped fibers are spun close to this borderline condition. Regular rayon is spun somewhere in the middle between the two speed limits described.

Sometimes the jet velocity is used as a reference point for indicating the amount of stretch imparted to the filaments. This might be useful for comparisons within a system of closely related conditions; in general, however, it is meaningless. As mentioned previously, the viscose, upon leaving the orifice, expands at first, thus reducing its speed; dehydration begins and the volume is quickly reduced to less than one-tenth. The filaments are now essentially coagulated, and stretching becomes meaningful. Up to this point the coagulating bath traveled at essentially the same speed as the filaments. In high-speed spinning, or spinning of slowly regenerating viscose, it is necessary to maintain the flow of coagulating bath for a certain minimum length at the speed of the filaments; this is done by spinning through tubes. As reference point, to which the beginning of stretch should be referred, should be taken the first point of holdback, which can either be a stationary guide, a thread-driven roller guide, or a driven wheel (lower godet) at the bath surface. Stationary guides can be used for regular rayon; high speeds or the spinning of high-performance fibers requires rotating holdback elements; the friction at the stationary guide would damage the "green" filament. The stretch is then calculated based on the speed differential between the yarn speed at the holdback and at the last wheel of the spinning process. Some shrinkage takes place between this last wheel and the takeup or the purification section of continuous machines. Tensions developed during stretching range from 0.4–1.2 g/den.

Occasional slipping of the yarn on the godets, eccentricities, and defective or improperly sized metering pumps can cause irregularities of denier, which in turn can cause nonuniformities in fabrics, especially when dyed. Figure 6 shows a typical example of a mass vibrometer denier trace of a commercially acceptable product (50/20 yarn). The indicated denier uniformity is approximately $\pm 5\%$.

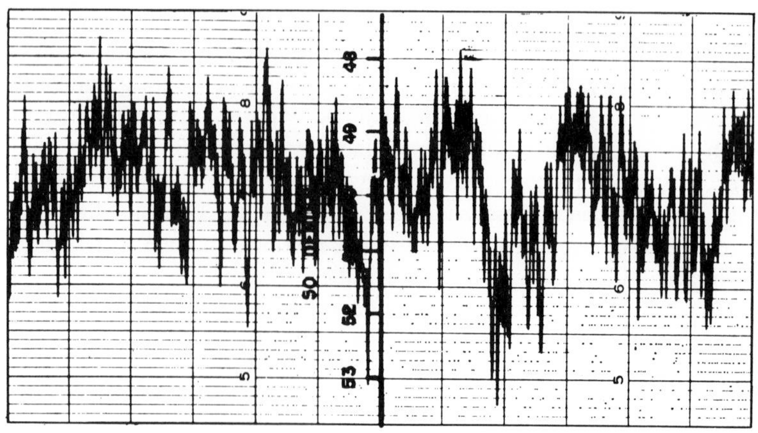

Fig. 6. Mass vibrometer denier trace of 50/20 yarn. Indicated denier uniformity ± 5%.

There are two basic principles of handling the spun filaments: collecting it in packages or immediately processing it further on the same machines as individual strands (continuous process).

Collecting the filaments in packages is the older form, and it is either done in pots—now by far the more common method—or on bobbins. On pot-spinning machines, the thread is fed from the upper godet downward through a funnel, which moves up and down, serving as traverse guide; it is pulled by centrifugal force. The advantage of this process is that twist is inserted, making succeeding handling easier. The textile industry is used to obtain rayon with at least 40 turns per meter; and this is one of the spinning speed limitations of pot machines, since the practical spindle speed is around 8,000–10,000 rpm.

The pot is stopped every 6–12 hr, depending on the denier and spinning speed, and the filament cake is removed (doffed). It represents about 1 kg of dried yarn. The wet cake weighs about 3 kg.

On bobbin machines, the yarn is wound up without twist. There are automatic doffing machines, machines with collapsible bobbins to reduce the inside-outside dyeing differences, and several other variations. However, lack of twist and the limitation to small takeup packages make bobbin processes less and less desirable.

All commercially successful continuous processes for viscose rayon textile yarns rely on the principle of advancing the individual threads on canted rolls. The machine developed by the Industrial Rayon Corporation uses interdigitating reels, which are, in effect, two canted rolls combined into one reel. All types of yarn, including tire yarn, can be made on these machines. As far as textile yarn is concerned, it is probably the gentlest way to handle yarn and the only continuous process allowing bleaching. The yarn is treated on a series of ten reels arranged to be self-threading. The total processing requires about 5 min, at a speed of 85 m/min, and includes neutralizing, desulfuring, bleaching, finishing, and drying.

Dobson and Barlow's Nelson machine utilizes two parallel rolls approximately 15 cm in diameter and 110–130 cm long. The yarn is spun on one side of the machine, traveling over the rolls to the other side; it is neutralized and partly desulfurized, passes through a finishing bath to a pair of dryer rolls, and is taken up on a down twister. Some older types of this machine combine the heating section on the same axis with the washing roll, and the finish is applied at the end of the wash roll.

Several other commercial processes utilize a third principle for continuously purifying filaments, one large roll, 25–30 cm in diameter and approximately 90 cm long, and one smaller-diameter roll, both supported on one side only.

Rayon made according to the later two principles has an even higher residual sulfur content than rayon purified on an Industrial Rayon Corporation machine; however, it can be used for many purposes with which the sulfur content and the slightly off-white color do not interfere. Furthermore, continuously purified and dried yarns, having been dried under tension, have a higher residual shrinkage than can be obtained with yarn dried in skein or cake form.

Yarn spun on batch machines is purified by drip-rinsing or by forcing the individual solutions through the packages either by centrifugal force or by hydraulic pressure. For pressure purification 4–6 yarn packages are combined on a spindle, with several spindles mounted on one carrier, either horizontally or vertically. The carriers are moved automatically from one purification station to the next. The finished packages are centrifuged, to remove excess moisture, and dried.

As with most commercial processes, all of the processes discussed above represent a compromise between process economy and market acceptance of the end product. Rayon filaments' competitive position is becoming more and more difficult, and many improvements and modifications to the above discussed basic process have been introduced.

While gray goods are often bleached to remove dirt accumulated during handling and weaving, the textile industry gives preference to cleaner and whiter yarn provided by the fiber manufacturer. It takes less severe conditions to purify and bleach gel yarn, or never-dried yarn so that a basically superior yarn results when the fiber manufacturer bleaches the yarn. Furthermore, better purified and bleached yarns are more suitable for dyeing in package form.

Continuous purification processes have at best several minutes (up to 5 min on the Industrial Rayon machine) available for purification and the yarn is under some tension. Neutralization requires little time, since it is an ionic reaction. Purification, however, is a comparatively slow process of dissolving impurities, leaching out, etc., and it can be done best when the yarn is relaxed. Bleaching also requires a good deal of time. At one time yarn was wound in skeins for purification and bleaching; this extra step in the process, however, became uneconomical.

Pressure purification processes have their limitations in the purity of the treatment solutions themselves, inasmuch as a rayon cake is a superior filter.

Du Pont developed an automatic drip-rinsing process with which rayon cakes of essentially absolute purity can be obtained. In principle this drip-rinse process is similar to most package purification processes, in which cakes are preconditioned, washed acid-free, desulfured, bleached, finished, centrifuged, and dried. The advantages of this process, however, lie in the savings of water, solution ingredients, and manpower. Furthermore, a significantly cleaner product is obtained; comparative data are given in Table III. Another advantage of the system is that undersized cakes can be purified as well.

TABLE III. Filament Yarn Impurities

	Rayon cake pressure wash	Typical continuously purified yarn	Automatic drip process
Ash, %	0.16	0.45	0.05
Sulfur, %	0.02	0.09	0.001
Lead, ppm	9	11	4
Iron, ppm	3	11	traces

The automatic drip washing process is initiated by an evacuation step. Rayon cakes, on a carrier used for transportation from the spinning areas, are completely submerged in water, and the container is evacuated down to 26 in of mercury. During the evacuation the CS_2 entrapped within the cake is removed, allowing faster and more uniform penetration of the various wash solutions and reducing the tendency of the solutions to channel in their passage through the cake. Furthermore, the cake is softened and the filaments are uniformly relaxed throughout the cake. The purification steps following the evacuation are carried out in a tunnel; the carriers are automatically advanced from station to to station by an indexing mechanism. The purified cakes are centrifuged and dried.

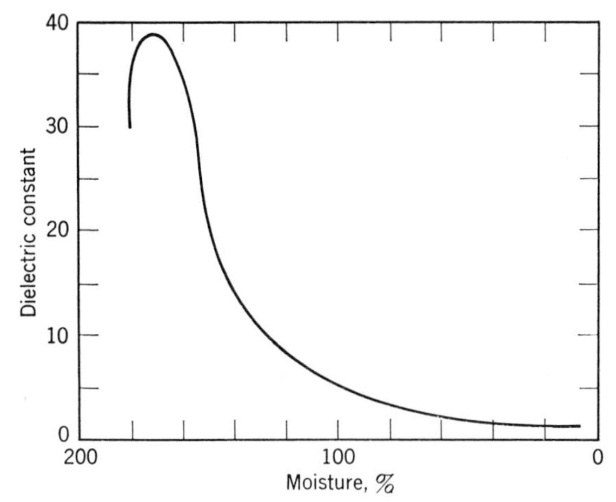

Fig. 7. Dielectric constant versus moisture content of rayon cakes.

Drying of rayon cakes is done either under carefully controlled wet-bulb conditions or in a high-frequency electrostatic field (dielectric drying). Uniform drying is very important to minimize outside-inside dyeing difference. If, for example, the outside layers are allowed to dry first, they would not be able to shrink against the still wet inner layers; the inner layers later dry unrestrictedly and a difference in residual shrinkage results, causing dyeing differences. Sometimes a rubber sleeve is put over the cake to further safeguard against the cake drying first on the outside.

Dielectric drying essentially eliminates inside-outside package dyeing differences. Furthermore, the drying time can be reduced to less than 30 min from as many as 160 hr—the time required to yield a product of acceptable dyeing uniformity in conventional dryers.

Rayon acts between the plates of a capacitor as a dielectric insulating material; its molecules are practically immobile, and it therefore has a low dielectric constant. Water molecules are mobile dipoles; wet rayon therefore has a high dielectric constant. Figure 7 shows the dielectric constant of rayon versus moisture content. A moistened rayon cake, placed between the plates of a capacitor connected to a high-frequency alternator (oscillator), is heated up due to the friction of the agitated water molecules, provided that the frequency changes fast enough. Since more heat is generated where there are more water molecules, drying and shrinkage proceed uniformly throughout the package; the lay of the yarn is not disturbed, and fewer breaks occur in subsequent unwinding. In spite of the savings in yarn, labor, and inventory, this process can be justified usually only where cheap power is available.

In practice, the rayon cakes are placed on a conveyor belt, which becomes one of the plates of the capacitor. As the cakes move into the dryer they come under a stationary plate, the electrode, and into the electrostatic field, alternated by an oscillator at about 300 Mc.

B. Yarn Characteristics

By far the most filament rayon produced for the textile industry is regular yarn in deniers from 50/18 (50 denier, 18 filaments per end) to 900/150. The average denier is close to 150, and in the United States more than half of the total production actually consists of 150-denier yarn. The relative proportions of the various deniers has changed only slightly over the past years.

Prices have remained fairly constant and, in the highly competitive textile field, close to the economic minimum. Only certain specialty yarns (see below) are able to demand a higher profit margin. The price in the United States of the "bread-and-butter" yarn, 150 denier, has settled at about $0.85 per pound, having been sold initially (1911) for $1.85, and having reached a high of $6.90 in 1920.

Breaking strength is not very important for a textile fiber, and the strength of regular rayon has not changed significantly during the past two or three decades; special products, however, have been developed with considerably higher strength, as shown in Table IV. While strength itself cannot be translated simply and directly into fabric performance, it is one of the few yarn parameters which can be easily and accurately measured, and it is therefore frequently used in the trade as the only specification. The importance of this fact should not be overestimated. Viscose filament yarn's secret for success is its drapability, dye recep-

TABLE IV. Filament Yarn Characterization (150/40 Bright)

	Regular (pot)	Regular (continuous)	High-strength (pot)
Tenacity (g/den), conditioned	2.1	2.0	3.8
wet	1.0	0.9	2.6
loop	1.8	1.7	1.5
Elongation (%), conditioned	22	17	16
wet	28	29	22
loop	16	12	8
Silk factor (ten. × elong), conditioned	46.2	34	60.8
Moisture regain (% 70°F, 65% R.H.).	13	13	13
Water imbibition	115	115	90

tivity, silky, rich look and hand, and its price. Stress–strain and other physical characteristics of viscose rayon fiber in general are discussed with viscose rayon staple.

IV. SPECIALTY FILAMENT YARN

A. High-Tenacity Textile Filament Yarn

In contrast to most synthetic fibers, the tenacity of viscose rayon fibers was originally quite low and was increased only very gradually during the nearly sixty years of their commercial use. Most synthetic textile fibers were introduced at high tenacity, and the tenacity of polyester fibers was even reduced for certain applications—for example, to reduce pilling.

Use of heavy metal salts in the coagulating bath to improve strength was suggested as early as 1911 (B.P. 406); with this and together with drawing between two godets, 2 g/den was reached in 1914. Lilienfeldt introduced a new concept by spinning into more concentrated (65%) sulfuric acid; a very plastic coagulum is obtained which can be stretched more than 100%, resulting in a brittle fiber of up to 6 g/den dry tenacity and 7% elongation.

A combination of regeneration retardants, zinc sulfate in the spin bath, and high stretch-spinning finally led to the present high-strength rayons. This development is being discussed in considerable detail in the chapter dealing with viscose rayon tire yarns.

Aside from chemical reactions, certain physical factors influence the formation of filaments and thus their final properties—for example, the shape of the spinneret holes, their arrangement in the spinneret, and the flow of the coagulating bath. Figure 4 illustrates schematically the formation of a filament and the theory of *tube spinning*.

The transition from the liquid, disordered phase to the solid, highly ordered phase is obviously the most critical operation in fiber-making, and presents more problems in wet-spinning than in dry- or melt-spinning. The nascent filaments are extremely tender, and even the slightest strain should be avoided. The coagulation bath supply must be absolutely free of turbulence, and equipment parts around the spinneret must be designed so as not to cause turbulence; this becomes more critical as process chemistry for high-strength fibers is used (delayed regeneration), and as the spinning speed is increased. The use of properly designed tubes helps to reduce turbulence around the spinneret, transferring much of the strain otherwise imposed on the nascent fiber by bath drag, to a stronger section of the fiber; their use also assures uniform bath supply. In an open bath turbulent conditions can cause return of used bath, and thus nonuniform bath composition at certain points.

TABLE V. Effect of Number of Filaments

	Textile "Cordura"[a]						Industrial "Cordura"[a]		
Denier	50	150	300	450	600	1100	1650	2200	3300
Number of filaments	20	60	120	180	240	720	1100	1650	2200
Tenacity (g/den), conditioned	2.05	2.40	2.87	2.91	2.96	5.05	5.20	5.05	5.03
Elongation (%), conditioned	20.7	20.5	17.3	15.6	15.8	11.5	11.0	12.0	13.4

[a] Du Pont registered trademark.

Neighboring filaments support each other to a certain extent; on the other hand, the conditions surrounding the nascent fibers become less uniform with increasing number of filaments. The sensitivity in regard to number of filaments per spinneret can be demonstrated by comparing the strength of commercial end products produced under conditions to yield an optimum product using similar technology (Table V). The most obvious variable between these products is the number of filaments, and the optimum is apparently somewhere around 1100 filaments.

As the number of filaments increases, the effect of the tube to support the nascent fiber probably becomes less important, and for staple fiber the prime effect of tubes is probably a more uniform and less turbulent bath supply. For filament yarn spinning, the use of tubes reduces the sensitivity to speed, allowing either higher spinning speeds at the same property level, or superior properties at a given speed. Practical maximum spinning speed for an open bath is 110 m/min; for tube spinning, 150 m/min.

While high-strength filament yarn has been very successful in industrial applications, having replaced cotton almost entirely in tires since World War II, it has proved of only limited interest in the textile trade.

B. Mixed Filament-Denier Yarn

The finer the denier per filament the softer the yarn; however, for certain fabrics a firmer hand is desired (taffetas and crepes). Heavier denier yields a stiffer yarn and the covering power is reduced. Yarn spun with mixed denier can give fabrics with a range of covering power and hand. The practical lower limit for viscose rayon is 1 denier per filament; 1.5 is most common. In Table VI approximate diameters of various filament-deniers are shown.

TABLE VI. Diameters of Viscose Rayon Filaments

Denier	1.0	1.5	2.5	6.0	15.0
Diameter, μ	10	12	15	25	38

C. High-Crimp Filament Yarn

High-crimp rayon filament is used in cut-end-loop pile fabrics, for example. Rayon is not particularly conducive to mechanical crimping; chemical crimping, however, yields very satisfactory products. The yarn is spun into a low-acid bath containing zinc sulfate, and is stretched before completion of coagulation. An unsymmetric cross section results (Fig. 5). The crimp is developed usually in the fabric by treating with dilute alkali solutions.

D. Strawlike Filament

Flat mono- or multifilament yarns have a harsh feel and strawlike appearance and are used primarily in the millinery trade, and finer denier for plush. They are spun through holes of various shapes and designs, to produce cross sections with specific length-to-width ratios, resulting in varying degrees of glitter, bulk, and resilience effects. Since the surface forces of the extruding viscose tend to form a circular cross section, regardless of the shape of the orifice, chemical conditions must be chosen so as to obtain rapidly a stable skin.

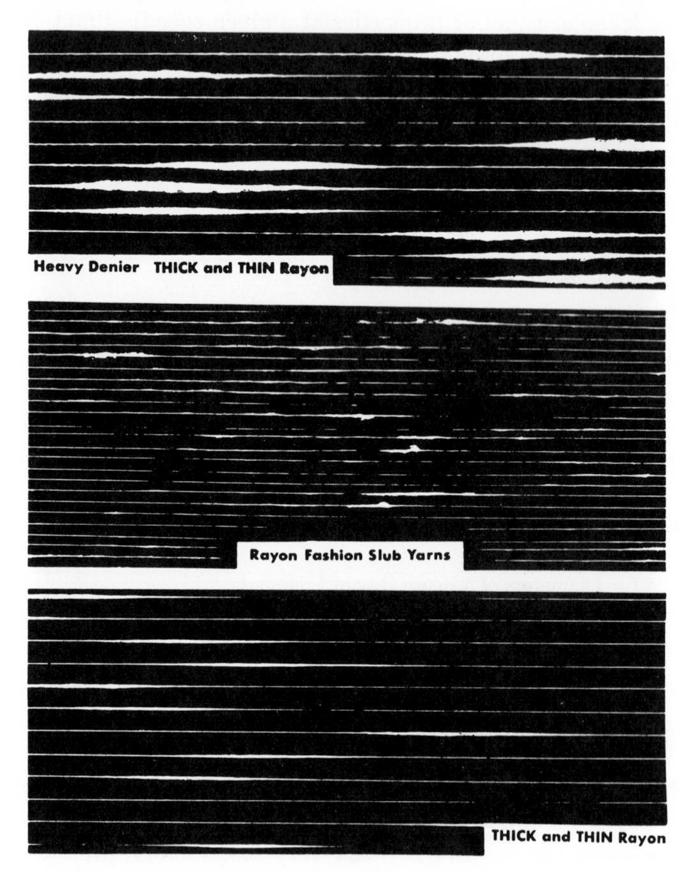

Figure 8

E. Hollow Filaments

With the incorporation into the viscose of blowing agents or the injection of air at the spinneret orifice, multifilaments or monofilaments can be produced containing hollow spaces.

Various types of fibers have been produced in this manner with the intention of increasing the covering power, improving the temperature-insulating effect, or utilizing the buoyance of these filaments with lower apparent specific gravity to replace kapok in life preservers. Spinning conditions can be chosen so that the hollow spaces are collapsed in the final yarn. Heavy denier yarn spun in this manner results in a straw-like product, which is used for handbags, braids, and in the millinery trade. Fine denier has a soft, but full hand, and greater covering power than conventional rayon.

F. "Thick and Thin" Filament Yarn

These special effect yarns can be produced either by an irregularly pulsating viscose supply, or by the formation of entangled slubs in the spun yarn at random frequency (see Fig. 8). The finer deniers are used in dress fabrics, and the heavier in drapery and upholstery fabrics.

The main problem in spinning these types of filaments is to generate the unevenness in a sufficiently long random pattern to avoid development of a pattern in the woven fabric. Satisfactory randomness can be delivered by proper process conditions for the slub formation in the spun filament. A viscose pulsating pattern can be generated either with a mechanical drive and hydraulic valve system with cams, or electronically—for example, with radioactive materials. The effect of this type of filament yarn is generally improved as more variations and combinations are used. High frequency of pulsation in the viscose supply (e.g., 3 per cm) can be obtained with an electromagnetic piston pulsator.

V. STAPLE FIBER

The standard of living of a civilization is based on man's ability to utilize the products offered by nature. The higher the standard of living, the more intricate becomes the refining process from nature's product to useful end products. No matter how refined a man-made product has become, the basic concept of nature's product, which it is supposed to supplement, is generally imitated and can be recognized as such.

The textile industry's most valuable fiber is silk. Silk is also the longest continuous natural fiber; no wonder man's first attempt to provide artificial raw materials for the textile industry resulted in continuous-filament, silklike products. Man-made silk, however, has the great advantages over nature's product of possessing uniformity and, for all practical purposes, endless length.

Only when the viscose rayon process had become cheap enough, so that the fiber could compare in price with cotton and wool, was the manufacture of staple considered. The use of staple fiber developed most rapidly in countries importing large amounts of cotton and wool—Germany, England, and later Japan. In the United States, with its abundance of cotton, rayon staple developed later and the production capacity equalled that of continuous filament only in 1953. Within the next ten years, the capacity for rayon staple was increased to about four times that of continuous filament. This success of rayon staple was based practically entirely on its low price.

A. Regular Rayon Staple Fiber

From the inception of rayon staple production, when it was produced from waste continuous filament, the process was oriented toward a cheap product. While the process for making viscose is the same as for continuous filament, various cost-reducing compromises are made. Cheaper viscose, with a higher ratio of cellulose to alkali, is produced under less critical specifications, since nonuniformities in the viscose, which may result in nonuniform fibers, can be blended out to a certain degree in the succeeding textile operations.

Fig. 9. Spinning machine (courtesy of Chemtex, Inc.).

Staple is spun from spinnerets with as many holes as feasible; in Fig. 3 a 12,000-hole spinneret is shown; even larger spinnerets are in use. Originally, the strands from each spinning position were led around various stationary guides for holdback, and several strands combined to a tow were pulled off and stretched by a set of heavy rolls at the end of the spinning machine. This method is limited in speed and amount

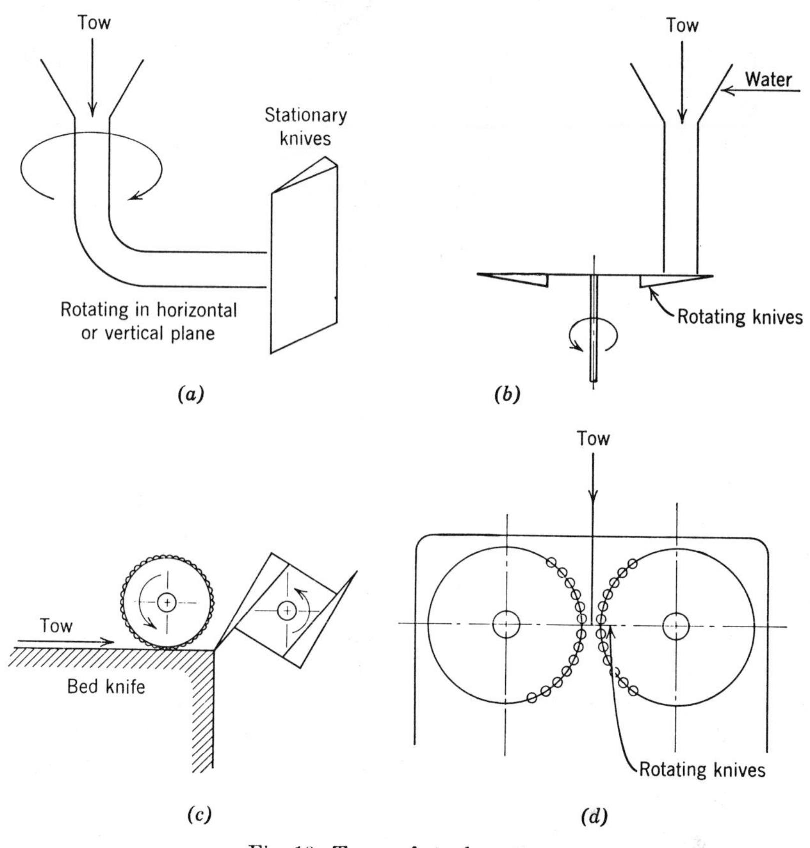

Fig. 10. Types of staple cutter.

of stretch. Modern machines provide godet wheels, similar to the continuous-filament spinning machines, and stretch is applied either in air or in a hot diluted coagulating bath between these godets and the stretch roll cluster. For the manufacture of highly crimped fibers a hot stretch bath is essential.

The stretched tow is now either cut to staple and processed in bulk, or the tow is purified, finished, and dried, to be used for direct conversion

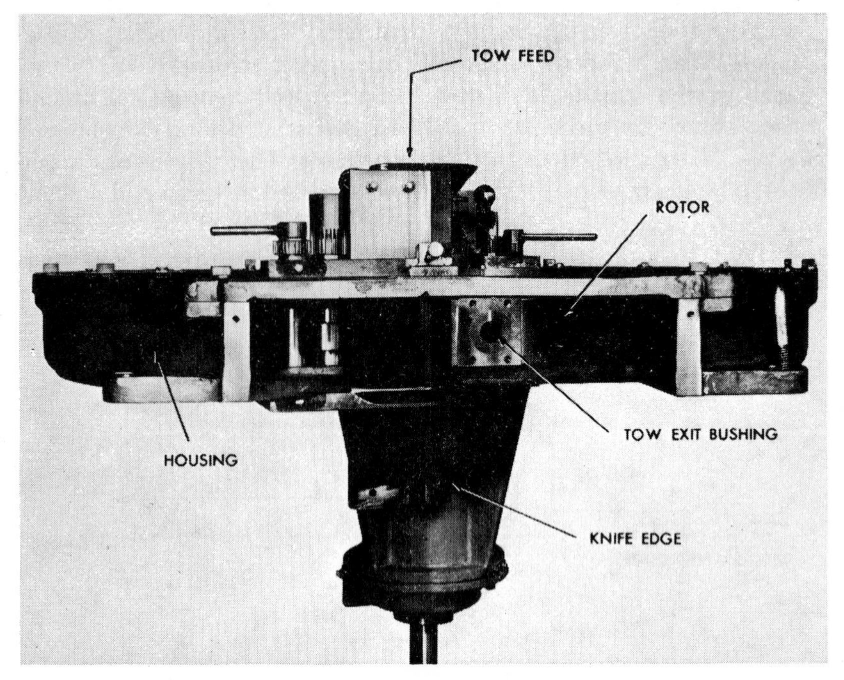

Fig. 11. Centrifugal cutter (courtesy of Chemtex, Inc.).

to spun yarns. Figure 9 shows part of a modern staple spinning machine.

During the developmental period of rayon staple, cutting of hot acid tow presented a problem of excessive maintenance because of corrosion. Various attempts were made to avoid cutting while the tow is still acid; however, because of process economics and improvements in cutter design, all staple is cut today right after stretching. Best crimp develops, if the fiber is desulfured (treatment with alkaline solution) in cut form, because it can shrink more freely than in tow form.

In Fig. 10, four cutter principles are shown which are most frequently used, and Fig. 11 shows a centrifugal cutter assembly. In the centrifugal cutter, (*a*) the tow is advanced by centrifugal force; one, two, or four stationary knives cut the tow as it exits from the rotor. Feed rate, rotor speed, and number of knives determine the cut length. In cutter (*b*) the tow is advanced by a stream of water and the knife rotates. In cutters made in accordance with principle (*c*), the tow is advanced by a pair of feed rolls and cut by rotary knives against a stationary bedknife. In example, (*d*), the tow is advanced and held in position during cutting by a series of opposing guides. This can be done, for example, with two wheels with slotted rims and rotating knives cutting the tow through the slots as the wheels turn.

Spare cutting machines are installed to allow sharpening of knives without interrupting the process. Knife lives are from several days for the centrifugal cutter to a few hours for cutter-types (*c*) and (*d*). Selecting the most suitable cutter generally requires a compromise between operating continuity, tow size, spinning speed, and staple diagram.

Staple diagram is an important end product characteristic, influencing further processing of the staple into yarn. Figure 12 shows a typical diagram obtained from the centrifugal cutter. The diagram is obtained

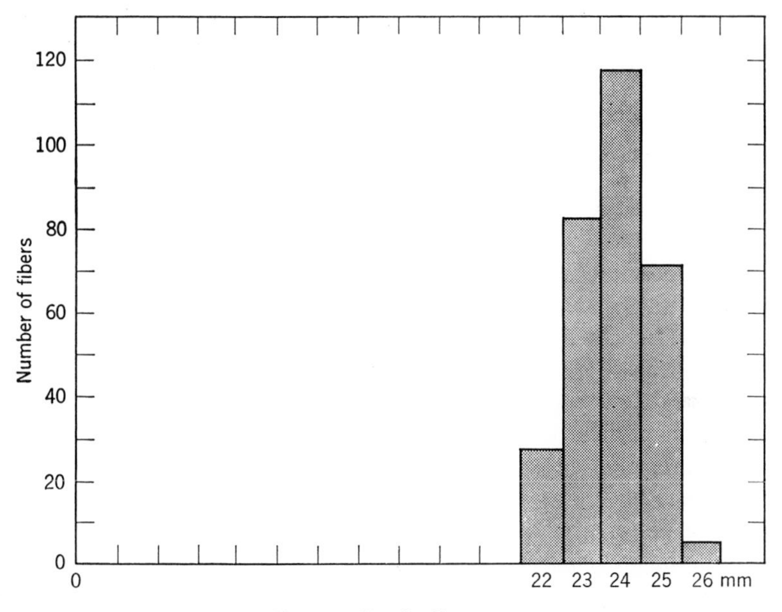

Fig. 12. Staple diagram.

by measuring the length of, generally, 300 sample filaments and recording the results in certain length groups. Customary cut lengths are from 32 mm to 160 mm. Fine denier (1.0–3.0), short cut lengths are sometimes referred to as cotton type rayon staple; heavier denier (3.4–5.5 and up to 30 for use in carpets), longer cuts as wool type, indicating the system on which they are most probably to be spun to yarn. A good staple diagram of a cotton type fiber should show more than 95% of cut fibers within ±1 mm of the desired cut length. Furthermore, there should be practically no very long or very short cuts; "overlength" fiber, in particular, may cause much trouble in the yarn spinning operations.

The staple chips fall from the cutter into a pan containing hot dilute acid. The remaining carbon disulfide is driven off, the chips open up and separate into individual fibers. The slurry of fibers is delivered into the purification machine, most frequently an endless sieve belt and, draining the acidic liquid, a 5–7 cm thick fleece is formed which is conveyed through washing, desulfuring, bleaching, and finishing. Excessive liquid is squeezed out, the fleece is dried and opened, and the fluffy staple fibers are pressed and baled for shipment. Bleaching is frequently omitted, since final fabrics are often bleached to remove dirt accumulated during textile processing. The finish is a combination of vegetable oils and fatty acid derivatives, depending on the type of fiber and the end use.

The entire process discussed above is fully continuous and oriented toward large capacity and low cost. Production lines have capacities up to 30 tons T/day and labor amounts to only up to 15% of the net manufacturing cost.

B. Converting

The textile industry requires long lengths of yarn for weaving, knitting, etc.; these can be either continuous filament yarn or yarn spun from short fibers, such as staple, cotton, or wool. The short fibers have to be parallelized to form the yarn; this requires several steps, such as carding, drafting, combing, and twisting. Cost savings may be expected if the parallel arrangement of the fibers in the tow is maintained. Furthermore, greater yarn uniformity and higher strength can be expected, since several steps of mechanical handling are avoided.

Three types of processes were found suitable for viscose rayon: (*1*) *direct* spinning, (*2*) *tow to top*, and (*3*) the types represented, for example, by the Pacific Converter. In direct spinning tows up to 10,000 denier are stretched until the individual filaments tear in random fashion, drafted and twisted; the tearing is sometimes assisted by an abrading surface. In the tow-to-top system tows up to 200,000 denier are broken under tension over sharp edges. Tows up to 2 million denier are fed to the Pacific Converter and actually cut with a helical knife. This process allows a certain amount of blending, since smaller tows can be combined for the feed tow. The tows, however, must be extremely uniform to assure satisfactory operation. The slivers resulting from these processes are handled further like slivers from carding machines. One of the main advantages of staple, the possibility of blending and thus averaging process nonuniformities, has been lost or greatly reduced in the tow to yarn processes.

C. Miscellaneous Uses

Rayon staple is being used in practically all fields of the textile industry, either pure, or in blends with natural and synthetic fibers.

Deniers from 5 to 15, at times even as high as 30, attained considerable importance as carpet fibers about 18 years ago. In fact, rayon was the first man-made fiber to compete with cotton and wool in carpets. Much of the production was "spin-dyed." The rapid increase, however, during recent years in the production of carpets from man-made fibers in the United States is based, practically entirely, on the superior performance of Nylon 66 and acrylic fibers. More recently, polypropylene is claiming a share of this market.

In Germany attempts were made to use "Flock" (short cuts from 0.2 to 7 mm) for cheap pile carpets. Flock is more often used for wallpaper, suede, case linings, and specialty paper.

In medicine, the high absorbency, safety in regard to static electricity, nonadherence to open wounds, and many other uses make this an important outlet for rayon.

D. Chemically Modified Rayon Staple Fiber

Viscose rayon fibers have been subjected to various treatments to modify their behavior in textiles. Examples in this regard are cyanoethylation of rayon staple, by treating it with acrylonitrile vapor, or acetylation by treating it with aceticanhydride vapor. The latter process has been perfected by Toyo Rayon; a product similar in properties to triacetate is obtained, although the chemical analysis indicates that only two hydroxyl groups have reacted.

Furthermore, rayon staple can be treated with cross-linking agents (aldehydes) to improve its handle (stiffer, less sleazy), increase its resistance to alkali, and reduce swelling in water, thus making it more compatible with cotton and improving its dimensional stability. It is believed, however, that in the long run only such treatments will be of commercial value which are applied to blends, such as for permanent press or wash-and-wear. It appears that 100% rayon fabrics treated to improve, for example, the abrasion resistance, dimensional stability, or microbiological resistance, will be replaced by blends with synthetics or 100% synthetic fabrics, as soon as the price of synthetics has been sufficiently reduced. Also, high-strength/high-modulus fibers will take over much of this application.

VI. HIGH-PERFORMANCE STAPLE FIBER (HIGH WET MODULUS, POLYNOSIC)

The highly competitive textile industry, which is exposed to such unpredictable influences as changes of fashion, constantly requires new and improved fibers. The rayon producers have therefore worked for many years on the development of improved staple fibers. These efforts were primarily directed toward improved dimensional stability, better abrasion resistance, and firmer hand of the final fabrics. It was not too difficult to make a tougher and stiffer fiber by applying the technology which had been developed for tire yarn; many high-strength fibers appeared on the market, however, with limited commercial success. It was more difficult to produce dimensionally stable fibers. The family of "high performance fibers" has reached a plateau of properties sufficiently high to justify investment in new production facilities and in applications research. Furthermore it has even been suggested that the improvement over regular rayon is so significant that this family should be classified by its own generic name; however, this has not been generally accepted.

Tachikawa made fibers in Japan with a degree of polymerization twice as high as conventional fibers. Compared with regular rayon processes, higher-viscosity viscose is spun into a coagulating bath of lower hydrogen ion activity; slower coagulation and regeneration allows stretching of about 200%, and a highly oriented fiber results, with low lateral order. Although the original "Toramomen" fiber (U.S. Pat. 2,732,279) was strictly a high-strength fiber, today's family of "polynosic fibers" is generally considered derived from this technology.

A second group of fibers evolved from high-strength fibers originally made by tire yarn technology. This group is generally referred to as "high-wet-modulus" (HWM or HM) fibers, because of its property now considered the most significant.

A. Formation of HWM Fibers

While the rayon spinning process has been described in principle previously, thoughts are advanced in this chapter to help explain processes of more recent development.

As the viscose solution comes into contact with the coagulating bath, a rapid coagulation must take place at the viscose-bath interface to provide the skin necessary for successful forming of a filament. As coagulation proceeds toward the center of the freshly launched filament, a dehydration and concentration of the structure occurs; the filament is neutralized, regeneration sets in, and effective structure formation begins. The relative rates at which these steps occur and the extent to which they proceed influence significantly the properties of the final yarn.

The initial skin or membrane is formed either by regeneration or by salting out, or a combination of both. The molecules are aligned to a certain extent parallel to the longitudinal axis because of flow orientation caused by "plug" flow of the viscose through the spinneret orifice. Besides being a casing, the skin serves as a membrane regulating the interaction between viscose and bath. Zinc salts, sulfur by-products, and "modifier" in combination give the proper rate of diffusion, the penetration of hydrogen ions (regeneration) is retarded, uniform coagulation proceeds from the filament surface inward, and the formation of a homogeneous, through-going network is approached, which, in its formation, squeezes out water by syneresis to yield a dense coagulum.

Stretch must be held at a minimum as long as lateral differences in the degree of coagulation exists, in order to avoid nonuniform buildup of the structure, which, in the final fiber, might result in uneven load distribution upon stressing. Therefore, drawoff stress and any stresses which might be caused by turbulent bath flow must be avoided prior to completion of coagulation.

While the chemical and physical changes leading to coagulation are fairly well understood, the chemistry of regeneration in the presence of zinc and "modifiers" is not completely clarified. As the pH within the filament changes from alkaline to acid, zinc ions probably deposit first above pH 7.5 as sodium zincate at the interface filament/spin bath, contributing to diffusion control. As the pH drops below 7.5, zinc ions become available and are able to penetrate as such the filament, forming zinc cellulose xanthate; being bivalent, it can cross-link two xanthates and at pH 4, the hydrogen ions, taking the place of the zinc are in proper position for a hydrogen bond. Governing the rate of these reactions is probably part of the function of "modifiers." A very large number of diversified chemicals have been found to be effective as "modifiers" such as amines and polyethylene glycol, and innumerable patents have been issued.

Summarizing the first phase of filament formation, a powerful coagulating system with limited regenerating effect is required; coagulation conditions must be selected to give a membrane structure of temporary nature to allow contraction as coagulation proceeds toward the center, resulting in a compact coagulum of uniform structure over the entire cross section, with the possible exception of a thin outermost layer. The better the gel yarn is protected from stresses during the formative stage (slow speed or tube spinning), the more favorable coagulation conditions can be selected and the more uniform will be the coagulum.

Having established a compact, uniform structure, but of near random orientation the next step is stretching to increase the degree of order. The structural characteristics of high-performance yarn are developed, such as (*1*) high orientation of the molecules in the direction of the fiber axis to equally carry load and (*2*) cross-links (hinge or junction points) to stabilize the oriented structure, but providing sufficient flexibility to assure low brittleness and good flex life (comparatively low lateral order but nevertheless with many small crystallites).

The prerequisites for effective stretching are (*1*) the existence of temporary cross-links which help align the molecules, themselves breaking up progressively (regeneration), and (*2*) low gel swelling so that permanent cross-links (primary and secondary bonds) can be formed as regeneration proceeds.

The importance of the gel swelling during stretching can be appreciated by considering gel swelling in this system to be analogous to temperature in the drawing of melt-spun fibers. Too high gel swelling in viscose spinning, comparable to too high a draw temperature in melt-spinning, causes flow within the filament and ineffective, non-structure-building stretch or draw.

While in the drawing of thermoplastic fibers cross-links are formed when the temperature drops at the end of the process when the rate of drawing decreases, in the stretching of rayon, cross-links are formed progressively, as regeneration proceeds. Thus, in drawing, the tension increases significantly at the end of the process, while in rayon stretching the resistance to attenuation increases steadily, throughout the process. Therefore, the rate-determining factor of structure-building (effective) stretching of a drawable polymer is limited by the rate of dissipation of the heat evolved, while it is the rate of regeneration which determines the rate of effective stretching of rayon.

The amount of effective stretching of the gel yarn depends on the degree of substitution of its reactive groups (degree of xanthation) and to a lesser extent on the temperature (degree of plasticization). Temperature, of course, has a dual effect, insofar as it influences the rate of dexanthation. The amount of stretch from the first roller guide to the cutter feed roll is 110–140%, as compared to 60–80% for regular rayon.

Further processing of HWM fibers is different from regular rayon only as far as it is related to the denser structure. Purification is somewhat slower and bleaching is generally inevitable to obtain an acceptable color. Because of lower water imbibition, drying requires somewhat less energy. HWM fibers dye lighter than regular rayon, in the same dye bath.

B. Microstructure

The physical and chemical behavior of this type of fiber seems to indicate a three-dimensional network of highly oriented aggregates, although of low lateral order; in other words, many small crystalline regions, interconnected by molecular chains or bundles, generally aligned parallel to the fiber axis. Any attempt to describe the structure briefly or to explain it with the help of sketches is certainly an oversimplification, and the various fibers represent most probably a wide spectrum of type and degree of organization. One thing seems to be certain however, that further improvements of the performance of textile rayons are independent of orientation building stretch, but entirely dependent on coagulation and regeneration conditions, with its effect on the crystalline-amorphous network.

Birefringence, electron microscopy, x-ray, conductivity, density, and accessibility measurements are some of the methods giving an insight into the structure of fibers, and the results provide food for speculation as to the mechanism of formation and the effect on performance.

One of the few variables in this regard, which has been fairly well defined, is the degree of polymerization. The optimum range for different types of fibers has been established. The upper limit is generally determined by practical considerations; for high-performance fibers, for example, it is around 550. In addition to the average chain length, the distribution is important, and the deleterious effect on properties such as swelling and solubility in caustic, can readily be related to the amount of low D.P. cellulose (below 100) present.

While natural fibers show fibrillar structure, the presence and possible effect on properties of a similar structure in regenerated fibers is not certain. It is possible, however, to fibrillate regenerated fibers by chemical and mechanical treatments.

Furthermore, the fiber structure includes microscopic and submicroscopic voids which have apparently no effect on properties.

C. Physical Properties

After the brief discussion of the mechanism of formation and the fine structure of high-performance rayon staple, its physical properties are shown in Table VII.

As mentioned previously, the physical properties of fibers cannot be readily translated into general fabric performance; however, their behavior under certain specific conditions may be predicted. High strength, for example, combined with the high breaking elongation indicates improved abrasion resistance, an ability to accept repeated de-

TABLE VII. Physical Properties of High-Performance Rayon Staple

	Regular	High tenacity	Polynosic	High wet modulus	Cotton
Denier	1.5	1.5	1.5	1.5	—
Tenacity (g/den)					
conditioned	2.5	4.1	4.0	5.0	3.7
wet	1.5	3.0	2.8	3.5	4.2
Elongation, %					
conditioned	22	30	10	15	10
wet	28	37	12	20	13
Wet modulus at 5% elongation	3	6	21	12	15
Loop tenacity (g/den) conditioned	0.65	1.2	0.6	1.2	1.7
Loop elongation % conditioned	1.7	6	1.0	3	—
Knot tenacity (g/den) conditioned	1.5	2.1	1.85	2.7	2.3
Knot elongation % conditioned	10.5	12	4.5	9.4	—
Ratio wet/dry tenacity	60	73	80	70	100
Water imbibition %	110	70	60	60	60
Weight loss in 5.5% NaOH at 20°C	11	4	1.5	2.5	1.5
Increase in diameter on swelling, %	26	—	12	15	13
Degree of polymerization	240	300	500	320	>2,000
Moisture regain, %	13	12	12	12	7

formation without substantial loss of properties, and higher residual strength after resin treatments. The lower accessibility as indicated by lower degree of swelling and higher resistance to caustic (less loss in weight) may predict better performance when wet (improved launderability) and higher residual strength after mercerization when blended with cotton. The resistance to caustic, in addition to being related to accessibility, probably depends also on the interior surface area, inasmuch as fibers with many but small crystallites have a larger area for attack by mercerizing caustic than the same amount of crystallinity represented by fewer but larger crystallites. While the former is probably typical for HWM fibers, the latter is a characteristic of the Toramomen (polynosic) types.

The properties of these two types of fibers are growing more similar to each other, and more recent HWM fibers show a promising combination of high strength, high wet modulus, and good caustic resistance.

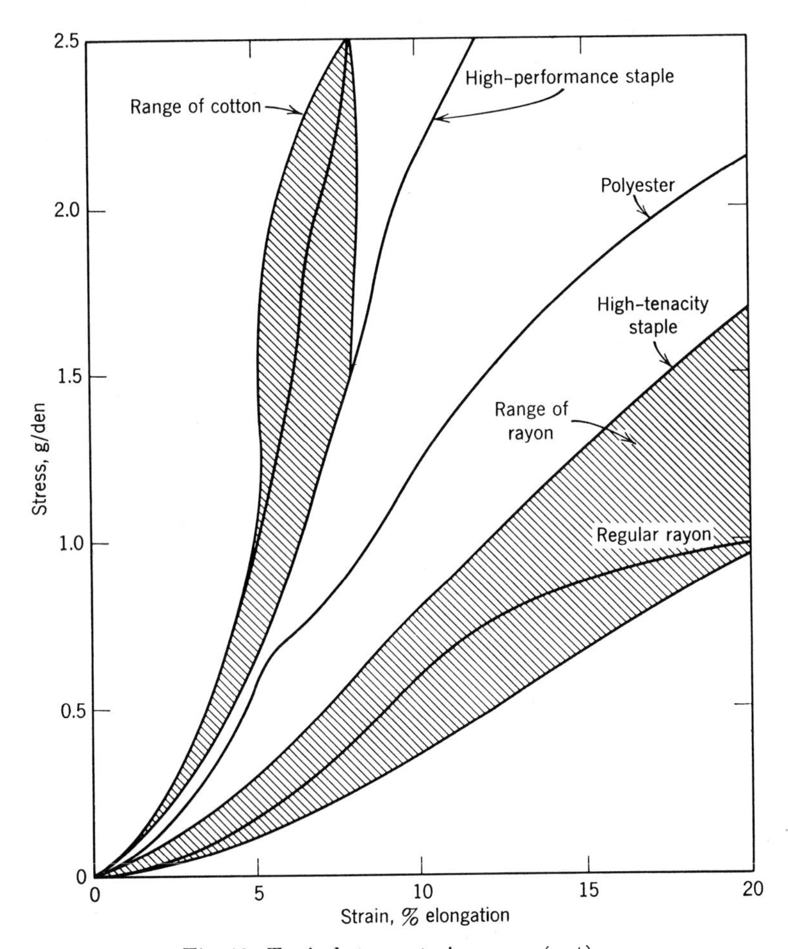

Fig. 13. Typical stress–strain curves (wet).

Referring to Fig. 13, the shape of the stress–strain curve of high-performance rayons is close to that of synthetic fibers, such as polyester. In blends of fibers maximum wear should be expected if the components have similar stress–strain curves.

High-performance rayons have a semi-dull, subdued luster, because of fine voids, probably formed by carbon disulfide during coagulation. It can be made completely dull by addition of dulling agents to the viscose. Because of the tighter molecular structure, these types of fibers dye lighter, less brilliant than regular rayon in the same dye bath, similar to cotton. Light fastness and fastness to washing is of course the same as for regular rayon.

As far as durable-press resin treatments are concerned, much more development work has been done with cotton than with rayon, and satisfactory performance of rayon alone or in blends with cotton or synthetics has not been proven conclusively as yet. In order to obtain acceptable crease resistance and recovery in regular rayon fabrics, twice as much resin has to be applied as for cotton. HWM fibers, however, require only approximately the same amount as cotton. This phenomenon is probably partly due to the improved elastic recovery *per se;* it is in the wet stage for regular rayon 65% (recovery from a loading of 0.5 g/den), as against 90% to 95% for HWM fibers. This improved elastic recovery, also present in the dry stage, gives fabrics improved resilience and makes it "livelier." Furthermore, the residual tensile properties, such as tear strength, important factors in case of wash-and-wear fabrics, are much higher after the resin treatment than for regular rayon, because the tensile properties are higher to begin with and, also, the loss due to resin finishing is less; the same applies for mercerization. Regular rayon cannot be mercerized by conventional cotton conditions, not only because the rayon would be seriously damaged, but also because of its high degree of swelling, which makes it difficult to wash the fabric free of caustic. HWM blends with cotton can be mercerized with conventional methods without difficulties.

Because of higher strength and better uniformity of yarns spun from HWM staple, finer counts can be spun, lighter and "cleaner" (fewer faults) fabrics can be obtained.

Furthermore, degradation processes, such as by acids to hydrocellulose by oxidizing agents to oxycellulose, and by light to photocellulose, are somewhat reduced in rate.

In general, these new fibers combine the desirable properties of rayon and cotton, essentially eliminating the shortcomings of both: dimensional stability, good wearing qualities, dyeability, uniformity and choice of properties of a manufactured fiber (denier, cut length, elongation, luster, spin-dyeing), to name the more important advantages. As opposed to regular rayon, high-performance rayons give fabrics of firm, yet rich and silky hand, which are nevertheless possibly not quite as "masculine" as cotton.

D. Dimensional Stability

The dimensional stability of fabrics containing viscose rayon depends primarily on (*1*) the resistance to deformation during the various textile operations such as dyeing and finishing, and during laundering, and (*2*) the degree of swelling.

During wet processing and laundering, fabrics are rarely stressed more than 0.5 g/den, and it was found to be important that such stresses allow elongation of less than 5%; higher elongation would partly remain in the finished fabric and appear as progressive shrinkage during subsequent laundering. At a stress of 0.5 g/den wet cotton is stretched about 2%, HWM fibers about 3%, and regular rayon about 10%. In other words, the wet modulus of HWM fibers is similar to cotton and much higher than that of regular rayon. Figure 13 shows the similarity of the initial portion of the stress–strain curves of high-performance rayons and cottons. Furthermore, high-performance rayons recover nearly completely from strains in this initial portion, and the resilience of these fibers is greatly improved.

The stress–strain curve of wet regular rayon is quite flat; this is explained by assuming that secondary bonding in the amorphous regions has been weakened by water and the molecules or crystallites slide past each other with little or no resistance. The fine structure of HWM fibers is such that resistance to initial deformation is provided even in absence of secondary bonds in the amorphous regions; the same structural characteristics give increased resistance to swelling. Swelling of a fiber causes longitudinal contraction. Some of this contraction is permanent and results in progressive shrinkage upon repeated wetting which for regular rayon can be up to 14%. Part of this contraction is temporary and is removed upon deswelling (drying), causing wet to dry length change, which, for example, make curtains made from regular rayon unacceptable, because of variation in length with relative humidity.

The practical advantages of the resistance to deformation and the lower swelling of HWM fibers are the feasibility of mechanical preshrinking of fabrics since these fibers can withstand the stresses of subsequent wet textile processes such as scouring and dyeing. Fabrics made from 100% high-performance fibers can thus be produced with less than 2% shrinkage. Regular rayon cannot be mechanically preshrunk since the compacting effect would be lost during wet processing or laundering.

In a fabric, a swollen fiber will cause an additional shrinkage, because the increase in diameter lengthens the path of the fibers woven across, thus reducing the dimension of the fabric in that direction. Lower swelling fibers, therefore, cause less fabric shrinkage.

Furthermore, the resistance to swelling causes high-performance fibers to be more resistant to caustic. Table VII shows that samples immersed for 10 min in 5.5% caustic at 20°C give a weight loss of 2.5% for HWM as against 11% for regular rayon. HWM rayons can be mercerized in blends with cotton without excess loss in strength.

VII. FURTHER READING

E. Ott and H. Spurlin, *Cellulose and Cellulose Derivatives,* Interscience, New York, 1954.
P. H. Herman, *Physics and Chemistry of Cellulose Fibers,* Elsevier, New York, 1947.
J. M. Matthews and W. R. Mauersberger, *Textile Fibers,* Wiley, New York, 1954.
R. W. Moncrieff, *Man-Made Fibers,* Wiley, New York, 1963.
R. H. Hill, *Fibres from Synthetic Polymers,* Elsevier, Amsterdam, 1953.

Viscose Rayon Tire Yarn

W. J. McGarry and M. H. Priest
Courtaulds Ltd., Coventry, England

CONTENTS

I. INTRODUCTION

A. General

Viscose rayon is the only major fiber whose formation, during spinning, depends upon chemical as well as upon physical reactions. Rayon fibers are wet-spun, and during their manufacture they pass from a highly swollen to a much less swollen state; hence they can be oriented by stretching in various degrees of molecular mobility. The fiber-forming process is thus highly complex, and therefore the process and product are very versatile. This versatility has been exploited to the extent that rayon fibers can be produced with tailor-made tensile properties, which cover most of the range of known fiber tensile properties; this status quo has been maintained for the last decade.

Much of the impetus for this achievement has been created by a continuing demand for more durable, faster-running, safer automobile tires. This demand has stimulated intensive research and technological developments, which have produced rayon tire yarns of increasing strength, fatigue life, and durability. These improved products have encouraged fundamental research, which is leading to a deeper understanding of the rayon tire yarn spinning process.

B. The Viscose Tire Yarn Spinning Process

In the wet-spinning of viscose rayon, the viscose, an aqueous alkaline solution of sodium cellulose xanthate containing impurities known as by-products, which are formed by reactions between sodium hydroxide and carbon disulfide, is pumped continuously through a jet (an assembly of parallel similar fine orifices) into a "coagulating-regenerating" bath. The gel obtained is transferred from the initial takeup roller or reel to a roller of higher circumferential speed, thus applying positive stretch.

The above stages are usually referred to collectively as the spinning process. Nowadays viscose tire yarns are usually continuously spun, and further stages of fixation, relaxation, washing, finishing, drying, and collection are added to the above stages to constitute the overall tire yarn manufacturing process.

All modern tire yarns are usually made with substances called modifiers added to the viscose, with spin baths consisting of sulfuric acid, zinc sulfate, and sodium sulfate, and with hot aqueous sulfuric acid stretch. To help a demand for new improved types of tires, such as radial ply tires, however, new high-modulus yarns are being made on an experimental scale which are based on a different spinning process.

II. HISTORY

Viscose rayon was first made commercially in Europe at the end of the nineteenth century. It is still the largest-selling man-made fiber. The

TABLE I. Development of the Strength of Tire Yarns

Yarn	Year	Conditioned tenacity, g/den	Wet tenacity, g/den	Cord breaking load, lb, (1650-den yarn)
Textile	1907	1.1	0.4	
Textile	1913	1.4	0.5	
Textile	1917	1.7	0.8	
Textile	1939	2.1	1.1	
Tenasco	1937	3.4	2.2	23
Low acid process	1950	4.0	2.8	28.5
Super 1	1953	4.3	3.1	32.5
Super 2	1957	5.0	3.8	35
Super 3	1962	5.5	4.4	38
Super 4 (in development)	1965	6.0	5.0	42

improvements in strength obtained for viscose rayon continuous-filament textile and tire yarn over the years are shown in Table I.

Important milestones in the early developments were the introduction of the Müller type bath in 1907 (sodium sulfate, which reduced weakness and dullness), the Napper bath in 1911 (containing 1% zinc sulfate), which produced a less hydrated and tougher filament, and various modifications to the stretching procedure, from 1911 onward.

It was the discovery of the "Tenasco" process (1) which first enabled rayon to be produced with sufficient tenacity to compete with cotton in the tire yarn market. The increase in tenacity, at the same extensibility, was obtained by two modifications: (*1*) The zinc sulfate concentration in the spin bath was increased from 1 to 4% (by weight). (*2*) The thread was stretched through hot dilute acid, enabling a much higher stretch to be applied and retained.

The strength of Tenasco increases as its water content is reduced, while the reverse is true for cotton. This was an immediate advantage, as the carcass of a tire loses moisture and remains dry during use. Furthermore, the higher extensibility of Tenasco conferred better flex and fatigue properties on the tire yarns, considerably increasing their life.

Under the impetus of World War II, rayon's share of the tire yarn market was substantially increased. The advent and growing importance of continuous spinning machinery, which made high quality rayon tire yarn cheaper to produce, also contributed to its rapid growth.

Postwar developments in the quality of dissolving pulps enabled better quality viscoses to be made. This enabled jets of smaller hole

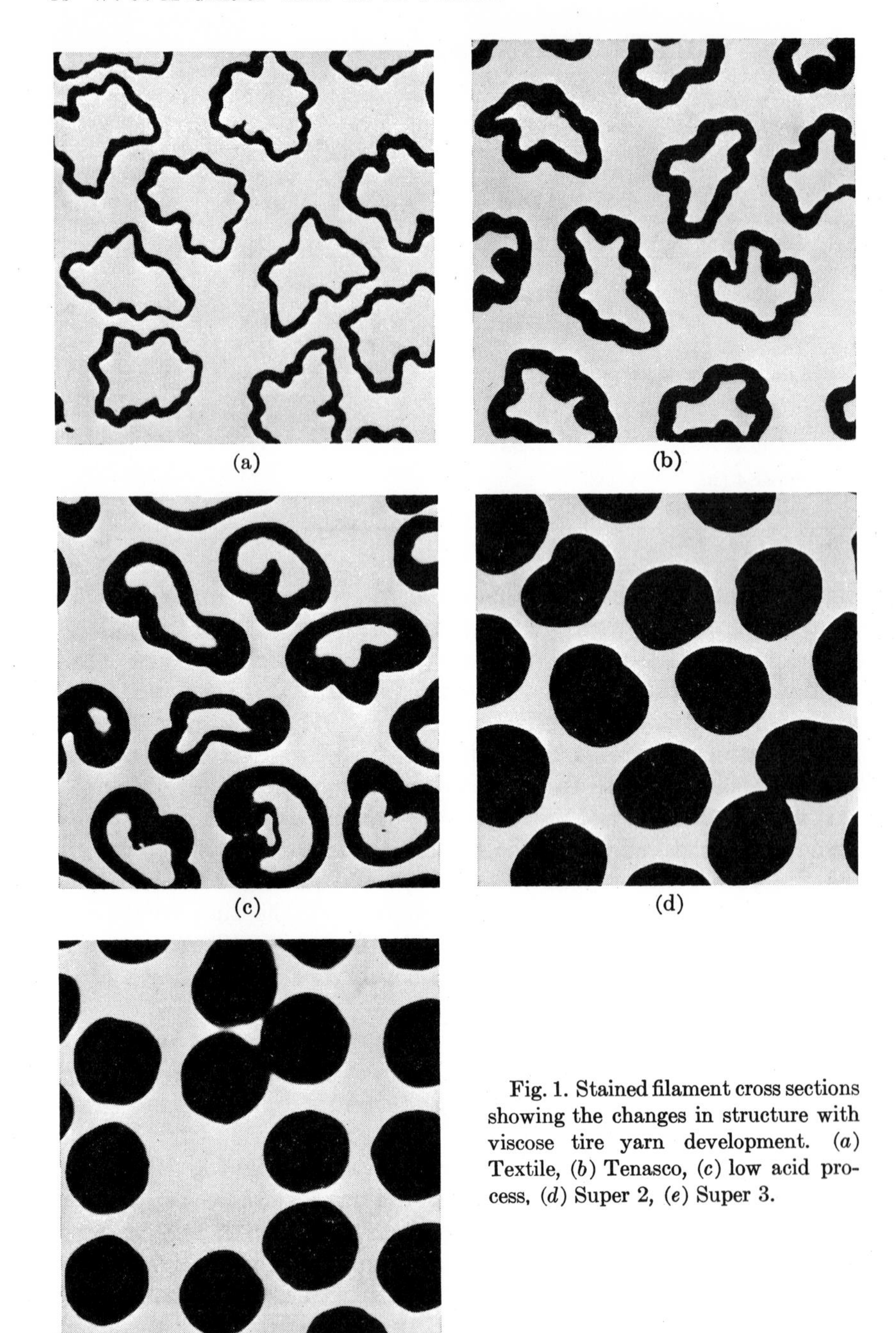

Fig. 1. Stained filament cross sections showing the changes in structure with viscose tire yarn development. (*a*) Textile, (*b*) Tenasco, (*c*) low acid process, (*d*) Super 2, (*e*) Super 3.

size to be used and led to the low acid process, when it was found that stronger yarns could be made by spinning at the minimum spin bath acid consistent with good yarn quality. Concomitant alterations in spin bath parameters (zinc sulfate concentration and temperature) and in stretching conditions, and the introduction of spinning aids which reduced bath drag on the tender filaments progressively led to further improvements in properties.

The next breakthrough in improved tire yarns followed the discovery of modifiers by Cox in 1946 (2). When added to viscose under certain conditions, modifiers gave rise to filaments of improved strength, with smooth cross sections and skin structure (see Fig. 1).

The action of modifiers will be discussed in detail later (see Section III C-2). Their discovery resulted in the production of the first Super tire yarns. [To the tire manufacturer a "Super 1 yarn" means a yarn that will give twofold 12 $\times$ 12 cord from 1650-den yarn of at least thirty pounds oven-dry breaking strength.]

Super 2 and Super 3 yarns, as well as experimental Super 4 yarns, have mainly resulted from technological modifications of the Super 1 process, involving the use of higher DP pulps of better quality, improved modifiers, jets of smaller hole size, lower spin bath acid concentrations, spin bath aids giving better conditions of spin bath flow (principally tube spinning—see Section IV B), and improved stretching techniques, all aided by continuing research, which has given rise to a better understanding of the mechanism of the tire yarn spinning process.

III. DEVELOPMENT OF STRUCTURE AND PROPERTIES

A. General Considerations

The properties of any fiber are determined by the relative arrangements of the molecules within the whole material. In the case of viscose rayon, due to the complexity of its formation a wide variety of configurations is readily achieved, and research is largely devoted to finding ways of achieving the most suitable morphology for particular end uses.

Appreciation of this follows from a consideration of the spinning process. Viscose solutions generally contain 5–10% of cellulose partially substituted with xanthate groups and 5–10% of sodium hydroxide by weight; the final fiber is cellulose. The essential reactions of fiber formation thus consist of a transfer of matter from the spinning filament to the bath, accompanied by chemical reaction. A large number of parameters can be varied to affect the relative rates of these reactions, with attendant effects on fiber structure.

The initial product, when viscose solution is extruded into a spin bath, is a gel. This is formed primarily by coagulation. Coagulation is dependent on the mutual assistance of a number of reactions; diffusion of ions from the spin bath to the filament (and vice-versa) accompanied by osmosis, salting-out effects, and chemical reactions between mutually diffusing ions and between diffusing ions and less mobile xanthate ions. Thus coagulation is critically dependent on both viscose and bath parameters; principally, upon the degree of xanthate substitution and the sodium hydroxide concentration, and upon the concentrations of acid and salts in the spin bath and its temperature.

The ratio of the alkali concentration in the viscose to the acid concentration in the bath is of particular importance in that it largely determines the extent to which regeneration accompanies or follows coagulation. The regeneration reaction is shown in Eq. 1.

$$\underset{\substack{\text{sodium}\\\text{cellulose}\\\text{xanthate}}}{\text{Cell—OCS}_2^-\text{—Na}^+} \xrightarrow{H_2SO_4} \underset{\substack{\text{cellulose}\\\text{xanthic}\\\text{acid}}}{\text{Cell—OCS}_2^-\text{—H}^+} \xrightarrow{H_2SO_4} \underset{\text{cellulose}}{\text{Cell—OH}} + CS_2 \qquad (1)$$

Regeneration may or may not be accompanied by compound formation (3). The most important example of this, which is generally considered to play an integral part in tire yarn formation is shown in Eq. 2.

$$\text{Cell—OCS}_2^-\text{—Na}^+ \xrightarrow{ZnSO_4} \text{Cell—OCS}_2^-\text{Zn}^{2+}\text{CS}_2^-\text{—O Cell} \xrightarrow{H_2SO_4}$$
$$\text{Cell—OCS}_2^-\text{—H}^+ \xrightarrow{H_2SO_4} \text{Cell—OH} + CS_2 \qquad (2)$$

The relative rates of coagulation and regeneration largely determine the rate and extent of filament shrinkage in the spin bath, and thus fiber shape and consolidation (the way the structure is laid down). This in turn affects the state of the gel at stretch, a critical factor in determining fiber properties and structure, as it determines the maximum stretch applicable, how this stretch is applied at the molecular level, and therefore potentially the final morphology of the product fiber.

Research has thus concentrated on the understanding of both filament formation and fiber structure, as a knowledge of each is essential for a fuller understanding of the other, and a knowledge of both is essential in order to obtain the best product.

A detailed account of how such studies have led to the development of modern tire yarns will now be given, and this will be followed by an appraisal of the present state of knowledge of viscose tire yarns.

B. Fine Structure

Viscose rayon fibers exhibit differences in both cross-sectional and longitudinal appearance. Furthermore, their structures can vary markedly across their cross sections. This feature is most readily shown by differential dyeing. Figure 1 shows stained cross sections which indicate change in tire yarn structure as development has proceeded. The dyeing treatment consists of a standard immersion in a given concentration of a suitable dye followed by a standard washing treatment, and, as is seen, different dye retentions are observed for different fibers, thereby indicating different states of fiber structure. Skin structure is said to retain the dye, while core structure does not (4).

It is seen that, as fiber strength has increased, the cross-sectional shape has changed progressively from highly crenellated to smooth, and the amount of skin structure has progressively increased. Modern tire yarns are composed of smooth-surfaced all-skin fibers; they have a uniform gross structure.

In addition to a skin-core or all skin structure, Super tire yarns possess a very thin outer layer or cuticle the existence of which has been demonstrated by optical microscopy (5). A number of authors hold the view that the cuticle is of considerable importance in determining overall fiber structure (see Section III C-3).

The submicroscopic or fine structure of tire yarns is generally interpreted by the fringe micellar theory. According to this theory, fiber structure, chemical reactivity, and mechanical properties are interpreted in terms of crystalline regions of high order which do not deform, and amorphous regions of low order which deform and largely confer the properties. The development of the theory has been reviewed by Frey-Wyssling (6) and Hermans (7); a useful background to the theory is given by Howsmon and Sisson (8), and a more modern appraisal is given by Hearle (9). While the theory provides a convenient model for interpreting structural measurements it is generally recognized that a whole spectrum of varying degrees of order exists within fibers.

The type of information obtained from, and the more important techniques used for studying the fine structure of rayons will now be briefly reviewed.

X-ray measurements have been used (*a*) to show that there are crystalline regions in rayons (10), and (*b*) following the methods proposed by Hermans (11) and Kast and Flaschner (12), to give a measurement of the size of the crystalline regions (crystallites). Low-angle scattering measurements based on the theories of Guinier (13) and Kratky (14) have demonstrated that the crystallites are longer (in the direction of the fiber axis) than they are broad, and that crystallite dimensions differ considerably for different types of rayons. The unit cell of cellulose II in viscose rayons has also been established by x-ray measurements (15). It has been further shown that the lattice is not disturbed when a fiber is immersed in water, implying that water does not penetrate the crystalline regions.

With this knowledge, measurements of moisture regains on rayon have been used to obtain further estimates of crystallite size (16), on the basis that if two rayons of the same crystallinity absorb different quantities of water vapor, the fiber with the smaller crystallites will absorb more water, because the surface area of the crystallites will be greater, and crystallite surfaces are accessible to water.

Estimates of crystallinity have also been obtained by infrared examinations of deuterated rayons. The basis of this method is that hydrogen can be readily replaced by deuterium-exchange in the accessible regions and the amount of exchange can be determined because the stretching frequencies of the OH and OD bonds are different. Lower values of crystallinity are obtained from infrared than from x-ray measurements.

TABLE II. Tensile Properties of Some Regenerated Cellulose Fibers (16)

	Tenacity, g/den		Extensibility, %	
Fiber	Conditoned	Wet	Conditioned	Wet
Normal textile viscose rayon	2.2	1.1	19.9	27.5
Tenasco	3.4	2.1	10.1	21.0
Low acid process	4.0	2.5	10.5	21.0
Super 1	4.1	3.1	13.5	25.0
Super 2	5.3	4.2	12.5	24.0
A polynosic rayon	5.4	3.8	6.0	7.3

Reasons for this are discussed in the review by Mann (17) of modern methods of determining crystallinity in cellulose. Infrared measurements have also shown that, in dry cellulose fibers, virtually all the hydroxyl groups are hydrogen-bonded (18)—an important consideration in the interpretation of mechanical properties. The infrared method of determining crystallinity suffers from the limitation that it can be much more easily applied to films than to fibers (17).

Density measurements, first proposed by Hermans (19), have provided a further criterion of the crystallinity of rayons (16).

Optical measurements, in particular birefringence measurements, have yielded information about the average orientation of chains within the fibers (16). The ratio of x-ray to optical orientation indicates the difference in orientation between the crystalline part of the fiber and the

TABLE III. Accessibility and Crystallinity of Some Regenerated Cellulose Fibers (16)

Fiber	Moisture regain, 60% RH (25°C), %	Accessibility, %	Density, g/cc	Crystalline cellulose II, %	Accessibility factor of crystalline region	Size of crystallite anhydroglucose units in side of square ends	Birefringence 65% RH, 25°C
Normal textile viscose rayon	12.5	76.6	1.512	45.2	0.48	4.3	0.027
Tenasco	12.9	79.1	1.509	42.9	0.51	3.9	0.032
Low acid process	13.4	82.3	1.509	42.9	0.58	3.1	0.032
Super 1	14.4	88.3	1.496	32.5	0.64	2.5	0.033
Super 2	14.1	86.4	1.508	41.5	0.67	2.0	0.037
A polynosic rayon	10.45	64.0	1.526	55.5	0.32	7.5	0.046

whole fiber (20). As has been pointed out by Wooding (21), tire yarns possess, at a given applied stretch, greater orientation in the crystalline regions than in the amorphous regions, whereas for polynosic fibers the orientations are more nearly equal.

Because of the different natures of their underlying assumptions, many of the methods used for determining structural parameters give different results. At present there is no published information which gives results for all the above methods over the range of tire yarn fibers. A fairly comprehensive set of data has been published by Tyler and Wooding (16), however. Some of their results are reproduced here, as they give a very good understanding of the fine structure of tire yarns. Table II shows the tensile properties of some fibers, and Table III shows the corresponding fine structural properties.

The authors themselves discuss in detail the manner in which the calculated results of Table III (accessibilities, crystallinities, accessibility factors of crystalline regions, and crystallite sizes) were estimated from the moisture regain and density measurements. The underlying assumptions are also fully discussed.

The data presented in Table III have contributed significantly to, and fits in very well with accepted views of the relationship between tire yarn structure and tensile properties.

As tire yarns have developed, their structure has become increasingly fine-textured and homogeneous. This allows a more even spreading of applied load than can occur in other rayons. Thus, tenacities and extensibilities are high because of the numerous small movements possible in the amorphous regions when stress is applied and because the structure can accommodate small-segment slippage leading to increased ordering effects. Tenacities are also high because individual molecules can pass through several crystallites, giving a cooperative effect and, because of the finer texture, the higher orientation is not accompanied by an increase in modulus and decrease in extensibility.

TABLE IV. Water Imbibition of Rayons, wt. %

Fiber	Water imbibition, %
Normal textile viscose rayon	95–100
Tenasco	80–90
Low acid process	70–75
Super 1	70–75
Super 2	70–75
Super 3	70–75
A polynosic rayon	65–70

In a homogeneous fine-textured structure, the many fine crystallites inhibit water swelling in the amorphous regions, and thus enhance the ratio of wet to dry strengths. This can also perhaps be stated as being due to the fact that a fine-textured structure reduces the number of hydrogen bonds broken during wetting, since to a first approximation the wet tensile curve for a rayon is similar to its dry curve above the yield point. (A detailed discussion of the tensile behavior of rayons and fibers in general is included in the review of Wakeham (22).)

The water imbibition of tire yarns, i.e., the percentage of water retained after a standard centrifuging treatment following a standard impregnation (23), does in fact decrease from Tenasco to Super 1, where it tends to level off. This is shown in Table IV.

Care is needed in the interpretation of water imbibition data, however, as the water imbibition is partly dependent on the orientation in the amorphous regions. Polynosic fibers generally have lower water imbibitions than tire yarns in spite of their coarser texture because of their higher overall orientation and their probably higher total crystallinity.

It is not easy on a microscopic basis to distinguish between Super 2 and Super 3 yarns; both are smooth sectioned and dye as all-skin. Dyeing as skin, however, probably corresponds to a certain degree of fineness of texture, and there is no reason to assume that an all-skin structure is homogeneous across the filament cross section. It seems probable on the basis of the evidence available, which is not as detailed as for earlier tire yarns and which has generally not been published, that Super 3 yarns are finer-textured and more homogeneous than Super 2.

Another method which has been used to measure structural parameters in viscose rayons depends on the fact that when an oriented cellulose fiber is immersed in sodium hydroxide solution it swells anisotropically, with the result that there is a change of length, which is generally a contraction. Contractions have been measured as a function of sodium hydroxide concentration for various rayon yarns immersed in solutions of sodium hydroxide of gradually increasing concentration (24). The contractions were interpreted as being due to the fact that regions of progressively increasing order, determined by size, shape, and perfection of ordered regions, are destroyed by progressively increased swelling. At the lower concentrations of sodium hydroxide the contractions are greatest for tire yarns, which is in accordance with tire yarns having a fine textured structure.

The fine structure of cellulose fibers has also been studied by electron microscopy. The fibers studied are generally first disintegrated, either mechanically or by acid or alkaline hydrolysis. Natural fibers break down into fibrils, whereas rayons do so to a lesser extent. Kaeppner (25) demonstrated that polynosic fibers have a fibrillar structure, whereas tire yarns do not. All the rayons have longitudinal striations on the surface, but whereas for Fortisan they are an expression of underlying fibrillar structure, for Super tire yarns they are confined to a very thin layer on the surface of the filaments—almost certainly the cuticle. Klare and Gröbe (26) have demonstrated that modifiers in the viscose give tire yarns with a more closely packed arrangement of striations in the structure.

The electron microscope can supply information which other techniques cannot. Kaeppner's results, for instance, suggest that bonding between crystallites is similar in both radial and tangential directions, and is probably stronger than bonding between the crystallites in the direction of the fiber axis.

Overall, the results are in accord with the accepted views of tire yarn structure.

It would be attractive if the interpretation of tire yarn fine structure which has just been discussed could be regarded as definitive. It is truer to say that it is the interpretation which is generally used by viscose scientists in their endeavors to explain and promote research and development of existing and new viscose fibers. The success achieved in the viscose industry is a measure of its utility.

This section would be incomplete, however, if it was not pointed out that there are a number of objections to the fringe micellar theory, in spite of its wide recognition and general use by fiber scientists. The existence of fibrils in rayons (although not in tire yarns), as demonstrated by electron microscopic measurements, is difficult to interpret on the basis of the fringe-micellar theory. However, it is worth remembering that the existence of fine fibrils has only been demonstrated for rayons which have been subjected to some form of disintegration treatment. A number of workers—Morgan (27), for example—have pointed out that x-ray measurements need not necessarily be interpreted in terms of crystallite size. They can equally well be interpreted in terms of imperfections in long fibrillar crystals. Kargin (28), on the other hand, concludes that it is possible to prove in several ways the absence of crystallinity in cellulose even when it is highly oriented. Electron diffraction measurements (29) have been interpreted as showing that cellulose is amorphous. Kargin also points out that differences between crystalline and amorphous regions in polymers are much less pronounced than in the analogous low-molecular-weight substances. Hearle (9) has discussed all these views in detail, and has proposed a fringed-fibril theory of cellulose structure.

The main attraction of the fringe-micellar theory for the interpretation of viscose rayon fine structure is that it fits in very well with the classical views of the mechanism of the viscose rayon spinning process. It is particularly attractive in its explanation of the skin-core and all skin structures of rayon tire yarns. Skin structure is considered to result from the intermediate formation of zinc cellulose xanthate in the spinning filament (see Section III-C-3). This results in a cross-linked gel. Numerous small crystalline nuclei are formed at the cross-linking points; these provide the basis of the fine-textured structure of the yarns. The validity of this theory is now in dispute, and the propounders of the alternative cuticle theory (see Section III-C-3) are already studying the manner in which their suggested mechanism fits in with tire yarn fine structure.

C. Mechanism of the Tire Yarn Spinning Process

1. General Considerations

As has already been stated, the structure and properties of a rayon fiber depend upon both viscose and bath parameters. These affect the state of the gel at stretch, thus constituting a very important factor in determining potential fiber properties.

The state of swelling of the gel is probably the most useful single criterion of the gel state, as it is dependent on gel structure, and these two factors together will determine molecular mobility during stretching. A highly swollen gel reflects an unconsolidated structure, and a shrunken gel a more organized structure. With a highly swollen gel the fiber structure is determined mainly at stretching; with a shrunken gel it is determined mainly before stretching.

Thus, with maximum stretch, a highly swollen gel will result in a fiber of high modulus (the factor most clearly related to molecular alignment) and low extensibility, because orientation occurs before crystallization; a highly shrunken gel will result in a fiber of low modulus and high extensibility, because crystallization precedes orientation.

This is borne out by the spinning conditions used for various fibers. Typically, polynosic rayons are spun from viscoses of high xanthate content into baths of low acid and salt concentrations at low temperatures; the reactions of coagulation and regeneration are thus slowed down. Tire yarns, on the other hand, are spun from viscose of lower xanthate content than polynosic yarns, into baths of higher salt but similar acid concentrations at higher temperatures; coagulation and regeneration are thus more rapid. The difference in regeneration is readily demonstrated by measurement of residual xanthate content at stretch.

Evidence for this view has been obtained by Clegg (30), who demonstrated that diameter shrinkages are much more rapid for tire yarns than for polynosic yarns by obtaining photographs of spinning monofilaments with a camera attached to a microscope.

This interpretation of the importance of the gel state is also indirectly demonstrated by a consideration of the primary gel swelling of different fibers, as shown in Table V. The gel swelling value is the swelling value, after a standard centrifuging treatment, of a fiber which has been completely regenerated in its own particular spinning bath without the application of stretch. (It is, of course, somewhat lower than the actual swelling of the gel state stretched in a conventional spinning process.) Nevertheless, the results indicate the shrunken nature of the tire yarn gel.

TABLE V. Film Gel Swellings of Some Regenerated Cellulose Fibers

Fiber	Gel swelling[a]
Toramomen type	6.8
Textile	3.0
Tenasco	2.5
Super 1	1.9
Super 2	1.8

[a] Unreported results of K. L. Gray (Courtaulds Limited).

Similar but more detailed results have been obtained by Vroom and Van Krevelen (31), who refer to the ultimate swelling value of a yarn, and who show that all-skin tire yarns have the lowest ultimate swelling value. That it is a very important quantity is shown by the fact that these authors refer to the ultimate swelling value as a "criterion of the spinning process as a totality."

Klare and Schmiedeknecht (32) have also carried out extensive gel swelling measurements and reviewed the work of previous authors.

However, both gel swelling and the state of the gel at stretch are determined by viscose and bath parameters. In addition to the appropriate balance of normal parameters, for Super tire yarns it is also essential that modifiers should be used in the viscose, and that a high concentration of zinc sulfate must be used in the bath. The reactions that occur with this system make the mechanism of Super tire yarn spinning unique, among viscose rayons, and it is gratifying to note that in recent years considerable effort has been devoted to obtaining a fundamental understanding of the "modifier-zinc" process.

2. *Modifiers*

Modifiers used today consist of a wide variety of different classes of chemical compounds. These include polyethylene glycols, primary, secondary, and tertiary amines, quadrilans, aromatic amines, ethoxylated phenols, etc. In addition, mixtures of compounds are frequently used, an important example being mixtures of amines and polyethylene glycols.

These widely different chemical substances have one important property in common with regard to their function in tire yarn spinning: they slow down the rate of initial acid penetration into the filament. This is shown by numerous measurements on neutralization points (sometimes called *D*-values) (31,33,34). The neutralization point is the distance from the jet at which the spinning thread just becomes neutral throughout its cross section. Neutrality is defined with respect to the pH change of an indicator added to the viscose. Table VI, taken from some of the authors' unpublished results, shows some typical measurements.

TABLE VI[a] Effect of Modifiers on Neutralization Point

Denier/filament	Neutralization point, cm (pK6)	
	Unmodified viscose	Modified viscose
2	4	6
4	7	13

[a] Conventional tire yarn spinning conditions were used.

Agreement on the effects of various viscose and bath parameters on the neutralization point is not always achieved between different authors. A probable reason for this is that precise viscose and bath parameters are not always quoted, and changes with respect to particular parameters would only be expected to be reproducible if other variables were the same.

It is accepted, however, that modifiers do decrease the rate of neutralization under technical tire yarn spinning conditions, and for this effect to be operative it is necessary that the relative acid and zinc sulfate concentrations in the bath lie within certain limits, appropriate to the viscose composition, and that by-products be present in the viscose.

A recent intensive study of neutralization points is included in the report of Vroom and Van Krevelen (31).

Many theories have been advanced to explain the role of modifiers in delaying initial regeneration, and also to explain their effects on Super tire yarn spinning in general. Literature reviews on these subjects are included in the papers of Klare and Gröbe (35) and Strübrer and George (36), and a more detailed review of a smaller number of papers is given by Wydrzycki (37).

The following is a summary of some of the more important effects claimed for modifiers.

1. Modifiers assist in the intermediate formation of zinc cellulose xanthate, which produces stronger deswelling and slower regeneration, and which is a necessary prerequisite to the formation of skin structure and tire yarn properties (3,31,34,36,38,39). This is frequently said to be due to the formation of a selective screen or membrane, which slows down the diffusion of hydrogen ions and allows a preferential penetration of zinc ions (3,38,39). Typically, the acid-resistant barrier is said to be due to the formation of salts, such as zinc dithiocarbamates in the case of amine modifiers and polyoxonium salts in the case of polyethylene glycol type modifiers (38).

2. Modifiers assist in the formation of a cuticle, usually specified to contain zinc cellulose xanthate (26,40–43). In particular, the cuticle is said to hinder the formation of the zinc cellulose xanthate inside its boundary either wholly (26,41,43), or at least in part (40,42). The cuticle promotes deswelling and slower regeneration and allows the particular type of coagulation responsible for tire yarn structure.

3. Modifiers cause increased deswelling (*a*) by reacting with metallic ions (44), (*b*) by reacting with free hydroxyl groups of the xanthate molecules, thus expelling water of solvation (45), (*c*) due to forming acid-resistant amine xanthates (46), although it has been shown that amine xanthates of lower xanthates are soluble (47), or (*d*) due to the formation of relatively insoluble oxonium xanthates (46).

4. Modifiers are active when added to the spin bath as well as to the viscose (2), but not always as effectively, as is shown by the fact that of the 200 or so patents listed on modifiers, a much greater proportion claim for addition to the viscose than the bath.

5. Modifiers act by physical processes in that they produce dispersions of particles of various sizes at the acid/alkali interface (48).

6. Modifiers have varying coagulative power, and effect coagulation due to their colloidal chemical action (49).

7. Modifiers reduce the size of fibrils of the surface structures formed in tire yarn baths (26).

8. Amine modifiers affect viscose ripening; warm aging produces round cross sections and good tensile properties; cold aging promotes crenelated cross sections and inferior tensile properties (50). Long ripening causes crenelations due to segregation effects (51).

9. Amine modifiers, for example dimethylamine, lead to thiourethane formation (52)—a possible explanation of the lower crystallinity of the resultant fiber.

10. Modifiers accelerate the sol–gel transition (53).

These investigations have led to two main theories of tire yarn formation, each supported by different groups of authors.

3. *Theories*

a. Zinc Cellulose Xanthate Theory. Skin structure and tire yarn properties are associated with the formation of zinc cellulose xanthate in the filament. Zinc cellulose xanthate is formed at some intermediate stage across the whole cross section of an all-skin yarn. Its formation is promoted by modifiers. It gives rise to a more shrunken gel than sodium cellulose xanthate, which assists in the formation of a finely textured structure. This is attributed to the formation of temporary cross-links which promote the formation of numerous small crystalline nuclei, and/or prevent the formation of large spreading crystalline regions. Furthermore, zinc cellulose xanthate decomposes more slowly than sodium cellulose xanthate in the presence of acids; consequently, the intermediate shrunken plastic gel exists for a longer time than a normal gel, and thus promotes the application of effective and rapid stretch.

b. Cuticle Theory. Tire yarn structure is due to the formation of a cuticle as the viscose stream emerges from the jet. The formation of the cuticle, which perhaps contains zinc cellulose xanthate, is promoted by modifiers. The cuticle is decisive in slowing down regeneration: it delays the exchange between the components of the spinning filament and the spinbath, and it prevents the formation of zinc cellulose xanthate inside the cuticle. These factors affect the course of coagulation in such a way as to give rise to skin structure and tire yarn properties. A further commonly expressed view is that modifiers react with by-products and zinc to form precipitates on the inside of the cuticle—for example, zinc dimethyldithiocarbamate—and that this precipitated layer is responsible for the slowing down of diffusion reactions.

c. Comparison of the Theories. The great contrast between these two theories provides an interesting and stimulating state of affairs to the scientist. In favor of the zinc cellulose xanthate theory, it may be said that it is simple, intuitively reasonable, and attractive. It explains the gradual transition from skin-core to all-skin yarns as the zinc sulfate concentration of the spin bath has been increased. It provided a basis for the origin of the fine-textured structure of tire yarns—via the formation of zinc cross-links. It fits in with the known rapid deswelling effect of zinc ions. It explains many of the observed reactions of modifiers and the slower rate of regeneration. It should be pointed out that it is not necessary to have the whole filament in the form of zinc cellulose xanthate at any time, only that some zinc cellulose xanthate should be formed in each part of the filament at some suitable degree of molecular mobility and pH, perhaps at different times. Also, the transient intermediate need not necessarily be zinc cellulose xanthate as such; it may be an ionic complex formed by interactions between zinc ions and xanthate ions. However, this theory does not attach any importance to the cuticle unless the semipermeable membrane which retards hydrogen ions but promotes the passage of zinc ions provides the cuticle. Furthermore, the evidence as to whether zinc actually penetrates the structure is ambiguous and disputed (26,54), and no direct proof of the existence of zinc cellulose xanthate in the spinning filament has been obtained.

The cuticle theory, on the other hand, gives a less precise interpretation of tire yarn formation. However, it is compatible with known facts on deswelling, and it does not depend on the (unproven) existence of zinc cellulose xanthate. Furthermore, no selective membrane needs to be invoked; the cuticle slows down all diffusion processes and satisfactorily explains the delay in initial regeneration. It explains why modifiers work in the bath as well as in the viscose. But it is more difficult to explain skin-core structure on a cuticle theory, and perhaps more difficult to explain the unique role of zinc in tire yarn spinning.

It is perhaps worth reviewing briefly some of the main evidence for and against the cuticle theory.

Klare and Gröbe (26) concluded that virtually no zinc cellulose xanthate is found in the filament for two main reasons:

1. Zinc cellulose xanthate is insoluble in water. However, when a modified viscose is spun into a tire yarn type bath, a freshly formed filament which has reached the neutralization point is soluble in water, except for a very thin skin (the cuticle). For a nonmodified viscose spun into the same bath, the filament is virtually insoluble.

2. Precise analytical investigations of freshly formed filaments at the neutralization point showed that, whereas about 40% of the xanthate is present as zinc cellulose xanthate for the unmodified case, virtually no zinc cellulose xanthate is present in the modified case (~1%). Furthermore, in the modified case, at later stages in the bath, the zinc content of the filament only increases slightly.

These results have been criticized by Van der Ven (54), who pointed out that Klare's report contained few details of the analytical techniques used. It did state, however, that the filament was washed with an acetate buffer.

Van der Ven produced evidence that washing filaments in buffers containing sodium ions produces an artificially low value for zinc content because of ion exchange (and we have results to support this). Using ice-cold water as a quench, he showed that although less zinc was found in the filament when modifiers were present in the viscose, there was still enough to correspond to a conversion of 15–30% zinc cellulose xanthate. Precise calculations are impossible, however, as other insoluble zinc compounds may well be present.

In answer to this, Klare and Gröbe (55) spun model filaments into baths containing radioactive zinc and showed that the zinc penetrates only into the periphery regardless of whether modifiers are present. However, the diameter of the model fibers was about 1 mm, and as the penetration region appears to exceed the diameter of a normal tire yarn filament, the evidence is indecisive.

More recently, Strübrer and George (36) have carried out more detailed experiments on the penetration of zinc into Super tire yarn filaments (using ice-cold water quenches). They have shown that even after allowing for a stoichiometric formation of zinc sulfide, excess zinc is available for the formation of 30–50% zinc cellulose xanthate. They conclude that zinc cellulose xanthate is necessary for the formation of a tire yarn structure, and that although there is no direct proof that it exists in the spinning filament as such, there is much indirect evidence to suggest that it does.

Further strong indirect evidence of the importance of zinc cellulose xanthate has come from measurements in which the stretching properties of filaments of cellulose, sodium cellulose xanthate, zinc cellulose xanthate, and other metal cellulose xanthates (zinc, ferric, cadmium, thallium, nickel, chromic, aluminum) have been compared (56). Model filaments of the last group are resistant to applied load and fracture easily. The first three can all be extended by about the same amount (approximately 100%), but only the zinc cellulose xanthate can be stretched rapidly. The filaments of sodium cellulose xanthate and cellulose fracture if stretched too quickly.

Vermaas has also published evidence in favor of the zinc cellulose xanthate theory (34). Using unmodified viscose only, he has shown that as a freshly formed filament moves down a spin bath, diffusion boundaries corresponding to successive stages of coagulation, neutralization, and acidification move progressively toward the center of the filament. With a bath containing zinc ions, a further long-lived zinc diffusion boundary is formed, which lies initially between the neutralization and acid boundaries. This is eventually overtaken by the acid boundary, and it marks the skin–core boundary of the filament. Skin structure is only formed when zinc cellulose xanthate is transiently formed, i.e., in the region where the zinc boundary precedes the acid boundary. It is worth stating here that, as far as unmodified tire yarns are concerned, no author seriously disputes the zinc cellulose xanthate theory.

A more sophisticated form of the zinc cellulose xanthate theory has been proposed by Serkov et al. (57). By model experiments, involving baths of hydrochloric acid and zinc sulfate, they have shown that the diffusion of both hydrogen and zinc ions is slowed down when modifier is present in the viscose. However, the actual ratio of zinc to hydrogen ions penetrating the filament is markedly increased. Moreover, more free sodium hydroxide is left in the filaments. They conclude that these effects of modifier promote the formation of zinc cellulose xanthate.

Cichowski (58) has also produced evidence in favor of the zinc cellulose xanthate theory. He has shown that the reaction of zinc ions with sodium cellulose xanthate depends on (*a*) the hydrogen ion concentration, (*b*) the zinc ion concentration, and (*c*) the sodium salt concentration in the solution, and concludes that the formation of skin structure depends on the intermediate formation of zinc cellulose xanthate. He has further demonstrated that zinc substitution causes a substantial increase in the plasticity of the cellulose xanthate gel and promotes that a zinc cellulose xanthate gel can be stretched much more rapidly than a sodium cellulose xanthate gel (56).

Structural information about the nature of the yarn during coagulation and regeneration has been obtained by x-ray studies of spinning filaments (59). This work showed that as the filament leaves the bath it has a molecular sheet structure of low orientation with a spacing of 4.4. Å within a single sheet. During regeneration the sheets come closer together, probably with some hydrogen bonding as the sheets pack into a swollen cellulose II structure. After drying, the yarn becomes largely crystalline cellulose II. It has been shown subsequently (60), however, that although this applies to an unmodified tire yarn, in the case of a Super tire yarn some cellulose II structure has been formed by the time the filament leaves the bath. Thus at the stretching stage a different structure is present in the two cases. The interpretation of this is a matter for speculation; it could be that either more or less zinc cellulose xanthate is present in the Super yarn.

Meanwhile, Klare and his collaborators have turned their attention to other aspects of the problem. They have discussed in detail, with a review of references, the role of gel swelling as a parameter of tire yarn structure (32), and find their results harmonious with the cuticle theory. They have studied the ordered coagulation of dilute solutions of sodium cellulose xanthate (ionotropic gel formation) and have shown that different ions, including zinc ions, produce different types of birefringent gel structures (61). They have also calculated the diffusion coefficient of bath components into the spun filament using different methods (62). In a recent paper they have again reviewed the present position of both theories (53). This paper is a very important one; it discusses Klare and Gröbe's latest views on the action of zinc and modifiers, the sol–gel transformation, and ordered coagulation.

A diffusion study has also been included in the paper of Vroom and Van Krevelen (31). They have drawn up three rules for cylindrical diffusion processes, in general, and have shown that these rules apply to viscose rayon spinning processes, with the exception of the Super tire yarn process, where the diffusion coefficient seems to alter numerically and become structure-(i.e., time-) dependent. This is attributed to the formation of zinc cellulose xanthate complexes of the form

$$Zn^{2+} + nX^- \rightleftarrows Zn\,X_n^{n-2} \tag{3}$$

which slow down regeneration.

A considerable amount of work which is relevant to these topics has been carried out in our own laboratories.

Film gel swelling measurements have been carried out using a two-bath system with a 1-sec immersion in the first bath and a 5-min immersion in the second bath (63). The gel swelling is always characteristic of the first bath, emphasizing the importance of the early stages of the reaction. Using a tire yarn viscose, a low-gel swelling is always obtained after a 1-sec immersion in a tire yarn bath, irrespective of the bath used for subsequent regeneration. Conversely, after 5 min regeneration in a tire yarn bath a high gel swelling is obtained, if this treatment is preceded by an initial 1-sec immersion in a bath of the same components (except at double the acid concentration).

A similar result was obtained for film neutralization point measurements. The neutralization time is effectively determined by the first 1 sec of immersion in the first bath.

The importance of the early stages of the reaction has also been demonstrated by measurements of pressure behind the spinning jet over a range of pulloff speeds from 0–30 m/min (64). The pressure drop, i.e., the change in pressure with pulloff speed, was recorded. The usual modifier–zinc–by-product interaction was observed, and in general it was found that tire yarn conditions give the lowest pressure drops. The interpretation is that the initial gel structure is less capable of transmitting tensions, as spinning conditions are changed toward tire yarn conditions.

A very significant illustration of the importance of the early stages of spinning has come from measurements of diameter, volume, and velocity of a spinning monofilament (65). Diameter changes were measured by photography and velocity changes using a focal plane shutter camera of known exposure time to photograph titanium dioxide particles of size distribution 5–15 μ added to the viscose. Volumes were computed from diameter and velocity measurements. It should be stated that experimental error in this work is such that only large differences can be regarded as real differences. The most striking effect observed was that modifiers cause a very rapid decrease in filament velocity within 0.5–1.5 cm of the jet face (at tire yarn spin-bath temperatures this applies irrespective of the presence or absence of zinc in the spin bath). To cite a specific example for zinc-containing baths, a 3-den monofilament extruded into a tire yarn bath at 20 m/min and pulled off at 16.5 m/min has a velocity of approximately 10 m/min after a 1-cm immersion for a modified viscose, and 16.5 m/min after a 1-cm immersion for an unmodified viscose. The diameter falls slightly during this distance (0–1 cm), so that the overall result for the modified viscose is a very rapid shrinkage (>50%), or at least a very rapid transfer of matter from the filament to the spin bath; subsequent diameter shrinkage from 1–10 cm is due largely to attenuation as the filament velocity rises to the pulloff speed, i.e., over the distance 1–10 cm volume shrinkage is only very slight. The small volume decrease over the range 1–10 cm immersion is probably slightly greater in a spin bath containing zinc, but the measurements are not sufficiently accurate to establish this with certainty.

The transfer of matter outward during the first 1 cm immersion (modified case) appears to be too rapid to be explained by diffusion or osmosis. A possible explanation is that it is due to the formation of a cuticle, which acts by exerting a mechanical pressure. The effective transfer of sodium hydroxide out of the filament provides a possible explanation of starting points (31).

It should be stated that the velocity and diameter changes were measured from a zero point of approximately 100 μ from the jet face (i.e., the maximum of the post extrusion swelling), and it is worth emphasizing that the velocity slowdown discussed above occurs after the post extrusion swelling.

d. The Present Position. There is general agreement in the literature that the structure of unmodified tire yarns is essentially determined by the intermediate formation of zinc cellulose xanthate during the spinning process.

With regard to modified or Super tire yarns two groups of authors hold differing views, which are generally regarded as being irreconcilable. The first group holds the view that the intermediate formation of zinc cellulose xanthate is assisted by modifiers and is of predominant importance; the second that the structure results from the formation of a cuticle which largely precludes the formation of zinc cellulose xanthate.

In the authors' view it is the very early stages of spinning which are decisive in determining Super tire yarn structure, and the most important reactions occur within the first centimeter of the jet face, where it is unlikely that a significant amount of zinc cellulose xanthate will have been formed. Modifiers are essential for Super tire yarn formation, because without them the tremendous shrinkage and early consolidation which determine the structure during this period would not occur. The early shrinkage alone, however, is not sufficient, because it occurs with modified viscoses even when zinc is absent from the spinbath.

Our own view is that the early shrinkage would not occur unless a cuticle of special properties was formed during the first meeting of the viscose and spin bath components. Why the cuticle should allow such a rapid shrinkage is not understood. We would suggest that its action is mechanical and should not necessarily be considered in terms of diffusion or osmosis.

At the present stage of knowledge, proposed mechanisms with regard to the manner in which the highly consolidated initial structure is transformed to the final tire yarn structure must be considered to be speculative. Evidence is accumulating that diffusion reactions are affected by modifier–zinc trithiocarbamate type complexes formed in or near the cuticle. However, it is still an open question whether or not zinc cellulose xanthate plays a vital role in subsequent structure formation.

In view of the above considerations we would suggest that the two main theories of tire yarn formation are not necessarily opposing and may well be considered to be complementary.

IV. TECHNOLOGY

Many of the developments in structure and properties discussed in Section III have only been made possible by corresponding advances in spinning technology. The various methods of viscose rayon tire yarn production currently in use along with some of the more important technological developments of recent years will now be discussed.

A. Machinery

In the early days of viscose rayon tire yarn development, the existing machinery then being used for textile yarn spinning was modified and adapted to the requirements of the new process. This mainly involved the incorporation of a zone whereby the yarn after withdrawal from the spin bath (by a roller or godet) could be submitted to a high degree of stretch in hot dilute sulfuric acid. The yarn was then collected as for textile yarn in a strain-free state, i.e., as a "cake" in a Topham box or by winding onto a spool. Full decomposition of the cellulose xanthate to cellulose was obtained by storage of the still acid yarn in conditions of relatively high humidity for some 24 hr. The yarn, still in the form as collected, was then washed free of acid, a suitable finish or lubricant was applied, and the yarn dried slowly at a medium temperature (45–50°C) in order to avoid differences in strain throughout the package. In order to confer to the yarn a higher modulus which would be more suitable for the requirements of tire reinforcement, the yarn was then "slashed," i.e., stretched 10% or so through water or aqueous finish and redried at this increased length. This process was normally carried out in the form of a warp, the general effect being to exchange some of the extension for strength and produce a yarn with higher tenacity, higher modulus, and lower extension to break. The yarn was then in a condition suitable for conversion into cord form by twisting two or more yarns together. (Before yarn slashing came into practice, it was customary to apply stretch in the dipping operation.)

At the present time, these methods are still in use by rayon producers around the world, although techniques and details have obviously been considerably improved. In addition, however, a number of continuous spinning systems have been developed. These replace the batchwise nature of the above processes by systems in which the yarn after hot-stretching is fixed, washed, finished, dried, and collected in a continuous operation. The resultant yarn, which is essentially held at constant length throughout this operation, is in no need of further slashing treatment and can be converted immediately into cord form.

There are three main types of continuous spinning machines in current use: (*1*) continuous warp processing; (*2*) processing on a pair of thread advancing rollers; (*3*) processing by means of a series of thread advancing reels. Each of these will now be briefly described.

1. Continuous Warp Processing

The yarns from one side of the spinning machine, after individual hot-stretching, are collected together to form a horizontal warp. The warp is then advanced by traction units, consisting of a number of parallel rollers, through long shallow troughs containing, in order, (*a*) hot dilute acid, (*b*) wash water, and (*c*) finish. Each treatment is effected by inducing the liquid to flow in a direction counter to that of the yarn movement, and spent liquor is progressively removed from the yarn by the squeezing action of a series of horizontal depressor guides. Finally, the yarns are transferred individually onto steam-heated reels or rollers for drying before final collection on bobbins. At the collection stage, a small amount of twist is normally inserted into the yarn.

2. Roller Spinning

One of the advantages of roller spinning is to compact the long processing lengths involved in warp spinning into a comparatively much smaller space. The yarn from the hot stretch zone is fed onto one end of a pair of rollers whose axes are set at a small angle to each other. Because of this angle, the yarn does not build up at one point but is advanced along the roller pair by small incremental amounts. While passing through this storage zone, the yarn is washed by water fed onto the top roller. (In this process, the hot-stretching zone is normally of sufficient length also to accomplish complete regeneration of the cellulose without a further fixation treatment.) At the end of the roller pair the yarn is passed through a finish bath and continuously dried on a steam heated roller, thread advancement and storage being provided by an angled "idling" roller of smaller diameter. Collection is often onto a cheese in the twistless state.

3. Reel Spinning

The principle of the thread self-advancing reel is identical to that of the thread self-advancing roller pair. However, in this case the rollers are made to fit concentrically together by suitably slotting (66). Thus, by having a number of these storage devices in series, the yarn can be passed from one to the other and submitted to a variety of processes. The usual system is to pass the yarn from the hot-stretch zone onto a reel for treatment with hot dilute acid, followed by successive washing, finishing, and drying reels. Collection is normally onto bobbins with the insertion of a small amount of twist.

B. Spinning Techniques

Over the years a number of spinning techniques have been developed which have made important contributions to the progressive optimization of viscose tire yarn processes.

One of the most important of these is the use now made of devices which give support to the yarn in the spin bath by means of streamlined flow along a tube (67–69). Such tube-spinning methods came into being along with the low-acid process and have remained as an essential component of subsequent developments which have all tended to produce filaments in the early coagulation stages which are more tender and easily damaged. The tube, along which the freshly formed filaments pass, can be vertical, horizontal, or at an angle, and flow of spin bath along it is normally induced by a suitable hydrostatic head. However, some vertical tubes take the form of larger-diameter "chimneys" placed above the spinning jet in a conventional open bath. Any flow of liquor up the tube in this case is merely induced by the pumping action of the moving filamentary bundle.

The application of hot stretch to the yarn before its complete regeneration is normally carried out in horizontal or inclined troughs or by treatment through a bath of hot dilute acid, with the yarn passing round a guide or roller fixed below the surface. Some advantage has been found in applying the stretch more gradually by the use of a pair of thread self-advancing rollers of conical shape (70). The yarn is led onto the cones at the point of minimum diameter and is progressively stretched as it advances toward the ends of larger diameter. If a stretch of 100% is required, it is common for 80% of the stretch to be applied incrementally, with the final 20% applied through a hot-stretch trough.

Techniques have also been developed by which the viscose is heated to a temperature approaching that of the spin bath immediately before extrusion (71,72). A number of methods are in use varying from heating the viscose in the pipeline before being fed to individual jets, to heating the viscose passing to each jet by means of a suitably coiled tube immersed in the spin bath or subsidiary water bath. It has been found that viscose heating in general renders a process less critical; that is to say, lower acid concentrations can be tolerated without adversely affecting spinnability, and higher acid concentrations can be allowed with less deleterious effects on tensile properties than would normally be the case. The mode of action of viscose heating is not yet clearly established, but is probably connected with the fact that (*a*) the viscose makes contact with the spin bath at a similar temperature, and (*b*) the resultant improvement in homogeneity of viscosity gives rise to better interfilament uniformity.

C. Viscose Making

In addition to these improvements and innovations to the spinning machine itself, significant advances have also been made in the field of viscose making. In order to satisfy the demand for progressive improvements in strength and uniformity, it has been found necessary to enhance the quality of the viscose used by paying particular attention to homogeneity and freedom from undissolved and dirt particles (73). In addition, productivity and increased production requirements have been met by the use of new and quicker methods of shredding the steeped alkali cellulose sheets.

Viscose solutions of improved quality have been obtained by the use of mixers which impart a higher shear to the system and hence are more efficient in their ability to dissolve "gels." In addition, recirculation during mixing has been improved, and this is often carried out via a subsidiary high-shear mixer/pump. After the viscose has been prepared it is now common practice to remove air bubbles (included in the mixing operation) by passing the viscose under reduced pressure as a thin film over a cone or plate (74–76). At this low pressure, any air bubbles expand and burst and the viscose, as finally collected, is substantially air-free. In many installations, such "continuous deaeration" has replaced the lengthier and more space-consuming batch deaeration in tanks. Finally, while being pumped to the spinning machines the viscose is kept homogeneous with respect to age by a series of multichannel pipe sections which act to displace the slowly moving viscose from the wall of the pipe to the faster moving central section, and vice versa (77). A number of such devices along the length of the viscose delivery pipeline minimize the proportion of old viscose of low degree of xanthate substitution arriving at the spinning jets.

V. APPLICATIONS

A. Tire Reinforcement

The textile component of a tire is the main load-bearing member and, as such, must have a high tensile strength and adequate modulus. However, it has been shown that under conditions of high sidewall deflection, the reinforcing material in the inner plies of the tire can be subjected to compressional strain (78,79). In order to withstand this cyclic compression as the tire rolls along, it has been found necessary to utilize the textile component not in yarn form but as a twisted cord structure, usually of either two- or three-yarn plies. Comparatively high levels of twist are used: for example, a twofold 1650-den cord will normally be used with 12 turns per inch in both singles and folding twist, balance being obtained by inserting this in the "Z" and "S" direction respectively. Most of the twist constructions in current use have been arrived at empirically but have also been the subject of recent published studies (80,81). It has been concluded that a certain minimum level of twist is necessary in order to avoid buckling and reduce filament stress and strain. In the past it has been suggested that cord breakup as a result of compressive strain cycling is caused by fatigue of the cellulose, analogous to the phenomena known to occur in metals. However, it is now widely recognized that so-called "fatigue" failure in a tire can cover a wide range of types of failure, and often includes failure of the adhesive bond between the cord and rubber and cohesive breakdown in the skin rubber adjacent to the cord fabric (82–85).

For a textile material to be considered for tire reinforcement purposes, it must at least be able to satisfy the following requirements: (*1*) High tensile strength; (*2*) adequate modulus; (*3*) low creep under static and dynamic loading; (*4*) good "fatigue" resistance (see above); (*5*) compatibility with rubber in conjunction with suitable bonding systems; (*6*) good impact resistance.

In order to meet the requirements of good fatigue resistance by the use of high-twist cord structures, it is necessary to relinquish perhaps 25% of the composite strength of the yarns used in the cord. As the tensile specifications of most tire companies are based upon cord strength, a great deal of effort has gone into developing methods of efficiently converting as much of the available yarn strength into cord strength. New methods of converting yarns into cords have been developed, and ringframe machines have to some extent been replaced by uptwisting, combined twisting, and direct cabling machines. The combined twisting and direct cabling machines obviously introduce large savings in time and handling and tend to give higher-strength yield efficiencies. In the case of the combined twisters, higher-strength yields are probably partly a result of the singles twist remaining in the yarn for a relatively short period of time, while with the direct cabler the singles yarn is only false-twisted, and the effects of such twist (which may lead to filament entanglement) are eliminated.

Apart from the obvious geometrical considerations of a cord structure, the yarn to cord strength yield has been shown to be influenced by filament cross-sectional shape, the extensibility of the yarns, the uniformity of filament properties (including denier), and the efficiency and uniformity of distribution of lubricant. Use of an efficient lubricant greatly influences the ability of filaments to resist entanglement during cording but primarily promotes the free interfilament movement and adjustment necessary for each filament to take an equal share of the applied load when being strained to break (86,87). As yarns have progressively increased in strength, so the need has arisen for improved lubricants to cope with the increased lateral pressure developed at the higher applied stresses.

Since it is the main load-bearing component of a tire, it is important for a tire cord to have a sufficiently high modulus to prevent undue dimensional change in the tire when inflated. In a tire reinforced with twofold 1650-den cords, a load of 2-3 lb will be induced in each cord by the tire inflation pressure (88). If the modulus of the cords is too low, tire stretch could be excessive and the dimensional changes would impose unwanted strains on the rubber with resultant tread and sidewall cracking.

Apart from the initial dimensional control required to withstand the inflation pressure, it is also necessary for the reinforcing cords to possess low creep characteristics when subjected to this inflation tension and the additional stresses of service. Due to the heat generated in a tire by hysteresis and friction, operating temperatures of around 100°C are commonplace. The factors affecting cord, and therefore tire growth are complex and involve initial extension and creep with time, both of which are influenced by moisture and temperature cycling. It is important for all these to be taken into account when designing laboratory tests (89,90).

Fatigue resistance has been dealt with already and has been shown to be closely associated with the strength of the adhesive bond between cord and rubber and the properties of the associated rubber. Over the years, adhesives have been developed which have progressively improved the bond between the rubber and the tire fabric and have moved from the use of resin natural rubber latex systems to the currently utilized resin/synthetic rubber latex systems. The resin is usually resorcinol-formaldehyde, and the most commonly used latices at the present time are vinyl pyridine–styrene–butadiene complexes (91).

Finally, but by no means least important, a tire must be capable of withstanding such impacts as collisions with a pothole or a rock at high speeds. Ultimate tire performance in this respect is difficult to predict, as much will depend on the mode of deformation of the tire when striking an obstacle. Thus a tire with a very rigid tread might well ride over the obstacle, whereas a tire with a more pliable tread will tend to envelope

TABLE VII. Effect of Strain Rate and Temperature on Rayon and Nylon Tire Cord

Fiber:		Super 2 rayon-dipped cord 2/1650, 12 × 12					Nylon-dipped cord 2/840, 12 × 12				
		Cond.	Oven-dry				Cond.	Oven-dry			
Temperature, °F :		75°	75°	150°	225°	300°	75°	75°	150°	225°	300°
Rate of extension of of sample, %/sec	Break										
0.0013%	lb	25.6	—	—	19.1	—	22.6	—	—	—	—
	elong.	12.7	—	—	8.0	—	18.0	—	—	—	—
	energy	1.82	—	—	0.80	—	1.71	—	—	—	—
1%[a]	lb	32.3	35.0	31.9	27.8	24.0	28.3	29.2	24.0	21.1	16.7
	elong.	13.5	10.2	10.4	10.8	11.3	19.9	20.8	18.9	20.5	22.2
	energy	2.45	2.08	1.94	1.69	1.51	2.50	2.69	1.92	1.93	1.82
1000%	lb	38.5	41.7	40.0	36.6	33.0	32.9	33.4	29.1	25.2	21.3
	elong.	13.8	10.4	11.4	12.5	13.5	17.6	21.1	20.9	21.1	21.3
	energy	3.24	2.66	2.70	2.78	2.75	2.80	3.12	2.59	2.51	2.05
3000%	lb	39.2	43.6	40.6	38.3	36.3	34.6	33.4	29.2	25.1	22.2
	elong.	14.2	10.4	12.7	13.3	14.2	18.5	20.6	20.1	19.5	20.2
	energy	3.17	2.76	3.07	3.08	3.12	2.83	2.94	2.58	1.98	1.91
6000%	lb	41.0	44.0	42.2	40.3	38.1	35.3	34.7	29.3	26.3	22.4
	elong.	13.7	10.3	12.4	13.3	15.0	17.5	21.0	19.8	19.5	19.0
	energy	3.21	2.55	3.07	3.18	3.32	2.75	3.01	2.35	2.18	1.79

[a] Instron Tensile Tester at 0.0013% and 1%/sec. Break elongation expressed in per cent. Break energy expressed in in.-lb/in. of cord.

the projection. To some extent, the energy absorbed in breaking a cord (i.e., work of rupture) can be taken as an indication of the potential impact resistance of a tire reinforced with that cord. However, it is essential to reproduce closely the likely operating conditions when carrying out a laboratory evaluation. Thus in order to simulate impact conditions for a tire running at 35 mph the rate of straining should be of the order of 6000%/sec carried out at an elevated temperature of 75–100°C (92). The normal laboratory method of tensile testing utilizes a rate of straining of 1%/sec which is equivalent to a speed of only about 0.006 mph. Table VII shows how important such considerations become when comparisons are made between two tire cords such as rayon and nylon. The break energy of the rayon cord, which is lower than that of the nylon cord at low strain rates, is considerably higher than that of the nylon when tested at higher temperatures and higher strain rates.

The degree to which all these needs are satisfied must obviously be the result of a compromise between sometimes conflicting requirements. Thus, it might be argued that a high extension to break could be used to bring about an increase in work of rupture, but this would inevitably be at the expense of modulus, creep resistance, and tensile strength. The excellent balance of properties which high-tenacity rayon possesses is the main reason for its recognition as an eminently suitable tire reinforcement material.

B. Other Applications

Apart from its major end use in tire reinforcement, high tenacity is extensively used in other fields where high strength, dimensional control and stability, and high impact or shock loading resistance is required. These include such important applications as transmission belting, conveyor belting, hose pipes, and coated fabrics. Each end use has its own stringent requirements, and the unique properties of high-tenacity rayon have for a long time made it an important reinforcing material in these applications.

VI. FUTURE DEVELOPMENTS

A. Higher Strength Levels

If the pattern of past developments is to be continued, the next logical step should be the production of a Super 4 level of strength, i.e., giving a 41–42 lb oven dry breaking load when tested in a 2/1650, 12 × 12 cord. Although such strengths have been obtained on a laboratory scale or in pilot plant production, commercially viable processes have yet to be put into operation. Such processes as are available tend to have a lower productivity, in that a lower spinning speed is required. Other aspects such as the use of higher-viscosity viscoses incur associated problems of uniform flow in pipework, etc., and the added difficulties involved in homogeneous dissolution of the cellulose xanthate.

It is sometimes asked whether increased tensile strength is really required and can be used by the tire industry. The same question has been asked repeatedly over the past 10 to 15 years as each new level has been reached. The answer may be found from the fact that the stronger yarns have come into increased usage, with the low-acid and Super 1 yarns gradually falling into disuse. With tire yarns of Super 2 and Super 3 level, tire designers have been able to develop safer yet at the same time cheaper tires. These can now be made with a reduced number of carcass plies while maintaining or even increasing the total casing strength. Another innovation which has led to reduced plies has been the concept of "giant cords" whereby the familiar 2/1650-den cord has been partially displaced by cords of 3/1650, 2/2200, and even 3/2200-den, in two-ply car tires in particular. Thus there can be little doubt that higher-strength cords at competitive prices would be used to full advantage by tire manufacturers.

B. The All-Textile Radial Ply Tire

The introduction of the all-textile radial ply car tire is one of the most significant developments in tire technology in many years. A conventional "cross-ply" tire is constructed with plies of cord fabric laid at opposite angles to each other and at approximately 40° to the tread circumference (Fig. 2). In comparison, an all-textile radial ply tire is composed of two or more carcass plies of textile cords laid at an angle of 90°, and a belt of several plies laid substantially circumferentially under the tread (Fig. 3). By virtue of the number of plies in this belt region (normally 4 or 6), the lower twists used in the cord and the low cord angle, such a belt has an extremely high stiffness in the plane of the tread when under the tension imposed by the tire inflation pressure, thus conferring a high degree of stability to the tread. The well-proven advantages of such tires are: (*1*) tread life increased by 60–80%, (*2*) improved grip, especially on wet roads, (*3*) safer cornering, (*4*) cool running for safe high-speed motoring, (*5*) lower rolling resistance giving improved fuel consumption figures, and (*6*) less "road roar" at medium to high speeds. The problem of a "harsh" ride at lower speeds can be successfully combated by suitable amendments to the design of the car suspension system (93).

The high strength and, more important, the comparatively high modulus of high-tenacity rayon has made it a natural choice for use in the belt region in conjunction with the more conventional higher-twist

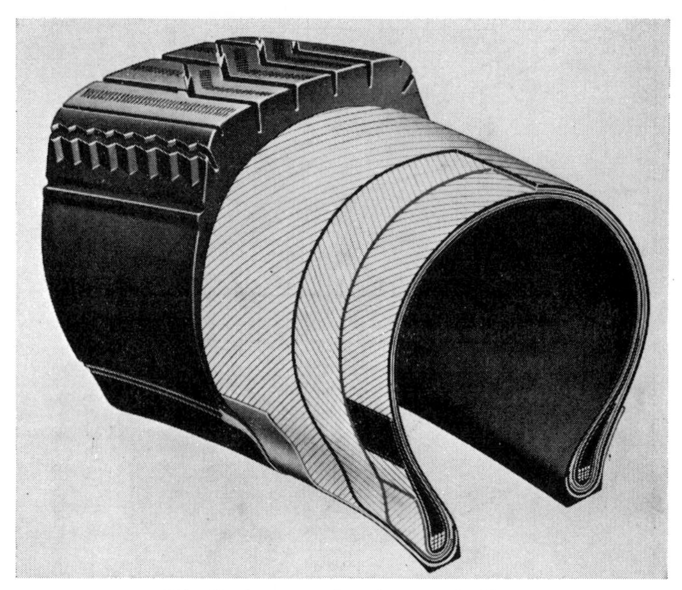

Fig. 2. A conventional cross-ply tire.

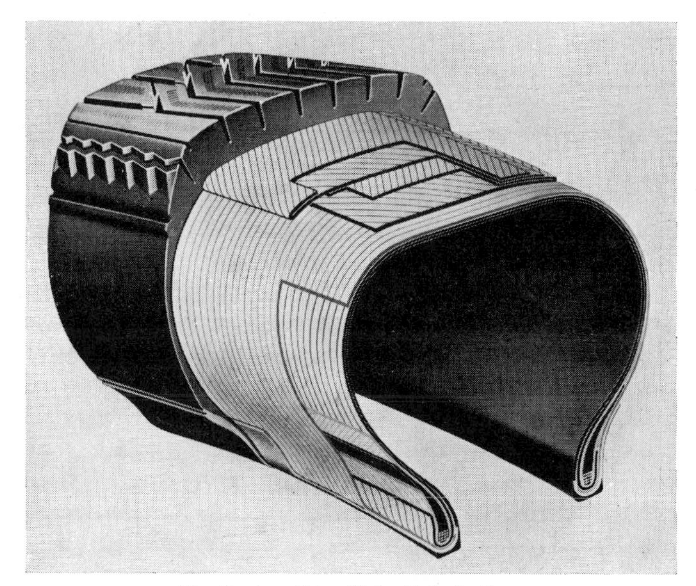

Fig. 3. An all-textile radial ply tire.

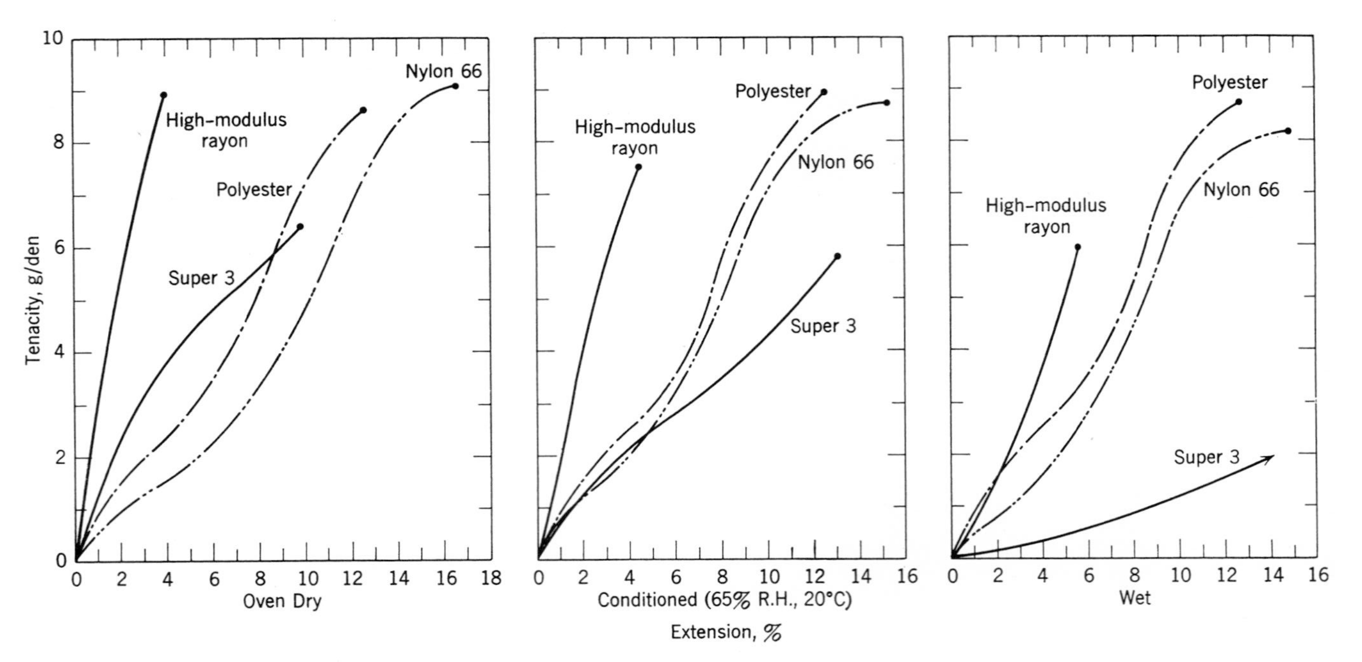

Fig. 4. Load extension curves for high-modulus rayon and other industrial yarns.

construction in the carcass. An ever-increasing number of car manufacturers are specifying all-textile radial ply tires as original equipment for the latest car designs, a pattern of development which is well advanced in Europe and which is developing in the United States and the rest of the world.

C. High-Modulus Rayon

An example of the versatility of the viscose process is illustrated by the recent development of a yarn specifically for end uses where increased strength, high modulus, and high dimensional stability are required. This special high-modulus rayon comes under the classification of a polynosic fiber. The principal properties of this type of yarn are listed in Table VIII and are shown graphically in Fig. 4 in comparison with other industrial yarns. In addition, the yarn has outstandingly good resistance to creep, and this combination of high strength, high modulus, and excellent dimensional stability has recommended it for use in industrial belting and hose. As a tire yarn, its unique properties immediately suggest it as a reinforcing material for the belt region of radial ply tires.

TABLE VIII. Properties of High-Modulus Rayon and Other Industrial Yarns

	High-modulus rayon	High-tenacity rayon—Super 3	Nylon 66 industrial	Polyester industrial
Tenacity, g/den.				
Oven dry	9.0	6.5	9.0	8.6
Conditioned (65% RH, 20°C)	7.5	5.5	8.7	8.6
Wet	6.0	4.4	8.2	8.6
Extensibility, %				
Oven dry	4.0	10	17	13
Conditioned (65% RH, 20°C)	5.0	14	16	13
Wet	6.0	24	15	13
Moisture regain at 65% RH	10.0	13.5	4.0	0.4
Oven-dry initial modulus, g/den	340	170	45	110
Contraction due to wetting, %[a]	0.5	7–10	0	0
Tension increase due to wetting, g/den[a]	0.12	0.1–0.2	0	0
Contraction (%) due to heating to 150°C[a]	0.1	1.2	4.1	5.0
Tension increase, (g/den) due to heating to 150°C[a]	0.14	0.3	0.6	0.61

[a] Values obtained with 100-g. pretension.

It is postulated that the higher modulus of the new yarn should enable it to be used in radial ply tire breakers either (*1*) in similar quantities to the currently used high-tenacity rayon to give an even stiffer breaker, or (*2*) to give the same level of stiffness by using less yarn. This latter approach is more likely and might enable either the cord denier to be reduced while retaining the present number of fabric plies or the number of plies to be reduced at the same cord deniers. The introduction of any new factor in tire design is a lengthy process and is finally dependent upon practical evaluation of the tire in extended service. The evaluation of the new high-modulus rayon is further complicated by the relative lack of experience with the textile radial tire itself, and the precise cord properties necessary to give optimum performance in the breaker region have not yet been fully established.

REFERENCES

1. Courtaulds Ltd., Fr. Pat. 467,500.
2. Du Pont de Nemours, U.S. Pats. 2,535,044; 2,535,045; 2,536,014.
3. W. A. Sisson, *Textile Res. J.*, **30,** 153 (1960).
4. J. M. Preston, *J. Soc. Chem. Ind.*, T199 (1931).
5. R. E. J. Cumberbirch, D. G. Drummond, J. E. Ford, and S. C. Simmons, *J. Textile Inst.*, **50,** T262 (1959).
6. A. Frey-Wyssling, *Submicroscopic Morphology of Protoplasm and its Derivatives*, Elsevier, New York, 1949, pp. 45–90.
7. P. H. Hermans, *J. Phys. Chem.*, **45,** 827 (1941).
8. J. A. Howsmon and W. A. Sisson, in E. Ott, H. M. Spurlin, and M. W. Grafflin, *High Polymers*, Vol. V, *Cellulose and Cellulose Derivatives*, Part I, 2nd ed., Interscience, New York, 1954, pp. 231–346.
9. J. W. S. Hearle, in J. W. S. Hearle and R. H. Peters, Eds., *Fibre Structure*, Butterworths, Manchester, 1963, pp. 209–234.
10. J. Henstenberg and H. Mark *Z. Kristallogr.*, **69,** 271 (1928).
11. P. H. Hermans, *J. Chim. Phys.*, **44,** 135 (1947); *J. Appl. Phys.*, **19,** 491 (1948).
12. W. Kast and L. Flaschner, *Kolloid-Z.*, **6,** 111 (1948).
13. A. Guinier, Thesis Series A, No. 1854, University of Paris, 1939.
14. O. Kratky, *Naturwissenschaften*, **26,** 94 (1938); **30,** 542 (1942); O. Kratky, A. Sehera, and R. Treer, *Z. Elektrochem.*, **48,** 527 (1942).
15. K. R. Andress, *Z. Physik. Chem.*, **34,** 190 (1929).
16. D. N. Tyler and N. S. Wooding, *J. Soc. Dyers Colourists*, **74,** 283 (1958).
17. J. Mann, *Pure Appl. Chem.*, **5,** 91 (1962).
18. J. Mann and H. J. Marrinan, *Trans. Faraday Soc.*, **52,** 481, 487, 492 (1956); T. Yurugi, *J. Soc. Textile Cellulose Ind., Japan*, **12,** 96 (1956).
19. P. H. Hermans, *Contribution to the Physics of Cellulose Fibres*, Elsevier, Amsterdam, 1946, p. 70.
20. P. H. Hermans, *Contribution to the Physics of Cellulose Fibres*, Elsevier, Amsterdam, 1946, p. 171.
21. N. S. Wooding, in *Fibre Structure*, J. W. S. Hearle and R. H. Peters, Eds., Butterworths, Manchester, 1963, p. 469.

22. H. Wakeham in E. Ott., H. M. Spurlin, and M. W. Grafflin, *High Polymers*, Vol. V, *Cellulose and Cellulose Derivatives*, Part III, 2nd ed., Interscience, New York, 1954, p. 1302.
23. W. C. Cameron and T. H. Morton, *J. Soc. Dyers Colourists*, **64**, 329 (1948).
24. N. S. Wooding, in *Fibre Structure*, J. W. S. Hearle and R. H. Peters, Eds., Butterworths, Manchester, 1963, p. 471.
25. W. M. Kaeppner, *Tappi*, **46**, 637 (1963).
26. A. Gröbe, H. Klare, R. Maron, H. Jost, and G. Casperon, *Faserforsch. Textiltech.*, **13**, 1 (1962).
27. L. B. Morgan (wrongly attributed to M. Magat), *Ric. Sci.*, **25A**, 755 (1955).
28. V. A. Kargin, *J. Polymer Sci.*, **30**, 247 (1958).
29. V. A. Kargin, V. L. Karpov, and Z. Pinsker, *Acta Phys. Chem. U.S.S.R.*, **7**, 646 (1937); V. A. Kargin and D. I. Leipunskaja, *Zh. Fiz. Khim.*, **14**, 312 (1930); **15**, 1011 (1941); *Kakinoki Proc. Phys. Math. Soc. Japan*, **21**, 66 (1939).
30. H. P. Clegg (Courtaulds Ltd.), private communication.
31. H. A. Vroom and D. W. Van Krevelen, *3rd European Symp. Chem. Reaction Eng.* Pergamon Press, New York, 1964.
32. H. Schmiedeknecht and H. Klare, *Faserforsch. Textiltech.* **14**, 219 (1963).
33. A. Gröbe, H. Klare, and R. Maron, *Faserforsch. Textiltech.*, **10**, 455 (1959).
34. D. Vermaas, *Textile Res. J.*, **32**, 353 (1962).
35. A. Gröbe and H. Klare, *Faserforsch. Textiltech.*, **13**, 1 (1962).
36. M. Strübrer and J. George, *Faserforsch. Textiltech.*, **15**, 289 (1964).
37. S. Wydrzycki, *Polimery*, **7**, 314 (1962).
38. D. K. Smith, *Textile Res. J.*, **29**, 32 (1959).
39. M. Levine and R. H. Burroughs, *J. Appl. Polymer Sci.*, **2**, 192 (1959).
40. R. J. E. Cumberbirch, J. E. Ford, and R. E. Gee, *J. Textile Inst.*, **52**, 7, T330 (1961).
41. K. Götze and V. Strach, *Mell. Textilber.*, **41**, 1326 (1960).
42. J. G. Witkamp and W. R. Saxton, *Tappi*, **45**, 650 (1962).
43. E. Elöd, *Mell. Textilber.*, **41**, 979 (1960).
44. St. Kalafut and L. Slivorsky, *Chem. Prumysl.*, **9** (34), 21, 104 (1959).
45. K. Götze and F. Hilgers, Research Report 18, March 1959, *Viscose Symposium*, Stockholm (1959).
46. K. Götze and F. Hilgers. March Report from the laboratory of Chem. Fabrik Stockhausen and Cie, Krefeld 1960.
47. B. Phillip and K. Müller, *Faserforsch. Textiltech.*, **13**, 54 (1962).
48. St. Kalafut and M. Fogeltanc, *Chem. Prumysl.*, **12**, 265 (1962).
49. A. Gröbe and H. Klare, *Monatsber. Deut.*, *Akad. Wiss. Berlin*, **1**, 573 (1959).
50. H. Klare, *Faserforsch. Textiltech.*, **11**, 582 (1960).
51. E. Zehmisch, *Faserforsch. Textiltech.*, **14**, 70 (1963).
52. S. Okajima, *Kogyo Kwagaku Zasshi*, **64**, 211 (1961).
53. A. Gröbe and H. Klare, *Oesterr. Chemiker-Z.*, **65**, 218 (1964).
54. A. M. Van der Ven, *Faserforsch. Textiltech.*, **13**, 262 (1962).
55. H. Klare, A. Gröbe, H. Jost, and R. Maron, *Faserforsch. Textiltech.*, **13**, 379 (1962).
56. N. S. Wooding (Courtaulds Ltd.), private communication.
57. A. T. Serkov, A. A. Konkin, I. M. Katomina, and G. A. Budnitskii, *Khim. Volokna*, **1963**, 40.
58. Z. Cichowski, *Polimery*, **9**, 1326 (1964).
59. L. Brown, A. W. Porter and J. G. Stenner, *Brit. J. Appl. Phys.*, **10**, 116 (1959).

60. L. Brown and J. G. Stenner (Courtaulds Ltd.), private communication.
61. H. Klare, A. Gröbe, H. J. Purz, and R. Maron, *Faserforsch. Textiltech.*, **14**, 347 (1963).
62. H. Klare, A. Gröbe, and J. Jost, *Faserforsch. Textiltech.*, **14**, 522 (1963).
63. W. J. McGarry, unpublished results.
64. E. V. Reeves and R. W. Yorke (Courtaulds Ltd.), private communication.
65. H. T. Cooper and P. Corke (Courtaulds Ltd.), private communication.
66. W. F. Knebusch, Brit. Pat. 413,414.
67. Cie Industrielle de Textiles Artificiels et Synthetique, Brit. Pat. 655, 516.
68. Du Pont de Nemours, U.S. Pat. 2,550,808.
69. Courtaulds Ltd., Brit. Pat. 782,585.
70. Courtaulds Ltd., Brit. Pat. 490,074.
71. American Viscose Corp., U.S. Pat. 2,745,640.
72. Glanstoff-Courtaulds GmbH, Fr. Pat. 1,264,394.
73. K. L. Gray and R. W. Yorke, *J. Polymer Sci.*, **61**, S5 (1962).
74. Courtaulds Ltd., Brit. Pat. 729,440.
75. Industrial Rayon Corp., U.S. Pat. 2,684,728.
76. Nereinigte-Glanstoffe-Fabriken A.-G., Fr. Pat. 837,025.
77. Algemeine Kunstzijde Unie N.V., Brit. Pat. 886,475.
78. D. L. Loughborough, J. M. Davies and G. E. Monfore, *Can. J. Res.*, **28F**, 490 (1950).
79. W. H. Bradshaw, *ASTM Bull.*, **136**, (1945).
80. W. J. Busby and E. V. Reeves, *Proc. Rubber Technol. Con. 4th* Heffer, Cambridge, 1962, p. 217.
81. J. O. Wood and G. B. Redmond, *J. Textile Inst.*, **56**, T191 (1965).
82. D. Entwistle, J. P. Jones, and G. A. Pittman, *Recent Advances in High-Tenacity Rayons*, Courtaulds Limited Publication, December 1958.
83. *Du Pont Tire Yarn Technical Review*, May 1959.
84. K. R. Williams, J. W. Hannel, and J. M. Swanson, *Ind. Eng. Chem.*, **45**, 796 (1953).
85. M. Wilson, *Textile Res. J.*, **21**, 47 (1951).
86. W. F. Kilby, *J. Textile Inst.*, **55**, T589 (1964).
87. H. L. Röder, *J. Textile Inst.*, **46**, 84 (1955).
88. H. G. Lauterbach and W. F. Ames, *Textile Res. J.*, **29**, 890 (1959).
89. J. O. Wood and W. F. Kilby, *Proc. Rubber Technol. Conf. 3rd*, Heffer, Cambridge, 1954, p. 711.
90. J. O. Wood, R. S. Goy, and F. S. Durawalla. *Textile Res. J.*, **29**, 669 (1959).
91. E. V. Reeves, *Adhesives Age*, **6**, 28 (1963).
92. F.M.C. Corporation Tech. Service Bull. V-21; E. W. Lothrop Jr., *High-Speed Testing*, Vol. V, Interscience, New York, 1965, p. 111.
93. V. E. Gough, C. W. Barson, J. C. Hutchinson, and D. H. James, *Proc. Inst. Mech. Engrs. London*, **1965**, Pt. 2A, 179.

Cellulose Acetate Fibers

Z. A. Rogovin and Yu. A. Kostrov
Textile Institute, Moscow, U.S.S.R.

CONTENTS

I. INTRODUCTION

Acetate fibers are one of the most important forms of widely used artificial cellulose-based fibers.

The first patents for the production of fibers from cellulose acetate appeared at the beginning of this century. They provided for the production of triacetate fiber from solutions of triacetylcellulose in chloroform by the wet method; this was naturally impossible in practice. Methods were soon proposed for obtaining acetone-soluble acetylcellulose and for the production of fiber by the dry method.

The production of acetylcellulose on an industrial scale began during World War I, for military applications: as fire-resistant lacquers used to cover airplanes, airships, and balloons, in preparing nonfogging and unbreakable glass, and composite nonsplintering glass (with a transparent acetylcellulose sheet glued between two pieces of glass), etc.

TABLE I. World Production of Acetate Fibers (in 1000 T)

Fibers	1929	1940	1945	1950	1956	1960	1963	1964	1965[b]
Acetate	19.9	106.0	175.0	267.7	211.0	240.0	296.0	345.0	366.4
All chemical fibers	199.1	1130.0	617.0	1664.4	2694.0	3317.0	4404.0	4980.0	5373.0
Percentage of acetate fibers[a]	10.0	9.4	20.3	16.1	7.8	7.3	6.7	6.8	6.6

[a] Percentage of the total production of chemical fibers.

[b] This quantity does not include the amount of acetate fiber used for cigarette filters. For this purpose, about 107,000 tons were used in 1965.

After the war the large capacity for the production of acetylcellulose was widely utilized, along with the production of sheets, lacquers, and plastics, for the production of fiber from cellulose acetate.

From then on until the fifties fibers were produced on an industrial scale exclusively from partly saponified acetylcellulose (the so-called acetate fiber).* In 1954–1955 the first publications appeared concerning the production of triacetate fiber by a dry method on an industrial scale. This fiber has, as will be indicated below, a number of specific advantages compared with the acetate fiber. At present these two types of cellulose acetate fibers are of basic importance. Partly acetylated cotton and viscose staple fiber are produced in relatively small quantities.

* Partially saponified acetylcellulose containing 230–250 acetyl groups per 100 elementary links of the macromolecule is soluble in acetone; this was one of the main reasons for its use in fiber production.

In 1965 world production of acetate fibers reached 366,000 tons (Table I).

During the past decade the increase in the production of fibers from cellulose acetate corresponded approximately to the general increase in the production of chemical fibers. The amount of acetate fiber manufactured constitutes 6.5–7.0% of the total amount of chemical fibers. Acetate fibers are basically delivered in the form of a continuous textile yarn. The production of staple acetate fiber in recent years has not exceeded 15% of the total world production of acetate fibers.

TABLE II. Price of Acetate Fiber (in dollars/kg) Compared with Other Types of Chemical Fibers (2)

Fiber	Filament yarn, 40 den	75 den	100 den	150 den	200 den	Staple fiber, 3-den
Acetate	2.47	2.18	2.00	1.63	1.54	0.88
Viscose	4.29	2.75	2.52	1.80	1.78	0.66
Nylon	4.53	3.77	3.65	3.52	3.28	2.45
Orlon	—	—	—	—	—	2.34
Dacron	4.84	4.00	3.85	3.75	3.39	1.85

Acetate fiber is one of the cheapest forms of chemical fiber. The price of acetate fiber in the United States is compared with that of other fibers in Table II (2).

II. THE PRODUCTION OF ACETYLCELLULOSE

The starting material for the production of acetate fiber is complex acetic acid cellulose ester—acetylcellulose. Since acetylcellulose is fully transportable, this cellulose ester can be produced either in the same plant in which the fiber is produced or in a separate plant. Certain methods of fiber production require, however, that these production units be located in a single plant. This is essential, above all, in the production of acetate fiber from acetylcellulose solutions in an acetylizing mixture (so-called liquors, see below).

In addition to the general rules which are characteristic of the synthesis of all types of complex cellulose esters, the production of cellulose acetates is characterized by a number of special features:

1. One cannot obtain highly substituted acetylcellulose under the action of acetic acid. Other esterification agents are therefore used: acetyl chloride, acetic anhydride, and ketene. Under industrial conditions this is usually accomplished with acetic anhydride (always in the presence of a catalyst). The esterification takes place according to the scheme:

$$[C_6H_7O_2(OH)_3]_n + 3n(CH_3CO)_2O \rightarrow [C_6H_7O_2(OCOCH_3)_3]_n + 3nCH_3COOH$$

2. The esterification reaction of cellulose with acetic anhydride is irreversible. It is therefore impossible to regulate the degree of esterification in the process of acetylation, as is done, for instance, in nitration. As a result of the acetylation one obtains cellulose triacetate and (if the process is not carried to the completion a mixture of triacetate and low-substituted cellulose acetates). Therefore, in order to obtain acetone-soluble acetylcellulose, one initially obtains cellulose triacetate and subsequently part of the acetyl groups is saponified in a homogeneous medium.

3. The acetylation of the cellulose always begins in a heterogeneous medium and is completed, depending on the composition of the acetylating mixture, in a heterogeneous or homogeneous medium. In the former case, the mixture contains a reagent, referred to as the diluent, which dissolves neither the cellulose nor the produced triacetylcellulose, and which is readily removed by distillation. When acetylation is completed in a solution of acetylcellulose in an acetylizing mixture, i.e., in a homogeneous medium (this is referred to below, for brevity, as "acetylation in a homogeneous medium"), a reagent is introduced into the acetylizing mixture, which is a solvent of cellulose triacetate.

Only acetic anhydride has found industrial application as an acetylizing agent.

Of considerable interest is the acetylation of cellulose by ketene:

$$[C_6H_7O_2(OH)_3]_n + 3nCH_2{=}CO \rightarrow [C_6H_7O_2(OCOCH_3)_3]_n$$

However, since ketene is a gaseous agent, the technology and instrumentation required to carry out this reaction causes difficulties. In addition, a side reaction of the polymerization of ketene always takes place. Nevertheless, acetylation by ketene is of interest for the following reasons:

1. Ketene is obtained in large quantities as an intermediate product in the synthesis of acetic acid from acetone.

2. The method of producing acetate fiber by acetylation of viscose staple fiber with the vapor of acetic anhydride, worked out in recent years by Japanese investigators, requires the regeneration of the produced acetic acid. The use of ketene as the esterification agent in this instance is of considerable interest.

A large number of various reagents are used as catalysts in laboratory investigations. Sulfuric and perchloric acids are used most extensively in industrial acetylation and almost exclusively as catalysts.

Perchloric acid is a more efficient catalyst than sulfuric acid. It does not form unstable cellulose esters—an advantage in using it. However, in acetylation in a homogeneous medium with the use of acetic acid as a solvent in the presence of perchloric acid, the viscosity of the triacetylcellulose solutions increases, leading to coagulation. Perchloric acid is the most widely utilized catalyst in the acetylation in a heterogeneous medium in the production of cellulose triacetate as the final product, without subsequent partial saponification.

Sulfuric acid is not only a catalyst in the esterification reaction, but also in the following stage of the process—the partial saponification of the cellulose triacetate. The main disadvantage in using sulfuric acid as a catalyst is the production of a small amount of cellulose ester sulfates in the process of esterification. These esters are unstable, and their saponification results in the production of sulfuric acid, giving rise to a gradual decomposition of the acetylcellulose (particularly at higher temperatures). Therefore, in spite of the fact that the major portion of the ester sulfates which are produced at the beginning of the acetylation will be saponified at the end of the process, particularly in the partial saponification of the triacetylcellulose, in using large quantities of sulfuric acid as a catalyst (with acetic acid as a solvent) it is essential to stabilize the acetylcellulose—to decompose the ester sulfates at a high temperature and to remove the sulfuric acid produced thereby.

The acetic acid salts of the alkaline metals, especially CH_3COONa, have found some application as catalyst in the acetylation of viscose fibers.

The third component of an acetylating mixture utilized in liquid-phase acetylation is selected in accordance with the method of acetylation. In the case of acetylation in a homogeneous medium the amount of the added solvent must ensure a sufficiently fast conduction of the heat released in the reaction, and the production of a uniform triacetylcellulose solution. As a solvent one uses acetic acid or a mixture of acetic acid and chlorinated hydrocarbons (commonly methylene chloride). Acetylation in a heterogeneous medium is carried out in the presence of a diluent, facilitating the removal of heat in the circulation or mixing of the acetylating mixture. Benzene, toluene, or carbon tetrachloride are used as diluents. These compounds are easily regenerated by distillation with water vapor and subsequent separation. A disadvantage in using carbon tetrachloride and benzene is their high toxicity.

Acetylation in a heterogeneous medium by an acetylating agent in gaseous form (acetic anhydride, ketene) is carried out without a third agent (the solvent), since in this instance the reaction occurs at high temperature, as a result of the use of catalysts which do not give rise to appreciable degradation of the cellulose.

The cellulose starting material for the production of acetylcellulose is chemically purified cotton fluff or refined wood cellulose with a minimum content of low-molecular-weight fractions. The stricter requirements of the cellulose utilized in the production of acetate fiber (compared with viscose fiber) are due to the absence in its production of special operations in the course of which hemicelluloses are dissolved (mercerization). Low-molecular-weight fractions of acetylcellulose are partially removed only as a result of their dissolution in the dilute acetic acid produced in the precipitation of acetylcellulose.

An essential operation, preceding both homogeneous and heterogeneous acetylation, is the activation of the cellulose. During activation the cellulose is swelled and correspondingly the intermolecular hydrogen bonds are partly destroyed; this facilitates the diffusion of the acetylating mixture in the esterification.

To activate it, the cellulose is treated with glacial acetic acid. The duration of the activation is shortened if it is carried out at a high temperature. In order to ensure uniform swelling, one must heat the substance uniformly; this is achieved by intense mixing, by the use of acetic acid vapor in the activation, etc. Thus, in treating cellulose with glacial acetic acid (40–60% of the weight of the cellulose) at 60°C the time of activation does not exceed 0.5 hr.

A greater degree of activation of the cellulose, i.e., more effective activation, takes place when the cellulose is treated with relatively dilute acetic acid. However, in this case the cellulose must be additionally treated prior to the esterification with glacial acetic acid, in order to avoid appreciable use of the acetic anhydride in the side reaction with water.

A. Acetylation in a Heterogeneous Medium

This method is used to produce only cellulose triacetate. A schematic diagram of technical acetylation in a heterogeneous medium is shown in Fig. 1.

Only a small amount of fiber (produced mainly by the wet method) is produced at present from cellulose triacetate obtained by acetylation in a heterogeneous medium.

In esterification in a heterogeneous medium the acetylating mixture contains 40–45% acetic anhydride, 15–20% acetic acid, about 35% diluent (benzene, toluene, or CCl_4) and a catalyst—perchloric acid (0.5–1% of the weight of the cellulose). The ratio of the acetylating

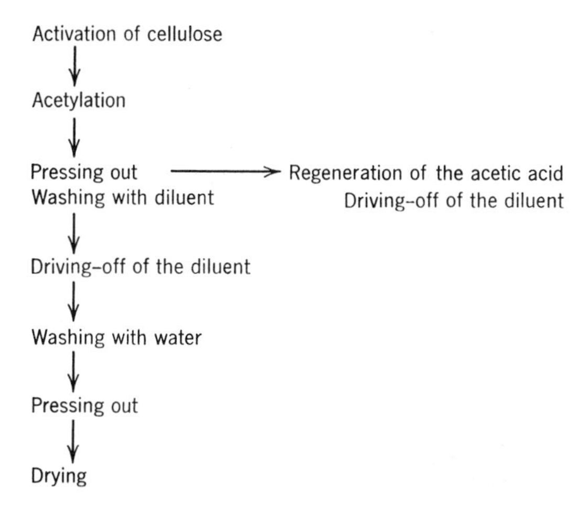

Fig. 1. Schematic diagram illustrating the production of acetylcellulose by acetylation in a heterogeneous medium.

mixture to the weight of the cellulose (the bath ratio) is about 15–20.

After completion of the acetylation the processed mixture is separated from the cellulose triacetate (for example, by centrifuging), and the diluent is driven off and can be reused. The duration of esterification is 2–3 hr, i.e., considerably less than in batch acetylation in a homogeneous medium. The acetylation, and often the other operations as well, are carried out in rotating drums or in vertical, jacketed vats with an agitator.

After completion of acetylation the product is washed with a diluent, which is then driven off with water vapor. The cellulose triacetate is washed with water, squeezed out, and dried.

B. Acetylation in a Homogeneous Medium

A schematic diagram of the technical production of acetylcellulose by esterification in a homogeneous medium is shown in Fig. 2. Acetic acid, or a mixture of acetic acid and methylene chloride, are used as the cellulose triacetate solvent in esterification in a homogeneous medium. The use of acetic acid only as the solvent makes it impossible to increase the volume of the batch apparatus because of difficulties in extracting the heat. Local overheating leads to degradation of the cellulose and of the produced acetylcellulose. Use of methylene chloride as the main component of the solvent mixture (the mixture contains acetic acid introduced by the activated cellulose and produced in the acetylation) can lead to a considerable increase of the volume of the acetylator, and

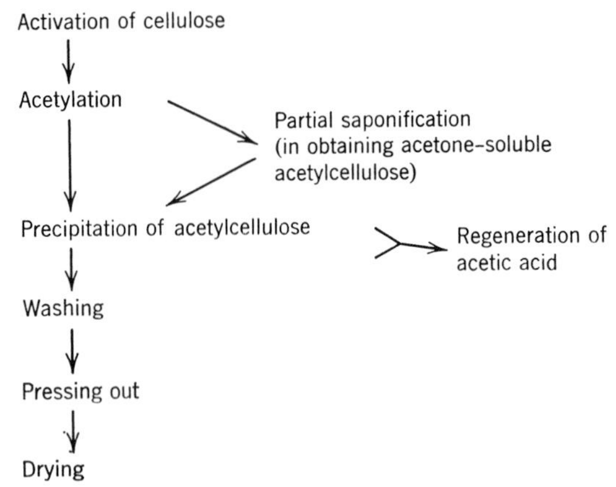

Fig. 2. Schematic diagram illustrating the production of acetylcellulose by acetylation in a homogeneous medium.

one can load up the apparatus with up to three tons of cellulose. This is due to the fact that while the boiling point of methylene chloride is 41°C, there is no superheating in the various zones and the excess heat is conducted away by evaporation of the methylene chloride and its subsequent condensation in a reflux condenser.

The duration of the acetylation is 8–10 hr. Acetylation in a homogeneous medium is usually carried out in so-called acetylators—a batch-action apparatus equipped with a powerful agitator and cooling jacket. Acetylators are made of acid-resistant steel, or are lined inside with phosphor bronze. The amount of acetic anhydride in the acetylating mixture is about 300%, while that of the solvent is 500–600% of the weight of the cellulose. The amount of sulfuric acid catalyst is 1–10% of the weight of the cellulose. The total amount of acetylating mixture exceeds the amount of cellulose in the load by a factor of 8–9. The acetylation is carried out at a temperature of up to 40–45°C.

The acetylation of cellulose in a homogeneous medium can be carried out not only by the batch method, but also by a continuous process. A number of variants have been proposed for the latter method which has appreciable technological and economic advantages; some of these have in recent years found practical application.

As is seen from the cited scheme, the sequence of subsequent operations depends on whether the final reaction product is cellulose triacetate or acetone-soluble (partially saponified) acetylcellulose. In the production of cellulose triacetate the completion of acetylation is followed by precipitation, washing, and drying. In the production of partially saponified cellulose acetate it is essential to carry out partial saponification of the cellulose triacetate which takes place in the presence of water and of a catalyst according to the scheme:

$$—C_6H_7O_2(OCOCH_3)_3—C_6H_7O_2(OCOCH_3)— + H_2O \rightarrow$$
$$C_6H_7O_2(OCOCH_3)_3—C_6H_7O_2(OCOCH_3)_2OH— + CH_3COOH$$

Under these conditions saponification of unstable cellulose sulfoesters takes place simultaneously.

The larger the water content in the saponifying mixture, the more rapid, but less uniform, the saponification. The water content of the acetylcellulose solution in the acetylating mixture during saponification does not usually exceed 15%. Sulfuric acid amounting to 15% of the starting weight of the cellulose is used as the saponification catalyst. The duration of the saponification depends on the required content of combined acetic acid in the acetylcellulose and on the temperature. At 40–45°C the duration of saponification until an acetone-soluble acetylcellulose is obtained is 8–10 hr. Saponification can be carried out in batches in a single unit and continuously, usually in several units equipped with agitators.

After saponification the acetylcellulose is precipitated from the solution by means of water or dilute acetic acid. The concentration of acetic acid after precipitation is 30–40%. Smaller concentrations of the acid in the solution after the precipitation lead to increased content of the low-molecular-weight fractions in the finished product and hamper the regeneration of the acetic acid.

The acetic acid is regenerated by extraction by means of various reagents, in particular by ethyl acetate which forms with it an azeotropic mixture. On completion of the extraction this reagent is distilled off and utilized in the following extraction cycle, whereas the acetic acid is vacuum distilled. The concentrated acetic acid is reused in the production of acetylcellulose, or for the production of acetic anhydride.

The precipitated cellulose is countercurrent washed with water, squeezed, and dried. These operations are carried out in batch-type (false-bottom vats, centrifuges, vacuum driers) and continuous apparatus (perforated conveyor belts, continuous-action centrifuges, or wringing rollers, tunnel or continuous-action belt driers, etc.).

III. PRINCIPAL PROPERTIES OF ACETYLCELLULOSE

A. Molecular Weight

The degree of polymerization of macromolecules of acetylcellulose used in the production of fibers is usually 250–300. Further increase in the degree of polymerization up to a given limit increases the strength of the resulting fiber and its resistance to wear and to multiple deformation. A certain additional increase in the degree of polymerization of cellulose employed in fiber produotion is therefore very expedient, regardless of the difficulty of preparing and processing more viscous spinning solutions.

B. Degree of Esterification

As has already been indicated, two types of acetylcellulose, differing in their degree of esterification, are employed in the production of fiber. In acetone-soluble acetylcellulose, for each 100 elementary macromolecular units 230–250 hydroxyl groups out of a possible 300 have been substituted by acetyl groups; this corresponds to a combined acetic acid content of 53.5–56%. In triacetylcellulose dissolved in methylene chloride and alcohol, each 100 elementary units contain 290–295 acetyl groups (combined acetic acid content, 61.5–62.2%).

A change in the optimum degree of substitution impairs the solubility of the acetylcellulose and increases the viscosity of the spinning solutions, leading thus to difficulties in the filtering of the solutions and in the forming of fibers.

C. Chemical and Physical Homogeneity

These properties of acetylcellulose are usually not determined in industrial practice (with the exception of the content of low-molecular-weight fractions) owing to the complexity and duration of the analyses; however, they exert a decisive influence on the properties of the solutions and the formation and quality of the fibers.

The properties of acetylcellulose solutions with equal mean values of the acetyl numbers often differ sharply, depending on the uniform distributions of acetyl and hydroxyl groups. It is natural that the requirement of chemical homogeneity is of main significance for incompletely esterified cellulose.

The chemical heterogeneity is determined by fractional solution or precipitation of acetylcellulose in solvents which dissolve acetylcellulose with high (for example, methylene chloride) or low (for example, ethyl alcohol at higher temperatures) values of the acetyl number.

The physical heterogeneity is determined by fractional precipitation or solution by means of reagents whose solvent action changes depending on the molecular weight of the acetylcellulose.

The presence of low-molecular-weight fractions (with degree of polymerization below 100–120) causes particular difficulties in the extrusion of

Fig. 3. Apparatus for dissolving acetylcellulose.

the fiber and impairs its quality. The content of these fractions in acetylcellulose should not exceed 5%. This fraction is determined in partly saponified acetylcellulose by dissolving it in an acetone (55%)-water (45%) mixture at room temperature.

D. Properties of Spinning Solutions

The properties of concentrated solutions of acetylcellulose depend to a considerable extent on its molecular weight, the degree of esterification, and their chemical and physical inhomogeneity. These indicators affect the solubility of acetylcellulose and the viscosity of its solutions.

E. Thermal Stability

This decomposition of acetylcellulose at high temperatures depends above all on the presence in acetylcellulose of small amounts of sulfoesters which are saponified at higher temperatures. The sulfuric acid released in the saponification of these esters causes the decomposition of the acetylcellulose and leads to its darkening. The darkening of acetylcellulose should occur at temperatures above 210°C.

The higher acidity has a detrimental effect, resulting in the possible corrosion of the pipes and apparatus, the entry of iron salts into the solutions, as well as causing a higher ash content of the acetylcellulose which (if it is due to salts or hydroxides of divalent metals) increases the viscosity of the concentrated acetylcellulose solutions.

IV. PRODUCTION OF FILAMENT YARN

The main stages of the technical production process of acetate filament yarn are: (*a*) preparation of the spinning solution; (*b*) spinning; (*c*) twisting and rewinding of the yarn.

A. Preparation of The Spinning Solution

In order to provide for uniform properties of the spinning solutions and of the produced fibers, the acetylcellulose of various batches is mixed prior to being dissolved.

In practice the solvent used in the production of filament fiber is a mixture of methylene chloride with alcohol, commonly ethyl alcohol (9:1) in the production of triacetate fiber, and a mixture of acetone and water (96:4), or of acetone and ethyl alcohol (85:15), in the production of fiber from partly saponified acetylcellulose. The use of the acetone–water mixture simplifies the process and allows one to obtain less viscous spinning solutions (when employing acetylcellulose which contains 54–55% combined acetic acid). The presence of a second component in the solvent mixture decreases the viscosity of the spinning solutions of acetylcellulose considerably.

The concentration of partly saponified acetylcellulose in spinning solutions amounts to 24–25%, whereas the concentration of triacetylcellulose in spinning solutions intended for the dry extrusion process amounts to 20–22%.

The acetylcellulose is dissolved in vertical or horizontal apparatus (dissolvers) with paddle or screw agitators and heating jackets. The duration of the dissolution in present-day batch apparatus does not exceed 8 hr.

The spinning solution is purified of mechanical impurities and gel particles by three- or fourfold filtration. The most widely employed filter materials are cotton fabrics and cotton wool, as well as special types of crimped paper. After filtration the air must be carefully removed from the solution. If the entry of air is prevented during the preparation of the spinning solution, the duration of its deaeration is minimized. For example, in a number of plants the solution is fed continuously into intermediate vats and continuously separated for extrusion. When a special deaeration operation is carried out, its duration does not exceed 6–8 hr.

It must be noted that, unlike viscose and cuprammonium solutions, the acetylcellulose solutions are stable, i.e., remain practically unchanged with time. Therefore the length of the preparation of spinning solutions and the thermal treatment (for example, in solution or filtration) have no effect of their properties.

B. Spinning Acetate Fiber

In principle one can produce cellulose acetate fiber from the melt or from solution (by the dry or wet process). However, the method of production of acetate fiber from the melt, in which the technological process is considerably simplified (it is no longer necessary to prepare the spinning solution and regenerate the solvents), has so far not progressed beyond the laboratory investigation stage (3). This is due to the fact that the melting of acetylcellulose is accompanied by its thermal degradation. In order to decrease the likelihood of thermal degradation, one must use acetylcellulose whose melting point occurs below its decomposition temperature and which contains no traces of free acetic acid, which intensifies the decomposition.

One of the methods of lowering the melting point is the addition of small amounts of low- or high-molecular-weight plasticizers (production from polymer mixtures). Chemical plasticizing is also possible; for example, one can obtain mixed esters or grafted copolymers of acetylcellulose (4). A successful solution of this attractive problem requires much investigation.

The filament yarn can be produced from solution by the wet or dry process. Acetate filament yarn is almost never produced by the wet process, owing to its uneconomic nature compared with the dry process. Until recently the wet process was employed in some countries to produce yarn from triacetylcellulose solutions in a mixture of methylene chloride and methyl alcohol in a low-temperature (-20 to $-25°C$) precipitating bath of methyl alcohol. However, at present this method is practically never used.

The dry process is used exclusively in the production of cellulose acetate filament yarn. This is due to the fact that the dry process has considerable economic advantages compared with the wet method: faster extrusion rates, avoidance of a number of technological operations connected with wet processing and the drying of the fiber, etc.

In the dry process the small jets of solution which turn into fibers after evaporation of the solvent move down from above, from a spinneret, through a shaft into which hot air is blown, to the takeup device. The yarn is wound on a bobbin, or through a takeup disc on a package, and mounted on a spindle (the yarn may also be twisted slightly).

Various constructions of spinning machines provide for cocurrent (along the direction of motion of the yarn), countercurrent, or combined air supply. With countercurrent air supply and an extrusion rate of 500 m/sec the shaft is generally about 3 m high.

The thermal range and rate of spinning depend on a number of factors, and above all on the vapor pressure and boiling point of the solvent, the amount and method of supply of the air, and the thickness of the elementary fiber. Thus, in forming fibers from solutions of partly saponified acetylcellulose in acetone, the air is supplied to the lower portion of the shaft at a temperature of 80–85°C; this provides for the rapid removal of the residue of the solvent from the yarn. Because of the heat used in evaporating the acetone, the temperature of the air removed from the upper portion of the machine is reduced to 60–65°C. The solvent vapor concentration in the gas–air mixture pumped out from the shaft is usually lower than the lower limit at which it becomes an explosion hazard (for acetone this lower limit occurs at 62 mg/l).

In the extrusion of triacetate fiber by the dry process the temperature of the gas–air mixture is lower (on account of the lower boiling point of methylene chloride).

The rate of extrusion of yarn by the dry process and in particular in the extrusion of acetate yarn is rather high—400 to 600 m/min.

The regeneration of the solvent in the production of acetate fibers is accomplished by adsorption from the gas–air mixture on charcoal and distillation of the water–solvent mixture which forms after desorption in fractionating columns.

C. Aftertreatment of the Acetate Yarn

To facilitate the textile processing, the fibers are lubricated. The surface-treated fiber is less electrifiable, has a smaller coefficient of friction, and is more compact. The yarn is usually lubricated on the spinning machine.

As a rule, the acetate filament yarn is produced with little twist (not exceeding 80 turns/m), providing considerable technological and economic advantages compared with other more twisted types of filament yarns.

V. THE PRODUCTION OF STAPLE FIBER

Acetate staple fiber is obtained both by the dry and wet processes (from cellulose triacetate), and also by acetylation of toughened viscose staple fiber.

A. Spinning of Staple Fiber by the Dry Process

Production can proceed on the same machines as used for textile yarn. The extrusion rate is somewhat reduced and the number of openings in the spinneret is larger by a factor of 5–10 compared to the number of the production of filament yarn. The fiber strands from each spinning location are lubricated, collected into a single ropelike strand, crimp is inserted by mechanical crimping (at high temperature), and the strand is then stapled by cutting to a given length.

In recent years the wet process has begun to be more widely applied.

B. Production of Staple Fiber by the Wet Process

In the production of fiber by this method one can, by the use of spinnerets with a large number of openings (up to 10,000 and more), ensure a high yield from each spinning location even at a relatively slow extrusion rate. The solvents used in the production of triacetate staple fiber are methylene chloride or acetic acid. Arnel-60 fiber, which has a number of advantages compared with triacetate fiber extruded by the process (5), is thus produced in the United States from solutions of cellulose triacetate in methylene chloride by the wet process.

Solutions of triacetylcellulose in an acetylating mixture obtained after acetylation in a homogeneous medium can be used directly for the production of staple fiber by the wet process. In order to prevent a decrease in the molecular weight and in the degree of esterification of the acetylcellulose in the process of preparation of this solution for production, the solution is stabilized by neutralization of the mineral acid (catalyst) with sodium acetate, urea, or with another organic base. Before extrusion the solution undergoes triple filtration and deaeration. Directly after extrusion the fiber is stretched 20–40%, rinsed, crimped, cut, and dried.

The process of producing the fiber directly from the acetylcellulose solution in the acetylating mixture has considerable economic advantages, since the number of technical operations is sharply reduced: there is no need for precipitation, washing, and drying in the production of cellulose triacetate, and there is also no need for crushing and dissolving triacetylcellulose in the production of triacetate fiber. One solvent regeneration plant is needed, rather than two. The consumption of solvent is reduced considerably.

The choice of the composition of the precipitating bath in extrusion depends on the nature of the solvent used in acetylation. Thus, when the solvent is methylene chloride, one can use alcohols in the composition of the precipitating bath, for example, ethylene glycol (6) or isopropyl alcohol (7).

When the solvent used is acetic acid, the precipitating bath can be water or, better, an aqueous solution of acetic acid (8). The precipitating bath can contain an admixture of certain salts.

Production from an acetylcellulose solution in an acetylating medium yields staple fiber whose properties do not fall below those of fiber obtained by dry extrusion.

C. Acetylation of Viscose Staple Fiber

This method is utilized in Japan to obtain the so-called Alon fiber (9) with the following composition. Strong viscose fiber produced from cellulose with a high α-cellulose content and with a high degree of polymerization is treated with an aqueous salt solution and dried. The salt (usually CH_3COONa) is a catalyst in the subsequent acetylation.

Continuous acetylation is carried out by means of acetic anhydride vapor at elevated temperatures (140–150°C). The use of such temperatures is possible because of the use of salts as catalysts instead of mineral acids; the latter would cause degradation of the cellulose at elevated temperatures. After acetylation the fiber contains 50–52% combined acetic acid. The fiber is then washed with water, bleached, lubricated, and dried. The technological and economic advantages of this method production of acetate staple fiber are not indisputable.

VI. PROPERTIES OF ACETATE FIBERS

A. Breaking Strength

Triacetate and acetate fibers produced by the dry process have approximately the same dry-air strength—1.2–1.6 g/den. The reasons for the low strength are apparently the insufficient uniformity of the structure, the inappreciable orientation of the macromolecules, and the low degree of polymerization of the acetylcellulose in acetate fibers. The strength of Arnel-60, which has a more uniform structure and a somewhat higher degree of macromolecular orientations is 2.0–2.2 g/den. The degree of polymerization of the acetylcellulose in Alon fiber is 430–350. The strength of Alon fiber is 2.8 g/den.

The loss of strength by wet acetate fiber depends on the degree of esterification of the acetylcellulose. Thus, for fiber from partly saponified acetylcellulose the decrease in wet strength is about 40%. The loss of strength of triacetate fiber (including Arnel-60) is about 20%.

B. Elongation

Acetate fibers of all types (except specially stretched fibers) have a breaking elongation of 22–30% when dry and 28–38% when wet. The elastic part of the elongation is approximately twice as large as that of viscose fiber; this is of considerable significance for a number of applications of acetate fibers.

The modulus of elasticity of triacetate and acetate fibers is 325 kg/mm^2 compared with 600 kg/mm^2 for viscose fiber. Arnel-60 has a higher modulus of elasticity—570 kg/mm^2.

C. Moisture Absorption. Laundering of Products

The absorption of moisture by acetate fiber (at 65% air humidity) amounts to about 6–7%. In the case of triacetate fiber the amount of absorbed water for the same air humidity is about 4.5% prior to thermal treatment and is reduced after thermal treatment of the fiber because of increasing crystallinity to 3–3.5%.

Owing to the considerably lesser swelling of acetate fibers in water, the drying of products manufactured from them is shorter by a factor of 3–5 than that of products manufactured from viscose fiber. Acetate fibers (especially triacetate fibers) almost do not shrink when laundered in hot water.

Triacetate-fiber fabrics and products neither shrink nor pull out after laundering: they dry quickly, retain their initial shape after laundering, and usually require no ironing. A big advantage of triacetate fiber products lies in the fact that they retain their strength after repeated laundering (10).

D. Stability Against Abrasion and Multiple Deformation

Dry-spun acetate fibers have a low stability against abrasion—almost half of that of viscose fiber. They are less resistant to multiple deformation than viscose fibers. Wet stability against abrasion is of greater importance under actual conditions of use (for example, during laundering). In this respect triacetate fiber surpasses fiber produced from partially saponified cellulose acetate, as well as viscose fiber.

The Alon and Arnel-60 fibers have a higher stability against abrasion and a better resistance to multiple deformation than the other types of acetate fibers.

E. Resistance to High Temperatures and Stability to Light

The thermoplastic acetate fiber begins to deform above 140–150°C. For this reason the ironing temperature of fiber from partially saponified acetylcellulose should not exceed 115–120°C. The ironing temperature of triacetate fiber is 190°C, and can after thermal treatment be increased to 220°C.

Triacetate fiber has a high thermal stability. Thus, after a two-week exposure to 130°C, heat-treated triacetate retains 68% of its initial strength, whereas cotton retains 38 and nylon only 20% (11).

Acetate, and particularly triacetate fibers, are highly stable against light, surpassing in this respect nylon, viscose, and cotton fibers.

Acetate fibers resist the action of microorganisms and are moth-proof.

F. Density

The specific weight of acetate fibers of various types varies between 1.28 and 1.34 g/cm³, and is thus smaller than that of viscose fiber (1.50–1.53).

G. Dyeing of Acetate Fibers

In practice disperse dyes are most widely used for dyeing fabrics made of acetate fibers. The difficulties encountered in dyeing acetate fabrics with dyes used for cellulose fibers are due to the lesser swelling of acetate fibers in water, the presence of a small amount of free hydroxyl groups, and the possibility of saponification of the acetylcellulose when using dye baths containing alkaline or acid solvents, particularly at high temperatures.

The majority of disperse dyes are azo dyes or anthroquinone derivatives. These dyes do not dissolve in water, but can be dispersed in it.

Triacetate fiber can be dyed at a higher temperature (up to 110–115°C) at a pH of up to 9.5. The dyeing of triacetate fiber to a dark color is usually carried out under pressure in the presence of carriers, i.e., substances which cause swelling of the fiber. The conditions for dyeing Alon fiber are similar to those for triacetate fiber.

In recent years a large amount of acetate fiber is dyed in the process of preparing the solutions for extrusion. This method has a number of economic advantages compared with the dyeing of fabrics at the finishing plants. Organic pigments and acetone-soluble dyes can be used in this method of dyeing. The dye can be added directly to the solvent (in the production of rayon, dyed to a given color over a long period of time) or into a special apparatus to be mixed with the spinning solution prior to extrusion. The latter method makes it possible to increase the color assortment and to change the colors more frequently.

The major portion of undyed rayon is produced with a dull finish by adding titanium dioxide (0.5–2% of the weight of the acetylcellulose).

H. Uses

The main use of acetate fibers is in the production of widely used consumer goods (12). Various fabrics and jersey goods are made of acetate fibers: men's shirts, women's blouses and clothing, underwear, ties, bathing suits, jersey jackets and sweaters, suit fabrics, coats, sports clothing, etc. As a result of the differences in the properties of various acetate fibers, each of them has its own specific area of application. Wash-proof creases can be introduced into triacetate fiber fabrics, rendering them useful for extensive application in the production of pleated and crimped goods.

Acetate staple fiber is used in mixtures with other fibers. By mixing it with viscose fiber one can increase the crease resistance of fabrics. Its use in mixtures with cellulose fibers makes it possible to produce color effects due to their different dyeing qualities.

In industry triacetate fibers are used to insulate cables.

VII. MODIFICATION OF THE PROPERTIES OF ACETATE FIBERS

A. Structural Modification

One method of structural modification which is widely employed is the change of the structure of the triacetate fiber by thermal treatment. Fabrics of triacetate fiber generally undergo thermal treatment. The thermal treatment results in an increase of the crystallinity and in a decrease of the internal stresses in the fiber. The triacetate fiber acquires more thermal stability, the ability to keep its shape better (pleats, crimp), and increased crease and shrink resistance after wet treatment.

The fiber or fabric is thermally treated with hot air (180–220°C) for 1–4 minutes (depending on the temperature). The triacetate fabric can also be heated with hot calender rolls, steam or water under pressure, infrared rays, and by means of certain other methods.

Possibilities of increasing the strength of acetate fibers by increasing the orientation of the macromolecules or aggregates of macromolecules have been investigated in recent years. These investigations have indeed led to positive results in working out the production techniques of Arnel-60 and Alon.

An increase in the strength of acetate fibers can also be achieved by changing the conditions under which the yarn is dry-extruded. Thus, soft extrusion and stretching of the fiber in dry extrusion enabled Japanese investigators to obain very strong acetate fibers under experimental conditions (13). Fibers produced from a 30% solution of acetylcellulose in acetone passed through a shaft which contained a high concentration of solvent vapor (above the upper limit at which it becomes an explosion hazard). The obtained fiber had a strength of 6.60 g/den for an extension of 29%. Further development of this new method of producing acetate fiber may lead to interesting and practically important results.

High-tenacity acetate yarn can be obtained by stretching plasticized acetate yarn by 500–2000%. This stretching is carried out in an atmosphere of steam under pressure at 130–145°C. A high-denier yarn is obtained (the elementary fiber is 0.7–1 den) with a strength of 4.5–5 g/den. Subsequent soft saponification results in a high-strength cellulose hydrate fiber—Fortisan. For a small elongation of 6–7% it attains a strength of 9 g/den. Owing to its high strength and high modulus of elasticity (2000–2500 kg/mm^2), this fiber can be used in a number of technological products.

Acetate fibers are thermoplastic; one can therefore obtain from them yarns with false twist (of the type, elastic helanca). The production of bulky yarns makes it possible to extend the assortment of goods made of acetate fibers.

B. Introduction of Small Amounts of Additives

Small amounts of additives which improve certain properties of acetate fibers can be introduced both into the spinning solution of the acetylcellulose before producing the fiber, and also in the form of finishing compounds used in the dressing of the fiber or fabrics.

Investigations have shown that the introduction of small amounts (up to 2% of the weight of the fiber) or certain compounds (aromatic amines or phenols) into the acetylcellulose solution increases the light stability of the acetate fibers (14).

The presence of small quantities of compounds which decrease the photooxidation degradation of acetylcellulose in the acetate fiber, such as, for example, 2,4-dioxybenzoquinone, diphenylamine, and β-naphthylamine, increase the light stability considerably.

Similarly one can introduce into the acetate fibers antistatic agents which decrease the electrifiability.

C. Production of Fibers from Mixtures of Acetylcellulose with Synthetic Polymers

An essential condition for obtaining such fibers is the ready solubility of the synthetic polymer in one of the solvents used for the cellulose acetates and the compatibility of the polymers.

Thus American investigators have obtained fibers from a mixture of solutions of partially saponified cellulose acetate and polyacrylonitrile in dimethylformamide by dry extrusion at 140–180°C (15). When the mixture contains at least 40% acetylcellulose the fiber properties are intermediate between the properties of acetate and polyacrylonitrile fiber and depend on the relative amounts of the components.

Soviet investigators (16) have obtained fibers from acetone solutions of chlorinated polyvinyl chloride and partially saponified acetylcellulose–acetochlorin. The acetochlorin fiber is fire-resistant and thermally more stable than the chlorinated polyvinyl chloride (chlorin) fiber. The shrinkage temperature of the acetochlorin fiber is higher by 20–25°C than that of chlorin fiber.

The processing of solutions of polymer mixtures is ma e difficult in a number of cases by the incompatibility of the polymers (stratification in storage). One can therefore measure out precisely and mix solutions of two or more polymers in a special apparatus directly before forming the fiber. The compatibility is improved when a small amount of grafted copolymer of acetylcellulose and of the same carbon-chain polymer is added.

D. Chemical Modification

The first method of chemical modification of the properties of acetate fibers was the production of fibers from mixtures of cellulose esters with acetic and certain other acids. This method found no practical application.

Further work to produce fibers from mixed esters can apparently be of some interest—above all, as a method of internal plasticization of acetylcellulose; for example, to increase the stability of acetate fibers against multiple deformation.

One of the interesting methods of chemical modification of acetate fibers is the use of predyed cellulose (17) in the production of acetate fiber. The cellulose is dyed with procion dyes which form chemical compounds with the macromolecules. These compounds are stable during acetylation and in the subsequent processing of the acetylcellulose until the finished acetate fiber is obtained.

The most promising prospect of obtaining fibers with new properties is the synthesis of grafted copolymers of acetylcellulose. The grafting of synthetic polymers can be carried out on the cellulose, acetylcellulose, and the finished fiber. In the first two instances the choice of grafted components is limited, since one must ensure the solubility of the grafted copolymer in the acetylcellulose solvents. However, an advantage of the method is the possibility of the participation of the grafted chain in producing the fiber structure in the process of its formation.

In principle one can by changing the type of grafted chains and their length obtain fibers from grafted copolymers of acetylcellulose which have a higher strength, stability against multiple deformation, high light stability, good dyeing qualities for certain types of dyes, and increased thermal stability.

REFERENCES

1. *Text. Organon,* **37** (6), 89 (1966).
2. *Mod. Textiles Mag.*, **46** (5), 57 (1965).
3. W. Germ. Pat. 818,577; Brit. Pats. 719,853, 726,900, 753,461, 758,442; U.S. Pats. 2,838,793, 2,902,383, 2,955,320; *Man-Made Textiles,* **32,** (375), 63 (1955).
4. A. Movsum-Zade, R. M. Livshitz, A. A. Konkin, and Z. A. Rogovin, *Vysokomolekul. Soedin.*, Coll. Cellulose and Its Derivatives, USSR Academy of Sci. Press, 1963, p. 186; P. V. Kozlov, R. M. Livshitz, A. Movsum-Zade, A. A. Konkin, and Z. A. Rogovin, *Vysokomolekul. Soedin.*, **6,** 1965 (1964).
5. B. S. Sprague, *Textile Res. J.*, **30** (9), 697 (1960).
6. Z. A. Rogovin, Yu. D. Sushkova, and A. P. Krainov, *Khim. Volokna,* **1959** (6), 27.
7. Z. A. Rogovin, F. M. Rozhanskaya, and L. P. Perepechkin, *Khim. Volokna,* **1959** (1), 48.
8. Z. V. Baibakova, F. M. Rozhanskaya, and Z. A. Rogovin, *Khim. Volokna,* **1961** (6), 46; L. P. Perepechkin and V. A. Troitskaya, *Ibid.*, **2,** 55 (1964).
9. Takeo Takagi and J. B. Goldberg, *Mod. Textiles Mag.*, **41** (4), 49 (1960); J. B. Goldberg, *Can. Textile J.*, **77,** (5), 59 (1960); R. W. Moncrieff, *Textile Monatssch.*, **85** (1020), 541 (1959); R. W. Moncrieff, *Fibers and Plastics,* **20** (8), 269 (1959).
10. A. F. Tesi, *Mod. Textiles Mag.*, **36** (12), 72 (1955).
11. *Mod. Textiles Mag.*, **35** (11), 36 (1954).
12. R. W. Moncrieff, *Man-Made Fibres,* London National Trade Press, 1959.
13. *Chemiefasern,* **6,** 409 (1963).
14. A. D. Virnik, K. Makhkamov, and Z. A. Rogovin, *Khim. Volokna,* **1963** (1), 47.
15. D. M. Cotes and H. J. White, *J. Polymer Sci.*, **20,** 155 (1956).
16. N. V. Mikhailov, Z. A. Ukhanova, and T. I. Karetina, *Khim. Volokna,* **1959** (3), 18.
17. U. Einsele, *Mell. Textilber.*, **42,** 427 (1961); L. S. Galbraikh, M. A. Chekalin, and Z. A. Rogovin, *Zh. Fiz. Khim.*, **35** (8), 1825 (1962); Swiss Pat. 357,383.

APPENDIX*

Spinning speeds for acetate and triacetate depend on the drying capability of the spinning apparatus and the physical property and quality requirements of the product, as well as other mechanical features of the spinning machine. The maximum drying capability of a given machine is substantially a constant (USP 3,272,638, Example 1). Consequently, drying capability can be described by a denier × speed factor. If a 50-den yarn can be adequately dried at up to 800 m/min, then a 500-den yarn can be adequately dried at up to 80 m/min. Thus, spinning speeds used in industry can vary widely in light of the various factors noted above, but are unquestionably measured in terms of hundreds of meters per minute.

* Private communications: J. L. Riley, Celanese Corporation.

Fibers of Cellulose Triacetate

K. C. Laughlin
Department of Consumer Sciences, University of California, Davis, California

CONTENTS

Cellulose triacetate is, by definition, cellulose which has been acetylated to the extent of at least 92% of the three available hydroxyl groups. As a fiber, it is a relative newcomer to the man-made fiber roster and is commercially produced in the western hemisphere only by Celanese Corporation and its subsidiaries. Because of their many similarities in chemical composition and methods of manufacture, this discussion will make frequent reference to triacetate's predecessor, cellulose acetate, which is made from the same raw material, cellulose, but is acetylated to the extent of only about 2.5 of the three available hydroxyl groups. In spite of the similarities in raw material and manufacturing processes, cellulose triacetate fiber has properties differing significantly from those of cellulose acetate fiber, and enjoys a market of its own which relies on these unique properties.

I. HISTORY AND ECONOMIC IMPORTANCE

The first commercial production of cellulose triacetate fibers was by the Lustron Company in the United States as early as 1914 (1,2). Production capacity was low—about 300 lb per day. Lack of knowledge regarding satisfactory dyeing and finishing procedures limited the acceptability of the yarn and the company closed in 1927. The next activity in this field was in England, where Courtaulds, Ltd. investigated triacetate yarns during the period 1946–1951. Comparisons with secondary acetate filament yarns showed that triacetate gave improved performance in crease resistance and in dimensional stability in washing. In the United States, laboratory studies were made by Bell Telephone Company on the annealing and quenching of triacetate yarns in 1941. In 1948 American Celanese conducted similar studies on triacetate yarns following the structural changes by means of x-ray diffraction. British Celanese experimented with melt-spinning of triacetate for a brief period starting in 1950, but later shifted to dry-spinning and wet-spinning techniques.

Commercial production of triacetate by Celanese Corporation and by British Celanese was announced in October, 1954, with Courpleta (Courtaulds) following in December, 1954. Canadian Celanese and the French and German Rhodiaceta Companies started production in 1955. American Celanese introduced, in 1960, a modified triacetate (Arnel 60) with about twice the strength of ordinary triacetate. This product was withdrawn from the market in 1962, presumably because the customer did not find the increase in strength to be worth the increased price.

Current producers of triacetate yarn, as listed in Textile Organon, June, 1965, are as follows:

United States	Celanese Fibers Company
Belgium	Amcel Europe, S.A.
Canada	Canadian Celanese Company
France	Société Rhodiaceta
Germany (West)	Deutsche Rhodiaceta A.G.
Mexico	Celanese Mexicana, S.A.
U.S.S.R.	Plant scheduled for 1966 at Kaunas, Lithuania
United Kingdom	British Celanese, Ltd. (Courtaulds)

In addition to these, *Index to Man-Made Fibers of the World*, 2nd ed., 1964, published by Harlequin Press, Ltd., lists Dainippon Celluloid Co., Ltd., and Nichitsu Acetate Co., Ltd., both of Japan. Mitsubishi Acetate Co., Ltd., is reported to be seeking a license to produce triacetate fiber.

Sales of triacetate continuous filament yarn in the United States, initiated in 1955, rose rapidly to 20 million pounds in 1959. Filament

TABLE I.

Denier and filament	Cones	Beams
55/LTDZ/15	—	$1.25
55/2Z/15	$1.32	1.33
75/LTDZ/20	—	1.21
75/2Z/20	1.26	1.27
100/LTDZ/26	—	1.09
100/2Z/26	1.14	1.15
150/LTDZ/40	—	0.90
150/2Z/40	0.95	0.96
200/2Z/52	0.92	0.93
300/2Z/80	0.87	0.88
450/2Z/120	0.86	0.87
600/2Z/160	0.85	0.86
2.5, 5.0 and 8.0 dpf staples 0.48		
2.5, 5.0 and 8.0 dpf tow 0.53		
Premium per pound:		
Solution-dyed	0.37	
Black	0.25	

sales in 1964 are estimated at 40 million pounds, with an additional 30 million pounds of staple and tow. The price of triacetate fiber is shown in Table I.

II. MANUFACTURING PROCESSES

A. Polymer Manufacture

Cellulose triacetate shares with other cellulosics the advantages and disadvantages of starting with a natural polymer. The methods of removing impurities from the native cellulose have been discussed in the chapter on viscose rayon tire yarns by McGarry and Priest. Since the molecular weight of the purified cellulose is usually higher than desired, one of the problems in acetylation is to control the rate of degradation so that the molecular weight of the product will be in the desired range. Several publications (3–6) describe in detail the effect of acetylation variables on molecular weight. Comparison of sulfuric acid, perchloric acid, methane disulfonic acid, sulfoacetic acid, and methanesulfonic acid showed that sulfuric acid was the best catalyst for acetylation of cotton linters, but that perchloric and methanedisulfonic acids were superior for regenerated cellulose acetylation. Kinetic studies on the rate of degradation and rate of acetylation as a function of temperature, acetic acid/anhydride ratio, catalyst, and catalyst concentration led to the conclusion that commercial manufacturing practice closely approximates the optimum conditions.

The commercial manufacturing process for cellulose triacetate resembles that for cellulose acetate, with the exception that the partial hydrolysis step is eliminated, and the final product is almost completely acetylated.

1. Batch Process

The batch process adheres rather closely to the process for secondary acetate (see the McGarry–Priest article).

A typical procedure is as follows:

The cellulose raw material, as for acetate, can be a good grade of wood pulp or cotton linters, according to the state of the market. After comminution in a shredder or mill the pulp is pretreated with 35% of glacial acetic acid in a horizontal, radial arm mixer. The acetylation reactor, a vertical vessel with high-viscosity agitator, is charged with a cold mixture of acetic acid and acetic anhydride containing sufficient anhydride to react with all of the cellulosic hydroxyls and the water in the system, plus 10–15% excess. Sulfuric acid catalyst is added, followed by the pretreated cellulose. The exothermic reaction causes a temperature rise to about 50°C. The viscous reaction mixture is neutralized with magnesium carbonate and is extruded into a dilute acetic acid bath, washed, and dried. This procedure results in a polymer with 61.5–61.9% acetyl value and 70–125 centipoise viscosity (of a 4.6% solution in 90/10 methylene chloride/methanol).

2. Continuous Processes

The continuous processes include one which produces the triacetate as a solution ready for spinning and one which retains the solid form of the original cellulose throughout the reaction.

In the first process, comminuted wood pulp is slurried in a 90/10 methanol mixture containing excess acetic anhydride. Sulfuric acid catalyst is added and the mixture is passed continuously through a series of at least ten agitated reaction vessels. The viscous solution so formed is neutralized in two stages with magnesium carbonate, filtered, and is then ready for spinning into fiber. This is the method of choice when acetylation and spinning occur at the same site.

In the second process, an inert solvent such as benzene or carbon tetrachloride is employed as a slurrying agent and perchloric acid is the preferred catalyst. Since the acetylated product is still in slurry form, it must be filtered, washed, and dried. This is the method of choice when acetylation and spinning are conducted at different locations.

3. Polymer Properties

From the standpoint of fiber manufacture, the important properties of the polymer are its melting point, thermal stability at temperatures above the melting point, and solubility in commercially available solvents. Triacetate does not have a sharp melting point and is relatively unstable at temperatures required to produce viscosities suited to spinning; hence melt-spinning is not attractive. Triacetate is readily dissolved in methylene chloride/methanol mixtures to give solution viscosities suited to dry or wet spinning.

B. Fiber Manufacture

Commercial spinning of cellulose triacetate is carried out in the same equipment as is used for acetate spinning except that the use of a different solvent requires changes in the solvent recovery system. When both fibers are produced in the same plant it is advantageous to have a single recovery system capable of handling both solvent mixes. Use of carbon-bed absorbers followed by fractional distillation columns in conventional arrangement imposes no unique engineering problems.

1. Dry-Spinning

The process for dry-spinning manufacture of continuous filament cellulose triacetate is shown in Fig. 1 and is described as follows:

The spinning dope is prepared by adding triacetate flake to a measured quantity of solvent plus filter aid and a delustrant (titanium dioxide) in a special turbine blade mixer. The viscous solution is discharged from the mixer to a storage tank from which it is pumped through three stages of filtration. The filtered dope from the last filtration stage is sent on to the spinning department.

There are two auxiliary systems in the dope preparation section. One system is the waste or residue dope system. All waste yarn and dope suitable for recovery are dissolved in the waste dope system and added to the regular dope mixers. The use of the waste recovery system results in a high material efficiency.

The other system is for the preparation of the delustering solution. Titanium dioxide and triacetate flake are added to solvent in a ball or pebble mill and blended to exact specifications.

The filtered spinning dope is distributed to the various machines for extrusion into the yarns. At each position an individual precision gear type pump accurately meters dope and forces it through the orifices of a

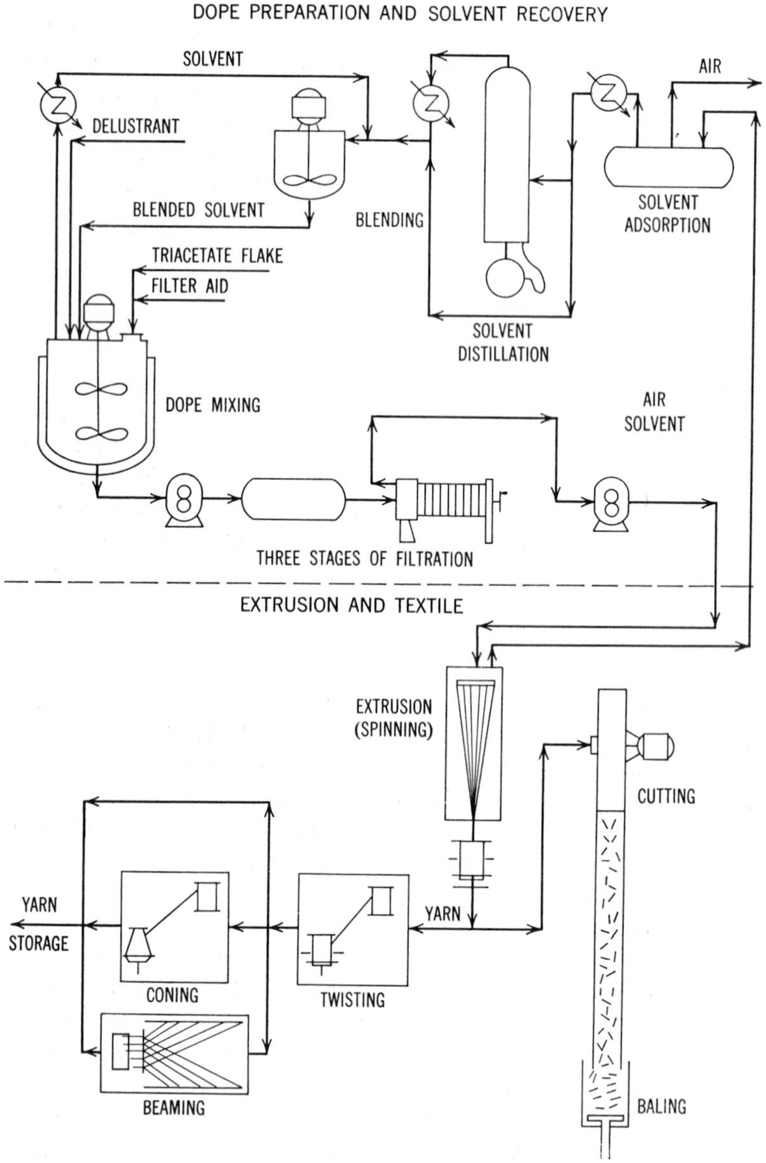

Fig. 1. Flow diagram for triacetate fiber plant.

spinneret. The filaments fall through a chamber into which hot air is circulated to evaporate the solvent. Triacetate yarn may be spun by either up- or down-draft methods. The filaments are gathered and wound over a feed roller whose speed is accurately controlled to ensure constant draw-down. The thread consisting of the required number of filaments is then ring-twisted and collected on a bobbin or taken up on other equipment as required. The bobbins are replaced on schedule to ensure constant yardage for the individual packages of yarn. A yarn lubricant is applied to the yarn between the cabinet and the feed roller.

The process for staple is the same, except that yarn from several spinning positions is combined into a tow which is dried, crimped, cut, and baled.

2. *Wet-Spinning*

The process for Arnel 60 (7), which produces fibers twice as strong as regular triacetate, is of technical interest even though it is no longer in commercial operation.

The features of the Arnel 60 process which differ from the regular triacetate staple process are presented in Fig. 2 and described as follows:

The Arnel 60 wet-spinning process uses the same spinning dope as employed for bright triacetate filament yarn. The dope is extruded into a spin bath with diminished solvent power for the polymer. The spin bath and tow pass upward through a spinning column to the head box where the tow is pulled out of the bath. The tow is mechanically freed of the spin bath followed by washing, air opening, and tow drying.

A small percentage of the cellulose triacetate from the spinning dope passes into the spin bath as dissolved and suspended solids. Before reuse, therefore, the spent spin bath is purified and distilled.

A conventional carbon absorber unit is used for recovery of solvents from the vapor-laden air exhausted from the dryer. Recovered solvents are separated in a distillation unit and then recycled to dope preparation and spin-bath makeup. Since the components of the solvents used for triacetate and Arnel 60 may be the same, the solvent recovery system can be common to both processes.

3. *Other Processes*

Cellulose triacetate fiber can also be produced by the acetylation of cotton and by the acetylation of viscose rayon. Two versions of the latter process exist, both of which are commercially feasible. The German process (8) uses liquid phase acetylation with phosphoric acid

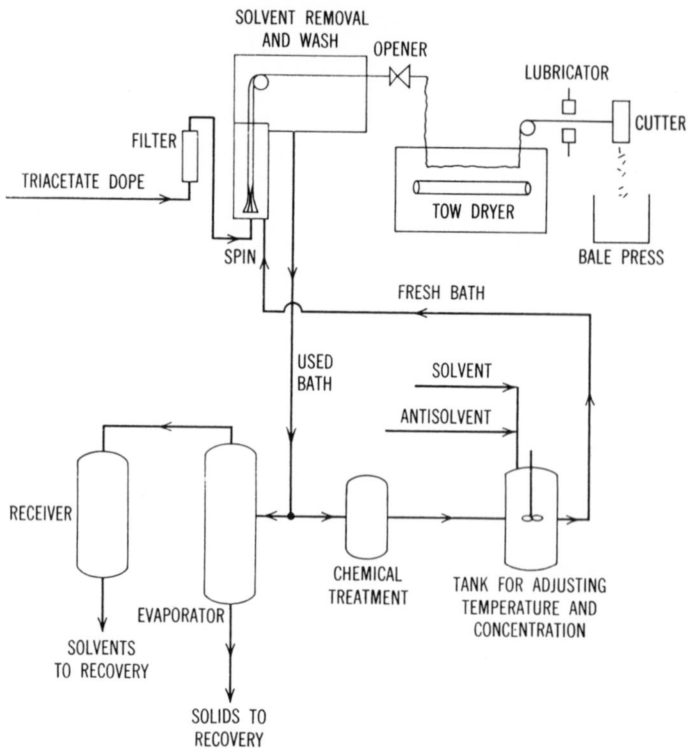

Fig. 2. Flow diagram for Arnel 60 fiber plant.

catalyst and without inert diluents. The Japanese process (9) operates with vapor phase acetic anhydride and requires somewhat longer reaction times than the German process. A typical Japanese (Acetovis) staple has a dpf of 2–2.5, a tenacity of 3.0 g/den, and 25% elongation. Fabrics constructed from Acetovis do not require heat treatment in order to achieve good color wash-fastness, a high safe ironing temperature, excellent resistance to glazing, and good dimensional stability. The appearance of dyed Acetovis cross section suggests that the surface of the fiber is completely acetylated, with the interior only partially acetylated, as might be expected from vapor-phase acetylation.

The acetylation of cotton has been studied by Conrad and others (10), who reached the following conclusions:

1. Heterogeneous acetylation is diffusion controlled.

2. Cotton crystalline structure decreases with progress of acetylation, disappearing at about the diacetate stage.

3. Glass transistion appears at the monoacetate stage and becomes more prominent at higher degrees of acetylation.

4. Triacetylated cotton melts at 310–315°C and loses acetyl at higher temperatures.

5. Breaking strength per end of yarn increases 50%, but tenacity decreases 20% due to increase in weight.

The acetylation of cotton is not regarded as commercially attractive under current United States cotton prices.

Numerous spinning modifications have been reported in the patent literature:

U.S.S.R. Patent 129,785 (1960) describes dry-spinning from methylene chloride/ethanol.

East German Patent 17,466 (1959) describes wet-spinning into a carbon tetrachloride bath.

British Patent 858,533 (1961) (to British Celanese) covers wet spinning into 18% acetic acid bath.

British Patent 828,071 (1960) (to Société Rhodiaceta) covers spinning with a solvent mixture of 72% dioxane, 4% ethanol, and 24% water.

Japanese Patent 783 (1961) covers wet-spinning into 20% acetic acid.

U.S. Patent 2,988,418 (1961) (to British Celanese) describes spinning into an aqueous ester bath.

U.S. Patent 3,033,846 (1961) (to British Celanese) describes wet-spinning into an acetic acid bath followed by a stretching operation.

U.S. Patent 3,081,145 (1962) (Wacker Chemie, to Celanese) describes wet-spinning from a 95/5 methylene chloride/pentanediol solution into a 5/58.5/31.5 bath of methylene chloride/pentanediol/water. Fiber physical properties are equivalent to Arnel 60.

Japanese Patent 221 (1963) (to Teikoku) covers dry spinning from a 96/4 methylene chloride/methanol solution.

Japanese Patent 18,325 (1962) and 13,524 (1962) (to Dainippon) describes wet-spinning into acetic acid with methyl isobutyl ketone and into 20% acetic acid containing titanium dioxide.

III. PHYSICAL PROPERTIES

The physical properties of cellulose triacetate differ from those of cellulose acetate fiber mainly by virtue of the increased hydrophobicity introduced by the higher degree of acetylation. Triacetate is manufactured in the United States only by Celanese Corporation, which markets a range of deniers in continuous-filament yarn and 2.5 and 5.0 dpf staple and tow. These fibers are available in solution dyed black. The physical properties are listed in Table II.

A typical stress–strain curve for triacetate is compared in Fig. 3 with acetate. The resistance to strength loss on heat aging is shown in Fig.

TABLE II. Physical Properties of Triacetates

Tenacity, g/den	
Standard conditions[a]	1.2–1.4
Wet	0.8–1.0
Knot, standard conditions	1.0–1.2
Loop, standard conditions	1.0–1.2
Elongation at break, %	
Standard conditions	25–28 (staple fiber 34–40%)
Wet	35–40
Initial modulus, g/den	35–40
Specific gravity	1.3
Refractive index	
Parallel to fiber axis	1.474
Perpendicular to fiber axis	1.471
Standard moisture regain, %	3.2
Water absorptivity (100% R.H.), centrifuge method	
Non-heat-treated	16–17
Heat-treated	10–11
Area cross-sectional swelling in water, %	
Non-heat-treated	4.0
Heat-treated	1.5
Melting point (copper block method), °C	315–320
Specific heat, cal/g/°C	0.32
Tensile recovery, %	
1% Stretch	100
3% Stretch	88
5% Stretch	75
10% Stretch	43

[a] 65% Relative humidity, 70°F.

4 in comparison with cotton and nylon. Figure 5 presents the effect of testing temperature on the stress–strain properties.

IV. CHEMICAL PROPERTIES

The chemical resistance of triacetate is listed in Celanese Bulletin TD-12A. In general, resistance to most solvents is good. Exceptions are acetic acid, hydrochloric acid, ammonium hydroxide, sodium hydroxide, phenol, and sodium hypochlorite (5%). It is resistant to attack by moths and carpet beetles, and was substantially unchanged in a twelve weeks' soil burial test. Strength retention on exposure to sunlight is in the same class as rayon, cotton, and acetate. Triacetate has unusually high resistance to degradation by chlorine in the concentration normally used in home washings.

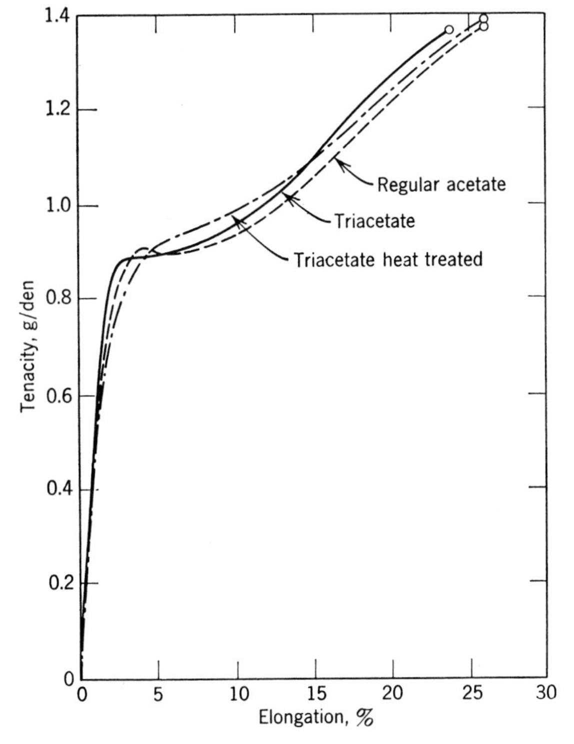

Fig. 3. Stress–strain curves of 150-den triacetate yarn.

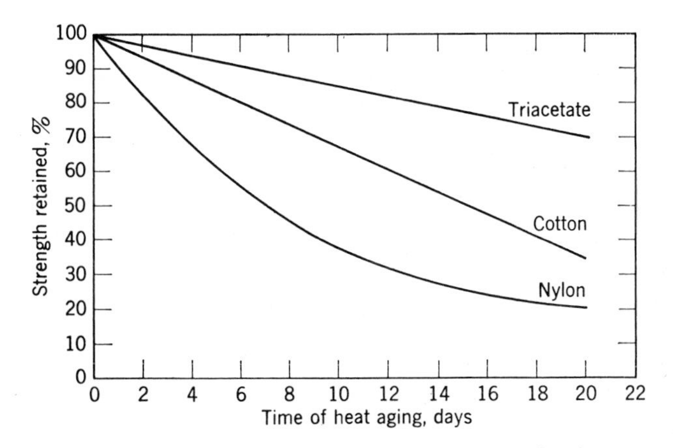

Fig. 4. Effect of aging on triacetate, cotton, and nylon.

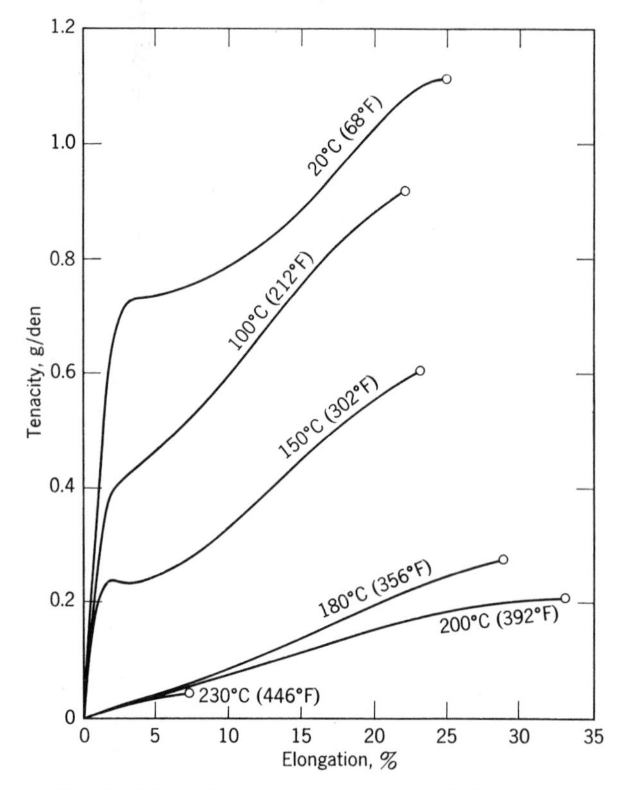

Fig. 5. Effect of temperature on stress–strain curves.

V. MORPHOLOGY

In 1957 Sprague, Riley, and Noether (11) reported studies on the morphology of cellulose triacetate fibers. Cellulose in the form of ramie, cotton, and wood pulp (cellulose I), Fortisan 36 (cellulose II), and high tenacity rayon tire yarn (cellulose IV) was acetylated to the triacetate (*a*) heterogeneously and (*b*) homogeneously. They concluded that:

1. Heterogeneous acetylation of cellulose I yields triacetate I.

2. Homogeneous acetylation of any form of cellulose results in triacetate II.

3. Any type of acetylation of cellulose II yields triacetate II.

4. Heterogeneous acetylation of cellulose IV prepared from cellulose II yields triacetate II.

Heat treatment studies showed that the triacetate I form was stable at temperatures up to 290°C, but that the triacetate II form resulted from heating at the melt temperature (about 315°C).

Treatment with swelling agents does not transform the crystalline form, but does change response to later heat treatment according to the agent employed. Acetone and acetic acid promote, dioxane and methanol inhibit, the response of triacetate II to heat treatment.

These studies indicated that the unit cell of the triacetate fiber closely resembles the parent cellulose, with the spacing between the chains being increased to accommodate the acetyl groups. The unit cell length in the fiber direction was 10.5 Å, corresponding to one cellobiose unit per repeat unit.

In recent work, Conrad and Creely (12) report that triacetylated cotton is converted from the triacetate I crystal form to the triacetate II form by treatment with formic acid. With acid concentrations of 75% and higher, the II form was retained on saponification. This behavior has not been explained.

Still more recently (13), Manley discussed the molecular morphology of native and regenerated celluloses. Based on his excellent work with high-resolution electron microscopy and x-ray, he formulated a model for the cellulose crystal which resembles a flattened figure eight spiral (achieved by compression of the figure eight along its vertical axis). This results in a ribbonlike structure 40 Å wide and 10 Å thick.

An important aspect of Dr. Manley's work is the conclusion that cellulosic fibers contain no amorphous regions as such since each microfibril is a very small single crystal. The crystalline structure observed in x-ray patterns results from orderly aggregation of these microfibrils, while the diffuseness observed arises from disorder in the arrangement of some of the microfibrils. It is expected that Dr. Manley will continue this work to include cellulose triacetate fibers, and confirm the expectation that similar morphology will be observed.

VI. FIBER AND FABRIC PROCESSING

A. Textile Processing

Triacetate staple can be processed on cotton, worsted, and wool systems. Performance is best when the temperature is 75–85°F and the relative humidity is 55–65%. The exact temperature and relative humidity within these ranges is not as important as the maintenance of uniform conditions. Conventional textile processing machinery can be used with settings and speeds within the normal range for natural fibers. Slashing usually employs size formulas consisting of starch or starch derivative, a softener, and a small amount of an adhesive. Size applications of 12–15% and stretch levels of about 3% appear to be optimum.

Triacetate filament yarns can be processed satisfactorily through the twisting, warping, slashing, quilling, and weaving operations on conventional, commercially available equipment with performance similar to that of acetate.

B. Dyeing of Cellulose Triacetate

Yarns and fabrics of cellulose triacetate can be dyed in a full range of shades using disperse dyes. Special equipment is not necessary, and heat treatment after dyeing with selected dyes will produce good wash-fastness. In line with its hydrophobicity, triacetate's dyeing rate with

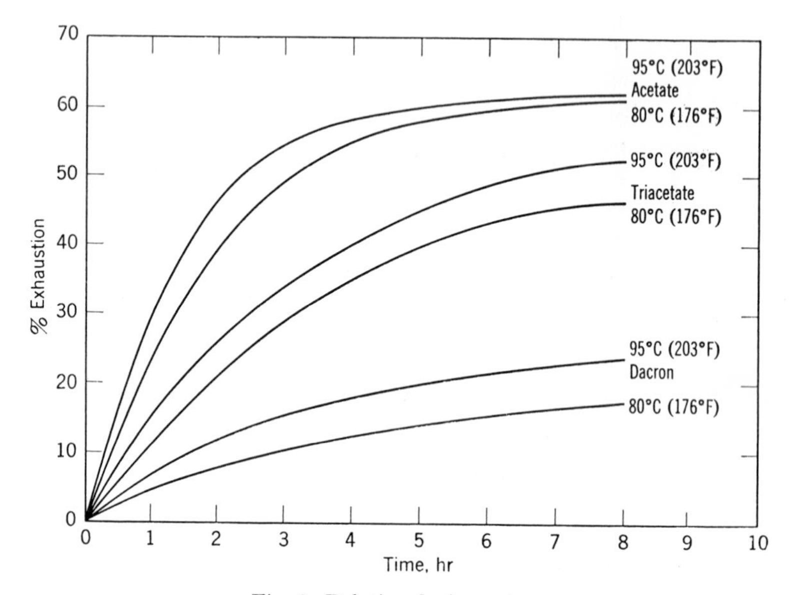

Fig. 6. Relative dyeing rates.

disperse dyes is slower than that of the secondary acetate, as shown in Fig. 6. Higher temperatures increase the rate of dyeing and the exhaustion of the dye bath, as shown in Figure 7. Accelerants can be added to the dye bath to increase dyeing rate and bath exhaustion. Suitable accelerants include methyl salicylate, butyl benzoate, orthophenyl phenol, biphenyl, phenyl salicylate, tripropyl phosphate, acetyl triethyl citrate, butyl cellosolve acetate, and triacetin.

Black and navy colors are produced by the use of developed azoic dyes. Dyeing procedures with these dyes are essentially the same as for secondary acetate, but even with 20–25°C higher temperature, longer times are required. Solution-dyed black yarns are commercially available at a $0.25/lb premium.

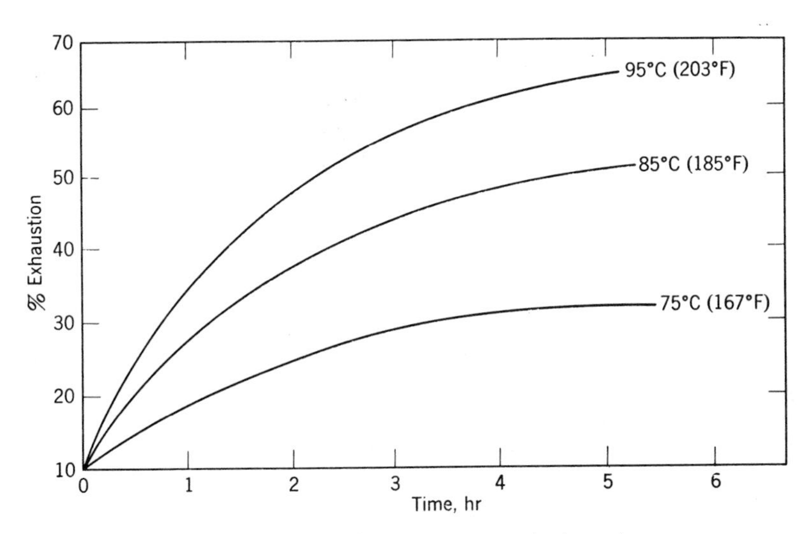

Fig. 7. Effect of temperature on dyeing rate.

Detailed information on dyes and dyeing procedures for cellulose triacetate will be found in a series of technical bulletins issued by Celanese.

C. Finishing of Triacetate Products

Triacetate fabrics can be finished with both durable and nondurable finishes, but the durable formulas are used more extensively, since triacetate is used most frequently in washable fabrics.

Silicone resins can be applied either before or after heat treatment. In some cases, silica dispersions are added to increase fiber-to-fiber friction.

Fluorinated polymers and antistatic finishes are applied after heat treatment. Because of the unreactive nature of triacetate, stiffening agents must be of the surface coating type.

A finishing treatment unique to triacetate is surface saponification achieved by treatment with caustic soda at elevated temperature. The surface film of regenerated cellulose results in antistatic properties, reduced soilage, increased resistance to "O"-fading, softer hand, increased safe ironing temperature, higher tear strength, and more versatility in resin finishing.

D. Heat Treating

Triacetate fabrics require heat treatment for the attainment of many desirable properties such as dye wash-fastness, higher safe ironing temperatures and decreased glazing, reduced shrinkage, and improved resistance to wrinkling. A variety of commercial heat treatment procedures can be used, and the choice depends largely on fabric construction and weight. For optimum results, a fabric temperature of 425°F should be maintained for about two seconds. Since triacetate fabrics can be easily stretched at this temperature, care must be taken to avoid application of tension to the fabric. Shrinkage and distortion can be avoided by proper restraint of the fabric. This is particularly important in wet heat treatment. By proper control of conditions, strength loss due to heat can be limited to 10–20%.

E. Printing

Triacetate can be screen- or roller-printed with disperse dyes to give prints of good definition, brightness, levelness, and color values. The color-fastness obtainable is equivalent to that of dyed fabric. The fixation conditions provide simultaneous heat treatment, so that the printed fabric does not stain on further processing or in consumer washing.

REFERENCES

1. *J. Textile Inst.*, **52,** 242–255 (1961).
2. *Text. Mfr.*, **87,** 219–222 (1961).
3. *Ind. Eng. Chem.*, **47** (5), 995 (1957); **53,** 363 (1961).
4. *Tappi*, **44,** 669–678 (1961).
5. *J. Polymer Sci.*, **51,** 11–122 (1961).
6. *Textile Res. J.*, **33,** 784 (1963).
7. U.S. Pats. 2,999,004; 3,057,039; 3,071,807; 3,081,145; 3,084,414; 3,109.697; 3,133,136; Belg. Pat. 612,915.
8. German Pat. 1,038,233 (to Wacker Chemie).
9. U.S. Pat. 2,780,511 (to Toho Rayon).
10. *Textile Res. J.*, **33,** 784, 794 (1963).
11. *Textile Res. J.*, **28,** 275–287 (1957).
12. *Textile Res. J.*, **35,** 184, 187 (1965).
13. Fiber Society Meeting, October 7, 1965; *Nature*, **204,** 1155–1157 (1964).

APPENDIX*

There is a range of conditions in which a triacetate fiber will undergo "heat setting." The most favorable of these has little or no effect on the initial tenacity and elongation of the fiber although the safe ironing temperature is very appreciably increased, the washfastness of any dye present during heat treatment is greatly improved, and the crystallinity is raised to values near 1.0. A fiber temperature of 204°C (400°F) for a duration of 20 sec will effect this set of changes (Celanese Fibers Marketing Company Technical Bulletin TBT-5). A longer exposure will produce neither a material improvement in washfastness and safe ironing temperature, nor an appreciable increase in crystallinity. However, the tensile properties will decline. At temperatures higher than 215°C, increasingly high crystalline order indices are obtained, but in the region of 230°C or higher, structural damage will occur to the fiber.

* Private communications: J. L. Riley, Celanese Corporation.

Characterization of Cellulose Fibers

Hans Krässig

Director, Research and Development, Chemiefaser Lenzing AG, Lenzing, Austria

CONTENTS

It is generally accepted that fibers are characterized with respect to their state and their properties by (*a*) the *molecular structure* and the molecular length of the fiber-forming polymer molecules, (*b*) the fine *structural arrangement* of the macromolecules into crystallites and fibrillar crystallite bands, and (*c*) the *morphological assembly* of the fibrils in the fiber.

Natural and man-made cellulose fibers are especially suitable for studying fiber characteristics and the effect of such characteristics on the physical properties of the fibers. Methods for molecular characterization, the relative ease with which the length of cellulose molecules can be altered by chemical degradation, the good crystallization tendency, and the well-defined morphology in cellulose fibers have made them excellent model substances. Many of the findings obtained with them have greatly helped the general understanding of fiber characteristics and their influence on properties, thus stimulating our knowledge of synthetic fibers.

It would therefore seem worthwhile to review our past knowledge of the characteristics of cellulose fibers and to describe the interrelations between molecular properties, fine structural arrangement, and morphological assembly and their effect on the technically important physical properties.

I. GENERAL CONSIDERATIONS

A. Cellulose Fiber Morphology and Fine Structure

The meaning of fine structural characteristics, such as crystalline order and crystallite orientation, as well as the understanding of the influence of molecular structure and molecular length of fiber-forming polymers on fiber properties, can only be derived from the relation of these properties to the morphology or architecture of fibers. It therefore seems opportune to begin our consideration of cellulose fiber characterization with a review of fiber morphology, its historical development, and its present status. Since this can only be a general account, the reader's attention is drawn to the excellent reviews already published by Leaderman (1), Frey-Wyssling (2), Hermans (3), Preston (4), Kratky and Porod (5), Treiber (6), Sippel (7), and Hearle (8).

The earliest scientific studies of fibers concentrated on the morphological aspects. The starting point for all the theories on fiber morphology has been the micellar theory advanced just over 100 years ago by Nägeli (9), suggesting that cell membranes are composed of submicroscopic crystalline particles called micelles, embedded in some undefined intermicellar substance. This concept is illustrated in Fig. 1. This was supported at an early date by x-ray diffraction measurements showing conclusively the existence of crystalline particles in fibers (10,11). The

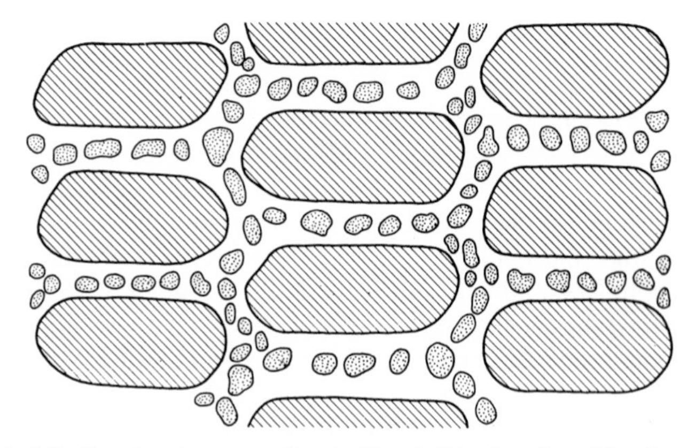

Fig. 1. Micellar structure according to Nägeli (9), after Frey-Wyssling (2)

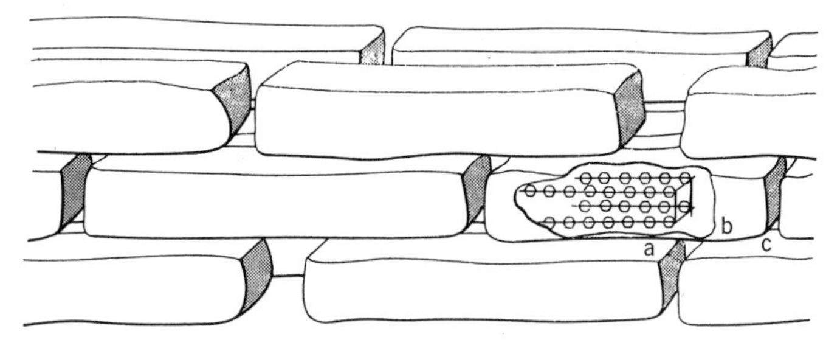

Fig. 2. Micellar structure according to Meyer (12) and Seifriz (13).

model devised by Meyer (12) and Seifriz (13) only extended Nägeli's theory with respect to details on the crystalline arrangement of the cellulose molecules inside the micelle, as shown in Fig. 2. At that time the actual length of cellulose and other fiber-forming molecules was still hotly disputed. In 1928 Hengstenberg and Mark (14) calculated from x-ray diffraction data that the micelle dimensions in ramie fibers were 600 Å in length and 50 Å in width, and in viscose rayon 300 Å in length and 40 Å in width. From this they supposed that the chain of the cellulose molecules consisted of sequences of 60–120 glucose units.

A completely new area was opened by Staudinger (15), who thought that the fiber-forming molecules were much longer, which was later proven to be substantially correct. The breakthrough was brought about by his famous work on polyformaldehyde (16). This new area is characterized by the development of the "fringe-micellar theory," combining the important aspects of both conflicting concepts, namely, that the structure of fibers is composed of long-chain molecules passing continuously through alternating crystalline and amorphous regions. Various models were suggested over the last thirty years, by Herrmann and Gerngross (17), Kratky and Mark (18), Frey-Wyssling (2), Kratky (19), Mark (20), Meyer and van der Wyk (21), Hermans (22), Hess and Kiessig (23), Hess, Mahl, and Gütter (24), and Hearle (25), among others. The various concepts only differ in the interpretation of more or less defined boundaries between the crystalline and amorphous phases. Models by Meyer and van der Wyk and by Mark illustrate these two extremes (Fig. 3).

In the textbook literature of the recent past various authors prefer structural models in which the crystallites are considered as distinct bricklike particles (26).

The fringe–micelle theory developed during the third decade of this century was quite stimulating to fiber research. It combined the knowledge gained from the newly developing macromolecular science with the

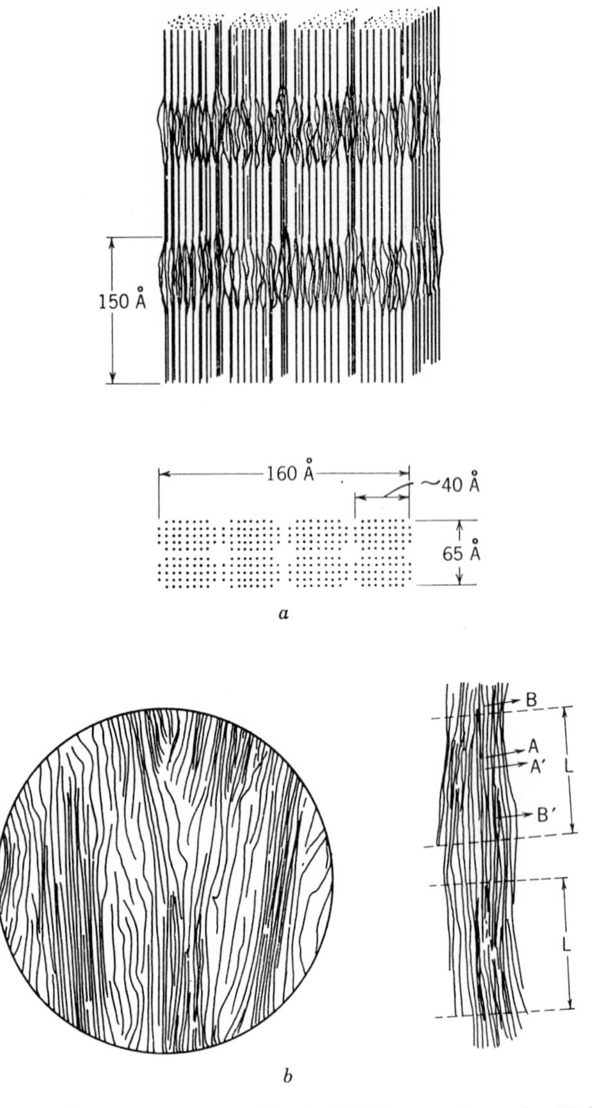

Fig. 3. Fringe-micellar structures according to (*a*) Meyer and van der Wyk (21) and (*b*) Mark (20).

existence of crystalline and less ordered phases proven by x-ray evidence and optical investigations. It helped to gain meaningful understanding of many other fiber properties, such as variations in moisture absorption, dye receptivity, and the effect of chemical attack. The assumption of the existence of inaccessible crystalline regions and of the role of the accessible less-ordered regions allowed a reasonable explanation not only of the chemical reactivity but also of the effects of mechanical forces in stretching, drying, and annealing. Changes in density and tensile and elastic behavior could be attributed to changes in crystalline–amorphous ratio and alignment of the crystallites or the molecules in the less ordered regions. Electrical properties, infrared observations, and nuclear magnetic resonance results were explained on the basis of this theory. It is therefore not surprising that the fringe–micelle theory is still being used by most fiber scientists as a fruitful working hypothesis.

From the early forties onward, the availability of the electron microscope opened a new area in fiber morphology and fine structural considerations. While according to the fringe-micelle theory the fiber was considered as a two-phase continuum structure, the electron microscope revealed the existence of distinct morphological units, namely, the elementary fibrils and fibrillar bundles of higher order. These observations have necessitated the more accurate distinction between gross morphology (laminae structures, skin-core structures in the light microscopy scale), morphology (fibrillar structures in the electron microscopy scale), and fine structure (architecture of the fibrils, crystallites, and their molecular interlinks).

The native and regenerated cellulose fibers have proven excellent and useful bases from which to gain an inside and generally applicable knowledge of fiber architecture from the macromolecular scale up to the macroscopic scale of the single fiber.

Information on the morphology of fibers by electron microscopy was obtained by (*a*) fragmentation involving or combining mechanical, ultrasonic, and chemical degradation methods, (*b*) investigation of ultrafine transverse and longitudinal sections, and (*c*) replication techniques. It is beyond the scope of this review to go into experimental details. An excellent description of the techniques and results of such investigations was presented very recently by Sikorsky (27).

Combining mild acid hydrolysis with moderate ultrasonic dispersion treatment on natural and regenerated cellulose fibers, and incorporating iodine electron microscopic observations, revealed, as shown by Husemann and Carnap (28), Hock (29), Morehead (30), Hess, Gütter, and Mahl (31), Kato and Yamada (32), and Mukherjee, Sikorski, and Woods (33), that distinct macro-fibrillar assemblies of elementary fibrils of a defined length exist. Together with Käppner (34), we could bring forward additional evidence enhancing the existence of such morphological units. The lengths of these larger morphological units range, according to these authors, from 1200 to 2500 Å (DP = 240–500) for natural cellulose fibers, such as ramie, cotton, and wood pulp, and from 650 to 1000 Å (DP = 130–200) for regenerated cellulose fibers, such as Fortisan and Toramomen rayon (see Table 1 in ref. 34).

Their existence was suggested some time ago by Staudinger et al. (35, 36), in an attempt to explain the observation of the loss of tensile properties, which occurs when native cellulose fibers are degraded below a DP of approximately 300–500 (1500–2500 Å), or regenerated cellulose fibers below a DP of 100–150 (500–750 Å). All the above-named authors found accumulation of macrofibrillar assemblies of average lengths in this order of magnitude.

The electron micrographs of Figs. 4 and 5 illustrate such findings.

The statistical evaluation of a large number of such micrographs, which ignored all fragments from isolated elementary fibrils, resulted in our own work on length distributions, as given in Fig. 6. We consider these macrofibrillar morphological units to be the actual building blocks of cellulose fibers interconnected and held together by interlinks from elementary fibrils and molecular strands of low order. As first found by Schulz and Husemann (37), and later by many others, prior chemical attack at these interlinks is also responsible for the accumulation of molecules with a DP of 400–500 and multiples thereof in celluloses degraded heterogeneously.

As the above electron micrographs clearly indicate, these morphological units are in essence assemblies of fragments of a still smaller basic morphological unit, namely the elementary fibril. This is also borne out by micrographs published by Mukherjee et al. (33). Mechanical fragmentation, including shearing forces, performed in the swollen state, and investigations on bacteriologically grown cellulose specimens have

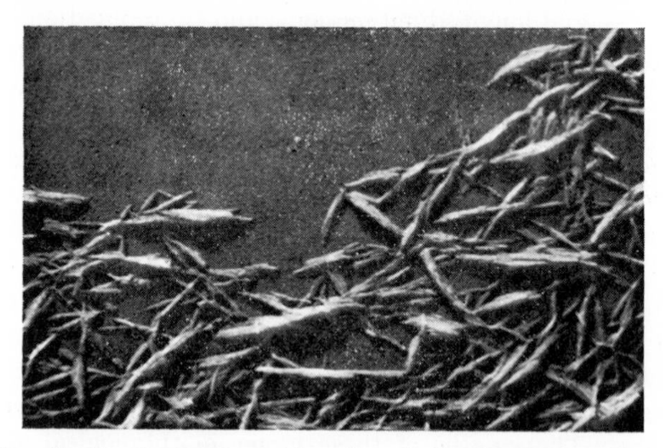

Fig. 4. Microfibrillar fragments and bundles of microfibrillar fragments of cotton hydrolyzed at 55°C with 1*N* HCl for 168 hr. (Electron micrograph; magnification 45,000; 1000 Å = 4.5 mm).

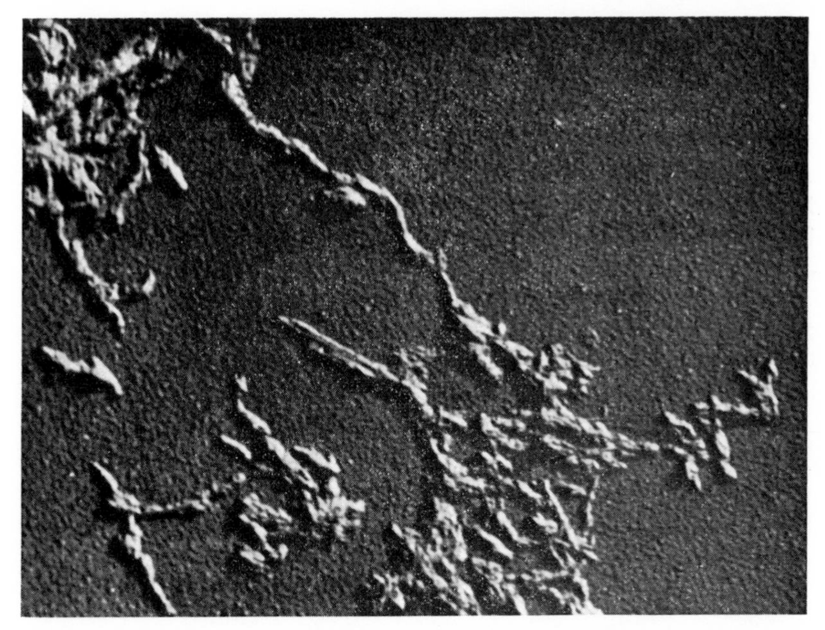

Fig. 5. Microfibrillar fragments and bundles of microfibrillar fragments of Fortisan hydrolyzed at 55°C with 1N HCl for 24 hr (electron micrograph; magnification 90,000; 1000 Å = 9.0 mm).

clearly established the existence of elementary fibrils of 25–100 Å width, similar thickness and seemingly indeterminate lengths in the range of microns (see Table 8.1 in ref. 24). It would be too tedious to name the numerous scientists who have contributed to this body of knowledge.

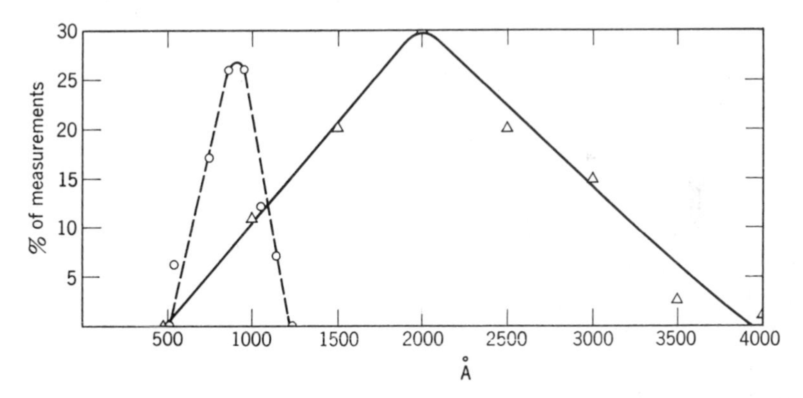

Fig. 6. Length distribution of bundles of microfibrillar fragments of cotton (——) and of Fortisan (– – –) hydrolyzed at 55°C with 1N HCl for 168 and 524 hr, respectively.

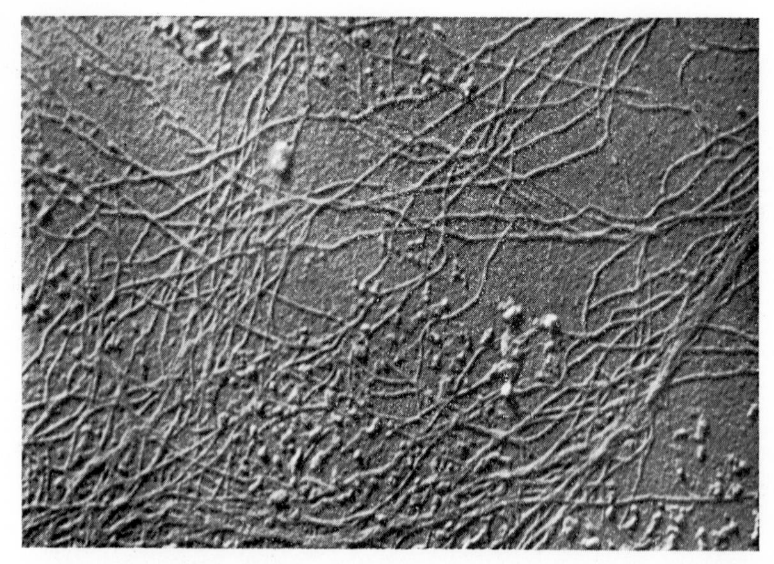

Fig. 7. Elementary fibrils from flax isolated by ultrasonic dispersion (electron micrograph taken by Mühlethaler (38); magnification 30,000).

The electron micrograph taken by Mühlethaler (38) and shown in Fig. 7 may serve as an example.

Although a sharp borderline between fiber morphology and fine structure cannot be drawn, the now clearly proven existence of morphological units of fibrillar assemblies and elementary fibrils allows at least some sort of distinction to be drawn. In light of the above newer results we tend to distinguish between the morphology of cellulose fibers and the fine structure inside the morphological units, thus reserving the term "fine structure" for the arrangement of the cellulose molecules inside the fibrils. For the latter the picture of a two-phase continuum structure still seems applicable. It would comprise a description of characteristics such as crystallinity, crystalline–amorphous ratio, and crystallite orientation.

The discovery of the existence of microfibrils has shifted the discussion of the structure of crystalline and amorphous phases to this newly discovered morphological element. Frey-Wyssling (2) was the first to apply the fringe–micelle theory within the fibrils. Morgan (39), at the other extreme, abandoned the fringe–micelle theory altogether and regards the fibril as a continuous crystalline phase. Hearle (8,40) extended two other views on the fine structure of the elementary fibrils, one considering the fibrils as originating from a cleavage of a fringe–micellar structure, and the other regarding the fibrils as part of a fringed-fibrillar structure in which the molecules pass continously through fringed crystalline fibrils and noncrystalline regions between the fibrils. This represents, in his own words, a union between two opposing viewpoints. similar to that which took place when the fringe-micelle theory was developed in the 1930's.

However, there is much to be said for considering the fibrils as bands in which crystallites and amorphous regions alternate. This view was first adopted by Hess (24,31). Long-period investigations on native and regenerated cellulose fibers by small-angle x-ray and electron microscopy in combination with suitable scatterers, such as iodine, lead, mercury, osmium, or thallium, resulted in long-period structures in the range of 100–400 Å. In 1950 Ranby and Ribi (41) succeeded in isolating a highly crystalline "micelle powder" from wood pulp by mild acid hydrolysis. They showed by electron microscopy that this powder consisted of relatively uniform particles of 50 Å thickness and 500 Å length, i.e., the same thickness as found for elementary fibrils but shorter in length. Together with Käppner (34) and with Kitchen (42) we found by applying a similar technique isolated microfibrillar fragments existing in cotton and Fortisan with thicknesses of approximately 60 Å in cotton and approximately 40 Å in Fortisan. The average length was determined as 400 Å and 200 Å, respectively, in good agreement with Mukherjee et al. (33). The length distributions which we found for these isolated fragments of elementary fibrils is illustrated in Fig. 8.

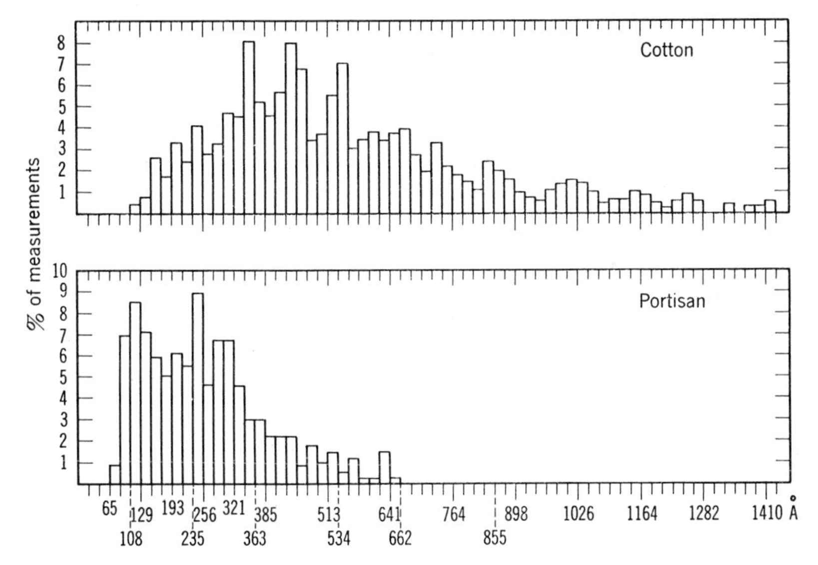

Fig. 8. Length distribution of microfibrillar fragments of cotton and Fortisan hydrolyzed at 55°C with 1*N* HCl for 168 and 524 hr, respectively.

Since from the width of x-ray wide-angle reflections the estimation of the cross dimensions of crystalline regions results in a similar range as the width of these fibrillar fragments observed by electron micrographs, there is strong indication that the view taken by Hess seems correct. This view is also in agreement with the "limiting DP values" at which the rate of hydrolysis in heterogeneous acid degradation slows down to nearly zero, being approximately DP = 100 for cotton and DP = 40–50 for regenerated cellulose fibers.

A question which is very much disputed today is the position of the macromolecules inside the crystallites. Until the early 1950's it was generally accepted that inside the crystallites, fiber-forming polymer molecules associate in extended form linearly one beside the other. In 1957, on the basis of results of x-ray studies on single crystals of polyethylene, Keller (43) suggested the possibility of chain-folding inside polymer crystals. Since then a number of scientists have attempted, and in some cases succeeded, in growing crystals from cellulose and cellulose derivatives (44). Although indications could be found that under special conditions folded structures may also be possible in the case of cellulose, the evidence is so far not convincing enough to change accepted views, as far as fiber characteristics are concerned. The average DP of cellulose isolated from the above-mentioned cellulose crystallites was found to be in the range 80–100 (400–500 Å) for cotton, and approximately 50 (200 Å) for Fortisan. Since this is in good agreement with the average lengths found from the evaluation of electron micrographs, there is a strong indication for the linear assembly of the molecules in these crystallites. Fine-focus electron diffraction measurements also attest to the alignment of the molecules along the longer axis of these particles.

A discussion on fiber morphology of cellulose fibers would not be complete without mentioning the aspects of gross morphology. It is known that in native cellulose fibers the fibrillar elements are deposited under varying spiral angles in distinct cell wall layers. The major part of the cellulose fibrils is laid down in a long outdrawn spiral, more or less aligned to the long cell axis and forms the "secondary wall." Toward the lumen and to the outside the fibers the fibrils are laid down in a crisscross pattern of layers with a narrow spiral angle. These layers are known under the terms "tertiary" and "primary wall." Especially in cotton the primary wall is particularly responsible for many of the specific properties of the fibers. In its restriction of lateral swelling the primary wall is responsible for the higher wet strength of cotton fibers, as we have shown by an acetylation peeling technique (45). Similarly, regenerated cellulose fibers show nonuniformities known as skin-core structure in their lateral order distribution throughout their cross section. The presence of a skin-core structure in viscose rayon was first demonstrated by Preston (46) and Ohara (47) and somewhat later by Schramek and Helm (48) by differences in dye receptivity and fastness throughout the cross section. While Preston et al. (46,49) explained the difference on the basis of a higher orientation in the skin portion, Morehead and Sisson (50) make the coagulation and crystallization conditions imparted by the composition of the spin bath and modifying additions to the latter responsible for the observed differences.

B. Cellulose Fiber Model and Features of Fiber Characterization

In conclusion to this short review of our general knowledge of fiber morphology, it is necessary to discuss a model for cellulose fiber structure. This model constitutes a compromise of all the outlined views, so that it is suited to be used as a working aid for our future considerations on cellulose fiber characterization.

Krässig and Kitchen (42), in their work on factors influencing the tensile properties of cellulose fibers, suggested the model shown in Fig. 9.

This model basically considers the structural state of a fiber in a simplified manner as a network of more or less defined morphological units consisting of assemblies of fibrils. The interlinkages between these morphological units are most probably constituted by molecules or bundles of molecules of lower order and higher accessibility. The existence of some fibrillar interlinks between the morphological units is suggested by the existence of some residual tensile strength even at high degrees of degradation.

From the model the following important characterization features derive: (*1*) the molecular length of the fiber-forming polymer molecule; (*2*) the degree of crystallinity or perfection of order; (*3*) the crystallite

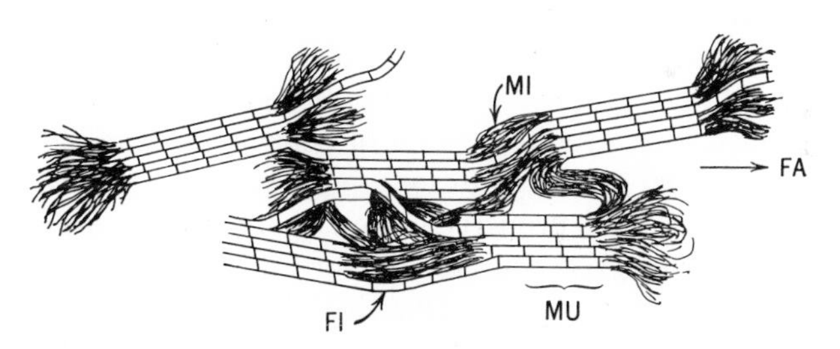

Fig. 9. Model of fiber morphology; FA = fiber axis; MU = morphological units, fibrillar aggregates of high lateral order and low accessibility; MI = molecular interlinks of low lateral order and high accessibility; FI = fibrillar interlinks of high lateral order and low accessibility.

size; (*4*) the size of the morphological units or fibrillar aggregates forming the network structure of the fiber; (*5*) the structural state of the regions interlinking the fibrillar aggregates; (*6*) the degree of alignment of the fibrillar aggregates and the interlinking elements toward the fiber axis, i.e., the degree of orientation; and (*7*) the degree and uniformity of packing, often designated as lateral-order distribution, including distribution of skin-core structures.

From theoretical considerations, *the tensile strength* of a fiber will be effected by the length of the polymer molecules, particularly by the number of intact molecular interlinks between the morphological units. Molecular breaks inside the well-ordered, crystalline fibrillar aggregates will not be as harmful as loose ends occurring in the less-ordered interlinking regions. Inside the crystalline regions the large number of secondary bonds exhibited by interactions, such as hydrogen bonds, will easily compensate for molecular breaks. The forces holding loose molecular ends in the regions of low order are much smaller however. Omo, Maeda, Fujawara, and Ishimoto (51) have presented additional evidence supporting this concept of ours (42). Furthermore, the tensile strength will be affected by the alignment of the fiber components with respect to the fiber axis and to a somewhat lesser extent by the perfection of the spatial arrangement of the molecules composing the morphological elements of the fiber. The better the degree of orientation along the fiber axis and the better the degree of crystallinity, the more uniform will be the distribution of acting stress, giving higher tensile strength. The effect of the degree of orientation was recognized as early as 1925 by Herzog (52) and Lilienfeld (53). The effect of the degree of crystallinity is much smaller, and has not yet been assessed with certainty.

The *elongation at break* is mainly effected by the degree of alignment of the fibrillar aggregates forming the network structure and of the interlinking elements toward the fiber axis. However, the size of the morphological units may exert effects of steric hindrance interfering with the extension theoretically possible. The *elastic modulus* is affected by the degree of crystallinity, the size of the morphological units and their steric hindrance, the structural state of the interlinking elements and regions, and the degree of orientation.

In a similar manner, properties such as *toughness, flexibility,* and *abrasion* can be analyzed and the factors influencing these phyiscal properties can be derived from setting them into relation with a suitable and valid fiber model. It is uncalled for to attempt in this short chapter a complete description of these interrelations. Comprehensive summaries have been given in the past, such as the ones by Wakeham (54) and Mark (55), or more recently in the excellent book by Morton and

Hearle (56). It should be mentioned, however, that in the past many scientists working on fiber characterization and interrelation with physical properties, particularly with respect to cellulose fibers, have unfortunately not considered the existence of defined morphological units. This is to some extent the reason why so many discrepancies exist in the literature even in well-known important factors such as the effect of the length of the fiber-forming molecules. We consider it therefore as one of the objectives of this chapter to bring forward the importance of morphological considerations in fiber characterization.

II. METHODS OF CHARACTERIZATION

In the following, it is intended to review the most important methods of determining fiber characteristics. This review can understandably not be very complete. It will be our goal to draw an overall picture and to give valuable hints. We will restrict ourselves to characteristics important to the understanding of the most concrete fiber properties, such as tensile strength and elongation.

A. Molecular Weight and Molecular Weight Distribution

It has long been recognized (first by Staudinger and Heuer (57)) that the viscosity of a polymer solution is closely related to the length of the chainlike molecules. Staudinger's original proposal was that at low concentrations

$$\eta_{\mathrm{sp}} = K_m \times M \times c_{\mathrm{gm}}$$

This relationship is now used most frequently in the form

$$[\eta] = K_m \times M$$

The *molecular weight determination* by viscosity is still the most simple and convenient means of determining this important characteristic, although in the last three decades modifications of this basic law have been found. Kuhn (58), Mark (59), and Houwink (60) suggested the formula

$$[\eta] = K_m \times M^{\alpha}$$

as an expression of more general validity. Kuhn and Kuhn (61), Kirkwood and Risemann (62), and Debye (63) proposed that the power itself may be a function of molecular weight.

However, most investigators accept today that for cellulose and cellulose derivatives the simple Staudinger equation, valid for stiff rodlike molecules, can be applied without substantial error. The α values reported range from 0.8 to 1.0.

Cellulose can be measured in various solvents, such as cuprammonium (61), cupriethylenediamine (64,65), quaternary organic bases (65), and various alkaline solutions of metal complexes (66).

Since it is known from evidence first presented by Clibbens and Ridge (67) and later confirmed by Staudinger et al. (68) and Davidson (69) that most cellulose contains alkali-sensitive links, in cases where the knowledge of the total length of the molecules is important many investigators prefer to transfer the cellulose prior to the determination into the trisubstituted nitric acid esters, commonly called cellulose nitrates. Staudinger and Mohr (70) have shown that this transfer can be performed "polymeranalog," e.g., without degradation. The cellulose nitrates can be measured in such solvents as acetone and ethyl acetate. In working with cellulose derivatives it is essential to work with fully substituted samples, since the degree of substitution has a great effect on the state of solution and the viscosity (71).

For the determination of the viscosity most investigators use capillary viscometers. They are thoroughly sufficient and easy to handle. For optimum results, however, the effect of shear rate should not be overlooked. In essence, the determination of the intrinsic viscosity $[\eta]$ comprises extrapolation of η_{sp}/c versus $c = 0$ and $G = 0$. For practical purposes the use of viscometers with several niveau bulbs is highly recommended. They allow the viscosity of a solution of given concentration to be determined at various shear rates. Shear-corrected $[\eta]$ values are then easily obtained from the viscosity by graphical extrapolation. Such results from several solutions of varying concentrations can be graphically extrapolated for zero concentration, giving

$$\lim \eta_{sp}/c = [\eta]$$
$$c \rightarrow 0, \qquad G \rightarrow 0$$

The viscometric method is in itself only a relative measure of molecular length of polymer molecules. It therefore has to be calibrated by one of the absolute methods, such as osmometry, light scattering, or sedimentation. Since in polymer characterization in many cases the number average molecular weight is more meaningful, a calibration toward osmotically determined molecular weight is recommended.

Excellent sources of information for the interested reader on the experimental methods of molecular weight determination of cellulose and cellulose derivatives are articles by Immergut et al. (72), Davis and Elliot (73), Peterlin (74), Lieser (75), Temming and Grunert (76), Cumberbirch and Harland (77), and the author (78).

In our work with Kitchen (42) on cellulose fiber characterization we successfully used the TAPPI Standard Method T 230 for molecular weight viscosity measurements of cellulose solutions in cupriethylenediamine. The concentration was usually 0.5%. When working with higher-molecular-weight samples, the concentration was adjusted so that the resulting η_{rel} did not exceed a value of 2.5. We measured the viscosity using a Cannon-Fenske viscometer and corrected for zero concentration by applying the formula suggested by Schulz and Blaschke (79). For the transfer of intrinsic viscosities into numerical average degree of polymerization (DP) we used the calibration suggested by Immergut et al. (72). This simplified procedure is justified under conditions where in the series of samples the molecular uniformity remains reasonably constant and the effect of alkaline-sensitive links in the samples is constant and small.

Useful procedures for the transfer of regenerated cellulose fibers into the corresponding cellulose nitrates and their use for the viscosimetric determination of the degree of polymerization were reported by Harland (77).

The *molecular weight distribution* is considered by many investigators of the fiber characteristics to be an important factor which helps to explain differences in properties between fibers of otherwise seemingly similar characteristics. Especially low-molecular-weight portions are considered detrimental, although the question of the extent of the practical importance of differences in distribution is still unsettled (80). A very comprehensive attempt to clarify this question has been undertaken by Cumberbirch (81), who produced model filaments from mixtures of a sharp acetate fraction of differing molecular weight.

Still the most reliable method of determining molecular weight distribution in cellulose samples is the precipitation fractionation procedure, which is unfortunately somewhat tedious. Most investigators perform this method on cellulose nitrates obtained by cautious nitration. By addition of suitable nonsolvents to the dilute cellulose nitrate solution in well-adjusted successive portions and intermediate isolation of the precipitate, the sample is subdivided into 10–12 fractions of preferably equal weight. Important for exclusive separation according to molecular weight is the application of a fully trisubstituted derivative in order to avoid interference from separation according to varying degree of substitution and differing solubilities. The evaluation technique was developed by Brønsted (82) and Schulz (83), Good descriptions of useful fractionation procedures for cellulose nitrate samples have been reported by Zapf (84), Roseveare and Poore (85), Mitchell (86), Harland (87), and Marx-Figini (88).

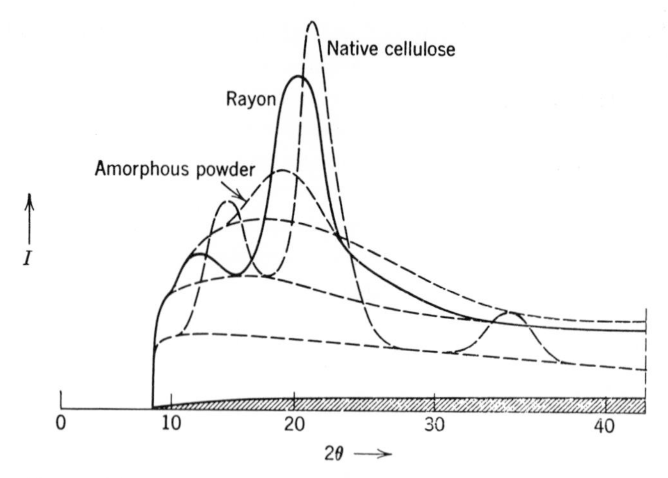

Fig. 10. X-ray diffraction curves and separation of continuous and discontinuous scattering for ramie, rayon, and a ball-milled amorphous cellulose powder, according to Hermans and Weidinger (118).

Since the precipitation fractionation method is time-consuming and tedious, a large number of efforts have been undertaken to develop simpler and ideally automated methods. Although these are not very recent, the interested reader is referred to the comprehensive summary given by Conrad (89), who in 1953 reviewed a series of other methods being explored, such as electron microscopy, chromatographic adsorption, turbidity titration, streaming birefringence, coacervation fractionation, resinographic replica technique, and dielectric dispersion. The newly developed gel permeation chromatography techniques seem especially promising.

As an example of the differences existing among various types of cellulose fibers, Fig. 10 illustrates some results obtained by Harland (87).

B. Size of Crystallites and Fibrillar Aggregates

The most direct and absolute method for the determination of crystallite size and dimensions of distinct fibrillar aggregates is given by *electron microscopic observations*. This method has already been referred to. Since electrons are readily absorbed by solid matter, this method requires the difficult task of fine distribution or sectioning without disturbing the texture of the material. Three methods are mainly in use to fulfil this condition, namely, mechanical distortion, treatment with ultrasonic waves, and partial hydrolysis. Besides these, microtome sectioning and replica methods have proven very useful.

Very useful summaries demonstrating the potential and techniques of electron microscopic investigations were given by several authors (90). Interesting preparation techniques for use with cellulose acetate fibers were published by Peck and Kaye (91). Some results obtained by various investigators of importance for the treatment of our subject were mentioned earlier. Unfortunately, only limited experimental results are reported dealing with regenerated cellulose fibers, and it seems a sensible suggestion that more attention be given in the future to the electron microscopic study of morphological differences between the numerous types of cellulose fibers.

From such investigations, the cross dimensions of crystallites were found to be in the range of 60 Å for cotton and 40 Å for Fortisan. The crystallite length for the same materials was determined with 400 Å and 200 Å, respectively (33,34,41,42).

In our own work with Kitchen (42), we found that longer periodicities in the length direction of the fiber seem of great importance for the physical properties. The length of fibrillar assemblies especially was found to enter the relation between molecular weight and properties. Hess et al. (31), in their electron microscopic studies on iodine-treated cellulose fibers, have found such long-range periodicities. Studies by various authors on the length distribution of the fragments from hydrolyzed and mechanically dispersed cellulose fibers have added further evidence of their existence (28–30,32–34). However, the information is still scarce and scattered.

X-ray methods are very widely used for the determination of crystallite dimensions. Although the wide-angle reflections and their line widths are influenced by crystal size and imperfections as well, a large number of investigators have tried to arrive at crystallite dimensions from the line width of wide-angle reflections. Hengstenberg and Mark (14) were the first to report such values for the width and length of crystallite in cotton and viscose rayon. They found the width to be 60 Å for crystallites from cotton and 40 Å for those from viscose rayon. These dimensions are in perfect agreement with those found later by direct electron microscopic observations. Using the Scherrer equation (92) on separated reflection by applying a special technique suggested by Gjønnes, Norman, and Viervoll (93), we found average distances from one imperfection face to the next rectangular to the $10\bar{1}$, 101, and 002 planes 60, 40, and 75 Å for Fortisan. For Meryl fibers the corresponding values were found to be 43, 30, and 62 Å, respectively (94). These values are somewhat higher than the direct electron microscopy observation revealed. However, the differences are tolerable. The result also shows that the crystallites and fibrils of Meryl are thinner and the crystallinity due to more disturbed interfaces must be lower than that of Fortisan.

Another tool for the determination of crystallite dimension is provided by *x-ray small-angle scattering*. Good summaries of the theory, methods, and results obtained on fibrous cellulose substrates have been given by Kratky and Porod (5), and by Kiessig (95). The theoretical background of small-angle scattering is still disputed (96), and the experimental techniques require very skilled workers. This makes the method unsuitable for routine testing.

The most important results obtained on regenerated cellulose fibers were reported by Hermans et al. (97), Kiessig (98), Heyn (99), Kratky et al. (100), and others (101). In the swollen state the equator reflection in the small-angle range become generally more expressed. The micelle thickness values reported for regenerated cellulose fibers range from 30–80 Å and are always found to be smaller for measurements performed in the dry state.

The length of the crystallites, i.e., alternations of ordered and disordered regions along the axis of the fibrils, should cause small-angle reflections on the meridian. For a high-tenacity tire cord, Kiessig (98) found a weak but definite meridional reflection corresponding to a periodicity of 150 Å. The appearance of these reflections can be enhanced by hydrolytic treatments, as demonstrated by Statton (102). For various samples of regenerated cellulose fibers he found after degradation crystallite length values in the range of 180–220 Å by small-angle scattering and DP measurements. These values agree reasonably well with the ones by Hess et al. (24,31,103), using electron microscopy on iodine-impregnated cellulose fibers. Similar investigations were also performed by Nukushina (104).

Concerning longer-range periodicities along the fiber axis, no evidence has been reported so far using small-angle scattering techniques.

Since electron microscopic and x-ray methods call for expensive instrumentation and skilled experimentors, often not available in industry, more simple *chemical methods* were developed by various workers in this field. These methods are all based on the concept of higher accessibility of the less ordered regions interlinking the crystallites in the elementary fibrils or linking together larger morphological units. They allow measurement of the length of the crystalline regions or of the morphological building blocks of the cellulose fibers to be obtained.

Japanese workers (104,105) have reported during recent years on crystallite size and crystallite size distribution measurements of rayon fibers. They prepared the crystallites by hydrolysis with strong sulfuric or hydrochloric acid at elevated temperature, sometimes combined with subsequent oxidation, and determined the DP distribution of the degraded products as a measure of crystallite size and crystallite size distribution. They found mean values for the crystallite length in the range 50–100 Å (DP = 10–20), with distinct variation for the various regenerated cellulose fibers.

In our own work with Kitchen (42) we developed a special method to determine the effective mean size of the larger morphological units, which from model considerations should be of even greater importance for the understanding of fiber tensile properties (see Fig. 9). The method comprises a study of the effect of hydrolytic degradation on tensile strength. We used for the hydrolytic degradation treatments with 1*N* hydrochloric acid at 50°C for extended periods of time. The neutralized, carefully washed and dried samples were tested for tensile strength, elongation at break, x-ray orientation, and crystallinity. As observed also by other authors (106) continued hydrolysis increases orientation and perfection of order. In accordance with experience gained by work on the influence of crystallinity and crystallite orientation on tensile strength, we normalized the measured tensile strength values and demonstrated interesting relations. Later in this chapter we shall discuss in greater detail this technique and the results concerning the size of the morphological units and their distribution in rayon fibers.

C. Crystallinity and Lateral Order

Polymer molecules in the solid state have the tendency to aggregate into a semicrystalline state. The crystallizing ability is determined by the chemical configuration and the regularity of the structure, by the presence of active groups able to form secondary interlinkages such as hydrogen bonds, and by the molecular flexibility. In the case of cellulose fiber formation the coagulation conditions and the drying are of utmost importance for the development of crystallinity (107). Since the technologically important physical properties are related to the structural state, the determination of the ratio of crystalline to amorphous regions has occupied scientific and technical researchers, since macromolecular substances have now become technically important.

The first hints that polymeric substances form semicrystalline structures were obtained in the early 1920's on cellulose and on caoutchouc by x-ray methods. In the following decades various methods for determining the crystalline–amorphous ratio on polymeric substrates were developed. The x-ray method, density determination, and calorimetric methods are generally applicable. In the case of cellulose, accessibility determination and substitution or degradation treatments have also gained importance.

New methods such as infrared spectroscopy, electron diffraction, and nuclear magnetic resonance have also revealed additional information. A very good summary of these various methods and results obtained for various polymers, including cellulose, has been given by Kast (108).

From these methods the *x-ray wide-angle diffraction* technique gives the most direct result, although the interpretation of the results and their evaluation is today still under discussion and is widely based on convenience.

The instrumentation for x-ray measurement on fibrous substrates has been greatly improved in the last decade. Useful cameras for quantitative work applying Geiger, flow, or proportional electronic counting for registration were described by various authors, such as Irvin and Breazeale (109), Segal and Conrad (110), Ruck and Krässig (111), Sukai and Kagawa (112), Ant-Wuorinen (113), and Trillat and Legrand (114). The most important experimental requirement for obtaining comparable results are constancy in primary beam intensity and constancy in sample weight and sample dimensions. In our paper with Ruck (111) we have described in great detail methods meeting these requirements.

As already mentioned, the interpretation and evaluation of x-ray wide-angle diffraction measurements is still under discussion. The first attempt to draw quantitative conclusions as to the crystalline–amorphous ratio from x-ray measurements on cellulose were made by Karagin and Michailow (115) and Mark et al. (116). Basing their research on work by Goppel (117), Hermans and Weidinger (118) were the first to suggest a crystallinity scale from their measurements on balled, milled "amorphous" cellulose powder, on a rayon fiber and on ramie sample. Their procedure includes a separation of the crystalline scattering and of amorphous background scattering, as indicated by Fig. 10. They determine J_{Cr} from the area of the scattering superimposed over the diffused amorphous background between $2\,\theta = 5\text{–}40°$. The amorphous background scattering they defined by the maximum height between $2\,\theta = 10\text{–}15°$. They derived their famous crystallinity scale for cellulose samples from measurements on samples widely different in perfection of order from the following equation (α = crystallinity);

$$J_{Cr_1}/J_{Cr_2} = \alpha_1/\alpha_2, \qquad J_{a1}/J_{a2} = (1 - \alpha_1)/(1 - \alpha_2)$$

A graphical method was suggested by Richards et al. (119). Kast et al. (120) and Kratky (121) have substantially contributed to the perfection of the experimental techniques and the evaluation method for determining crystallinity. These methods have also been widely used in the past for the crystallinity determination of other polymers.

During the last decade a number of authors have suggested other methods for the qualitative and quantitative evaluation of x-ray wide-angle reflection patterns with respect to degree of crystallinity values or crystallinity factors. Based on work by Hermans and Weidinger (118), various integration methods have been proposed and used successfully by Kast and Flaschner (120), Kratky and Krausz (121), Wakelin et al. (122), Ellefsen et al. (123), Jayme et al. (124), and Bonart et al. (125). From the area of the crystalline and amorphous scattering they derive a crystallinity index

$$\mathrm{KI} = A_{\mathrm{Cr}}/(A_{\mathrm{Cr}} + A_a)$$

which multiplied by 100 can be used as a measure of percentage crystallinity.

Another group of investigators, such as Segal et al. (126) and Ant-Wuorinen and Visapää (127) form ratios between the height of the 002 reflection in the case of cellulose I and the 101 reflection in the case of cellulose II with the height of the amorphous reflections at $2\theta = 18°$ or $2\theta = 16°$, respectively They suggested a crystallinity index term which is calculated using the following formula:

$$\mathrm{CrI} = 1 - \mathrm{Am}\ h/\mathrm{Cr}\cdot h = 1 - \mathrm{Am}\ h/(\mathrm{total}\ h - \mathrm{Am}\ h)$$

Both methods are demonstrated in Fig. 11, taken from Jayme and Knolle (124). These authors compared the two methods and came to the conclusion that the integral method is superior. On the other hand, we have used successfully in our work with Kitchen (42) the empirical method suggested by Ant-Wuorinen (127) for the practical characterization of the crystallinity on rayon fibers, as will be demonstrated later in this chapter.

Some years ago, Gjønnes et al. (93) proposed a new and very promising method to evaluate x-ray wide-angle patterns of cellulose substrates.

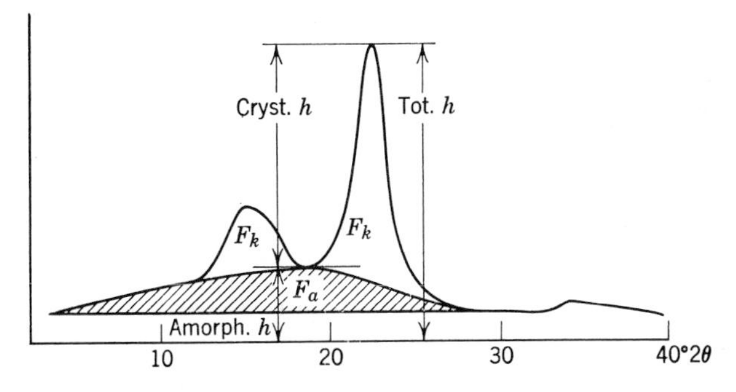

Fig. 11. Methods for the determination of x-ray crystallinity (taken from Jayme and Knolle (124)).

The method allows a separation of overlapping reflection under the assumption that the intensity curves of the reflections have the shape of Cauchy distributions and that the wide-angle pattern is the result of the following summation:

$$I(s) = \sum K_i \frac{\alpha_i}{\alpha_i^2 + (s - s_{oi})}$$

where $s = 4\pi \cdot \sin \theta/\lambda$, s_{oi} = peak position, α = half-width of the ith reflection at half of the maximum intensity, and K_i is constant depending on the structural factor of the ith reflection. We have used this method for the evaluation of x-ray wide-angle diffractograms of native and mercerized cellulose samples and of rayon (128). We could confirm the findings of Gjønnes et al. concerning the resolution of the diffractograms of native cellulose. In the case of samples mercerized heterogeneously by steeping, we found that a complete resolution without the assumption of underlying amorphous scattering is equally possible assuming the presence of approximately 20–25% cellulose I, remaining either from incomplete transfer or formed by recrystallization in cellulose I structure during drying. For Fortisan and Meryl samples we found that their x-ray wide-angle reflection patterns contain solely cellulose II reflections. We have referred to conclusions drawn from this evaluation earlier in this chapter. We feel that further attention should be given to this method.

Beside x-ray wide-angle diffractometry, *the density determination* has been widely used. The knowledge of the specific volumes of the crystalline and amorphous state gives a useful method for the determination of the crystalline/amorphous ratio. The method is applicable in all cases where outside factors, such as the presence of inaccessible voids in the fiber, do not interfere with the accurate determination of density. The specific volume for the completely crystalline state of native cellulose (cellulose I) was determined by Meyer and Misch (129) as 0.628 cm^3/g. The determination of the same value for regenerated cellulose (cellulose II), as present in rayon fibers, has proved to be much more difficult. The drying condition (130) and the presence of voids in some newer types of rayon fibers are of definite influence on the result. From the work of Legrand (131), Kiessig (132), Kratky and Treiber (133), Hermans et al. (134), and Kast (135), the specific volume of the completely crystalline regenerated cellulose is now accepted to be 0.622 cm^3/g. The specific volume for the amorphous state of cellulose was first determined by extrapolation from x-ray crystallinity and density data of samples of varying crystallinity and was thus assumed to be 0.680 cm^3/g. Da Gupta (136) later confirmed this value by density measurements on dried, spontaneously coagulated cellulose gels. From these values the

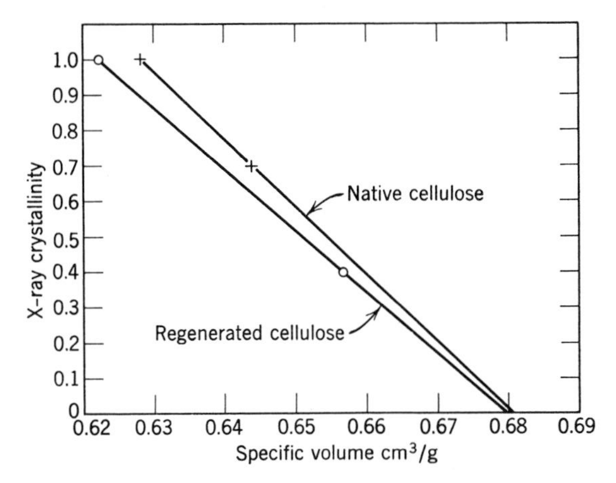

Fig. 12. Combination of volumetric and x-ray data of native and mercerized celluloses. Extrapolation for the specific volume of noncrystalline cellulose, according to Kast.

interrelation between x-ray crystallinity and specific volume can be represented by the graph shown in Fig. 12.

A review of the various methods and the experimental techniques used in fiber density measurements has been given by Bobeth et al. (137). Recommendations for well-specified drying procedures were published recently by Kozlowski and Mrozowski (138).

Another method is based on *caloric measurements*, mainly on the determination of the heat of solution and the heat of recrystallization. Hermans et al. (139), Ward and Reeves (140), and Balcerzyk et al. (141) have reported investigations in this field. However, this technique has not found wide application.

Infrared spectroscopy has proven a very useful additional tool for detecting differences in crystalline/amorphous ratio, as shown by the work O'Connor et al. (142), Hurtubise and Krässig (143), and Rau (144). However, it has to be stated that this far no systematic application in the characterization of rayon fibers is known to the author.

Methods which have gained great importance in the determination of crystalline/amorphous ratio and of lateral order distribution, and which are specific in the characterization of cellulose fibers, are those based on the accessibility and reactivity in degradation and substitution reaction. Nevertheless, we must state clearly that one should in such investigation never fail to consider the interference of morphological factors. Nickerson and Habrle (145) and Conrad and Scroggie (146) reported accessibility studies using a combination of hydrolytic and oxidative treatments. Philipp et al. (147) and Krässig and Kitchen (42) have investigated the

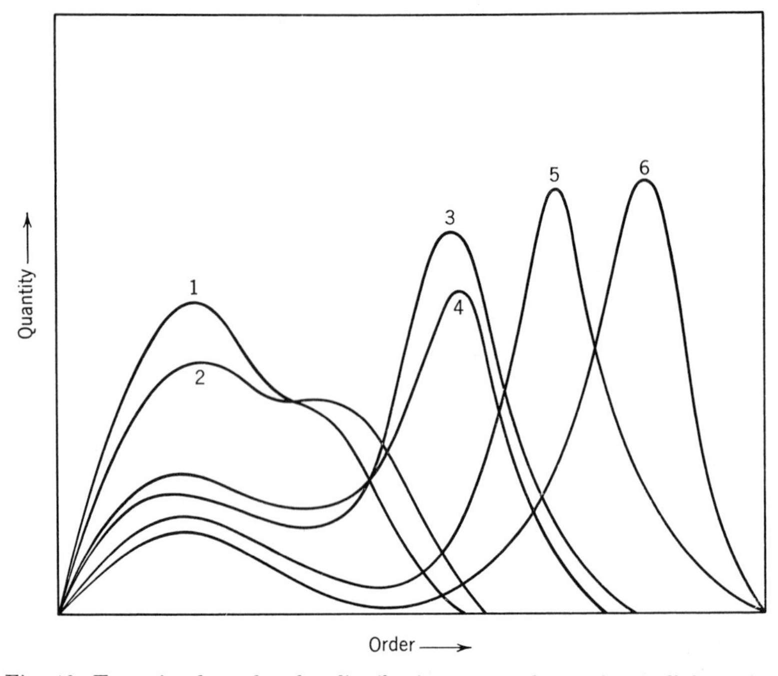

Fig. 13. Tentative lateral order distribution curves for various cellulose fibers. Curves: (*1*) high-tenacity rayon; (*2*) textile rayon; (*3*) high-strength, low-elongation rayons; (*4*) mercerized native fibers; (*5*) wood pulp; (*6*) cotton (see ref. 162).

behavior in acid hydrolysis. Kato and Yamada (148), Mitsuishi (149), and Philipp and Baudisch (150) used ethanolysis sometimes in combination with alkali treatments to study lateral order differences. Goldfinger, Mark, and Siggia (151) and Timell (152) described observations using oxidation with periodate. Reactivity measurements revealing the availability of the hydroxyl groups were described by Purves et al. (153), Reeves and Thompson (154), Timell (152), Mark et al. (155), and others (156). They used reactions with thallium ethylate, diazo methane, metallic sodium in ammonia, formic acid esterification, and deuterium exchange. Physical methods, such as water regain or sorption isotherm studies, have complemented the results obtained from chemical reactivity investigations. Iodine adsorption was used by Bréquet and Chareyron (157), Hessler and Power (158), and by French investigators (159). Typical examples of such work were presented by Howsmon (160) and by Hailwood and Horrobin (161). From such studies lateral order distributions were derived, as suggested by Howsmon and Sisson (162) and illustrated in Fig. 13.

Later in this chapter the usefulness of hydrolytic studies with respect to the characterization of fibers for their lateral order perfection will be demonstrated on examples taken from our own work (42).

D. Orientation of Crystallites and Morphological Units

In the aggregation of fiber-forming macromolecules to crystallites, fibrils, and larger morphological elements of higher order into a fibrous state, the alignment of these units with respect to the fiber axis is of great importance. In the case of artificially produced fibers the alignment is produced by stretching in the plastic or gel-like state. The degree of alignment or, as it is commonly termed, the "orientation," will influence the uniformity of the distribution of an acting stress, thus affecting the tensile properties of the fiber. It will determine its flexibility, extensibility, and elasticity, thus influencing the wear properties and wear life.

The importance of the degree of orientation for fiber qualities was already recognized in 1925 by Herzog (52) and Lilienfeld (53).

It is beyond the scope of our present discussion to review all the various theories and views concerning different types of orientation brought about by the geometry of the crystallites and their effect on the outcome of the results of x-ray and other methods of measuring orientation. A very comprehensive description of these aspects and their effect on the outcome of x-ray diffraction measurements was first published by Sisson (163). Reviews of the theories of orientation in polymer substrates helpful to interested readers were later given by Howsmon and Sisson (162), by Kratky (164) for the x-ray determination of orientation, and by Stuart (165) for other determination methods.

The degree of orientation can be determined by microscopic studies, by the study of extinction angles and dichroism in polarized light, or by the evaluation of x-ray wide- and small-angle diffraction patterns. In the use of single-fiber investigations the optical methods are in most cases preferred. However, the data obtained from measurements on single fibers suffer from the fact that they are only specific for the localized area observed.

Contrary to the optical methods, the *x-ray diffraction* technique for the determination of orientation is based on the diffraction from bundles of many well-aligned fibers and is thus not subject to local irregularities. However, it is today still a widely accepted view that from x-ray diffraction measurements only the crystallite orientation can be derived.

If the crystallite orientation is random the x-ray diffraction appears in the form of continuous circles, as known from powder patterns. If the

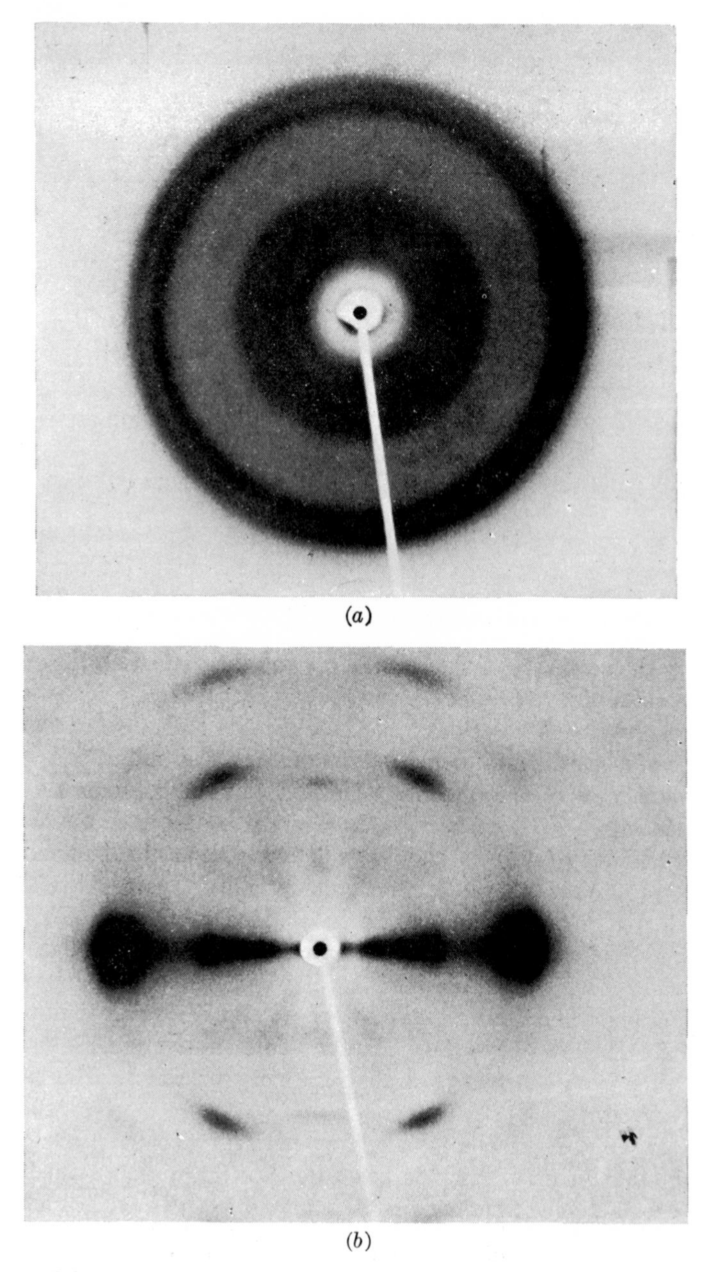

(a)

(b)

Fig. 14. Wide-angle diffractogram of an unstretched (a) and highly stretched (b) cellulose hydrate fiber.

crystallites are oriented with respect to a given axis, such as along the length of a fiber, the reflections appear as arcs. These arcs narrow as the degree of orientation improves. This is illustrated by the photographs of x-ray diffraction pattern taken with the flat film camera shown in Fig. 14.

The intensity distribution along these arcs can be measured by densitometry in the case of photographic registration. Today, the use of electronic counters allows direct measurement by setting the counter at the Bragg angle of maximum diffraction for a given crystallographic plane and slowly turning a bundle of well-aligned fibers exposed at a right angle to the x-ray beam. Examples of intensity distribution curves obtained by this technique are given in Fig. 15. The latter technique and a suitable camera arrangement have been described by Ruck and Krässig (111) and in our work with Kitchen (42).

The first systematic application of x-ray wide-angle scattering for orientation measurements on cellulose fibers was performed by Sisson and Clark (166). Based on the concepts of Polanyi (167), they developed an evaluation procedure giving percentage distribution curves with respect to the deviation of crystallite planes from the fiber axis. Their method was later considerably improved in theory and practice by Kratky (168), Hermans et al. (169), Kast (170), Berkeley and Woodyard (171), Segal et al. (172), Krässig et al. (111,42), and Creely and Conrad (173).

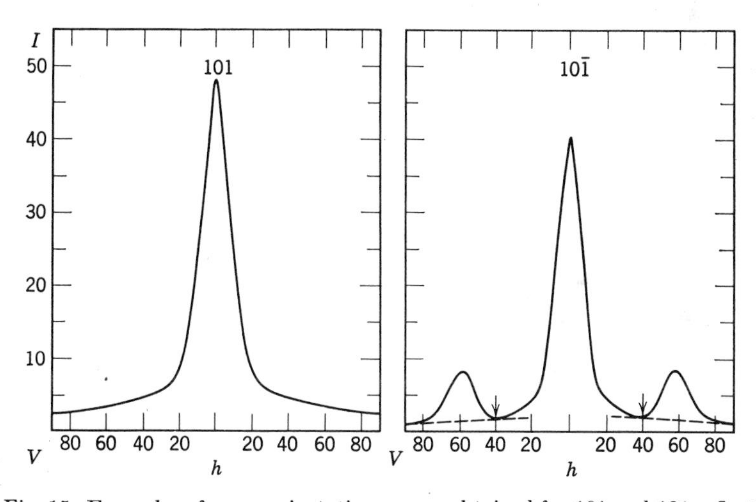

Fig. 15. Examples of x-ray orientation curves obtained for 101 and 101 reflections by slow turning of the fiber bundles in the x-ray beam with the proportional counter set at 12° and 20° respectively. The method of extrapolation to eliminate interference from the 021 reflection is indicated in the drawing on the right.

In our work with Kitchen (42), we have successfully used the evaluation method suggested by Hermans et al. (169). According to this method the weight–average sine square of the angle β, by which the molecular chains deviate from the fiber axis, may be calculted from $\overline{\sin^2 \alpha}$ of the paratropic $101 = A_0$ and $10\overline{1} = A_3$ reflections using the relationship

$$\overline{\sin^2 \beta} = \overline{\sin^2 \alpha_0} + \overline{\sin^2 \alpha_3}$$

The weight–average sine squares are calculated from the intensity distribution obtained from the above-described azimuthal scans through the 101 and $10\overline{1}$ diffraction arcs using the equation

$$\overline{\sin^2 \beta} = \int_0^{\pi/2} d\alpha \sin^2 \alpha \cos \alpha\, I(\alpha) / \int_0^{\pi/2} d\alpha \cos a\, I(a)$$

In order to obtain a measure of the overall orientation in the fibers, we made no deductions for amorphous scattering from the total intensity curves in our evaluations. In the case of overlapping by other reflections we suggested well-standardized extrapolation procedures.

In some cases, such as for Fortisan, Meryl, high-wet-modulus rayons or tire yarn rayons, where the diatropic 020 reflection is strong enough for good resolution, we made parallel measurements using the tilting technique suggested by Kast (174). Reasonably good agreement between the values from this direct measurement of $\overline{\sin^2 \beta}$ with the values obtained according to Hermans et al. (169) from paratropic planes was found (see Table I in ref. 42).

From $\overline{\sin^2 \beta}$ an orientation parameter, $f_r = 1 - {}^2/_3\, \overline{\sin^2 \beta}$, can be formed following a suggestion by Hermans et al. (169). This parameter was found very useful for expressing the effect of orientation on physical fiber properties.

Other more empirical values were suggested by a number of authors, such as: (*a*) the angular length in degrees of the corresponding reflection arc at half maximum intensity or any convenient fraction thereof, (*b*) the reciprocal of the half maximum angle which increases with improved orientation, or (*c*) the ratio of the maximum intensity to the intensity at some angle to the fiber axis (175). Kast (176) made a comparative study and found that such methods can also be used successfully to determine the quality and quantity of orientation.

The x-ray small angle scattering also allows conclusions concerning the orientation as shown by Heyn (177) and Kratky et al. (178). X-ray small-angle scattering is, however, very demanding in instrumentation and in interpretation and has therefore found only limited application.

From the *optical methods* the orientation birefringence and the dichroism studies have gained similar acceptance as has the x-ray wide angle method. Quantitative expressions for the orientation of molecules within a fiber were first derived from birefringence by Hermans (179) and from dichroism of dyed fibers and films by Morey (180) and Preston (181). For the study of orientation problems on rayon fibers such methods were applied in the recent past by a number of authors (182). An especially interesting attempt was published by Smith et al. (183). In combining accessibility studies using deuterium exchange with infrared dichroism investigations, an attempt was undertaken to characterize various rayon fibers for the lateral order and orientation differences in their noncrystalline but highly ordered regions. Russian authors recently reported the use of dielectric anisotropy measurements as a means for determining orientation in fibers (184). Many of these authors named above and active in this field point out that the combination of x-ray techniques for determining crystallinity and crystallite orientation with accessibility studies and optical investigations of orientation will allow conclusions on the lateral state and molecular alignment in the noncrystalline portions of regenerated cellulose fibers, which widely determine the dynamic properties.

E. Gross Morphology of Regenerated Cellulose Fibers

Although a short review as given here can never be complete, it is felt that a summary of the methods of characterization of cellulose fibers would have gaps unless short reference was made to the methods of studying gross morphology of fibers.

It has long been known that regenerated cellulose fibers have a gross morphology, generally known under the term "skin-core structure." This gross morphology is not nearly so distinct as it is in naturally grown cellulose fibers. Morehead and Sisson (50) first showed, and their finding was later confirmed by many others, that the development of skin-core structures is specifically connected and influenced by the coagulation conditions in fiber spinning. A comprehensive summary on the interrelation between the coagulation condition in fiber formation and the skin-core structure was given by Sisson (185). Electron microscopic studies on this subject were presented by Kassenbeck (186).

Dyeing techniques with suitable dye mixtures (187) helped to differenitate between skin and core in rayon fibers. Electron microscopic studies (185) revealed that the skin consists of much smaller crystallites than those composing the core. Peeling techniques, such as the repeated topochemical acetylation or nitration combined with extracting with suitable solvents the trisubstituted top layer formed, helped in the study of density distribution (188), lateral order distribution (189), and the orientation and crystallinity differences in the various layers (190) throughout the cross section of the fibers. Also, diffusion and hydrolysis studies allow an inside view into the gross morphology of rayon fibers (191).

III. FACTORS INFLUENCING TENSILE PROPERTIES

In the following the relations between fiber characteristics and fiber properties will be shown and the potential and practical value of fiber characterization illustrated. Data obtained in our own work with Kitchen (42) will be used to discuss our findings in comparison with results obtained by other investigators. Understandably, the discussion will have to be restricted to a number of basic properties, such as tenacity and elongation.

A. Effect of Crystallinity

The effect of crystallinity has never been assessed with certainty. So far mostly qualitative information is available. From such information Mark (192) and Hermans (193) concluded that the physical properties of cellulose fibers, such as tenacity, elongation, and elasticity, are closely related to the amount and kind of crystalline material, whereas reactivity and swelling are associated with the state of the amorphous areas. Baker et al. (194) have demonstrated that toughness and extensibility in cellulose esters are favored by local molecular disorder. Ward (195) has shown that for cotton fibers of constant orientation the elongation increases with decreasing degree of crystallinity. Tyler and Wooding (196) have found qualitative relations between the differences in crystallinity and the differences in properties among various rayon fibers. More than ten years ago Mark (55) had already pointed out that quantitative data on the effect of crystallinity are hard to obtain since it is difficult to isolate the effect of crystallinity from the effect of differing orientation and molecular and morphological variations in fibers. This is especially so, since these other characteristics have a much more pronounced effect on the physical properties.

From our numerous data on various rayon fibers (42) we were able to select a few examples of fibers only different in "crystallinity index" (CrI) but having equal orientation parameter (f_r) and equal $1000/DP_L - 1000/DP$, as a measure of the intact molecules in the areas of lower-order interlinking morphological units of the average length corresponding to DP_L. These examples are given in Table I.

TABLE I. Effect of Crystallinity on Tenacity of Rayon Fibers in the Conditioned and Wet State at Similar Orientation and Similar Status of the Interlinks between the Morphological Units

CrI	$1000/DP_L$ − 1000/DP	f_r	Tensile strength Cond.	Tensile strength Wet	Elongation cond.
0.66	6.91	0.42	3.36	2.26	10.0
0.76	7.81	0.42	4.14	3.11	11.3
0.64	9.73	0.45	4.91	3.39	10.4
0.68	9.38	0.45	5.16	3.63	11.5

These few examples clearly indicate that increasing crystallinity at otherwise constant structure characteristics definitely improves conditioned and wet tensile strength but has apparently no effect on conditioned elongation.

B. Effect of Orientation

Much more clearly established are the quantitative aspects of the effect of orientation on cellulose fiber properties, such as tenacity, elongation, swelling, and dyeing. Mark (55) has qualitatively stated the effects of increased orientation.

Based on x-ray orientation measurements Berkeley et al. (171,197) and Sisson (175) demonstrated that for cotton a close linear relationship exists between orientation and tensile strength. However, it was noted that this relationship may be different for different species of cotton. Ingersoll (175) showed that definite relationships exist between orientation and dry or wet elongation and tenacity. As a general rule, according to Ingersoll's results, the tenacity increases linearly, while elongation decreases hyperbolically with increasing orientation. He already recognized that other characteristics also affect these properties. The use in viscose spinning of coagulation baths containing zinc resulted in much higher tenacities and elongations at the same degree of orientation than observed for rayons spun from spin baths not containing zinc. He attributed this to differences in lateral order distributions and assumed that a more uniform lateral order distribution results in better properties. Suleimanova and Kargin (198) and Tanzawa (199) attribute differences in deformability and extensibility to variations in degree of orientation, packing of the cellulose chains, and the network structure of the amorphous part of the fiber.

In our work with Kitchen (42) we performed an extensive study of the effect of different stretch and orientation achieved thereby on the dry

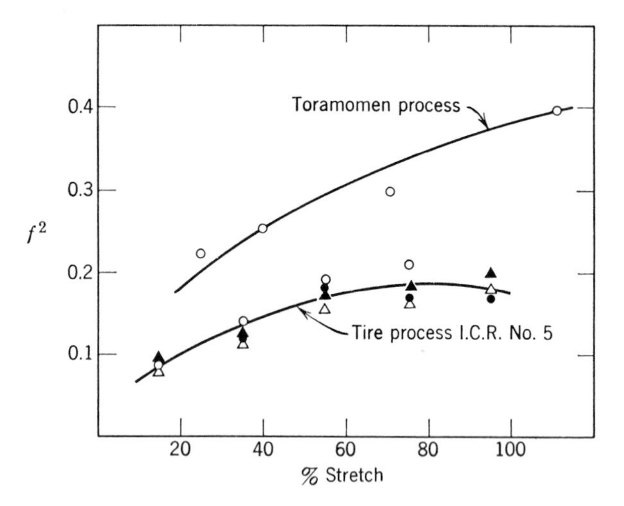

Fig. 16. Improvement in orientation parameter (f_r^2) with stretch. Effect of Toramomen process and tire yarn process.

and wet tenacity and elongation. In this study we found that applying different stretch on a gel filament bundle formed in a given spin bath only alters the degree of orientation. The degree of crystallinity and the size of the morphological units determining the effect of DP in accordance with the expression $1000/DP_L - 1000/DP$ does not change appreciably during stretching. This allows the influence of orientation on properties to be clearly established.

In Fig. 16, taken from our work (see Fig. 34 in ref. 42), the effect of various amounts of stretch on the establishment of orientation for two widely different spinning processes is given. It is interesting to note the different response of the gel filament bundles toward the stretch under various coagulation conditions. We attribute the better response of the gel filaments toward the orienting force to the larger morphological units formed under the Toramomem coagulation conditions.

In considering the *relationship between orientation* (f_r) *and tensile strength* we found that a linear relationship of high statistic probability exists between f_r^2 and conditioned tensile strength. A similar linear relationship of equal statistical probability was found between $f_r^{2.5}$ and the wet tensile strength. The use of powers 2.0 and 2.5 of the orientation parameter was suggested on the condition that a realistic relationship has to result in a defined residual strength even for samples of low order and low degree of orientation. Both relations are illustrated by Fig. 17. Any change in crystallinity on wetting cellulose fibers has not to be considered. Hermans and Weidinger (200) found no indication of a differ-

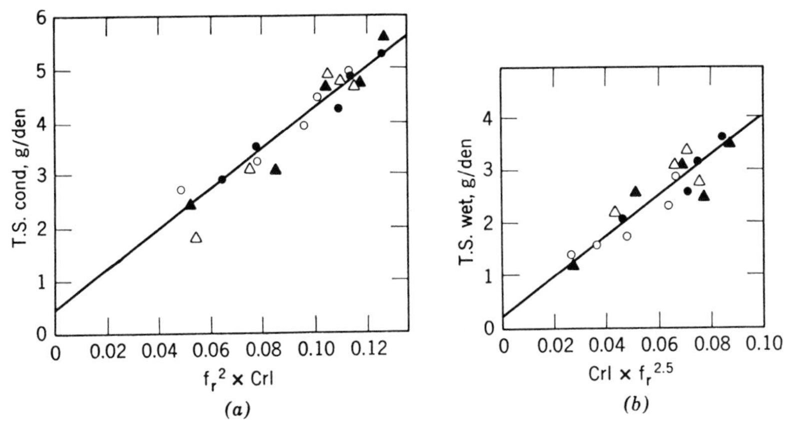

Fig. 17. (*a*) Relationship of the product of the square of the orientation parameter and the crystallinity index to the observed tensile strength of the conditioned yarns. $TS_{\text{cond}} = 0.4 + 38.1 \times f_r^2 \times \text{CrI}$. (*b*) Relationship of the product of the $f_r^2 \times$ CrI value and the square root of f_r to the observed tensile strength of the wet yarns. $TS_{\text{wet}} = 0.2 + 38.8 \times f_r^{2.5} \times \text{CrI}$.

ence in crystallinity in swollen and in dry fibers. In own work this was confirmed conclusively.

In dealing with the *relationship between orientation and breaking elongation* of conditioned and wet fibers we had restricted ourselves to a consideration of the "inverse breaking modulus" as represented by the ratio $\%E/TS$. In doing so, we were aware of the fact that this approach will only describe an overall behavior and will not allow any statement concerning specific elongation characteristics of the fibers in question.

The theoretical elongation of a system in which the individual elements deviate from a common axis by an average angle α is given by the expression $(1 - \cos \alpha)/\cos \alpha$. This consideration does not, however account for effects of steric hindrance on the mobility of the individual morphological elements. Since the square root of f_r changes in a first approximation in a similar way to $\cos \alpha$ over the range of interest, we decided to use the ratio $(1 - f_r^{0.5})/f_r^{0.5}$. There exists a definite relationship between this parameter and the "inverse breaking modulus" of conditioned fibers. A linear fit is achieved when the second power of the parameter is used. The relation between $\%E/TS_{\text{cond}}$ and $(1 - f_r^{0.5})^2/f_r$ found is illustrated in Fig. 18. The relationship explains 84% of the variability. This seemed to us a useful working basis. We attribute deviations from this relationship to the difference in the after-stretch and relaxation treatments which chiefly affect the portions of the fibers responsible for their plastic deformation properties. Since these

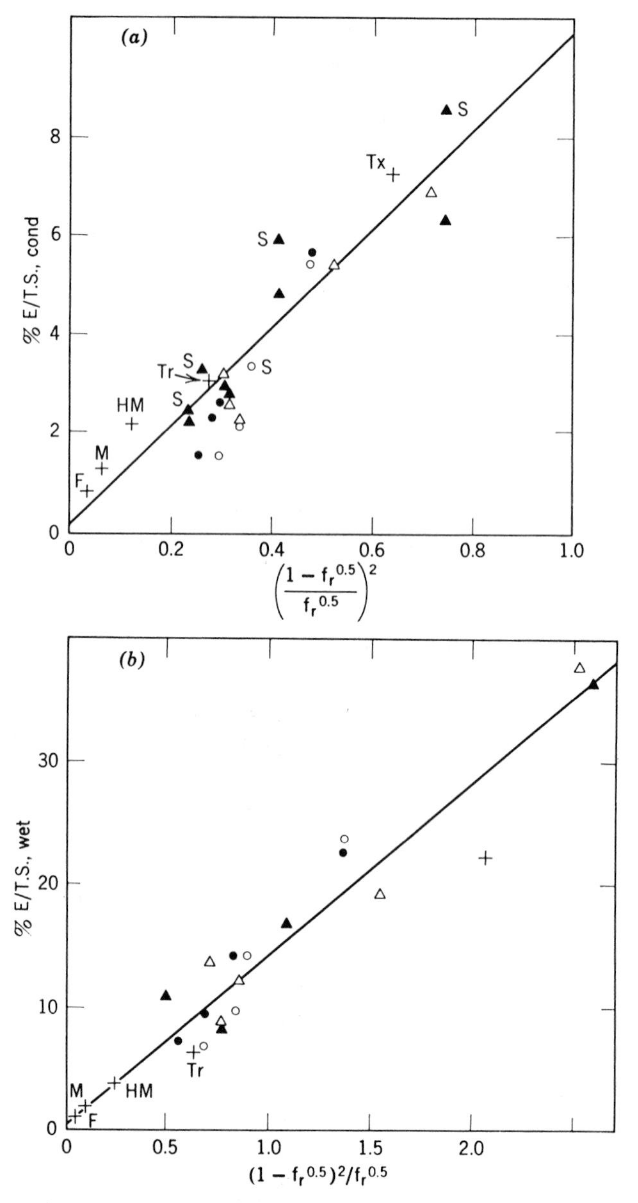

Fig. 18. (*a*) Relationship of $[(1 - f_r^{0.5})/f_r^{0.5}]^2$ to the ratio $\% \ E/TS$ of the conditioned yarns. $\% \ E/TS_{\text{cond}} = 0.1 + 10.1 \ [1 - f_r^{0.5}/f_r^{0.5}]^2$. (*b*) relationship of $(1 - f_r^{0.5})^2/f_r^2$ to the ratio $\% \ E/TS$ of the wet yarns (commercial samples Tx = textile rayon; Tr = Tire yarn; M = Meryl; HM = high wet modulus rayon; F = Fortisan are included for a comparison). $\% \ E/TS_{\text{wet}} = 0.6 + 13.9 \ (1 - f_r^{0.5})^2/f_r^2$.

portions are most probably the less ordered regions, x-ray methods are not able to resolve differences of that nature.

In considering the "inverse breaking modulus" of wet fibers two things have to be taken into consideration. This value will be higher than the corresponding property of conditioned fiber because of the increase of elongation upon wetting and the subsequent decrease in tensile strength usually observed in the wet state. Since we had seen that the decrease in tensile strength upon wetting is proportional to the factor $f_r^{0.5}$, we have used the additional factor $1/f_r^{0.5}$ to account for the decreased tensile strength. It was natural to use the square of the resulting expression also to account for the increased elongation caused by the wetting. The resulting parameter $(1 - f_r^{0.5})^2/f_r^2$ was actually found to be linearly related to the "inverse breaking modulus" of wet fibers, as illustrated in Fig. 18.

C. Effect of Molecular Weight and Size of Morphological Units

It has been shown in the past that a minimum molecular length seems necessary for the development of any useful tensile properties in cellulose or other fibers. In the case of native cellulose fibers, this minimum value where hydrolytically or oxidatively degraded fibers loose their tensile properties is reported to be in the range of DP = 300–500 (35). For regenerated cellulose fibers a minimum DP of approximately 100–150 (36) is required for the existence of useful tensile properties. Characteristic differences in the morphological structure of native and regenerated cellulose fibers have been suspected to be responsible for this intrinsic difference. This explanation was supported by the results of many investigators (28–34,42), as thoroughly discussed earlier in this chapter.

The second significant fact concerning the effect of molecular length on tensile properties originated from Staudinger et al. (201), who in 1937 demonstrated a linear relation between the reciprocal DP ("Lückenzahl") and tensile properties. Flory (202), in interpreting results obtained by Sookne and Harris (203), showed that on theoretical grounds the tensile strength should be a linear function of the reciprocal of the numerical average DP. A number of investigators (204,205) have in general confirmed this conclusion.

Earlier in this chapter the concept for a fiber model was also outlined. From this it was concluded that the tensile strength of a fiber will be determined by the length of the polymer molecules, in particular by the number of intact molecular interlinks between the morphological units forming the network of the fiber structure. Molecular breaks inside the

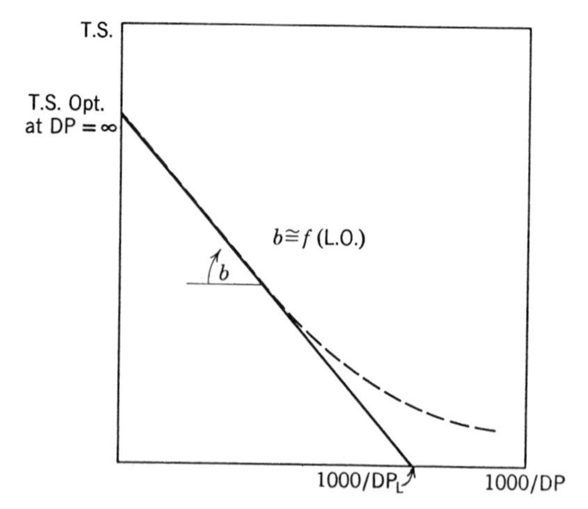

Fig. 19. Theoretical relationship between 1000/DP and tensile strength. The slope b of the solid straight line is assumed to be related to the perfection of order and the degree of orientation.

well-ordered, crystalline fibrillar aggregates will not be as harmful as loose ends occurring in the less ordered interlinking regions. Inside the crystalline regions the large number of secondary bonds, numerous in the case of cellulose, will hold the molecules together and easily compensate for molecular breaks.

In the case of a continuous structure where no defined morphological units exist, the fraction of still existing bonds at a given DP is directly related to the expression $1 - 1/\mathrm{DP}$. The existence of defined morphological units, as proven to exist in cellulose fibers, alters this fraction to $1/\mathrm{DP_L} - 1/\mathrm{DP}$, where $\mathrm{DP_L}$ is the length of morphological units expressed in number of glucose units. This formula should relate the effect of the degree of polymerization to the tensile properties under the following conditions: (*a*) the size of the morphologial units of high order is relatively uniform; (*b*) the interlinks between the morphological units are regions of low order and have a relatively small density of secondary bonds from cellulose molecule to molecule. In the case of series of varying degree of polymerization produced by a degradation treatment this relation will only be fulfilled when the following additional conditions hold: (*c*) the degradation occurs preferably in the interlinking areas and topochemical degradation of molecules on the surface of the morphological units does not effect the measurement of the effective molecular weight; and (*d*) the degradation does not alter the lateral order and orientation of the system appreciably. Under these conditions the tensile strength should be linearly related to 1/DP, as shown in Fig. 19.

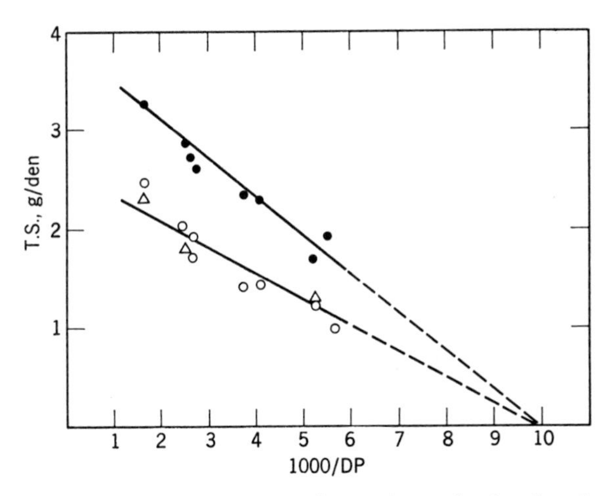

Fig. 20. Dependence of tensile strength on the molecular length of the fiber-forming molecules of rayons and acetate fibers, according to examples selected from Cumberbirch and Harland (205). (●) Conditioned rayon samples, (○) wet rayon samples, (Δ) cellulose acetate fibers in conditioned state.

Cumberbirch and Harland (205) have spun from fractions of differing molecular weight rayon and acetate model fibers using throughout the same spinning conditions and varying stretch ratios. Since they have characterized their resulting fibers using birefringence, we were able to

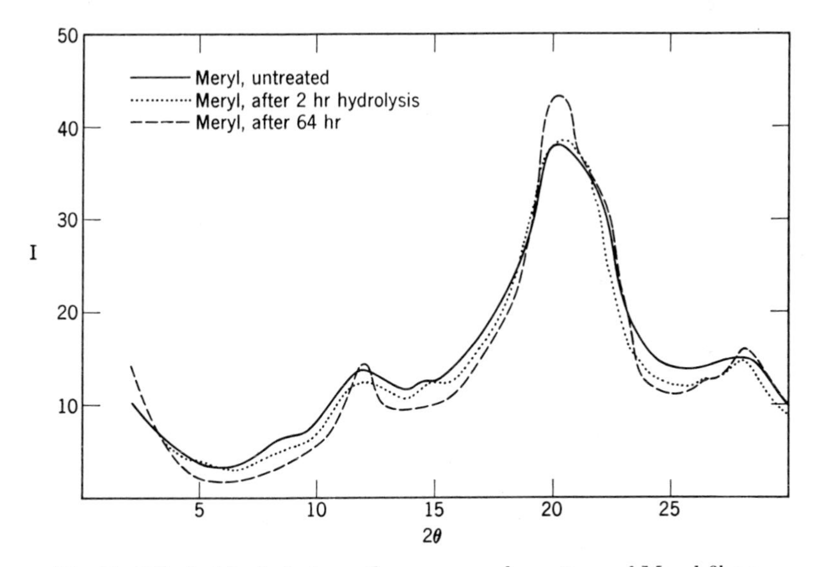

Fig. 21. Effect of hydrolysis on the x-ray powder pattern of Meryl fibers.

select samples of similar orientation and most probably similar crystallinity. Presented in a strength against 1000/DP plot, their data excellently confirm the validity of the above-described concept, as shown in Fig. 20. It may be mentioned that the degradation of cellulose fibers with high-energy radiation gives principally the same results. However, the decay of tensile strength with decreasing DP is much slower than in the case of heterogeneous hydrolysis. This may be attributed to the fact that radiation causes statistical degradation throughout crystalline and amorphous regions, from which only molecular breaks in the amorphous regions are effective in lowering tensile strength (51,206).

Many investigators (207) have observed that the tensile strength of fibers degraded to various degrees does not drop linearly with 1/DP but tapers out slowly, as shown by the dotted line in Fig. 19. This is probably due to the fact that one or more of the conditions discussed above are not fulfilled. One of the objects of our experimental work with Kitchen (42) was to investigate this phenomenon. For this purpose we hydrolyzed cotton and a number of rayon fibers for various lengths of time. The samples were then submitted to viscosity determinations, to tensile measurements, and to x-ray investigations to study the effect of the hydrolysis treatment on the molecular state, the tensile behavior, and the lateral order. In order to determine the effect of DP on the tensile properties it would have been desirable to find conditions which alter the degree of polymerization without affecting the lateral order, namely crystallinity and orientation. It soon became evident from the x-ray powder diffraction studies of the hydrolyzed samples that the hydrolysis resulted in an improvement of the perfection of order or crystallinity. This is demonstrated in Fig. 21 using the results obtained

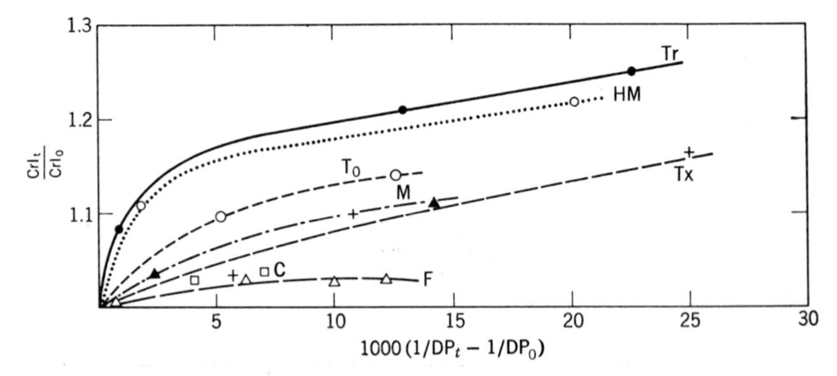

Fig. 22. Degree of recrystallization with progressing degradation (F = Fortisan, C = cotton, Tx = textile rayon, M = Meryl, To = Toramomen, HM = high-wet-modulus rayon; Tr = tire yarn).

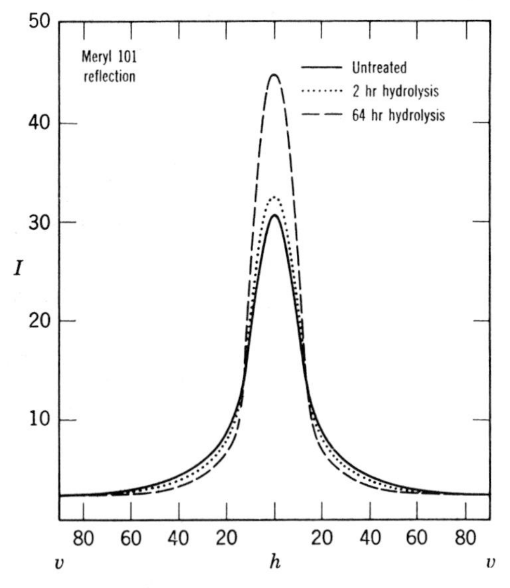

Fig. 23. Effect of hydrolysis on the azimuthal intensity distribution of the 101 reflection of Meryl.

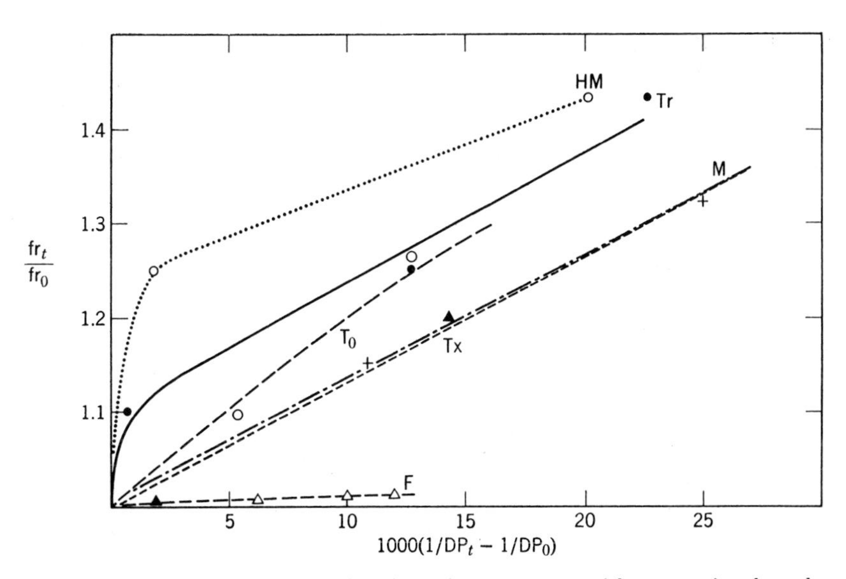

Fig. 24. The fractional increase in orientation parameter with progressing degradation (F = Fortisan, Tx = textile rayon, M = Meryl, To = Toramomen, Tr = tire yarn, HM = high-wet-modulus rayon).

on Meryl. This recrystallization tendency during the course of hydrolytic treatments is the more expressed, the lower the original degree of crystallinity of the untreated sample. The recrystallization increases from cotton (CrI_0 = 0.89) and Fortisan (0.86), to textile rayon (0.76), to Meryl (0.74), to Toramomen (0.74), to high-wet-modulus rayon (0.70), and to tire yarn rayon (0.65), as illustrated by Fig. 22.

X-ray orientation measurements revealed that a marked improvement also occurs during the hydrolysis treatments. This is indicated by the considerable increase in the sharpness of the intensity distribution

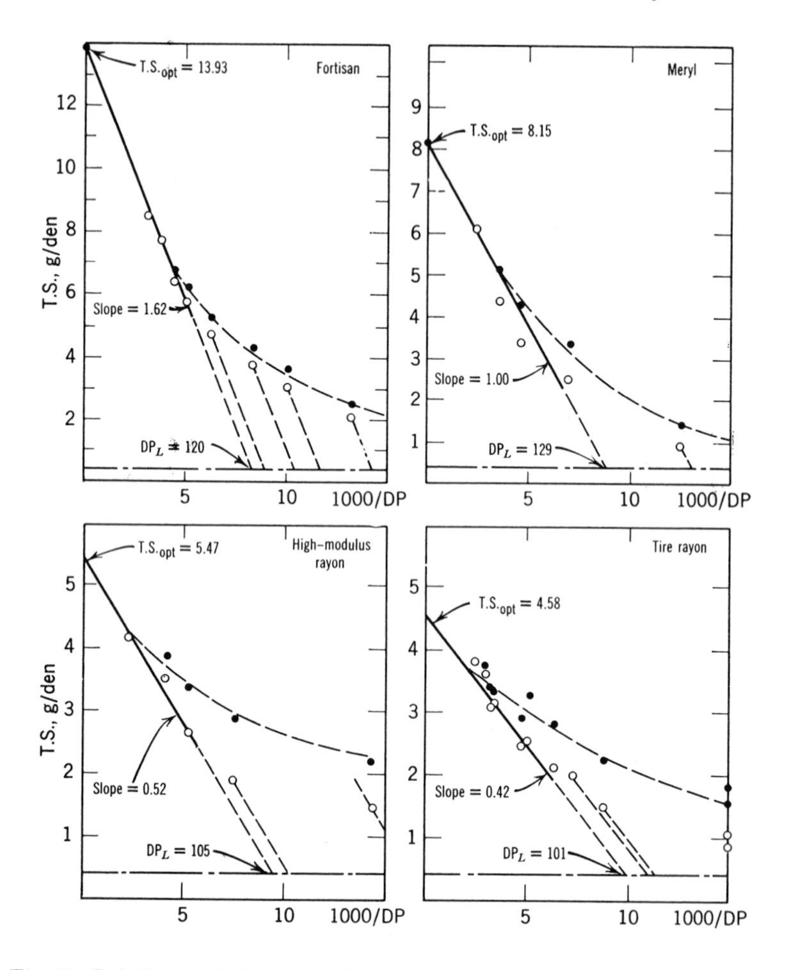

Fig. 25. Relationship between tensile strength of conditioned yarns and 1000/DP. In each series the DP was changed by acid hydrolysis. (●) Observed values of TS_{cond}; (⊙) TS_{cond} corrected for the improvement in fine structure during hydrolysis.

curves obtained by azimuthal scanning through the reflection arcs, as shown for the 101 reflections of Meryl samples hydrolyzed to various degrees in Fig. 23. The improvement of orientation during hydrolysis is not as strictly related to the degree of crystallite orientation in the original fibers. For cotton and Fortisan ($f_{r0} = 0.71$) the improvement of orientation during hydrolysis is negligible, while it increases from Meryl (0.58) and textile rayon (0.31), to Toramomen (0.58), to tire yarn (0.44), and to high-wet-modulus rayon (0.50) in the same order as observed for the improvement in crystallinity (Fig. 24). This suggests that recrystallization is the primary cause of reorientation and that the mechanism of this improvement of order is the agglomeration of fibrillar crystallite bands to thicker regions of high order. Similar observations were made by a number of investigators (208).

Since we had thus obtained quantitative evidence that the lateral order improves during the course of the hydrolysis treatments, we felt that any consideration of the effect of degree of polymerization on tensile

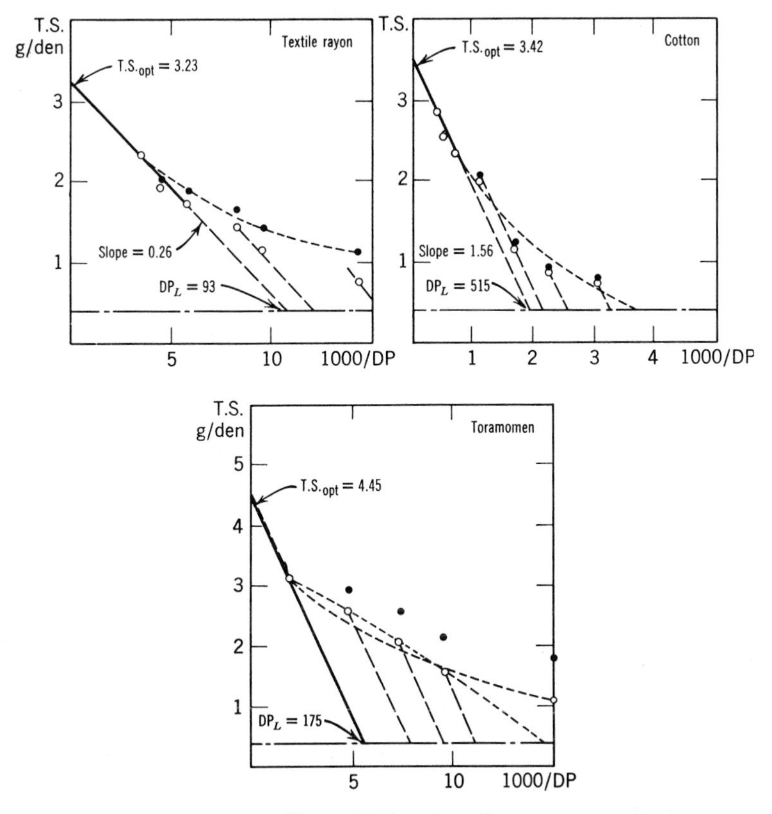

Figure 25 (*continued*)

properties should take these changes and their effect into account. On the basis of our above-described results on the effect of crystallinity and orientation on tensile strength, we therefore corrected the observed tensile strengths for the changes in lateral order by multiplying with the factor $CrI_0 \times f_{r0}^2/CrI_t \times f_{rt}^2$. Figure 25 demonstrates the effect of this treatment on the relationships between 1/DP and conditioned tensile strength for cotton, Fortisan, Meryl, high-wet-modulus rayon, tire rayon, Toramomen, and textile rayon.

It can be seen from Fig. 25 that correcting for the effect of improvement in lateral order during hydrolysis tends to straighten out the plots of tensile strength versus 1/DP and brings them more in agreement with the concept demonstrated by Fig. 19. It does not, however, bring all the points onto a common straight line. This suggests that there exists a distribution in the length of the morphological units. In the case of regenerated cellulose fibers, another possibility as cause for the tapering off in tensile strength could be the existence of less accessible interlinkages between the morphological units surviving extended hydrolysis. Extensive topochemical degradation on the surface of the morphological units, interfering with the measurement of effective DP, could be called a third reason for the deviation from our concept.

The slopes of the straight lines in Fig. 25, expressing the initial decay of tensile strength with 1/DP, were found to be linearly related to the original order characterized by the factor $CrI \times f_r^2$ (Fig. 26). Only Toramomen with 1/DP showed a rather peculiar behavior. The initial

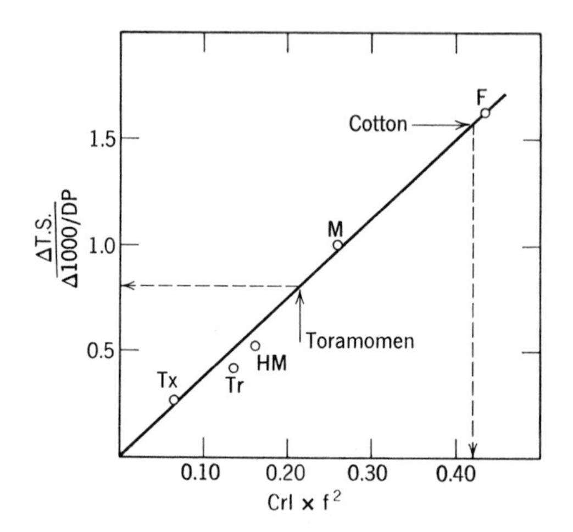

Fig. 26. Relationship between the rate of decay of tensile strength with 1/DP and the original lateral order of the fibers, as expressed by the parameter $CrI \times f_r^2$. (F = Fortisan, M = Meryl, HM = high-wet-modulus rayon, Tr = tire yarn).

loss of tensile strength with 1/DP is in this case much slower than expected from the crystallinity and the relatively high degree of orientation. It seems reasonable to assume that in the case of Toramomen the three possibilities outlined above act together in bringing about the observed result. Since for Toramomen we could not interpolate an initial rate of decay of tensile strength with 1/DP from the data in Fig. 25, we appointed a corresponding value on the basis of its crystallinity and orientation from the graph shown in Fig. 26.

From the straight lines, expressing the initial decay of tensile strength, the effective length of morphological units was found as an interception on the abscissa. Table II summarized our results and compares them

TABLE II. Length of Morphological Units Derived by Interpolation from Strength versus 1/DP Plots and "Sensitive Links" Calculated According to Sippel (209)

Sample	DP_L, from 1/DP versus *TS* corr.	"Sensitive links" according to Sippel (from *TS* corr.)	DP_L/SL
Cotton	515	624	0.82
Fortisan	120	147	0.81
Meryl	127	173	0.74
High-wet-modulus	111	98	1.13
Tire yarn	112	120	1.07
Toramomen	175	84	2.09
Textile rayon	93	119	0.78

with values calculated according to Sippel (209) from DP and corrected tensile strengths.

Here also the peculiar behavior of Toramomen is quite evident. In all other cases we found reasonable relative agreement between the values obtained by our interpolation method and the values calculated according to Sippel. In the case of Fortisan the values DP_L = 120 or 147 (600 or 750 A) are also in reasonably good agreement with the result of our electron microscopic study (42).

By interpolation with parallel lines to the initial rate of decay of tensile strength with 1/DP we attributed for all points not situated on the initial line of strength decay an effective DP_L. By treating the TS_t/TS_0 fractions and the corresponding DP_L in a similar manner to that for polymer fractionation data we arrived at length distributions for the morphological units, as illustrated by Fig. 27 for cotton, tire yarn, and Toramomen.

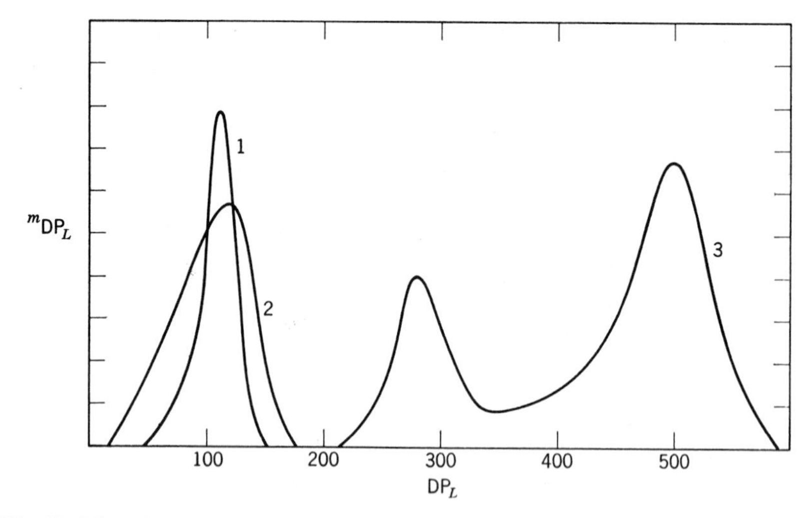

Fig. 27. Mass distribution of morphological units of various lengths (DP_L) for cotton (*3*), Toramomen (*2*), and tire yarn (*1*).

From these length distributions the peculiarity of Toramomen becomes quite evident. Toramomen seems to have a very wide spread length distribution of its morphological units, while all the other regenerated cellulose fibers show very narrow length distributions.

It may be mentioned that our hydrolysis studies also revealed an interesting inverse relation between the structural factor $\mathrm{CrI} \cdot f_r$ and the initial rate of hydrolysis, as demonstrated in Fig. 28.

Also here Toramomen with its high rate of hydrolysis does not fall in line with the other fibers. Simple geometric considerations suggest that long morphological units could account for a rather high accessibility of sensitive bonds. Indeed, the use of a parameter $DP_L/\mathrm{CrI} \times f_r$ instead of $1/\mathrm{CrI} \times f_r$ also brings Toramomen in line with the other fibers. The high apparent DP_L is in agreement with the findings of Drisch and others (210), who found a very expressed fibrillar nature for polynosic fibers.

Summarizing these results we tested the relation between the tensile strength of conditioned fibers from our hydrolysis experiments and the parameter $\mathrm{CrI} \cdot f_r^2 \times (1000/DP_L - 1000/DP)$ by multiple regression analysis. As illustrated in Fig. 29, a correlation of very high statistic probability was found.

The same applies to the relation between the wet tensile strength of the fiber samples from our hydrolysis experiments and the parameter $\mathrm{CrI} \cdot f_r^{2.5} \times (1000/DP_L - 1000/DP)$, as demonstrated by Fig. 30.

Earlier, in analyzing the effect of orientation on the "inverse breaking modulus" of conditioned fibers we had shown a correlation between

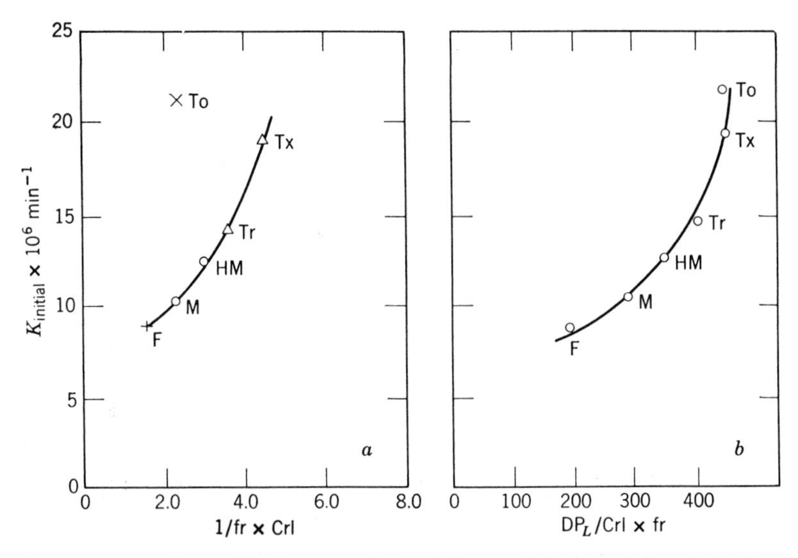

Fig. 28. (*A*) Relationship between the initial rate of degradation and the lateral order, expressed by the product CrI $\times f_r$. (*B*) Relationship between the initial rate of degradation and the parameter DP_L/CrI $\times f_r$. (F = Fortisan, M = Meryl, HM = high-wet-modulus rayon, Tx = textile rayon, Tr = tire yarn, To = Toramomen).

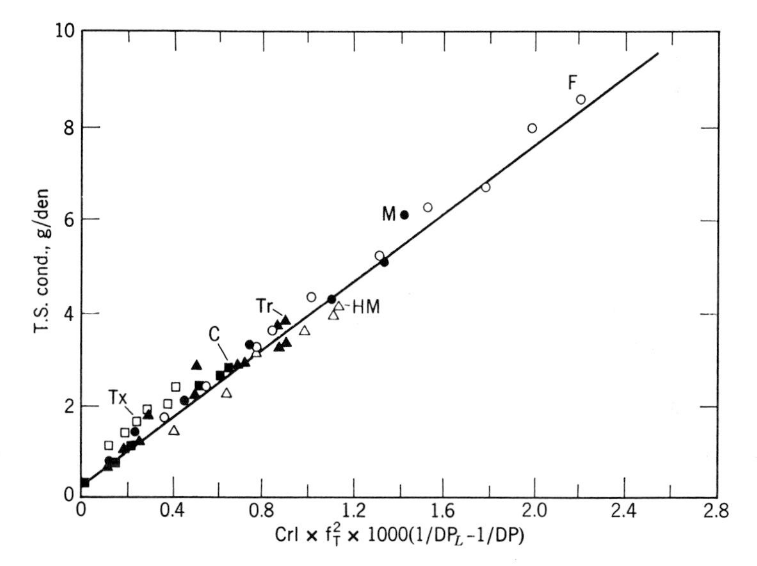

Fig. 29. Relationship between the parameter CrI $\times f_r^2 \times$ (1000/DP_L − 1000/DP and the observed tensile strength of conditioned yarn from hydrolysis series (F = Fortisan, M = Meryl, HM = high-wet-modulus rayon, Tr = tire yarn, C = cotton, Tx = textile rayon). $TS_{\text{cond}} = 0.4 + 3.63 \times \text{CrI} \times f_r^2 \times (1000/DP_L - 1000/DP)$.

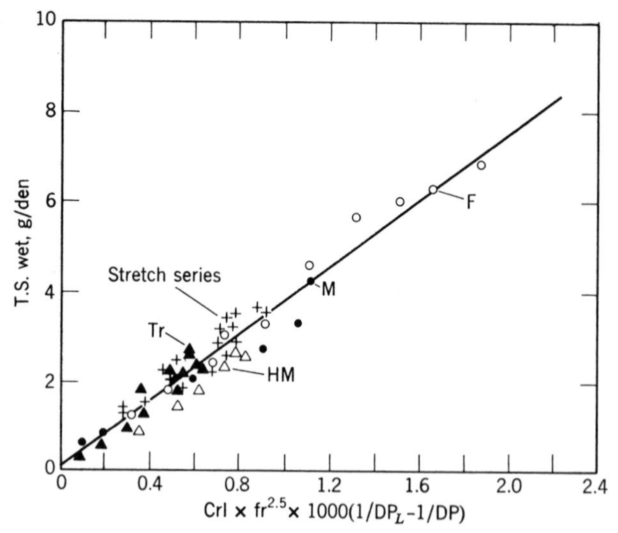

Fig. 30. Relationship between the parameter CrI $\times f_r^{2.5} \times (1000/\mathrm{DP_L} - 1000/\mathrm{DP})$ and the observed tensile strengths of wet yarns from the hydrolysis series (F = Fortisan, M = Meryl, Tr = tire yarn, HM = high-wet-modulus rayon). $TS_{\mathrm{wet}} = 0.08 + 3.70 \times \mathrm{CrI} \times f_r^{2.5} \times (1000/\mathrm{DP_L} - 1000/\mathrm{DP})$.

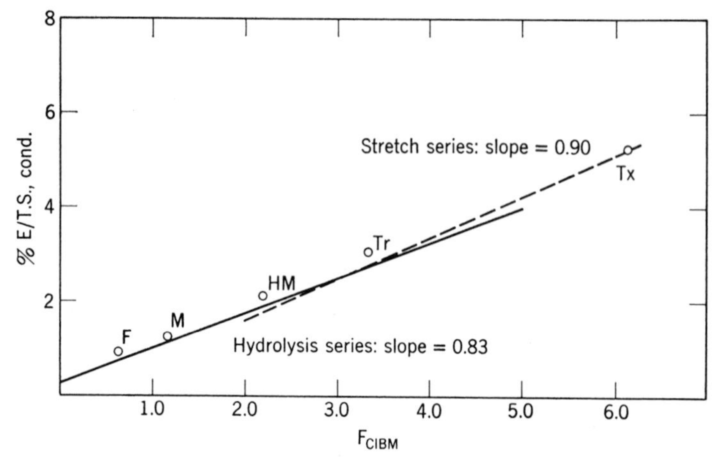

Fig. 31. Relationship between the parameter F_{CIBM} and the ratio $\% E/TS$ for conditioned samples. (F = Fortisan, M = Meryl, HM = high-wet-modulus rayon, Tr = tire yarn, Tx = textile rayon). $\% E/TS_{\mathrm{cond}} = 0.28 + 0.83 \times F_{\mathrm{CIBM}}$.

$\%E/TS$ and the parameter $(1 - f_r^{0.5})^2/f_r$. Since the tensile strength is directly related to the parameter $1000/\mathrm{DP_L} - 1000/\mathrm{DP}$, and since long morphological units may exert more steric hindrance reducing elongability, we tested the applicability of the parameter:

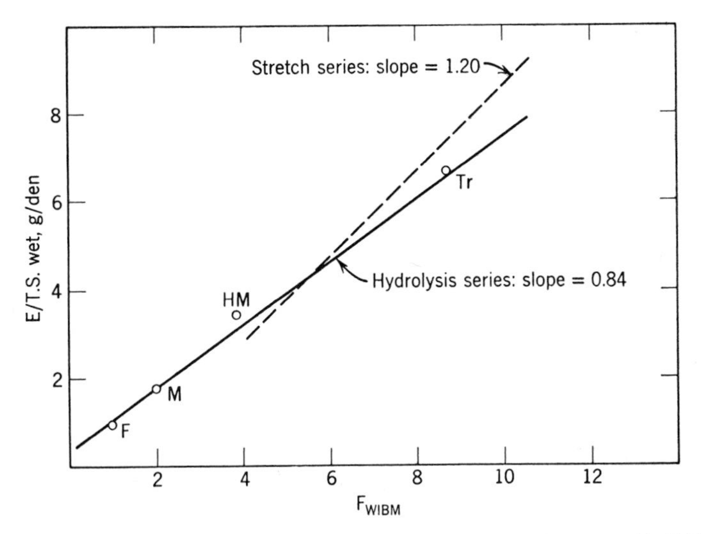

Fig. 32. Relationship between the parameter F_{WIBM} and the ratio % E/TS for wet samples (F = Fortisan, M = Meryl, HM = high-wet-modulus rayon, Tr = tire yarn). % E/TS_{wet} 0.28 + 0.84 × F_{WIBM}.

$$F_{\text{CIBM}} = (1 - f_r^{0.5})^2/f_r \times 10/(1000/\text{DP}_\text{L} - 1000/\text{DP}) \times \frac{1000}{\text{DP}_\text{L}}$$

in its relation to %E/TS. Figure 31 illustrates that a good correlation exists.

Finally, in analogy with the procedure used for the "inverse breaking modulus" of wet fiber samples from the stretch series, we extended the above parameter by the reciprocal of f_r, arriving at

$$F_{\text{WIBM}} = (1 - f_r^{0.5})^2/f_r^2 \times 10/(1000/\text{DP}_\text{L} - 1000/\text{DP}) \times \frac{1000}{\text{DP}_\text{L}}$$

Figure 32 illustrates that a reasonably good correlation exists between this parameter and the %E/TS values of wet fiber samples.

IV. CHARACTERIZATION OF COMMERCIAL RAYON SAMPLES

In our study with Kitchen (42) a large number of experimental and commercial rayon samples were characterized by viscosity for degree of polymerization and by x-ray investigations for crystallinity (CrI) and orientation (f_r). From the tensile strength of the samples in the conditioned state we computed the unknown DP_L using the regression formula

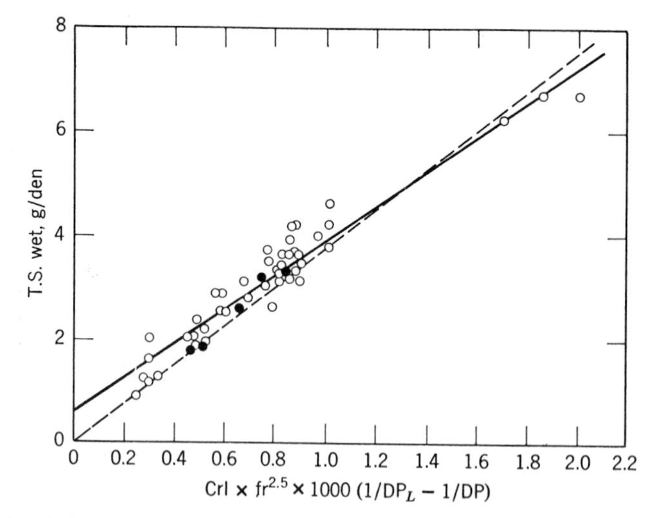

Fig. 33. Relationship between the parameter CrI $\times f_r^{2.5} \times$ (1000/DP$_L$ – 1000/DP) and wet tensile strength of commercial rayon samples (Solid circles are from Toramomen stretch series.) $TS_{wet} = 0.6 + 3.33 \times \text{CrI} \times f_r^{2.5}$ (1000/DP$_L$ – 1000/DP).

relating conditioned tensile strength with the parameter CrI $\times f_r^2 \times$ (1000/DP$_L$ – 1000/DP) derived from our hydrolysis experiments (see Fig. 29). Thus the effective length of the morphological units in number of glucose units was obtained. From this treatment the commercial rayon fibers can be grouped according to their characteristics as shown in Table III. A test of the validity of our concept and the calculation of DP$_L$ in the way described above was made using this calculated parameter to estimate the wet strength and compare it with the observed values. Figure 33 shows that a good agreement was reached.

Although it does not list all types of cellulose and cellulose derivative fibers, the table shows the wide variety of regenerated cellulose fibers which one has learned to spin at will suitable for a wide spectrum of uses.

According to the results of fiber characterization discussed above, the various types of rayon fibers can be characterised as follows:

The morphological units forming the network structure of *regular textile rayons* are of intermediate length (DP$_L$ = 90–100) and perfection of order (degree of crystallinity; CrI = 0.74–0.79): the crystallinity index may be taken as an indication of the average cross-sectional dimension of the morphological units. The orientation of these morphological units with respect to the fiber axis is the lowest of all the rayon types, as indicated by the low f_r value of approximately 0.31.

TABLE III. The Various Types of Rayon Fibers, Their Structure Characteristics and Properties

Type	DP	DP_L	CrI	f_r	*TS*, g/den		% *E* at break	
					Dry	Wet	Dry	Wet
Textile rayon								
normal	290	97	0.79	0.312	2.33	1.17	22.1	25.4
medium tenacity	295	80	0.66	0.356	3.16	2.07	15.5	25.5
high tenacity	285	77	0.69	0.358	3.82	2.92	22.3	30.3
high-wet-modulus	470	111	0.67	0.495	4.19	2.66	8.8	8.8
polynosic	500	172	0.74	0.538	3.38	2.58	7.0	9.9
Tire yarn								
normal	290	97	0.66	0.421	3.36	2.26	10.0	18.3
medium tenacity	340	93	0.76	0.416	4.14	3.11	11.3	26.3
high tenacity	500	70	0.66	0.409	5.32	4.21	10.9	31.4
Meryl	490	124	0.76	0.571	5.83	4.66	6.7	7.8
Fortisan	310	120	0.85	0.712	8.55	6.78	7.0	7.0

The *medium- and high-strength textile rayons* are both spun under conditions which create a network of shorter (DP_L = 65–85) and thinner (CrI = 0.65–0.69) morphological units. The degree of orientation of these units with respect to the fiber axis increases with the strength of these yarns (f_r = 0.30–0.35 for medium-strength textile rayon; f_r = 0.36–0.39 for high-strength rayon). Both the shorter length of the morphological units and the higher degree of orientation are responsible for the improvement in tensile strength and the changes in elongation. This will be discussed further below.

In considering the results obtained on the *high-wet-modulus rayon* samples it is apparent that the rayon industry is taking at present two basically different approaches. The one, known as the Toramomen process, giving fibers generally known under the term "polynosics," is based on the use of high DP viscose and results in fibers whose network structure is formed of morphologial units which appear to be rather long (DP_L = 170–180), relatively thick or perfectly ordered (CrI = 0.74), and well aligned along the fiber axis (f_r = 0.54–0.60). There are indications for a rather densely interlinked structure of polynosic fibers, as was pointed out before. The other approach, generally followed first by some American rayon producers, creates rather shorter and equally thick or perfectly ordered morphological units (DP_L = 100–120; CrI = 0.74–0.75) which are not quite as well oriented along the fiber axis. The concept outlined here explains why the Toramomen process makes use of high DP viscose necessary ($TS \cong f[1/DP_L - 1/DP]$), and shows that the high strengths and low elongations are mainly the result of the high degree of orientation.

The *regular strength tire yarns*, originally on the market some years ago, were essentially improved textile rayons having a higher degree of orientation (DP_L = 90–100; CrI = 0.66–0.70; f_r = 0.39–0.42). The improvement in tensile strength achieved in the case of the *improved and super tire yarns* was mainly the result of a higher perfection of order (DP_L = 90–100; CrI = 0.69–0.76) and a still higher degree of alignment along the fiber axis (f_r = 0.42–0.50). In considering the *Super II and Super III qualities*, two approaches are apparent. One group of tire yarn manufacturers continued to improve the tensile properties by further improvements in the degree of orientation, without changing the average length or width of the morphological units. The exponent of this approach spins average DP viscose into tire rayon of DP_L = 100–110, CrI = 0.71–0.72, and f_r = 0.51 – 0.53. Most other manufacturers have followed this approach, and further extended it. Another group of tire yarn producers is spinning with extensive modification to produce shorter and thinner morphological units (DP_L = 70–85; CrI = 0.64–

0.66); they have further enhanced the effect of DP by using high DP viscose. Their yarns, however, have much lower degrees of orientation (f_r = 0.41–0.45). An obvious conclusion of our concept is that a combination of the two approaches, namely to spin high DP viscose into yarns having short, well-ordered morphological units with a high degree of orientation, may lead to tire yarns with conditioned yarn strengths well over 6.5 g/den with still acceptable elongation behavior.

The *Meryl and Fortisan* processes lead to fibers having relatively long (DP_L = 110–130), well-ordered morphological units (CrI = 0.73–0.76 for Meryl; CrI = 0.81–0.86 for Fortisan). The units in these fibers are very well aligned along the fiber axis (f_r = 0.57–0.60 for Meryl; f_r = 0.70–0.72 for Fortisan), accounting for their high tensile strength and low elongation.

REFERENCES

1. H. Leaderman, *Elastic and Creap Properties of Filamentous Materials and Other High Polymers*, Textile Foundation, Washington, 1943, Chapter III.
2. A. Frey-Wyssling, *Submikroskopische Morphologie des Protoplasmas und seiner Derivate*, Gebrüder Bornträger, Berlin, 1938; revised English edition: *Submicroscopic Morphology of Protoplasma*, Elsevier, Amsterdam, 1948 and 1953.
3. P. H. Hermans, *Physics and Chemistry of Cellulose Fibers*, Elsevier, Amsterdam, 1949.
4. J. M. Preston, in *Fibre Science*, 2nd ed., J. M. Preston, Ed., The Textile Institute, Manchester, 1953, Chapter I.
5. O. Kratky and G. Porod, in *Physik der Hochpolymeren*, Vol. 3, H. A. Stuart, Ed., Springer-Verlag, Berlin, 1955, Chapter V, Section A.
6. E. Treiber, in *Physik der Hochpolymeren*, Vol. 3, H. A. Stuart, Ed., Springer-Verlag, Berlin, 1955, Chapter VI.
7. A. Sippel, *Reyon Zellwolle Chemiefasern*, **8,** 24 (1958).
8. J. W. S. Hearle, in *Fiber Structure*, J. W. S. Hearle and R. H. Peters, Eds., The Textile Institute, Manchester, 1963, Chapter 6.
9. Nägeli, C., "Micellartheorie," Original papers reprinted in *Oswalds Klassiker* as No. 227 (Edited by A. Frey), Leipzig, 1928.
10. K. H. Meyer and H. Mark, *Chem. Ber.*, **61B,** 593, 1928.
11. K. H. Meyer and H. Mark, *Der Aufbau der Hochpolymeren Naturstoffe*, Leipzig, 1930.
12. K. H. Meyer, *Kolloid-Z.*, **53,** 8 (1930).
13. W. Seifriz, *Am. Naturalist*, **63,** 410 (1929).
14. J. Hengstenberg and H. Mark, *Z. Krist.*, **69,** 271 (1928). H. Mark and K. H. Meyer, *Z. Physik. Chem.*, **B 2,** 115 (1929).
15. H. Staudinger, *Die hochmolekularen, organischen Verbindungen, Kautschuk, und Cellulose*, Springer-Verlag, Berlin (1932).
16. H. Staudinger, H. Johner, R. Signer, G. Mie, and J. Hengstenberg, *Z. Physik. Chem.*, **126,** 425 (1927).
17. K. Herrmann and O. Gerngross, *Kautschuk*, **8,** 181 (1932).
18. O. Kratky and H. Mark, *Z. Physik. Chem.*, **B 36,** 129 (1937).

19. F. Breuer, O. Kratky, and G. Saito, *Kolloid-Z.*, **80,** 139 (1937); O. Kratky, *Angew. Chem.*, **53,** 153 (1940); B. Baule, O. Kratky, and R. Treiber, *Z. Physik. Chem.*, **B 50,** 255 (1941); O. Kratky, *Kolloid-Z.*, **96,** 301 (1941).
20. H. Mark, *J. Phys. Chem.*, **44,** 764 (1940).
21. K. H. Meyer and A. J. A. van der Wyk, *Z. Elektrochem.*, **47,** 353 (1941).
22. P. H. Hermans, *Kolloid-Z.*, **97,** 231 (1941).
23. K. Hess and H. Kiessig, *Z. Physik. Chem.*, **A 193,** 196 (1944).
24. K. Hess, H. Mahl, and E. Gütter, *Kolloid-Z.*, **155,** 1 (1957).
25. J. W. S. Hearle, *J. Polymer Sci.*, **28,** 432 (1958).
26. C. W. Bunn, in *Fibres from Synthetic Polymers*, R. Hill, Ed., Elsevier, Amsterdam, 1953, Chapter 10; H. Mark, in *Cellulose and Cellulose Derivatives*, 2nd ed., E. Ott, H. M. Spurlin, and M. W. Graffin, Eds., Part I, Interscience, New York, 1954, Chapter IV; P. C. Scherer, in *Matthews' Textile Fibers*, 6th ed., John Wiley, New York 1954, Chapter II; P. Alexander and R. F. Hudson, *Wool: Its Chemistry and Physics*, Chapman and Hall, London, 1954, Chapter XII; W. Kast, O. Kratky, G. Porod, and H. A. Stuart, in *Die Physik der Hochpolymeren*, H. A. Stuart, Ed., Vol. 3, Springer-Verlag, Berlin, 1956, Chapter V; F. W. Jane, Ed., *The Structure of Wood*, Black, London, (1956), Chapter 8; O. A. Battista, *Fundamentals of High Polymers*, Reinhold, New York, 1958, Part II, Chapters 3 and 5; W. P. Hohenstein and R. Ullman, in *Unit Processes in Organic Synthesis*, 5th ed., P. H. Groggins, Ed., McGraw-Hill, New York, 1958, Chapter 15.
27. J. Sikorsky, in *Fibre Structure*, J. W. S. Hearle and R. H. Peters, Eds., The Texttile Institute, Manchester, 1963, Chapter VIII.
28. E. Husemann and A. Carnap, *Naturwissenschaften*, **32,** 79 (1944).
29. C. W. Hock, *Text. Res. J.*, **20,** 141 (1950).
30. F. F. Morehead, *Text. Res. J.*, **20,** 549 (1950).
31. K. Hess, E. Gütter, and H. Mahl, *Kolloid-Z.*, **158,** 115 (1958).
32. K. Kato and K. Yamada, *Text. Res. J.*, **29,** 368 (1959).
33. S. M. Mukherjee, S. Sikorski, and H. J. Woods, *Nature*, **167,** 821 (1951); *J. Text. Inst.*, **43,** T 196 (1952).
34. H. Krässig and W. Käppner, *Makromol. Chem.*, **44/46,** 1 (1961).
35. H. Staudinger, M. Sorkin, and E. Franz, *Melliand Textilber.*, **18,** 681 (1937); H. Staudinger, *Textil-Rundschau*, **4,** 3 (1939); H. Krässig, *Melliand Textilber.*, **36,** 55 (1955).
36. H. Staudinger, *Melliand Textilber.*, **18,** 53 (1937). H. Staudinger and F. Reinecke, *Melliand Textilber.*, **20,** 109 (1939). H. Staudinger and M. Staudinger, *Z. Textilind*, **56,** 805 (1954).
37. E. Husemann and G. V. Schulz, *Z. Physik. Chem.*, **B52,** 23 (1942); Naturforschung, **1,** 268 (1946); E. Husemann and A. Carnap, *Naturwissenschaften*, **32,** 79 (1943); E. Husemann, *Makromol. Chem.*, **1,** 140 (1947); E. Husemann and M. Goecke, *Makromol. Chem.*, **2,** 298 (1948); E. Husemann and R. Lötterle, *Makromol. Chem.*, **4,** 278 (1950); E. Husemann and U. Consbruck, *Makromol. Chem.*, **5,** 179 (1950); E. Husemann, E. Loes, and R. Lötterle, *Makromol. Chem.*, **6,** 163 (1951); L. A. Hiller, Jr., and E. Pascu, *Text. Res. J.*, **16,** 490 (1946); E. Pascu, *Fortschr. Chem. Org. Naturstoffe*, **5,** 129 (1948); H. J. Philipp, M. L. Nelson, and H. M. Ziifle, *Text. Res. J.*, **17,** 585 (1947); H. Krässig, *Makromol. Chem.*, **26,** 17 (1957); L. F. McBurney, in *Cellulose and Cellulose Derivatives*, E. Ott, H. M. Spurlin, and M. W. Grafflin, Eds., Part I, Interscience, New York, 1954, Chapter III, Section C.

38. K. Mühlethaler, *Biochim. Biophys. Acta,* **3,** 15 (1949); *Z. Schweiz. Forstverein,* **30,** 55 (1960); *Papier,* **17** (10a), 546 (1963), K. Mühlethaler, in *Cell-Biochemistry, Physiology, Morphology,* J. Brachet and A. E. Mirsky, Eds., Academic Press, New York–London, 1961; A. Frey-Wyssling and K. Mühlethaler, *Makromol. Chem.,* **62,** 25 (1963); K. Mühlethaler, in *Cellular Ultrastructure of Woody Plants,* W. A. Côté, Ed., Syracuse University Press, Syracuse, New York, 1965, pp. 51, 191.
39. L. B. Morgan, *Simp. Intern. Chem. Macromol., Suppl. Ric. Sci.,* **25,** 755, 1955; L. B. Morgan, *J. Appl. Chem.,* **4,** 160 (1954).
40. J. W. S. Hearle, *J. Polymer Sci.,* **28,** 432 (1956); *J. Textile Inst.,* **53,** P 449 (1962); *J. Appl. Polymer Sci.,* **7** (4) ,1175, 1193, 1207 (1963).
41. B. G. Ranby, *Acta Chem. Scand.,* **3,** 649 (1949); B. G. Ranby and E. Ribi, *Experientia,* **6,** 12 (1950).
42. H. Krässig and W. Kitchen, *J. Polymer Sci.,* **51,** 123 (1961).
43. A. Keller, *Phil. Mag.,* **2,** 1171 (1957); A. Keller, in *Fiber Structure,* J. W. S. Hearle and R. H. Peters, Eds., The Textile Institute, Manchester, 1963, Chapter 10.
44. R. St. J. Manley, *J. Polymer Sci.,* **47,** 509 (1960); *J. Polymer Sci. A,* **1,** 1875, 1893 (1963); R. St. J. Manley, *Proc. 1st Can. Wood Chem. Symp., Toronto,* 1963, p. 247; *C.A.,* **64,** 2270c (1966); R. St. J. Manley and S. Inoue, *J. Polymer Sci., B,* **3,** 691 (1965); B. G. Ranby and R. W. Noe, *J. Polymer Sci.,* **51,** 337 (1961); H. Dolmetsch and H. Dolmetsch, *Kolloid-Z.,* **185** (2), 106 (1962); H. Bittiger and E. Husemann, *Makromol. Chem.,* **75,** 222 (1964); **80,** 239 (1964).
45. H. Krässig and H. Schenkel, unpublished work.
46. J. M. Preston, *J. Soc. Chem. Ind.,* **50,** 199 T (1931).
47. K. Ohara, *Sci. Papers Inst. Phys. Chem. Research (Tokyo),* **25,** 152 (1934); *C.A.,* **29,** 924 (1935).
48. W. Schramek and J. Helm, *Kolloid-Z.,* **85,** 291 (1938); *Cellulosechemie,* **18,** 1 (1940); *Monatsschr. Textil-Ind.,* **55,** 64 (1960).
49. J. M. Preston and R. V. Bhat, *J. Textile Inst.,* **39,** T 211 (1948); J. M. Preston and K. I. Narasimhan, *J. Textile Inst.,* **40,** T 327 (1949), J. M. Preston and G. D. Joshi, *Kolloid-Z.,* **122,** 6 (1951).
50. F. F. Morehead and W. A. Sisson, *Text. Res. J.,* **15,** 443 (1945).
51. R. Ono, H. Maeda, S. Fujiwara, and A. Ishimoto, *Sen-i Gakkaishi,* **19** (6), 428 (1963); *C.A.,* **62,** 13299c (1965).
52. R. O. Herzog, *J. Phys. Chem.,* **30,** 457 (1926).
53. L. Lilienfeld, Brit. Pats. 253,853 (June 17, 1925), 274,521, and 274,690 (January 1, 1926).
54. H. Wakeham, in *Cellulose and Cellulose Derivatives,* E. Ott, H. M. Spurlin, and M. W. Grafflin, Eds., Interscience, New York (1954), Part III, Chapter XI.
55. H. Mark, in *Cellulose and Cellulose Derivatives,* E. Ott, H. M. Spurlin, and M. W. Grafflin, Eds., Interscience, New York (1954), Part I, Chapter IV.
56. W. E. Morton and J. W. S. Hearle, *Physical Properties of Textile Fibers,* The Textile Institute, Manchester (1962).
57. H. Staudinger and W. Heuer, *Chem. Ber.,* **63B,** 222 (1930); *Z. Physik. Chem. Leipzig,* **153,** 391 (1931).
58. W. Kuhn, *Z. Angew. Chem.,* **49,** 858 (1936).
59. H. Mark, *Der feste Körper,* Hirzel Verlag, Leipzig (1938), p. 103.
60. R. Houwink, *J. Prakt. Chem.,* **155,** 241 (1940).

61. W. Kuhn, *Z. Physik. Chem. Leipzig*, **161**, 1 (1932); W. Kuhn and H. Kuhn, *Helv. Chim. Acta*, **26**, 1394 (1943); **28**, 1553 (1946); **29**, 71 (1946); **30**, 1233 (1947); W. Kuhn, *Helv. Chim. Acta*, **32**, 735 (1949).
62. J. G. Kirkwood and R. Risemann, *J. Chem. Phys.*, **16**, 636 (1948).
63. P. Debye, *J. Chem. Phys.*, **14**, 436 (1946).
64. H. Staudinger and B. Ritzenthaler, *Chem. Ber.*, **68 B**, 1225 (1935); H. F. Launer and W. K. Wilson, *Anal. Chem.*, **22**, 455 (1950).
65. L. J. Jolley, *J. Textile Inst.*, **30**, T 4, T 22 (1939).
66. G. Jayme and W. Verburg, *Reyon, Zellwolle, Chemiefasern*, **32**, 193, 275 (1954); G. Jayme and F. Lang, *Kolloid-Z.*, **144**, 75 (1955); G. Jayme and K. Neuschäffer, *Papier*, **9**, 663 (1955).
67. D. A. Clibbens and B. P. Ridge, *J. Textile Inst.*, **19**, T 389 (1928).
68. H. Staudinger and A. W. Sohn, *J. Prakt. Chem.*, **155**, 177 (1940); H. Staudinger and E. Roos, *Melliand Textilber.*, **22**, 369 (1941); E. Roos, *Ueber Oxycellulosen*, Diss. Univ. Freiburg (Germany) (1941).
69. G. F. Davidson, *J. Textile Inst.*, **25**, T 174 (1934); **27**, P 144 (1936); **29**, T 195 (1938); *J. Soc. Dyers Colourists*, **56**, 58 (1940).
70. H. Staudinger and R. Mohr, *Chem. Ber.*, **70**, 2303 (1937).
71. H. Wannow, *Kolloid-Z.*, **102**, 29 (1943); Ch. H. Lindsey, and M. B. Frank, *Ind. Eng. Chem.*, **45**, 2491 (1953); H. Krässig, *Makromol. Chem.*, **26**, 1 (1957).
72. E. H. Immergut, B. G. Ranby, and H. F. Mark, *Ind. Eng. Chem.*, **45**, 2483 (1953); Ch. H. Lindsley and M. B. Frank, *Ind. Eng. Chem.*, **45**, 2491 (1953); A. F. Martin, *Ind. Eng. Chem.*, **45**, 2497 (1953); E. H. Immergut and F. R. Eirich, *Ind. Eng. Chem.*, **45**, 2500 (1953).
73. W. E. Davis and J. M. Elliott, in *Cellulose and Cellulose Derivatives*, E. Ott, H. M. Spurlin, and M. W. Grafflin, Eds., Interscience, New York (1955), Part III, Chapter X.
74. A. Peterlin, in *Die Physik der Hochpolymeren*, H. A. Stuart, Ed., Springer-Verlag, Berlin (1953), Volume II. Chapter V.
75. Th. Lieser, *Kurzes Lehrbuch der Cellulosechemie*, Gebrüder Borntraeger. Berlin-Nikolassee (1953), Chapter C.
76. H. Temming and H. Grunert, *Temming-Linters*, Peter Temming AG, Glückstadt (1965), Chapter III.
77. W. G. Harland, *J. Textile Inst.*, **45**, T 678 (1954); R. J. E. Cumberbirch and W. G. Harland, *J. Textile Inst.*, **50**, T 336 (1958).
78. H. Krässig and H. Müller, *Chemiker-Z.*, **78**, 209 (1954).
79. G. V. Schulz and F. Blaschke, *J. Prakt. Chem.*, **158**, 130 (1941).
80. R. S. Neiman, Z. Rogovin, and R. Obogi, *Org. Chem. Ind.* (*USSR*), **2**, 461 (1936); *C.A.*, **31**, 3264 (1937); R. S. Neiman and E. A. Fokina, *Org. Chem. Ind.* (*USSR*), **5**, 742 (1938); *C.A.*, **33**, 5180 (1939); H. M. Spurlin, *Ind. Eng. Chem.*, **30**, 538 (1938); W. Schieber, *Zellwolle*, **5**, 266 (1939); H. Mark, *Paper Trade J.*, **113** (3), 34 (1941); *Rayon Textile Monthly*, **22**, 409 (1941); W. E. Davis, *Ind. Eng. Chem.*, **43**, 516 (1951); N. Drisch and L. Soep, *Textile Res. J.*, **23**, 513 (1953); S. Mukoyama and K. Yamada, *J. Chem. Soc. Japan, Ind. Chem. Sect.*, **59**, 99 (1956); *C.A.*, **50**, 17433b (1956); H. Hara, N. Kimura, S. Ando, and I. Kimura (Kanegafuchi Spinning Co., Ltd., Osaka), Paper Presented at the 132nd Meeting of the American Chemical Society, Sept. 8–13, 1957, in New York, B. A. Zakharov, V. I. Ivanov, and G. A. Krylova, *Khim. Volokna*, **1959**, (3) 32: *C.A.*, **53**, 22907i (1959); R. J. E. Cumberbirch and W. G. Harland, *J. Text. Inst.*, **50**, T 311 (1959).

81. R. J. E. Cumberbirch, *J. Textile Inst.*, **50,** T 528 (1959).
82. J. N. Brønsted, *Z. Physik. Chem.*, Bodenstein-Festband, p. 257 (1931).
83. G. V. Schulz, *Z. Physik. Chem.*, **B 46,** 137 (1940).
84. F. Zapf, *Makromol. Chem.*, **10,** 61 (1953).
85. W. E. Roseveare and L. Poore, *Ind. Eng. Chem.*, **45,** 2518 (1953).
86. R. L. Mitchell, *Ind. Eng. Chem.*, **45,** 2526 (1953).
87. W. G. Harland, *J. Textile Inst.*, **46,** T 483 (1955).
88. M. Marx-Figini, *Makromol. Chem.*, **32,** 233 (1959).
89. C. M. Conrad, *Ind. Eng. Chem.*, **45,** 2511 (1953); A. Mueller, and L. N. Rogers, *Ind. Eng. Chem.*, **45,** 2522 (1953); R. L. Scott, *Ind. Eng. Chem.*, **45,** 2532 (1953).
90. P. Kassenbeck, *Melliand Textilber.*, **39,** 55 (1958); J. J. Trillat and Cl. Sella, *Bull. Inst. Textile France*, **92,** 35 (1961).
91. V. Peck and W. Kaye, *Textile Res. J.*, **24,** 295,300 (1954).
92. P. Scherrer, *Göttinger Nachr. Math. Phys.*, **1918,** 98.
93. J. Gjønnes, N. Norman, and H. Viervoll, *Acta Chem. Scand.*, **12,** 489 (1958); J. Gjønnes and N. Norman, *Acta Chem. Scand.*, **12,** 2028 (1958); **14,** 683 (1960).
94. H. Krässig, unpublished results.
95. H. Kiessig, *Papier*, **12,** 117 (1958); *Norelco Reptr.*, **7,** (3), 99 (1960).
96. A. Guinier, *Compt. Rend.*, **204,** 1115 (1937); Thèses, Ser. A. Nr. 1854, Univ. Paris (1939); *Ann. Phys.*, **12,** 161 (1939); *J. Chim. Phys.*, **40,** 133 (1943); O. Kratky and A. Sekora, *Naturwissenschaften*, **31,** 46 (1943); O. Kratky, *Monatsh. Chem.*, **76,** 325 (1947); *J. Polymer Sci.*, **3,** 195 (1948); O. Kratky and G. Porod, *Z. Elektrochem.*, **60,** 188, 190 (1956); **58,** 918 (1954); G. Porod, *Proc. Intern. Congr. Biochem., 4th* Vienna, 1958, **9,** 237; R. Hosemann, *Z. Phys.*, **113,** 751 (1939); **114,** 133 (1939); **127,** 16 (1950); **128,** 1 (1950); *Kolloid-Z.*, **117,** 13 (1950); **119,** 129 (1950); *Z. Elektrochem.*, **60,** 190 (1956); **58,** 923 (1954); G. Porod, *Kolloid-Z.*, **124,** 83 (1951); **125,** 51 (1952).
97. D. Heikens, P. H. Hermans, P. F. van Welden, and A. Weidinger, *J. Polymer Sci.*, **11,** 433 (1953); P. H. Hermans and A. Weidinger, *Makromol. Chem.*, **13,** 30 (1954); *J. Polymer Sci.*, **14,** 397 (1954); D. Heikens, P. H. Hermans, and A. Weidinger, *Verhandl. Kolloid-Ges.*, **18,** 15 (1958); D. Heikens, *J. Polymer Sci.*, **35,** 139 (1959).
98. H. Kiessig, *Physik. Verhandl.*, **5,** 87 (1954), H. Kiessig, *Kolloid-Z.*, **152,** 62 (1957); *Papier*, **12,** 117 (1958); K. Hess and H. Kiessig, *Kolloid-Z.*, **130,** 10 (1953); *Naturwissenschaften*, **31,** 171 (1943); *Z. Phys. Chem. Leipzig*, **193,** 196 (1944).
99. A. N. J. Heyn, *Nature*, **172,** 1000 (1953); *Textile Res. J.*, **23,** 782 (1953); *J. Polymer Sci.*, **14,** 403 (1954); *J. Appl. Phys.*, **26,** 519, 1113 (1955).
100. O. Kratky, A. Sekora, and R. Treer, *Z. Elektrochem.*, **48,** 587 (1941); H. Janeschitz-Kriegl and O. Kratky, *Z. Elektrochem.*, **57,** 42 (1953); O. Kratky and G. Miholic, *Monatsh. Chem.*, **94,** 151 (1963); *J. Polymer Sci., C,* **2,** 449 (1963).
101. N. Kasai, M. Kakudo, and T. Watase, *Kogyo Kagaku Zasshi*, **59,** 786 (1956); *C.A.*, **52,** 6799c (1958); I. Sakurada, Y. Nukushina, and H. Tanzawa, *Kobunshi Kagaku*, **17,** 21 (1960), *C.A.*, **55,** 12862g (1961).
102. W. O. Statton, *J. Polymer Sci.*, **22,** 385 (1956).
103. K. Hess, *Papier*, **11,** 553 (1957).
104. Y. Nukushina, *Kogyo Kagaku Zasshi*, **64,** 38 (1961); *C.A.*, **57,** 4898 b (1962).
105. T. Koshiro, K. Yagami, E. Shiratsuchi, and T. Fujimura, *Bull. Chem. Soc. Japan*, **31,** 606 (1958); *C.A.*, **53,** 22911d (1959); T. Koshiro and T. Fujimura, *Bull. Chem. Soc. Japan*, **34,** 476 (1961); *C.A.*, **56,** 1628c (1962); S. Takehara, *Kogyo Kagaku Zasshi*, **62,** 1044 (1959); *C.A.*, **57,** 14014d (1962).

106. P. H. Hermans and A. Weidinger, *J. Polymer Sci.*, **4,** 317 (1949); A. Meller, *J. Polymer Sci.*, **4,** 619 (1949); H. G. Ingersoll, *J. Appl. Phys.*, **17,** 924 (1949); J. A. Howsmon, *Textile Res. J.*, **19,** 1952 (1949).
107. S. Mukoyama, H. Tanzawa, and Y. Nukushina, *Kobunshi Kagaku,* **15,** 751 (1958); *C.A.*, **54,** 20213e (1960); A. Nakai, *Kogyo Kagaku Zasshi,* **62,** 467, 470 (1959); *C.A.*, **57,** 16910i, 16911e (1962); S. Okajima and A. Nagai, *Sen-i Gakkaishi,* **18** (8), 657 (1962); *C.A.*, **62,** 16425g (1965).
108. W. Kast, in *Die Physik der Hochpolymeren,* H. A. Stuart, Ed., Springer-Verlag, Berlin–Göttingen–Heidelberg (1955); Volume III, Chapter V, B.
109. B. Irvin and F. B. Breazeale, *Rev. Sci. Instr.*, **24,** 627 (1953).
110. L. Segal and C. M. Conrad, *Am. Dyestuff Reptr.*, **46,** 637 (1957).
111. H. Ruck and H. Krässig, *Norelco Reptr.*, **7,** (3), 71 (1960).
112. K. Sukai and I. Kagawa, *Kogyo Kagaku,* **61,** 605 (1958); *C.A.*, **55,** 11995 b (1961).
113. O. Ant-Wuorinen and A. Visapää, *Paperi Puu,* **43,** 105 (1961).
114. J. J. Trillat and C. Legrand, *Bull. Inst. Textile France,* **96,** 7 (1961).
115. V. A. Karagin and N. V. Michailow, *Acta Physicochim. URSS,* **11,** 343 (1939).
116. H. Mark, *J. Phys. Chem.*, **44,** 764 (1940).
117. J. M. Goppel, *Proefschrift Delft,* **1946,** *Appl. Sci. Res. Sect. A,* **1,** 18 (1947).
118. P. H. Hermans and A. Weidinger, *J. Appl. Phys.*, **19,** 491 (1948); *Kolloid-Z.*, **115,** 103 (1949); *Bull. Soc. Chim. Belges,* **57,** 123 (1948); *J. Polymer Sci.*, **4,** 135 (1949); *Textile Res. J.*, **31,** 558 (1961).
119. J. L. Matthews, H. S. Peiser, and R. B. Richards, *Acta Crystallogr.*, **2,** 85 (1949).
120. W. Kast and R. Flaschner, *Kolloid-Z.*, **111,** 6 (1948).
121. O. Kratky, F. Schlossberger, and A. Sekora, *Z. Elektrochem.*, **48,** 409 (1942); O. Kratky and A. Sekora, *Kolloid-Z.*, **108,** 169 (1944); O. Kratky and A. Krausz, *Kolloid-Z.*, **151,** 14 (1957).
122. J. H. Wakelin, H. S. Virgin, and E. Crystal, *J. Appl. Phys.*, **30,** 1654 (1959).
123. Ø. Ellefsen, E. W. Lund, B. A. Tønnesen, and K. Øien, Norsk Skogind., **9,** 349 (1957).
124. G. Jayme and H. Knolle, *Papier,* **18,** 249 (1964); **19,** 106 (1965).
125. R. Bonart, R. Hosemann, F. Motzkus, and H. Ruck, *Norelco Reptr.*, **7** (3) 81 (1960).
126. L. Segal, J. J. Creely, A. E. Martin, Jr., and C. M. Conrad, *Textile Res. J.*, **29,** 786 (1959); **30,** 404 (1960).
127. O. Ant-Wuorinen, *Paperi Puu,* **37,** 335 (1955); cf. O. Anker-Rasch, *Ibid.*, 551, O. Ant-Wuorinen and A. Visapää, *Valtion Tek. Tutkimuslaitos Tiedotus Sarja I,* **4,** Pts. 1-4, 57 pp. (1961); *Norelco Reptr.*, **9,** 47 (1961); *Paperi Puu,* **47** (5), 311 (1965); *Textile Res. J.*, **30,** 402 (1960).
128. H. Krässig and K. Füger, unpublished work.
129. K. H. Meyer and L. Misch, *Helv. Chim. Acta,* **20,** 232 (1937).
130. P. H. Hermans and A. Weidinger, *J. Colloid Sci.*, **1,** 185 (1946); W. Kast and R. Schwarz, *Z. Elektrochem.*, **56,** 228 (1952); W. Kast, *Z. Elektrochem.*, **57,** 525 (1953).
131. Ch. Legrand, *Compt. Rend.*, **227,** 529 (1948).
132. H. Kiessig, *Z. Elektrochem.*, **54,** 320 (1950).
133. O. Kratky and E. Treiber, *Z. Elektrochem.*, **55,** 716 (1951).
134. P. H. Hermans, J. J. Hermans, and D. Vermaas, *Kolloid-Z.*, **109,** 5 (1944); *J. Polymer Sci.*, **1,** 149, 156, 162 (1946); P. H. Hermans, *J. Chim. Phys.*, **44,** 135 (1947), *J. Textile Inst.*, **38,** 63 (1947); *Contribution to the Physics of the Cellulose Fibers,* Elsevier, Amsterdam (1946).
135. W. Kast, *Z. Elektrochem.*, **57,** 525 (1953).

136. DasGupta, Manchester Sci. Tech. Thesis (1938).
137. W. Bobeth, A. Mally, G. Piechottka, and U. Schroeter, *Faserforsch. Textiltech.*, **16** (2), 83 (1965).
138. W. Kozlowski and M. Mrozowski, *Tworzywa-Guma-Lakiery,* **5** (6), 178 (1960); *C.A.*, **55,** 7848e (1961).
139. E. Calvet and P. H. Hermans, *J. Polymer Sci.*, **6,** 33 (1951); P. H. Hermans and A. Weidinger, *J. Amer. Chem. Soc.*, **68,** 2547 (1946).
140. K. Ward, Jr. and R. E. Reeves, *J. Polymer Sci.*, **6,** 778 (1951).
141. E. Balcerzyk, P. Boivinet, E. Calvet, and K. Hempel, *Compt. Rend.*, **256,** 3674 (1963).
142. R. T. O'Connor, E. F. DuPré, and D. Mitchum, *Textile Res. J.*, **28,** 382 (1958).
143. F. G. Hurtubise and H. Krässig, *Anal. Chem.*, **32,** 177 (1960).
144. J. H. Rau, *Melliand Textilber.*, **44,** 1098, 1197 (1963).
145. R. F. Nickerson, *Ind. Eng. Chem.*, **34,** 1480 (1942); R. F. Nickerson, and J. A. Habrle, *Ind. Eng. Chem.*, **37,** 1115 (1945); **38,** 299 (1946).
146. C. C. Conrad and A. G. Scroggie, *Ind. Eng. Chem.*, **37,** 592 (1945).
147. H. J. Philip, M. L. Nelson, and H. Ziifle, *Textile Res. J.*, **17,** 585 (1947).
148. K. Kato and K. Yamada, *Textile Res. J.*, **29,** 368 (1959).
149. Y. Mitsuishi, *Seni-i-Gakkaishi,* **18,** 585 (1962); *C.A.*, **63,** 1930c (1965).
150. B. Philipp and J. Baudisch, *Faserforsch. Textiltech.*, **16** (4), 173 (1965).
151. G. Goldfinger, H. Mark, and S. Siggia, *Ind. Eng. Chem.*, **35,** 1083 (1943).
152. T. Timell, Thesis, Stockholm (1950).
153. A. G. Assaf, R. H. Haas, and C. B. Purves, *J. Am. Chem. Soc.*, **66,** 59 (1949).
154. R. E. Reeves and H. H. Thompson, *Contrib. Boyce Thompson Inst.*, **11,** 55 (1939).
155. V. J. Frilette, J. Hanle, and H. Mark, *J. Am. Chem. Soc.*, **70,** 1107 (1948).
156. G. Champetier and R. Viallard, *Compt. Rend.*, **205,** 1385 (1937); *Bull. Soc. Chim. France,* **5** (5), 1042 (1938); H. Sobue, and S. Fukuhara, *Kogyo Kagaku Zasshi,* **61,** 767 (1958), *C.A.*, **55,** 20417i (1961).
157. A. Bréquet and C. Chareyron, *Mém. Serv. Chim. État Paris.* **37** (3), 249 (1952); *C.A.*, **48,** 9071a (1954).
158. L. E. Hessler and R. E. Power, *Textile Res. J.*, **24,** 822 (1954).
159. Anon., Centre Rech. Ind. Text. Rouen, France, *Bull. Inst. Textile France,* **102** 945 (1962).
160. J. A. Howsmon, *Textile Res. J.*, **19,** 152 (1949).
161. H. J. Hailwood and S. Horrobin, *Trans. Faraday Soc.*, **42B,** 84 (1946).
162. J. A. Howsmon and W. A. Sisson, in *Cellulose and Cellulose Derivatives,* E. Ott, H. M. Spurlin, and M. W. Grafflin, Eds., Interscience, New York (1954), Chapter IV, B; J. A. Howsmon, Am. Chem. Soc. meeting, New York, September 1951.
163. W. A. Sisson, *J. Phys. Chem.*, **40,** 343 (1936).
164. O. Kratky, in *Die Physik der Hochpolymeren,* H. A. Stuart, Ed., Springer-Verlag, Berlin (1955), Volume III, Chapter V, C.
165. H. A. Stuart, in *Die Physik der Hochpolymeren,* H. A. Stuart, Ed., Springer-Verlag, Berlin–Göttingen–Heidelberg (1955); Volume III.
166. W. A. Sisson and G. L. Clark, *Ind. Eng. Chem., Anal. Ed.*, **5,** 296 (1933).
167. M. Polanyi, *Z. Physik,* **7,** 149 (1921).
168. O. Kratky, *Z. Physik. Chem.*, **B50,** 255 (1941); *Z. Elektrochem.*, **48,** 587 (1942).
169. J. J. Hermans, P. G. Hermans, D. Vermaas, and A. Weidinger, *Rec. Trav. Chim.*, **65,** 427 (1946); P. H. Hermans, *Physics and Chemistry of Cellulose Fibers,* Elsevier, New York (1949), pp. 214–240.
170. W. Kast and A. Prietschk, *Kolloid-Z.*, **114,** 23 (1949).

171. E. E. Berkeley and O. C. Woodyard, *Ind. Eng. Chem., Anal. Ed.*, **10,** 451 (1938); E. E. Berkeley, O. C. Woodyard, H. D. Barker, T. Kerr, and C. J. King, *U.S. Dept. Agr., Tech. Bull.*, No. 949 (1948), p. 3–14, 57–61.
172. L. Segal, J. J. Creely, and C. M. Conrad, *Rev. Sci. Instr.*, **21,** 431 (1950).
173. J. J. Creely and C. M. Conrad, *Textile Res. J.*, **35** (9), 863 (1965).
174. W. Kast, "Feinstruktur-Untersuchungen an künstli chen Zellulosefasern verschiedener Herstellungsverfahren," Forschungsber. Wirtsch. Verkehrsministerium Nordhein-Westfalen. No. 35 (1953), No. 261 (1956).
175. H. G. Ingersoll, *J. Appl. Phys.*, **11,** 924 (1946); W. A. Sisson, *Textile Res. J.*, **7,** 4255 (1937).
176. W. Kast, *J. Polymer Sci., C,* **2,** 429 (1963).
177. A. N. J. Heyn, *J. Am. Chem. Soc.*, **72,** 2284 (1950).
178. O. Kratky, *Kolloid-Z.*, **68,** 347 (1934); O. Kratky, A. Sekora, and R. Treer, *Z. Elektrochem.*, **48,** 587 (1942).
179. P. H. Hermans, *Physics and Chemistry of Cellulose Fibers,* Elsevier, New York (1949), pp. 214–240.
180. D. R. Morey, *Textile Res. J.*, **4,** 105 (1934); **5,** 483 (1935).
181. J. M. Preston, *J. Soc. Dyers Colourists,* **47,** 213 (1931); J. M. Preston and D. C. Tsien, *J. Soc. Dyers Colourists,* **62,** 368 (1946).
182. S. Okajima, Y. Kobayashi, and T. Kikuchi, *Bull. Chem. Soc. Japan,* **27,** 471 (1954); *C.A.*, **49,** 13643a (1955); K. Hájek, Věda Vyzkum Prumyslu Textil., **1,** 23 (1956); *C.A.*, **52,** 5828c (1958); D. S. Jackson and A. Sandig, *Proc. Cellulose Conf., 1st,* Syracuse, **1958,** 96; H. de Vries, *J. Polymer Sci.*, **34,** 761 (1959); A. N. Zakhar'evskii and L. A. Fedin, *Optika i Spectroskopiya,* **6,** 701 (1959); *C.A.*, **53,** 17518h (1959); H. Hara, H. Sado, and I. Hashimoto, *Sen-i Gakkaishi,* **17** (10), 1002 (1961); *C.A.*, **62,** 13302b (1965); M. S. Parthasarathy and N. Ramanathan, *J. Sci. Ind. Res. (India),* **21D** (4), 111 (1962); V. A. Berestnev, L. S. Dubova, and V. A. Kargin, *Khim. Volokna,* **1963** (4), 32; *C.A.*, **59,** 11709g (1963); K. C. Ellis and J. O. Warwicker, *J. Appl. Polymer Sci.*, **8** (4), 1583 (1964); B. E. M. Bingham, *Makromol. Chem.*, **77,** 139 (1964); V. A. Berestnev, L. S. Dubova, T. S. Pryanikova, and L. A. Fedin, *Vysokomolekul. Soedin.*, **6** (7), 1302 (1964); *C.A.*, **61,** 9621a (1964); R. J. E. Cumberbirch and J. D. Owen, *J. Textile Inst.*, **56** (7), T 389 (1965).
183. J. K. Smith, W. J. Kitchen, and D. B. Mutton, *J. Polymer Sci., C,* **2,** 499 (1963).
184. I. Z. Eifer, E. Z. Fainberg, and N. V. Mikhailow, *Khim. Volokna,* **1965** (2) 48; *C.A.*, **63,** 1929b (1965); *Vysokomolekul. Soedin.*, **7** (3), 411 (1965); *C.A.*, **63,** 1927e (1965).
185. W. A. Sisson, *Textile Res. J.*, **30** (3), 153 (1960).
186. P. Kassenbeck, Bull. Inst. Textile France, **43,** 43 (1953); P. Kassenbeck, *Ann. Sci. Textiles Belges,* **4,** No. 1, 176 (1956).
187. J. M. Preston, *Modern Textile Microscopy.* Emmott and Co., London (1933); P. H. Hermans, *Textile Res. J.*, **18,** 9 (1948); F. F. Morehead and W. A. Sisson, *ibid.*, **15,** 443 (1945); W. Schramek and J. Helm, *Kolloid-Z.*, **85,** 291 (1938); H. Sieburg, *Zellwolle, Kunstseide, Seide,* **46,** 215 (1941); J. M. Preston, *J. Soc. Chem. Ind.*, **50,** 199 (1931); J. M. Preston and D. C. Joshi, *Kolloid-Z.*, **122,** 6 (1951); K. Kato, *Textile Res. J.*, **27,** 803 (1957); **29,** 661 (1959); K. Kato, *Sen-i Gakkaishi,* **15,** 494 (1959); *C.A.*, **53,** 15572g (1959); A. Nakai, *Sen-i Gakkaishi,* **15,** 478 (1959); *C.A.*, **53,** 15573g (1959); *Ibid.*, **15,** 708 (1959); *C.A.*, **53,** 22962i (1959); E. Rockstroh, *Deut. Textiltech.*, **10,** 363 (1960); K. Kato, *Sen-i Gakkaishi,* **16,** 831 (1960); *C.A.*, **54,** 25844f (1960); R. J. E. Cumberbirch and

J. E. Ford, *J. Textile Inst.*, **51,** T 132 (1960); R. J. E. Cumberbirch, J. E. Ford, and R. E. Gee, *ibid.*, **52,** T 330 (1961); W. Bubser and H. Eichmanns, *Textil-Praxis,* **19** (1), 81 (1964); E. Wuensch and S. Hoffrichter, *Mitt. Inst. Textiltechnol. Chemiefasern Rudolfstadt,* **6,** 181 (1964).

188. E. Elöd and H. G. Fröhlich, *Textile Res. J.*, **18,** 487 (1948); E. Elöd, *Textil-Rundschau,* **9,** 13 (1954); *Melliand Textilber.*, **34,** 1 (1953); *Tinctoria,* **50,** 425, (1953).
189. A. Nakai, *Bull. Chem. Soc. Japan,* **32,** 1037 (1959); *C.A.*, **54,** 14699i (1960).
190. S. Okajima, Sh. Hayama, and K. Watanabe, *Bull. Chem. Soc. Japan,* **26,** 322 (1953), *C.A.*, **48,** 6132 b (1954); S. Okajima and Sh. Hayama, *Bull. Chem. Soc. Japan,* **27,** 544 (1954); *C.A.*, **49,** 12839 h (1955); S. Okajima and T. Kikuchi, *Kogyo Kagaku Zasshi,* **60,** 1559 (1957); *C.A.*' **53,** 16534e (1959); *Ibid.*, **61,** 880 (1958); *C.A.*, **55,** 19251 b (1961); *Ibid.*, **61,** 601 (1958); *C.A.*, **55,** 9884 e (1961); Sh. Hayama, *Kogyo Kagaku Zasshi,* **60,** 1066 (1957); *C.A.*, **53,** 10769 i (1959); T. Yurugi, *J. Chem. Soc. Japan, Ind. Chem. Sect.*, **58,** 970 (1955); *C.A.*, **50,** 13447 i (1956); H. Sobue and S. Fukuhara, *Kogyo Kagaku Zasshi,* **61,** 250 (1958); *C.A.*, **53,** 20880 a (1959).
191. Sh. Hayama, *J. Chem. Soc. Japan, Ind. Chem. Sect.*, **58,** 984 (1955); *C.A.*, **50,** 13448 g (1956); T. Skwarski, *Przemyl Wlókienniczy,* **11** (2), 69 (1957); *C.A.*, **54,** 25844 i (1960); Y. Tsuda, *Toyo Rayon Shuho,* **11,** 45 (1956); *C.A.*, **52,** 1620 g (1958); Y. Tsuda and S. Mukoyama, *Textile Res. J.*, **27,** 945 (1957). V. I. Sharkov and V. P. Levanova, *Vysokomolekul. Soedin.*, **1,** 1034 (1959); *C.A.*, **54,** 18967 a (1960); *Ibid.*, **5** (5), 729 (1963); *C.A.*, **59,** 4157 h (1963); R. S. Neiman and V. I. Gryaznova, *Khim. Volokna,* **3** (5), 47 (1961); *C.A.*, **59,** 15426 g (1963); R. J. E. Cumberbirch, *Rept. Progr. Appl. Chem.*, **46,** 233 (1961).
192. H. Mark, *J. Phys. Chem.*, **44,** 764 (1940).
193. P. H. Hermans, *J. Phys. Chem.*, **45,** 827 (1941).
194. W. O. Baker, C. S. Fuller, and N. R. Pape, *J. Am. Chem. Soc.*, **64,** 776 (1942).
195. K. Ward, *Textile Res. J.*, **20,** 363 (1950).
196. R. N. Tyler and N. S. Wooding, *J. Soc. Dyers Colourists,* **74,** 283 (1958).
197. E. E. Berkeley, *Textile Res. J.*, **19,** 363 (1949).
198. Z. I. Suleimanova and V. A. Kargin, *Zh. Fiz. Khim.*, **32,** 811 (1958); *C.A.*, **52,** 21065f (1958).
199. H. Tanzawa, *Kogyo Kagaku Zasshi,* **63,** 2186 (1960); *C.A.*, **57,** 1102 e (1962); *Ibid.*, **64,** 197 (1961); *C.A.*, **57,** 4892c (1962).
200. P. H. Hermans and A. Weidinger, *Makromol. Chem.*, **18/19,** 75 (1956).
201. H. Staudinger, M. Sorkin, and E. Franz, *Melliand Textilber.*, **18,** 681 (1937).
202. P. J. Flory, *J. Am. Chem. Soc.*, **67,** 2048 (1945).
203. A. M. Sookne and M. Harris, *Ind. Eng. Chem.*, **37,** 478 (1945).
204. H. M. Spurlin, *Ind. Eng. Chem.*, **30,** 538 (1938); H. Staudinger, *Papier-Fabrik,* **36,** 473 (1939); H. Staudinger and J. Jurisch, *Melliand Textilber.*, **20,** 693 (1939); *Zellwolle, Kunstseide, Seide,* **44,** 375, 377 (1939); *Kunstseide, Zellwolle,* **21,** 288 (1939); H. Staudinger and F. Reinicke, *Papier-Fabrik,* **36,** 489 (1939); P. C. Scherer and B. P. Rouse, *Rayon and Synthetic Textiles,* **30** (11), 42, (12), 47 (1949); P. C. Scherer and R. D. McNear, *Rayon and Synthetic Textiles,* **31,** (2), 53, (4), 54 (1950); H. Klare, *Faserforsch. Textiltech.*, **7,** 199 (1956); **8,** 262 (1957); V. W. Tripp, R. S. Orr, H. M. Ziifle, and C. M. Conrad, *Text. Res. J.*, **28,** 404 (1958); S. S. Trivedi and A. G. Chitale, *J. Textile Inst.*, **50,** T 390 (1959).
205. R. J. E. Cumberbirch and W. G. Harland, *J. Textile Inst.*, **50,** T 311 (1959); R. J. E. Cumberbirch, *J. Textile Inst.*, **50,** T 528 (1959).
206. H. Krässig, J. Schenkel, and L. Géczy, unpublished work.

207. A. Sippel, *Kolloid-Z.*, **113,** 74 (1949); **127,** 79 (1952); N. N. Winogradoff, *Nature,* **165,** 72 (1950); R. J. E. Cumberbirch and C. Mack, *J. Textile Inst.*, **52,** T 382 (1961).
208. H. G. Ingersoll, *J. Appl. Phys.*, **17,** 924 (1946); J. A. Hosmon, *Textile Res. J.*, **19,** 152 (1949); A. Meller, *J. Polymer Sci.*, **4,** 619 (1949); H. Sobue and H. Minato, *Kogyo Kagaku Zasshi,* **60,** 327 (1957); *C.A.*, **53,** 5667e (1959); A. Nowakowski and M. Wronski, *Zeszyty Nauk. Politech. Lodz, Chem.*, **15,** 105 (1965); *C.A.*, **63,** 16516 e (1965).
209. A. Sippel, *Melliand Textilber.*, **38** (8), 898 (1957); *Papier,* **13,** 413 (1959).
210. N. Drisch, *Svensk Papperstid.*, **65** (4), 118 (1962); Cl. Cella, D. Chaperot, and and J. J. Trillat, *Compt. Rend.*, **252,** 2349 (1961).

Nylon 66

H. Hopff

Swiss Federal Institute of Technology, Department of Industrial and Engineering Chemistry, Zurich, Switzerland

CONTENTS

I. INTRODUCTION

Nylon 66 is the first synthetic polyamide to be developed of technical importance. It was invented by W. H. Carothers in the laboratories of DuPont in February 1935 and has opened a new era in the field of synthetic fibers.

The history of the development of nylon is described by Bolton (1) and Mark and Whitby (2). It is a member of the large group of polycondensation products of dicarboxylic acids and diamines with fiber-forming properties, according to the following equation:

$$x\mathrm{HOOC}\cdot(\mathrm{CH_2})_n\cdot\mathrm{COOH} + x\mathrm{H_2N}\cdot(\mathrm{CH_2})_m\cdot\mathrm{NH_2} \rightarrow \mathrm{HOOC(CH_2)}_n\cdot\mathrm{CONH(CH_2)}_m\mathrm{NHCO}\cdot(\mathrm{CH_2})_n\cdot\mathrm{CONH(CH_2)}_m\cdot\mathrm{NH}\ldots$$

From among these the product from adipic acid and hexamethylene diamine was selected as the best and was manufactured by DuPont under the name of nylon. Later, as other polyamides were developed, a numerical system was chosen to express the chemical composition of the polyamides. A two-figure combination indicates a polyamide obtained from a diamine and a dicarboxylic acid; the individual numbers refer to the numbers of carbon atoms respectively in the diamine and dicarboxylic acid chains, with the diamine number given first. Thus, nylon 66 is derived from hexamethylene diamine, $NH_2(CH_2)_6NH_2$ and adipic acid, $HOOC(CH_2)_4COOH$.

At the time of the invention of nylon, neither adipic acid nor hexamethylene diamine were technically available, and therefore much work was necessary until production on a larger scale could be started. In 1939 the first production plant went into operation in Seaford, Delaware. From this time, the development of nylon production has increased rapidly, and present production (1966) has surpassed 500,000 tons a year. Nearly all countries with textile industries have taken a license from the du Pont Company.

For the production of high-molecular polyamides it is essential to use the intermediates in carefully balanced quantities. Since the technical starting materials, adipic acid and hexamethylene diamine, normally contain small amounts of impurities, it is important to prepare a salt of equimolecular amounts of both starting materials in methanol solution, whereby the impurities remain in the mother liquor. Nylon salt (AH salt) forms snow-white crystals (m.p. 190–191°), readily soluble in water with pH 7.2–7.3. It is stable in storage and can therefore be shipped without difficulty.

Nylon 66 production comprises four steps: (*1*) salt preparation; (*2*) polycondensation; (*3*) extrusion and milling; (*4*) spinning. For the production of the intermediates, various processes have been developed which will be discussed in detail in the following chapters.

II. ADIPIC ACID MANUFACTURE

A. Oxidation of Cyclohexanol

Adipic acid can be obtained from a number of starting materials, such as cyclohexane, cyclohexene, cyclohexanol, cyclohexanone, cyclohexylamine, tetrahydrofuran, aniline, hexanediol, etc. Of all these products only cyclohexane, cyclohexanol, and cyclohexanone are interesting from the technical point of view. Although various oxidizing agents can be used ($KMnO_4$, CrO_3, ozone), only nitric acid and oxygen can be used economically. The most important process is the oxidation of cyclohexanol with 50% nitric acid at 60–70°. In a stainless steel kettle the cyclohexanol is added to the acid under cooling and stirring. The escaping nitrous gases are absorbed and regenerated to nitric acid. On cooling the adipic acid crystallizes out. Oxalic, succinic, and glutaric acids and small amounts of lower fatty acids and nitro compounds are formed as by-products. The crude acid is crystallized from water. The yield exceeds 85% of theoretical (3).

The process can be carried out continuously by pumping the reactants through tubes (4) or kettles (5).

Instead of cyclohexanol, hexanediol-1,6 can be used, but the temperature must be lower because of the faster reaction of this glycol with nitric acid. Economically, this method has no importance, as hexanediol is best prepared by hydrogenation of adipic acid esters.

B. Oxidation of Cyclohexanone

The oxidation of cyclohexanone with nitric acid demands higher temperatures than cyclohexanol. Much better than this method is the catalytical oxidation with oxygen or air in the liquid phase (6). The cyclohexanone is oxidized in the presence of acetic acid as diluent and with 0.1% manganese acetate or nitrate at about 80–100°. The yield is about 70%. Succinic and glutaric acids are obtained as by-products. When nylon production was in its infancy, DuPont used this method.

For nylon 66 a very pure adipic acid is necessary. Small traces of impurities give rise to a colored product. The acid number should be 768, the ester number 0, and ash content below 0.01%. The color must be white, and the melt of the adipic acid must remain water-clear for hours.

C. Direct Oxidation of Cyclohexane

The simplest method for the production of adipic acid seems to be the direct oxidation of cyclohexane. Oxidation with nitric acid is possible (7), but gives only a yield of 35% with considerable amounts of nitrocyclohexane and lower dicarboxylic acids. Cyclohexene gives good yields with 50% nitric acid (8), but is too expensive.

More interesting is the catalytic oxidation with air by soluble manganese or cobalt catalysts (naphthenates, stearates) at 120–150°. The reaction is interrupted at a conversion of 10–15% and leads always to a mixture of cyclohexanol and cyclohexanone in equal amounts, and adipic acid, cyclohexanol adipate, lower aliphatic acids, and tarry residues. The unchanged cyclohexane is recycled and the crude oxidation product fractionated. Since cyclohexane is an important petrochemical product, much of the production of cyclohexanol and cyclohexanone is based on this process.

D. Other Methods

All other patented methods using cyclohexylamine (9), tetrahydrofuran (10), or hexahydroacetophenone (11) as starting materials are not economical.

III. ADIPODINITRILE MANUFACTURE

The dinitrile is the intermediate for the production of hexamethylene diamine. It can be produced by different methods.

A. Vapor Phase Process from Adipic Acid and Ammonia

One method involves condensation from ammonia and adipic acid in the vapor phase. The process is executed as shown in Fig. 1. Adipic acid is vaporized and let with an excess of ammonia gas (mol. ratio 20:1) at 350° over a catalyst of boron phosphate (BPO_4). The reaction is endothermic at 57 cal/mole (12). The yield is 87.5% with b.p. 147–148°/10 mm, m.p. 2.4°, n_D = 1.4370, d^{25} = 0.9600; it is soluble in

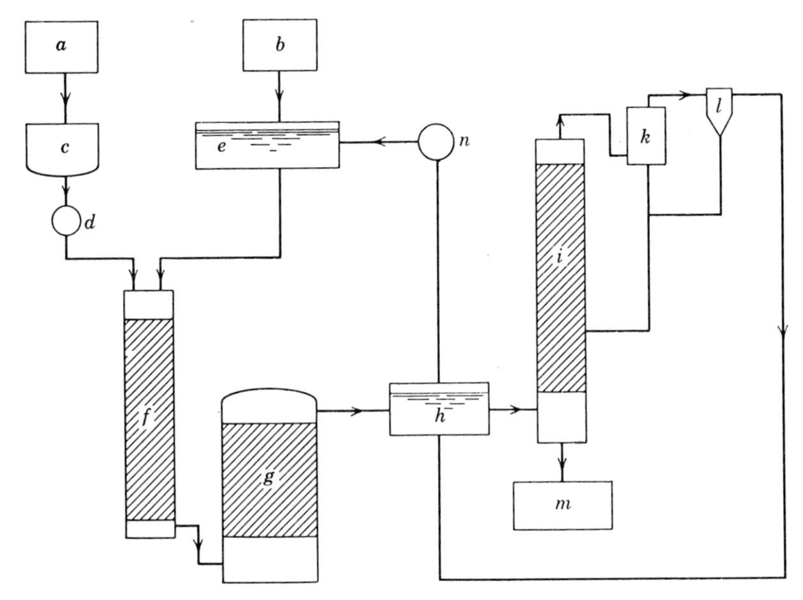

Fig. 1. Adipodinitrile plant. (*a*) Tank for adipic acid; (*b*) tank for liquid ammonia; (*c*) fusion pot for adipic acid; (*d*) rotameter; (*e*) ammonia preheater; (*f*) evaporator for adipic acid; (*g*) reactor; (*h*) heat exchanger; (*i*) distilling column; (*k*) cooler; (*l*) cyclon separator; (*m*) tank for adipodinitrile; (*n*) tank for ammonia.

alcohols, benzene, toluene, insoluble in water and gasoline. Cyclopentanone and high-boiling residues are formed as by-products. The catalyst is prepared from boric acid and phosphoric acid and heated to 400° after drying. It is a hard mass which is ground into small pellets.

B. Liquid Phase Process

In a liquid phase process, ammonia is introduced in molten adipic acid at 200–250° in the presence of such catalysts as alkyl or aryl phosphates in 0.1–0.5% phosphoric acid or boron phosphate (13). The yield amounts to 86%.

C. 1,4-Dichlorobutane and Sodium Cyanide

The reaction of 1,4-dichlorobutane with sodium cyanide is carried out as follows. 1,4-Dichlorobutane can be obtained either by treatment of butanediol-1,4 or tetrahydrofuran with HCl. More economical is the addition of chlorine to butadiene, giving 1,4-dichlorobutene. This can be converted to 1,4-dicyanobutane-2 by NaCN (14). Dry sodium cyanide is mixed with adipodinitrile as diluent, and the calculated amount of 1,4-dichlorobutane is added at 185–190°. By addition of water, the oily layer is distilled. The yield is about 95% (15).

Adipodinitrile can also be obtained by reacting butenediol-1,4 with HCN (16).

D. Electrohydrodimerization of Acrylonitrile

A more recent and interesting process is the electrohydrodimerization of acrylonitrile by Baizer, whereby yields higher than 82% are reported. Monsanto is using this process in a large plant at Decatur, Alabama. The optimum value of pH was found to be about 9 and the current density between 2 and 30 A/dm². The cathode potential was found to be independent of pH above 2.5. The overall reaction can be described by the following formula:

$$2CH_2{:}CH{\cdot}CN + 2H^+ + 2e^- \rightarrow NC(CH_2)_4CN$$

The simultaneous dimerization and reduction of acrylonitrile was first described by DuPont (17).

According to a Japanese patent, Appl. No. 2415/65, adipodinitrile can be obtained from acrylonitrile in aqueous HCl solution with rubidium or cesium amalgam with 100% yield (?).

Another process is described for adipodinitrile from butadiene comprising chlorination to dichlorobutene and reaction of the latter with hydrogen cyanide.

$$\underset{\text{(butadiene)}}{CH_2{:}CH{\cdot}CH{:}CH_2} + Cl_2 \rightarrow \underset{\text{(1,4-dichlorobutene-2)}}{ClCH_2{\cdot}CH{:}CH{\cdot}CH_2Cl}$$

$$ClCH_2{\cdot}CH{:}CH{\cdot}CH_2Cl + 2HCN \rightarrow \underset{\text{(1,4-dicyanobutene-2)}}{CH_2(CN){\cdot}CH{:}CH{\cdot}CH_2(CN)} + 2HCl$$

The first step in this synthesis leads to an isomeric mixture of dichlorobutenes with some higher chlorination products. The desired product is 1,4-dichlorobutene-2, which is formed in good yield only at low temperatures (18). Very high yields were obtained by Muskat and Northrup (19) by chlorination at low temperatures with chloroform as diluent.

Commercial Solvents Corporation has described a vapor phase chlorination which provides yields of 75–78% of theoretical. The reaction is exothermic. Besides 1,4-dichlorobutene-2, the reaction product contains 3,4-dichlorobutene-1 in approximately equal amounts. The chlorinated products can be purified by distillation. The conversion of the dichlorobutenes to adipodinitrile demands a weakly acidic medium (pH 4–6) and gives yields exceeding 80% of theoretical. For the absorption of the hydrogen chloride, a basic acceptor must be present; calcium carbonate has proved advantageous. Small amounts (0.5–

2 mol. %) of cuprous chloride are favorable. As diluent, water or organic solvents can be used. The reaction requires temperatures higher than 60°. The hydrogen cyanide is added according to its consumption by the reaction. A slight excess of HCN and $CaCO_3$ is necessary. As a practical example, Farlow (20) has suggested 2000 parts water, 15 parts cuprous chloride, 3 parts copper powder, 3.6 parts concentrated hydrogen chloride, and 6.9 parts potassium chloride. To this mixture, 525 parts of finely powdered calcium carbonate together with 1000 parts water are added at 80° under vigorous agitation. Then 625 parts dichlorobutene and 308 parts liquid HCN are added gradually, while the temperature is maintained below 95°. The liquid reaction product is cooled to 60°, a small amount of chloroform is added, and the adipodinitrile is extracted with an organic solvent. After distillation, 509.5 parts dicyanobutene-2 (95.9% theoretical) are obtained.

The most promising method for the production of adipodinitrile would be the direct addition of 2 molecules of HCN to butadiene, but this process has not yet been realized, although it is mentioned in *Kirk-Othmer's Encyclopedia of Chemical Technology*, 2nd ed., Vol. 6, 1965, p. 1583.

IV. HEXAMETHYLENE DIAMINE MANUFACTURE

Hexamethylene diamine is manufactured exclusively by the hydrogenation of the dinitriles, 1,4-dicyanobutane, or -butene in the presence of catalysts. DuPont (14) suggests palladium as catalyst. In Germany, a catalyst of nickel, copper, and manganese on kieselguhr was used. Another effective catalyst was cobalt oxide mixed with calcium oxide. In all cases, the reaction must be carried out in the presence of excess ammonia to avoid the formation of hexamethylene imine. Figure 2 shows a diagram of the apparatus.

Pure hexamethylene diamine is a colorless crystal mass with strong aminelike odor, melting at 40°; b.p. 100°/20 mm; readily soluble in water, alcohols, ketones.

V. NYLON 66 SALT (AH SALT)

A high-molecular-weight nylon 66 is only obtained if equimolecular amounts of the components are used, since an excess of one of the components would terminate the chain by formation of an acid or amino end group. For this reason, the salt of 1 mole adipic acid and hexamethylene diamine (AH salt) is used as intermediate. The process is shown in Fig. 3.

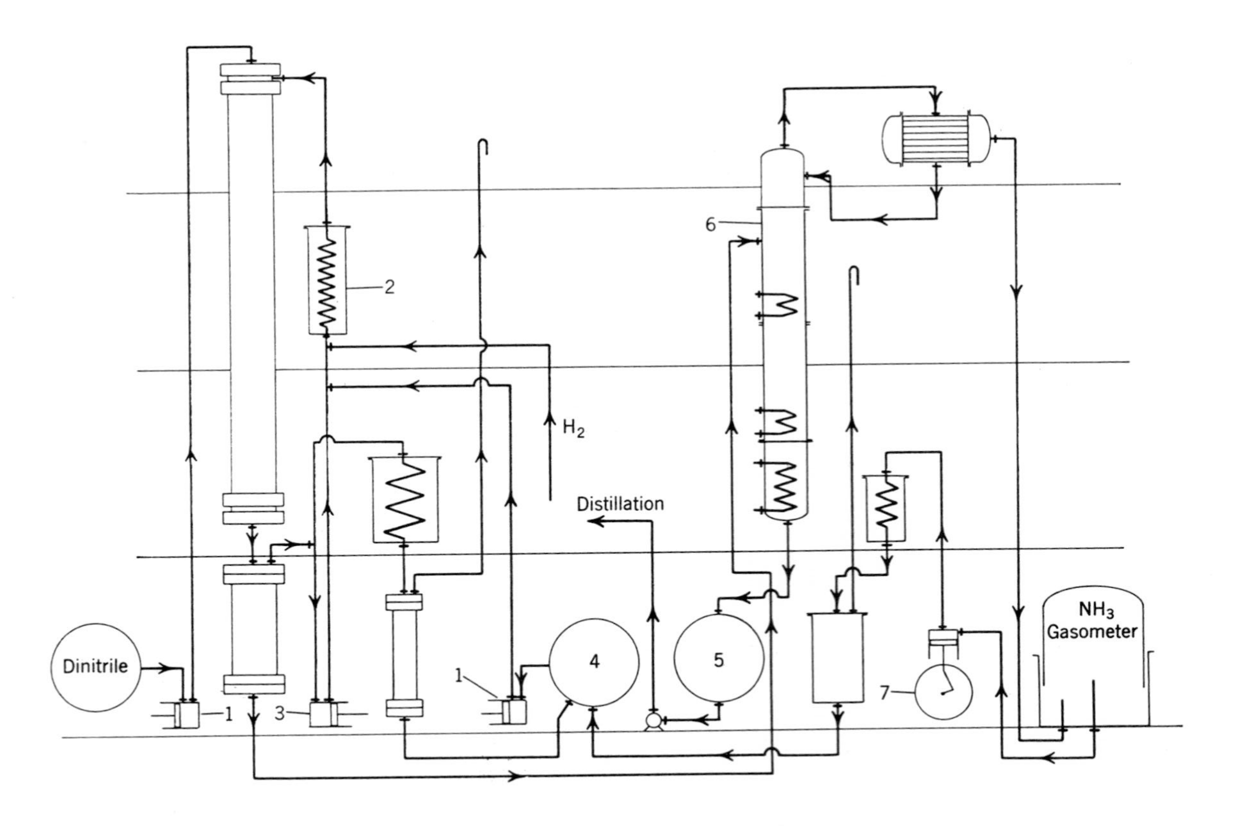

Fig. 2. Hexamethylene diamine plant.

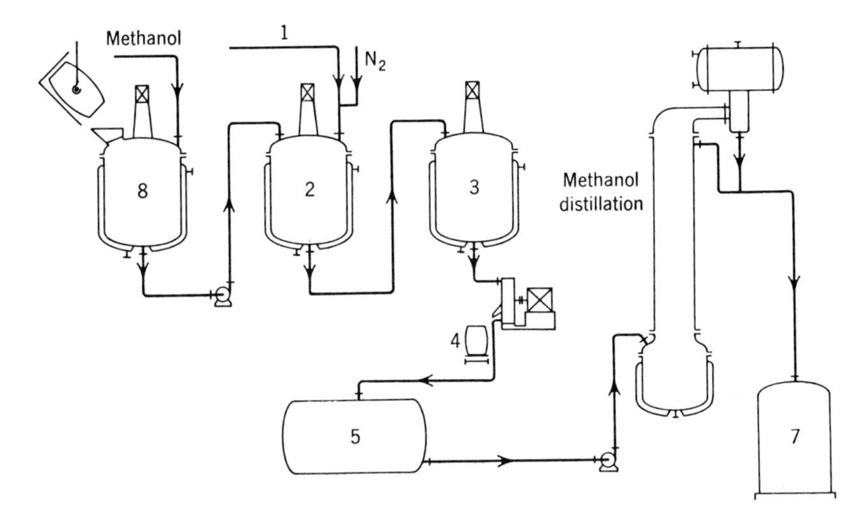

Fig. 3. Nylon 66 salt plant.

The hexamethylene diamine is used as a 60–70% solution and the adipic acid as a 20% solution in boiling methanol. The heat of neutralization is removed by the refluxing methanol. The separated salt is centrifuged and washed with methanol. It contains only small amounts of the alcohol, so that it can be used directly for the polycondensation in aqueous solution. It is stored as a 60% solution in distilled water. If pure adipic acid and pure hexamethylene diamine are available, the two components can be neutralized directly from the aqueous solution of the two components and easily pumped to the storage tank.

VI. POLYCONDENSATION

A. Melt Condensation

The equipment for the polycondensation is illustrated in Fig. 4. To a 50–60% aqueous solution of the nylon salt in distilled water, a small percentage of viscosity stabilizer (0.5% acetic acid) is added, and this solution is pumped into an autoclave lined with stainless steel or enamel which can be heated to 260–280°. The autoclave contains an internal heating coil and an external heating system and normally has a capacity of 500–1500 gal. As heating medium of either Dowtherm or high-pressure steam of 65 atm is used.

Before the condensation starts, the autoclave is purged with very pure nitrogen (less than 0.005% O_2) to avoid discoloration during the

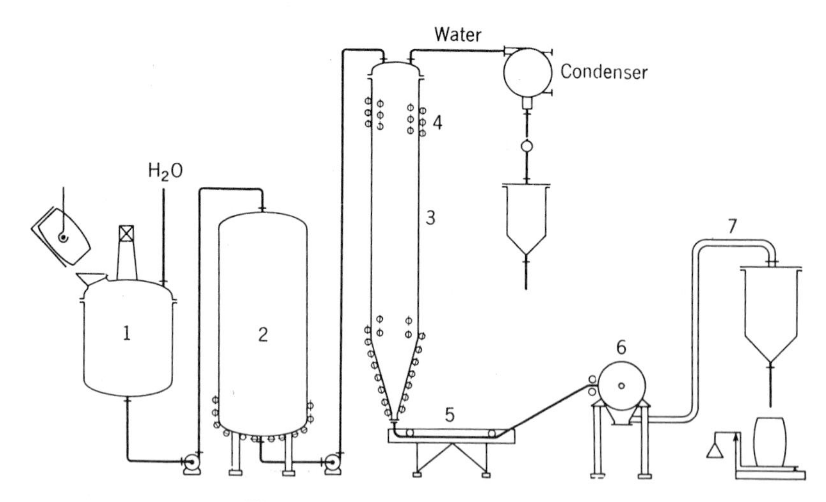

Fig. 4. Nylon 66 salt condensation.

condensation. During the heating of the autoclave, a pressure of 15–16 atm (210–220 psi) is built up. At this point, the pressure is released by opening a valve, and the heating is continued until all water has been distilled off. Toward the end of the distillation, the autoclave is evacuated. The polymer is obtained as a clear, low-viscous melt which is removed from the autoclave by pressure with pure nitrogen. As the melt is not stable at the high temperature, it must be extruded soon after the removal of the water. By using the electrically heated slot in the bottom of the autoclave instead of a wheel, the melt can be conducted directly into a vat filled with cold water, where it solidifies to a ribbon which is broken into small chips; these can be blown directly into the barrels for shipping. As the material is still hot, a special drying process is not necessary. The product contains small amounts of oligomers (20a):

$$\begin{array}{l} CO\cdot(CH_2)_4\cdot CO \\ | \qquad\qquad\quad | \\ NH\cdot(CH_2)_6\cdot NH \end{array} \qquad \begin{array}{l} CO\cdot(CH_2)_4\cdot CO\cdot NH\cdot(CH_2)_6\cdot NH \\ | \qquad\qquad\qquad\qquad\qquad\qquad\quad | \\ NH\cdot(CH_2)_6\cdot NH\cdot CO\cdot(CH_2)_4\cdot CO \end{array}$$

B. Interfacial Condensation

Besides the melt condensation, the so-called "interfacial" polycondensation has found practical interest. It was first discovered by Orthner (21) for the production of polyurethanes from dichloro carboxylic esters of diols with diamines in the presence of alkalies or an excess of diamine. Morgan (22) and Wittbecker and Morgan (23) later prepared polyamides by the same method. The reaction takes place at the interface between a solution of a dicarboxylic acid chloride in a water-insoluble organic solvent and a water solution of a diamine containing an acid acceptor. The product formed on the surface of the interface can be continuously removed until the entire amount of the components is used up. The reaction is so rapid that a precise equivalency of reactants in the solution is not necessary, and high-molecular-weight products are obtained. By this method, even polymers which are unstable at their melt temperatures can be easily prepared. Copolymers can be obtained in the same way. If the reaction is carried out under stirring, the product is obtained in the form of a white powder. A detailed description of this important method of polycondensation is given in the book by Morgan (24).

VII. CHARACTERIZATION OF THE POLYMER

Nylon 66 melts at 251–252° and gives a colorless melt with low viscosity. It is hygroscopic and must therefore be protected against moisture on storage. It is turbid because of crystallinity. It has the best mechanical properties of all polyamides of the type dicarboxylic acid/diamine. Its most important application is in fiber-spinning, but its use as a plastic material for shaped articles is also of great importance. For the latter application, one prefers a product with a higher molecular weight which can be obtained by using a smaller amount of acetic acid during the polycondensation. In Germany, 0.2% acetic or adipic acid is used.

All physical properties of nylon 66 depend on the molecular weight; this is especially the case with tensile strength as seen in Fig. 5. For the

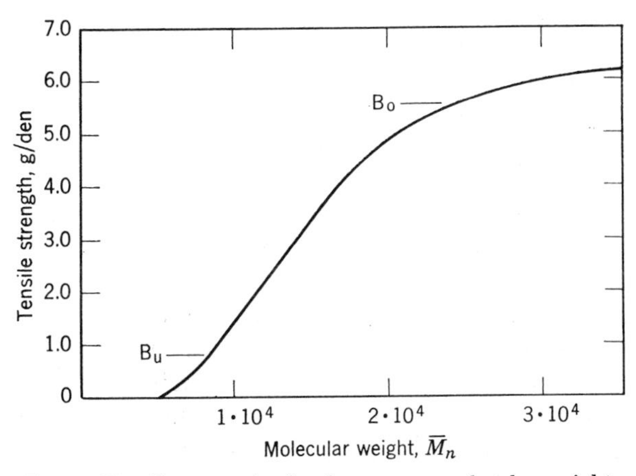

Fig. 5. Tensile strength of nylon versus molecular weight.

determination of the molecular weight, all the usual methods have been investigated: cryoscopy, osmotic pressure, ultracentrifuge sedimentation, viscosimetry, isothermal distillation, light scattering, and turbidometric and end-group titration. We have to distinguish between number-average molecular weight $\overline{M}_n$ and weight-average molecular weight $\overline{M}_w$. The latter is best obtained by light scattering or ultracentrifuge sedimentation.

For the characterization of Nylon 66, the viscosity average molecular weight is used very often. It is the simplest and most generally used method, although it is not an absolute one and has to be calibrated for each polymer–solvent system by another absolute method such as osmotic pressure. Normally, the intrinsic viscosity

$$[\eta] = \lim \frac{\eta_{sp}}{c}, \qquad \eta c_{sp} \rightarrow 0 \tag{3}$$

is used, where $\eta_{sp} = (\eta_{r-1})$ and η_r = viscosity of solution/viscosity of solvent $= \eta/\eta_0$. In all these definitions, the concentration c is measured in g/100 cc. The solvent and concentration must always be specified in addition to the numerical value.

The empirical relationship between the intrinsic viscosity and the molecular weight of a high polymer can be expressed by the formula

$$[\eta] = K\overline{M}_v^{\alpha}$$

where K and α are constants for any given polymer–solvent system and $\overline{M}_v$ is the viscosity average molecular weight. Calculations have shown that this equation is of the form predicted by theory, and that α can be expected to vary between the limits of 0.5 and 1, depending upon the shape of the polymer molecule in solution. The determinations of α by different researchers for various polymer–solvent systems have shown values between the limits of 0.5 and 1.

The values of K and α for a given polymer–solvent system can be determined by measuring the intrinsic viscosity of homogeneous fractions whose molecular weights have been determined by osmotic pressure or light scattering.

As solvents for the determination of the viscosity molecular weight, sulfuric acid, *m*-cresol, and chloral hydrate can be used. Concentrated sulfuric acid at normal temperature does not influence the viscosity on standing for hours. The values for K and α which are published in the literature differ considerably. Taylor (25) gives a K value of 11 $(K \cdot 10^4)$ for nylon 66 in 90% formic acid solution and 0.72 for α. Normally the molecular weight of technical nylon 66 lies between 10,000 and 20,000. The inherent viscosity

$$\eta_{inh} = \ln \eta_{rel}/C$$

for polyamides is 0.8 in 1% solution. For comparison of different products it is normally sufficient to determine only the relative viscosity.

The solution behavior of nylon 66 was studied in different solvents by Elias and Schumacher (26). Solution properties and molecular weights were determined by measurements of light scattering, osmotic pressure, solution viscosity, and by end group determinations. The relationship between intrinsic viscosity $[\eta]$ and viscosity average of molecular weight M_v can be expressed by formulas of the type

$$[\eta] = A + K \cdot M_v^{\alpha} \text{ (ml/g)}$$

for 25° and a range of molecular weights between 146 (adipic acid) and about 50,000. The following values for the constants A, K, and a were found: 90% formic acid (2.5, 0.0132, 0.873); 95% sulfuric acid (2.5, 0.0249, 0.832); *m*-cresol (1.5, 0.0353, 0.792), $2M$ KCl in 90% formic acid (0, 0.142, 0.559); $2.3M$ KCl in 90% formic acid (0, 0.253, 0.500); and $0.1M$ sodium formate in 90% formic acid (1.0, 0.0516, 0.687). Divergent values of some data of the literature could be shown to depend on an excessively small range of molecular weights, the use of molecular weight averages unfit for calibration such as end-group determinations, and on wrong assumptions for the calculation of intrinsic viscosities from one concentration, i.e., of nylon 66 associated in dichloroacetic acid. The effect can be explained by intermolecular solvatophobic bonding between the methylene groups of the polymer molecules. A comparison of thermodynamic properties and dimensions points to intramolecular solvatophobic bonding of nylon 66 in other solvents.

The values characteristic for the theta state were calculated by the theories of Stockmayer and Fixman (27) and Krigbaum (28). The values of K_θ by both methods agree quite well. Exceptions are discussed. The molecular weight dependence of the second virial coefficient A_2 can be expressed by

$$A_2 = \text{const } M^{-\gamma}$$

for measurements in $2M$ KCl in 90% formic acid. The exponent γ exhibits a value of 1.42 in the range of molecular weights from 2000 to 16,000, much too high to be explained by existing theories. For molecular weights higher than 16,000 the value of γ decreases. All measurements in any solvents can be expressed by a formula

$$(A_2)_v M_v/[\eta] = 1.90\ (1 - \alpha^{-3}) \qquad (7)$$

if A_2 is taken as the viscosity average and if the expansion factor α is calculated by the theory of Krigbaum.

The ratio of weight average to number average of molecular weights was $M_w/M_n = 1.80$ for four technical products, about 2.3 for samples synthesized with more than 1.2:1 molar excess of adipic acid, and about 1.6 if an excess of hexamethylene diamine was used.

A knowledge of the *melt viscosity* is required for the design of optimum spinning conditions if the nylon 66 is converted into fibers. The relationship between melt viscosity and weight-average molecular weight is therefore extremely helpful. Flory and co-workers obtained the following empirical relationship

$$\log \eta_m = A + B\overline{M}_w^{1/2} + \frac{C}{T} \tag{8}$$

where η_m is the melt viscosity measured at an absolute temperature T, $\overline{M}_w$ is the weight-average molecular weight, and A, B, and C are constant for a given polymer. The relation fits remarkably well over a wide range of molecular weights for linear polyamides. The values of the constants A, B, and C can be determined by measuring the melt viscosity of a series of homogeneous fractions, whose molecular weights have been measured by other methods (osmometry or light scattering). The melt viscosity can be measured by the falling sphere method or by the rate of flow of the molten polymer through a capillary tube (29,30).

VIII. END GROUP DETERMINATION

A simple and useful method for determining the number-average molecular weight of a polymer is to measure the number of end groups present in a given weight of polymer. As nylon 66 has titratable NH_2 and COOH groups at the end of the chain and is not branched, this method can be used for the determination of the molecular weight with the formula

$$\overline{M}_n = \frac{\text{(weight of polymer) (no. end groups/molecule)}}{\text{total no. measured end groups}}$$

The end group titration method is only accurate for molecular weights of up to about 20,000. In polymers of higher molecular weight, the end group concentration becomes too low to be measured accurately by normal methods.

The method has proved to be invaluable for measuring the molecular weight of nylon 66; the number-average molecular weight of the

TABLE I. Consumption of HCl and NaOH by Nylon 66

Sample	Molecular weight (titrimetric), acid and alkali	Molecular weight (titrimetric), acid only	Molecular weight (viscosimetric)	Remarks
1	11,000	6,523	10,450	
2	17,700	11,200	18,088	
3	22,200	17,500	19,950	
4	4,520	13,862	3,445	Excess of carboxylic groups
5	3,666	1,942	5,080	Excess of amino end groups

polymer is about 10,000 and hence is outside the range of the osmotic method.

Rafikow and Korshak (31) determined the consumption of HCl and NaOH by nylon 66 and found the data indicated in Table I. From the consumption of acid (a) and NaOH (b) the molecular weight was determined by the formula

$$M_n = 200{,}000/(a + b) \tag{10}$$

The values are comparable with those determined by the viscosity method of Staudinger. The absorption of hydrochloric acid was studied by several investigators.

Boulton (32) investigated the absorption of some acids by nylon 66 whereby the results were obtained which are shown in Fig. 6.

TABLE II. Determination of M_n of Nylon 66 in 90% Formic Acid by Viscosimetric Methods

Sample	M_n (found)	$[\eta]$ (found)
1	7,800	0.66
2	9,000	0.75
3	9,800	0.78
4	11,700	0.93
5	13,600	1.01
6	20,000	1.39
7	22,500	1.60
8	24,400	1.76

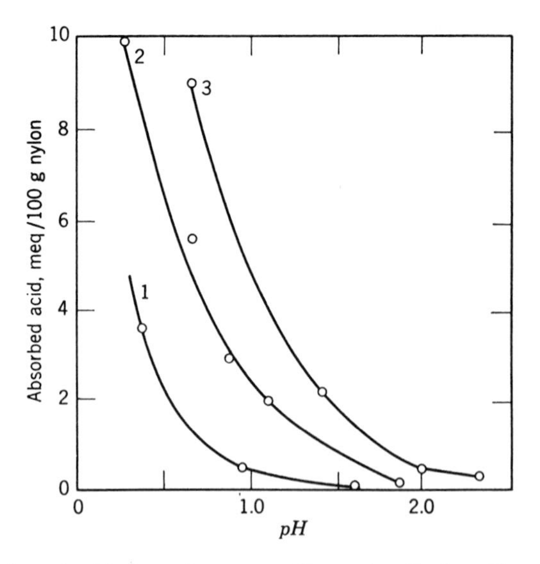

Fig. 6. Absorption of acids by nylon yarn. Curve *1*, sulfuric acid; curve *2*, benzo sulfonic acid; curve *3*, dodecyl sulfonic acid.

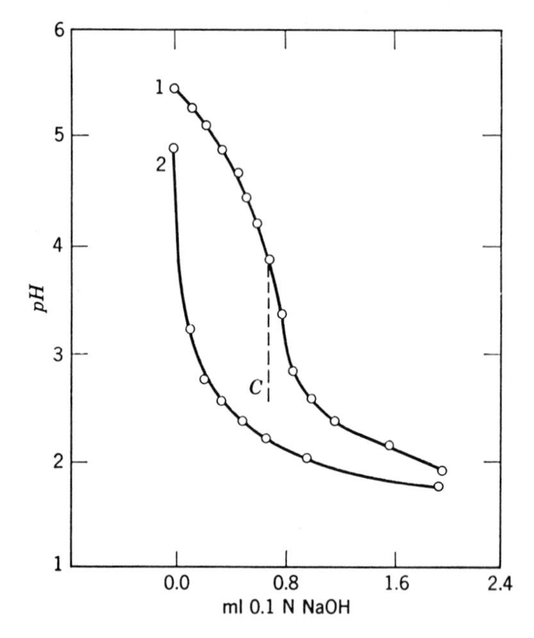

Fig. 7. Molecular weight determination of nylon by potentiometric titration of the amino end groups. Curve *1*, nylon sample; curve *2*, blank test. *C*, equivalence point.

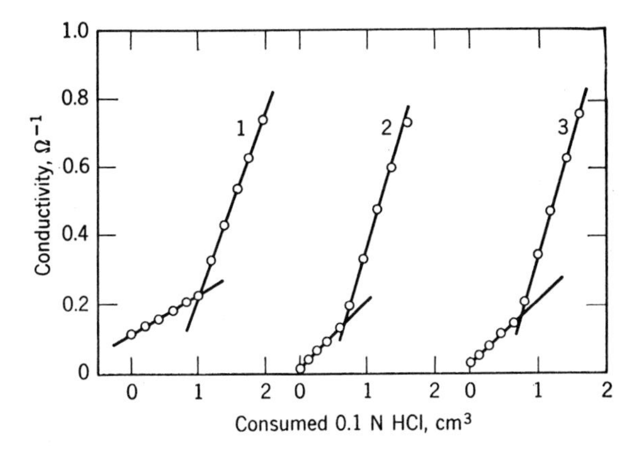

Fig. 8. Molecular weight determination of nylon by conductometric titration of the amino end groups. Curve *1*, AH salt; curve *2*, low polymer; curve *3*, technical nylon.

Waltz and Taylor (33) determined the amino end groups of nylon 66 in phenol and the carboxyl end groups in boiling benzyl alcohol by potentiometric and conductometric titration. They obtained the curves shown in Figs. 7 and 8. The data obtained are in accordance with those by viscosimetric methods in 90% formic acid as solvent, as is shown in Table II, as well as the melting point of nylon 66. This points to the fact that the product is very uniform. Korshak and Samjatina (34) prove this by fractionation of several nylon products, as shown in Table III. From these data it seems that nylon 66 is uniform, to an extent of 85%. The titration values give much higher molecular weights.

TABLE III. Fractionation of Several Nylon Products (34)

Starting material	Percentage	Molecular weight (viscosimetric)	Molecular weight calculated from Korshak titration
Starting material	100	9,620	14,300
Fraction 1	28.6	10,811	21,700
Fraction 2	28.8	9,680	18,100
Fraction 3	28.5	9,500	16,100
Fraction 4	4.7	7,514	11,800
Fraction 5	7.3	5,701	10,400
Fraction 6	2.1	2,803	

Many other authors have used this method (35–39). (A detailed description of all known methods for the determination of the molecular weights of polyamides can be found in the book of W. N. Dawydoff, V. E. B. Verlag Technik, Berlin (1959).)

IX. MOLECULAR WEIGHT DETERMINATION BY OSMOTIC PRESSURE

Nylon 66 is soluble only in strong polar solvents such as sulfuric acid, formic acid, acetic acid, phenols, and cresols for which suitable membranes and osmometers are difficult to find. Successful measurements by the static method were reported by Hoshino (40) and Nichols (41) with the modified two-chamber osmometers of Herzog and Spurlin (42).

Schumacher and Elias (43) described dynamic osmotic determinations. According to measurements of a sample of nylon 66 in 90% formic acid at 25° and in *m*-cresol at 60°, the number-average molecular weight can be determined by dynamic osmometry at glass membranes. The molecular weights thus obtained agree with those of end group determinations within the limits of error.

X. GLASS TRANSITION TEMPERATURE

The glass transition temperature T_g or second-order transition temperature is determined by measuring the change in some physical properties of the polymer (e.g., thermal coefficient of expansion, specific volume, dynamic modulus of elasticity, heat capacity, or dielectric constant). A change in slope of the curves so obtained is regarded as the glass transition temperature. For nylon 66 the glass transition temperature has been determined as 50° and the melting point as 265° (44).

Among the other data for the characterization of nylon 66, the thermal properties play an important part.

XI. MOLECULAR WEIGHT DISTRIBUTION

For the characterization of polymers, the molecular weight distribution is sometimes important. By fractionation of a Nylon 66 solution with a nonsolvent and plotting the weight of molecules in each fraction against the measured molecular weight, the molecular distribution can be determined. It is normally represented in graphical form, as shown in Fig. 9.

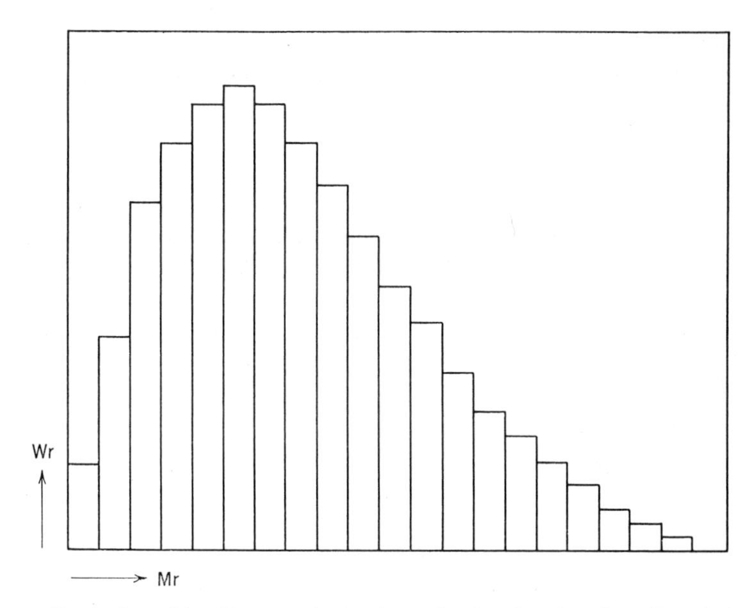

Fig. 9. Typical steplike diagram obtained on plotting fraction data directly in the form of a differential weight distribution diagram.

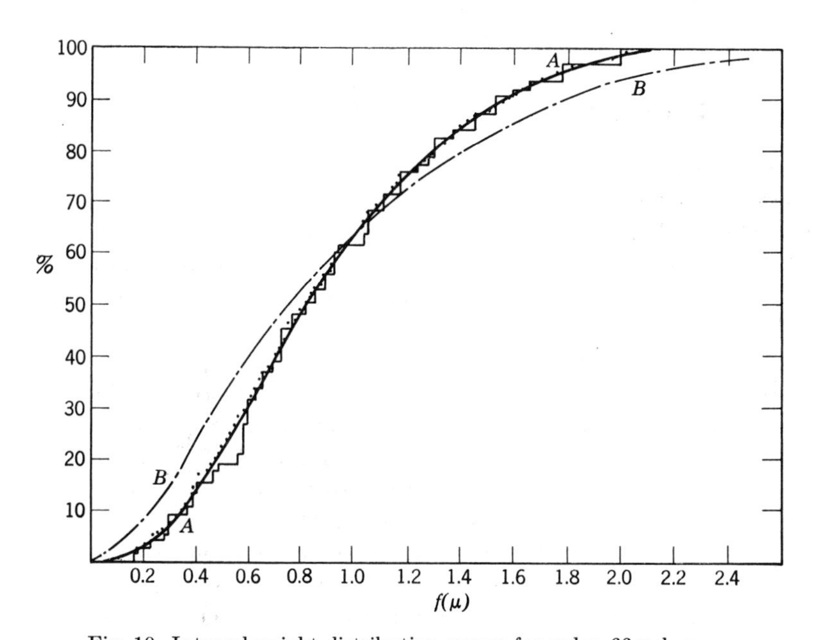

Fig. 10. Integral weight distribution curves for nylon 66 polymer.

Figure 10 shows a typical integral weight distribution curve, obtained by Taylor (45). He obtained the following relationship between intrinsic viscosity and number-average molecular weight:

$$\overline{M}_n = 13{,}000\ [\eta]^{1.39}$$

Curve *A* shows weight per cent against intrinsic viscosity in formic acid solution. The fractionation can be made using fractional precipitation or fractional solution. A continuous fractionation, using phenol–water, is described by Duveau and Piguet (46). Furthermore, one may use the chromatographic methods, the molecular distillation technique, or the method of ultrafiltration through graded membranes—the partition between two immiscible solvents and the turbidimetric titration—but one must bear in mind that, with respect to molecular weight, completely homogeneous fractions can never be obtained.

A detailed description of the methods has been published by Cragg and Hammerschlag (47).

For the comparison of the molecular weight distribution of a number of samples of the same polymer, the turbidimetric titration is useful (48). The method is based upon fractional precipitation, where a very dilute solution of the polymer is titrated with a nonsolvent.

A new and elegant method for the determination of the molecular distribution is gel permeation chromatography, about which little information has as yet been published.

XII. MOLECULAR STRUCTURE

As with all fiber-forming polymers, nylon 66 forms long chains of high molecular weight, normally exceeding 10,000. The structure of nylon 66 is practically linear, as can be shown by x-ray measurements. As do most fiber-forming polymers, nylon 66 has a two-phase structure, and infrared spectra show some typical bands of hydrogen bonding (3800–2200 cm^{-1}). Perturbed NH stretching frequencies, both in the fundamental (49) and overtone (50) regions (3308 and 6523 waves/cm respectively), are evidence of hydrogen bond formation; the fact that in sheets exhibiting plane as well as chain orientation the dichroism of the 3308 NH band is very similar to that of the symmetrical CH_2 band, is taken as evidence that the NH bond is parallel to the bisector of the H–C–H angle; this direction lies near the plane of the sheet.

Detailed studies on the infrared spectra of polyamides have been published by Schnell (51), Cannon (52), and especially Heidemann and Zahn (53). These authors synthesized nylon 66 which was deuterated in the α-position to the amide group either in the amine (N-vicinal) or acid (CO-vicinal) component by interfacial polycondensation using either hexamethylene-diamine-1.1.6.6,N,N'-d_8, or adipoyl-2.2.5.5-d_4 chloride. The infrared spectra of films made from these samples showed clearly the following relatively strong bands of the nylon 66 spectrum which could be assigned:

Scissoring mode of the N-vicinal CH_2-group at 1474/cm, scissoring mode of the CO-vicinal CH_2-group at 1416/cm, twisting mode of the CO-vicinal CH_2-group at 1198/cm and twisting mode of the N-vicinal CH_2-group at 1179/cm. The position of the scissoring modes of these groups is dependent on the conformation relative to the amide group. As a result of rotation out of the ideal *trans*-conformation, the $\delta CH_2(N)$ and $\delta CH_2(CO)$ coincide at 1435/cm. The difference in band positions and intensities as well as their dependence on conformation is qualitatively explained. Based on these results one must postulate an intramolecular interaction between the CH-groups adjacent to the amide group on the amine side and the π-electron system of the amide group.

X-ray diffraction methods give only detailed information if the specimen studied is crystalline. Therefore, only drawn specimens will show the crystalline regions which are oriented with a molecular chain axis parallel to the direction of drawing. A bristle of nylon 66 after drawing exhibits the picture shown in Fig. 11 (54). The corresponding x-ray diagrams *a*, *b*, and *c* were made at the corresponding spots of the fiber. The draw ratio of nylon 66 is about 400%. Incomplete drawing shows a typical shoulder effect (Fig. 12). The corresponding x-ray diagrams are shown in Fig. 13.

The x-ray diagram of the drawn nylon 66 allows the determination of the identity period in the direction of the chain axis. The chains have a plane zigzag configuration.

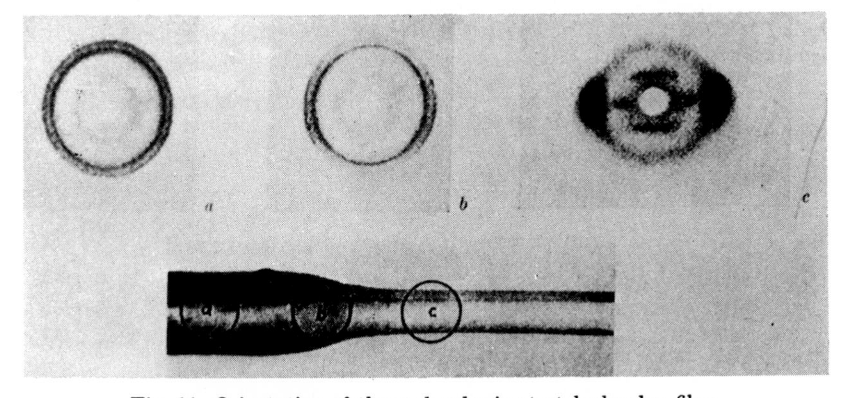

Fig. 11. Orientation of the molecules in stretched nylon fiber.

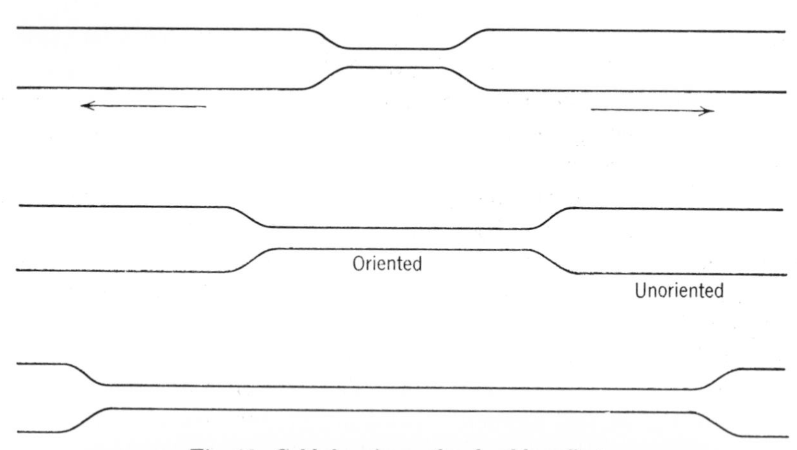

Fig. 12. Cold-drawing: the shoulder effect.

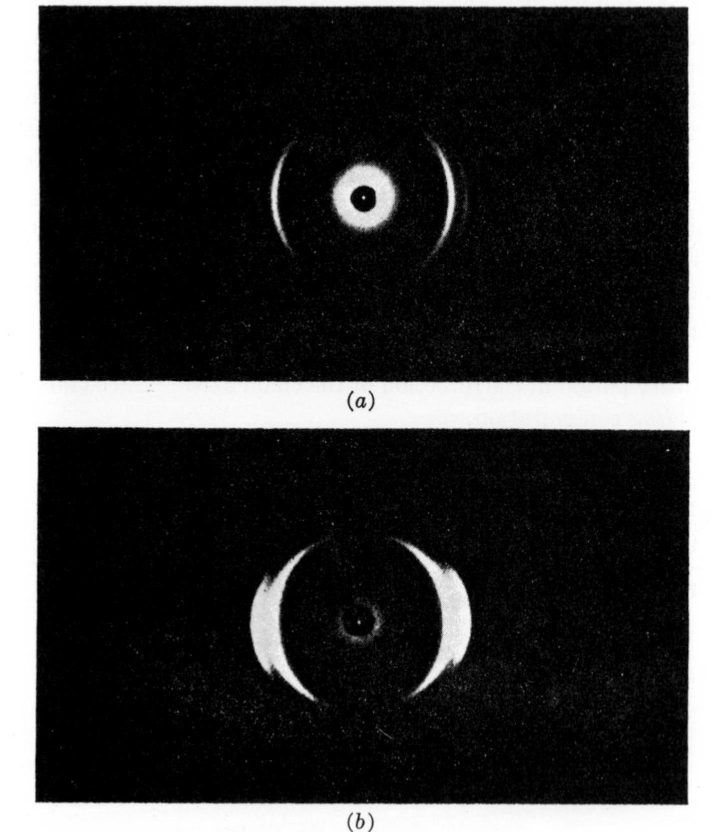

(a)

(b)

Fig. 13 X-ray diffraction photographs of nylon 66 yarns of different draw ratios. (a) Undrawn; (b) drawn 100%.

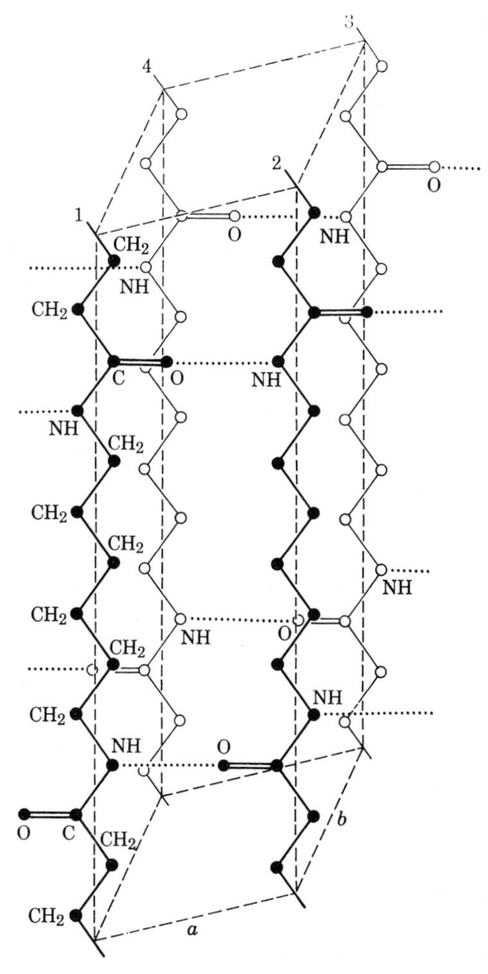

Fig. 14. Structure of α-crystal of Nylon 66, showing hydrogen-bonded sheets.

There exist two crystal forms, α and β, in normal specimens. Bunn and Garner (55) and Brill (54) have shown that the fiber diagram of the α-form of Nylon 66 can be described by a triclinic axis system with a = 4.9 Å, b = 5.4 Å, c (fiber axis) = 17.2 Å, $\alpha = 48.5°$, $\beta = 77°$, $\gamma = 63.5°$. The molecules are fixed by hydrogen bonds to form sheets, and a simple packing of these sheets gives rise to the triclinic cell of the α structure. Information on the β-form is scanty, but it is interesting to find that the crystal structures of these polyamides appear to correspond in several aspects to that of natural β-keratin (Fig. 14).

The evidence for hydrogen bonding is that the CO groups of one molecule are always opposite to NH groups of neighboring groups, whereby the distance between oxygen and nitrogen atoms is 2.8 Å, which is shorter than that expected for van der Waals forces and agrees well with distances in other crystals having hydrogen bonds between those groups.

The determination of atomic position in the unit cell has completely substantiated the expected molecular structures (54,55), and infrared absorption spectra are also consistent with these crystal structures (50,56). The possibility of other groupings in the amorphous regions cannot be excluded.

XIII. FIBER-FORMING CONDITIONS

All chain polymers of high molecular weight which soften below the decomposition temperatures can be spun into fibers by suitable methods. Nylon 66 has been found to give fibers and monofilaments for textiles or other miscellaneous uses of high quality. In fact, nylon 66 gives fibers of high tensile strength, great flexibility, and abrasion resistance and is superior in this respect to nearly all other known fibers.

As mentioned before, the molecular orientation of the fiber is essential for good mechanical properties. The molecules or sections of molecules of good fibers are not only parallel to the fiber axis, but are also arranged side by side with the full free dimensional order. Nylon 66 and other polyamide fibers are highly crystalline.

The factors which influence essential fiber properties are described by Atlas and Mark (57).

XIV. SPINNING OF NYLON 66

For the rapid development of the nylon 66 fiber, it was essential that a new spinning process could be applied: the melt-spinning process. It was first developed for nylon 66. Due to the sufficient stability of the melt and its low viscosity, nylon can be spun in the molten state with unusual velocity (up to 2000 m/min). This method makes nylon spinning very economical. For endless fibers, the apparatus shown in Fig. 15 is used. The feed in the form of small chips is filled into a container (Fig. 16) whose base has a coil of stainless steel (Fig. 17) heated above the melting point of the polymer by Dowtherm or superheated steam. The molten polymer flows through the grid and, after passing a series of sieves filled with pure sand, to the spinneret (Fig. 18). The melt is pumped through this system and solidifies immediately on contact with the air. To assist the solidifying, a cross air blast is applied.

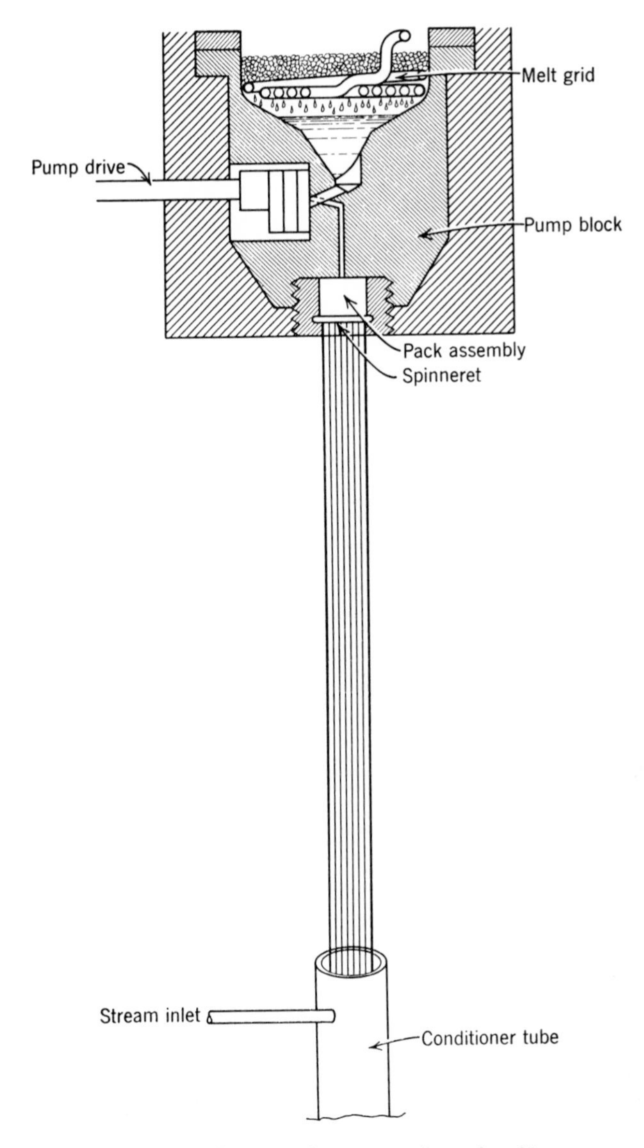

Fig. 15. Melt-spinning process for nylon 66.

As the fiber at the exit of the spinneret is completely free from water, it has to be treated with a certain amount of steam in a chamber and then with a preparation of either mineral oil or another substance before it is wound on the bobbin. The spinneret normally has a certain number of holes for 24–48 fibers which are brought together to a single fiber and

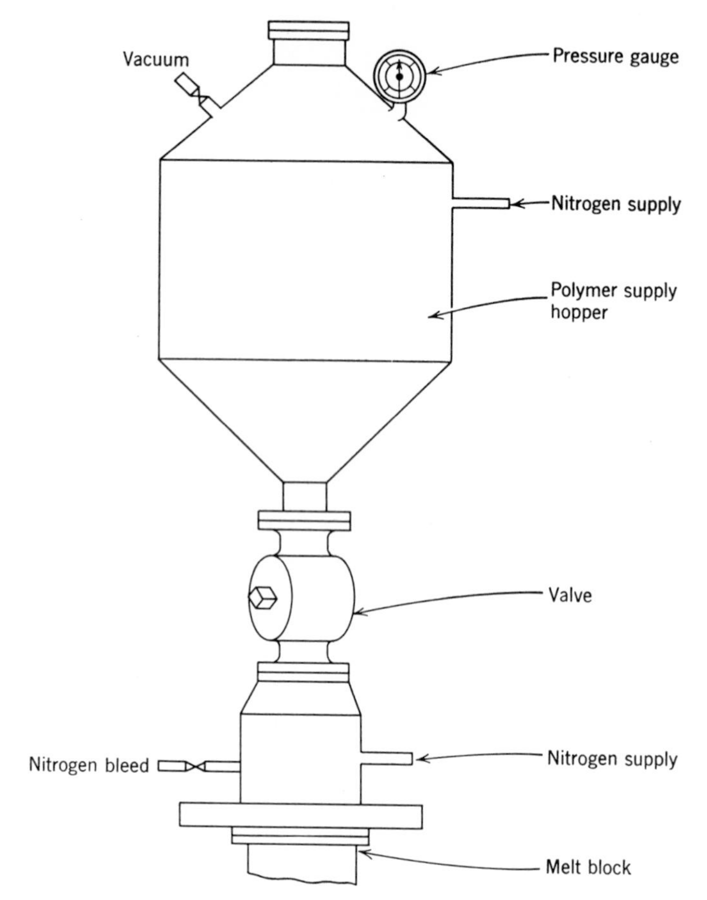

Fig. 16. Container for the melt-spinning process.

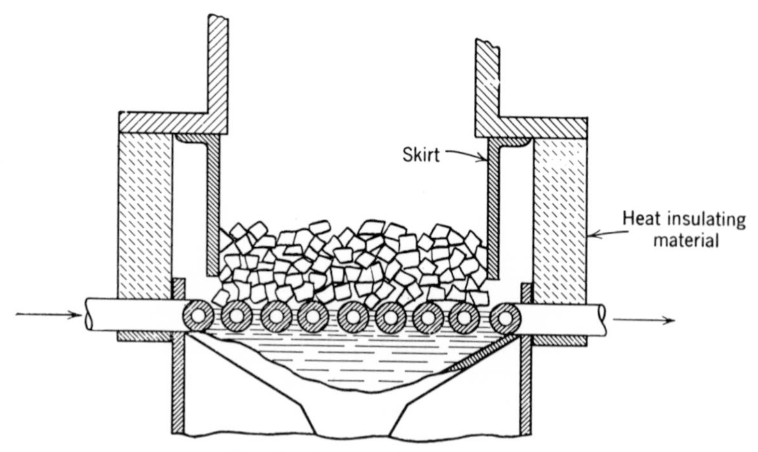

Fig. 17. Base of the container.

then stretched in the cold to about 400%. Only by this process, which causes a parallel orientation of the chain molecules, are the outstanding properties of the fiber obtained. The stretching begins with the formation of a typical shoulder, which on further stretching disappears. Higher temperatures allow to stretch the fiber with moderate stress. The equipment for the stretching process is seen from Fig. 19.

The fiber comes from a pair of feed rolls and is wound around a highly polished rod of agate which acts as a brake and is then wound around another pair of rolls, moving about four times velocity of the first pair before winding on the bobbin. The stretching process decreases the

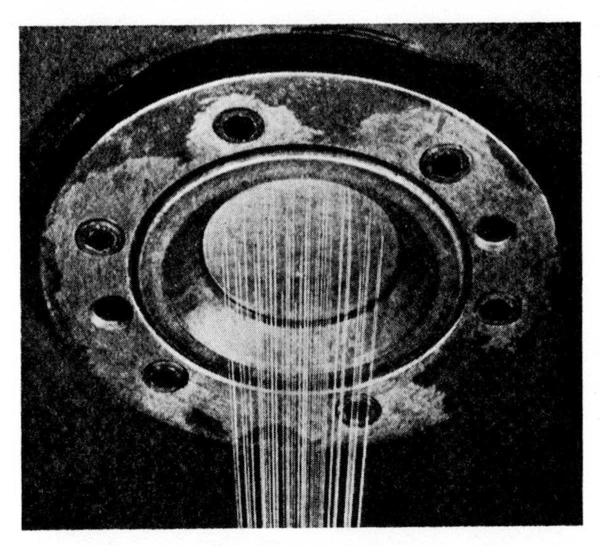

Fig. 18. Spinneret.

elongation which is necessary for the production of tire cords. Higher temperatures allow additional stretching after the cold stretching. For better heat stability, the stretched fiber is treated with steam. Crimping can be achieved mechanically by passing the tow of the fibers through a gear or by treatment with hot water, eventually with dilute sulfuric acid or phenols. Delustering of the fibers is normally made by adding titanium dioxide during the polycondensation or by adding it to the melt before the extrusion.

The pumps used for the spinning are of special construction adapted to the high temperature. They are gear pumps, as shown in Fig. 20. Normally the speed of spinning is between 800 and 1200 m/min.

Fig. 19. Draw twister for nylon.

XV. PROPERTIES OF POLYAMIDE FIBERS

Commercial production of nylon 66 began in 1939 (58). The largest market for the fiber is in stockings, where natural silk has been completely replaced by nylon. Blends with wool and cotton have a large market. Other uses for the fiber include rope production and tire cords, especially for airplanes.

A. Mechanical Properties

The resistance to deformation is generally defined by the modulus which depends on the type of stress to which the fiber is subjected, the

Fig. 20. Gear pump for nylon spinning.

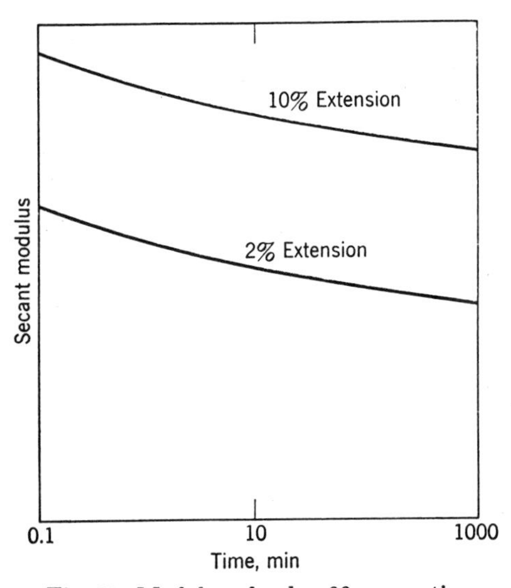

Fig. 21. Modulus of nylon 66 versus time.

load-extension-time conditions, the ambient conditions of temperature and humidity to which the fiber is exposed, and the manufacturing and processing of the fiber. Young's modulus is 30 g/den per 100% extension, similar to that of wool and acrylic fibers. Bending modulus and torsional rigidity modulus are low, even by comparison with the tensile modulus. The modulus depends, of course, on the conditions of loading or extension. It decreases with loading time as with other fibers, because the contribution of primary and secondary creep to the observed deformation is greater at longer loading times (Fig. 21).

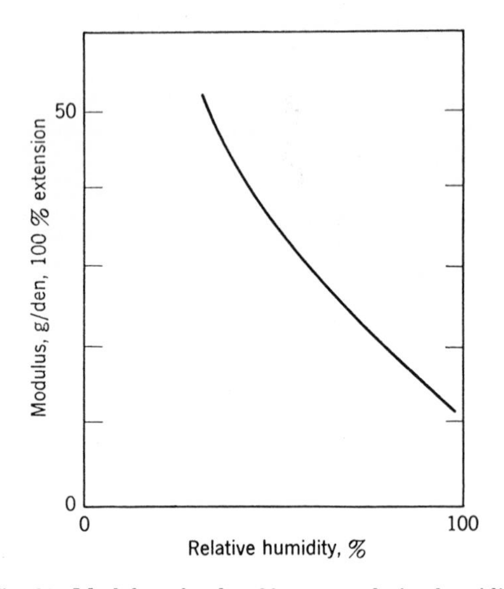

Fig. 22. Modulus of nylon 66 versus relative humidity.

Moisture has less influence on the mechanical properties of nylon 66 than of other fibers, due to nylon's high crystallinity and relatively hydrophobic character, as seen from Fig. 22. The torsional rigidity of Nylon 66 in saturated air is nearly 40% of that of the dry fiber compared with 10% in wool. The modulus of nylon 66 drops from 48 to 30 g/den per 100% extension after conversion of the yarn to fabric and to 12 g/den per 100% extension after boiling the fabric. Relaxation by water or heat treatment below 150° also reduces the modulus. With increasing molecular orientation by the stretching process, the modulus also increases. A 10% increase in the drawing will increase the modulus by about 20%. Disorientation will therefore decrease the modulus.

B. Tensile Strength

Nylon 66 has high tenacity. Depending on the degree of molecular orientation, it can vary between 6 and 10 g/den and may range even higher. It depends on the conditions and time of loading, the temperature, and the humidity, although the latter conditions exert no great influence. The effect of humidity on breaking extension is greater than on breaking load, and the effect of temperature is greater at high humidity than at low. Cold drawing increases the tensile strength consider-

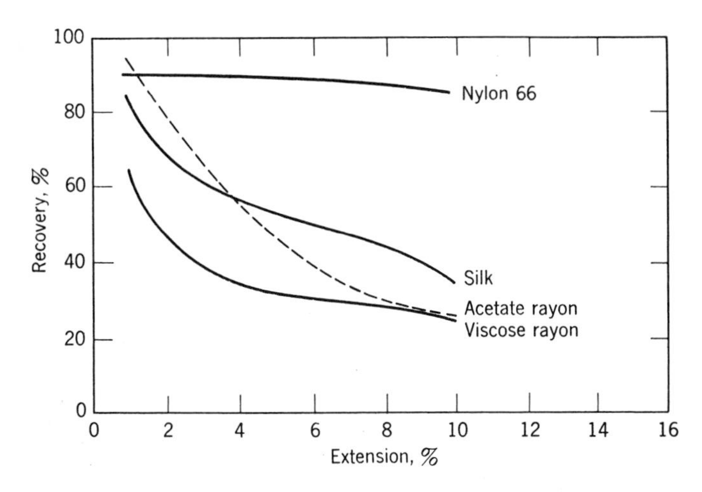

Fig. 23. Recovery of various fibers as a function of extension.

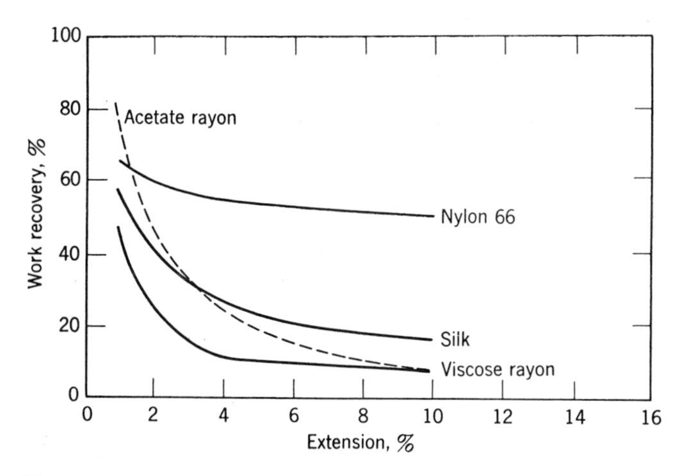

Fig. 24. Work recovery of various fibers as a function of extension.

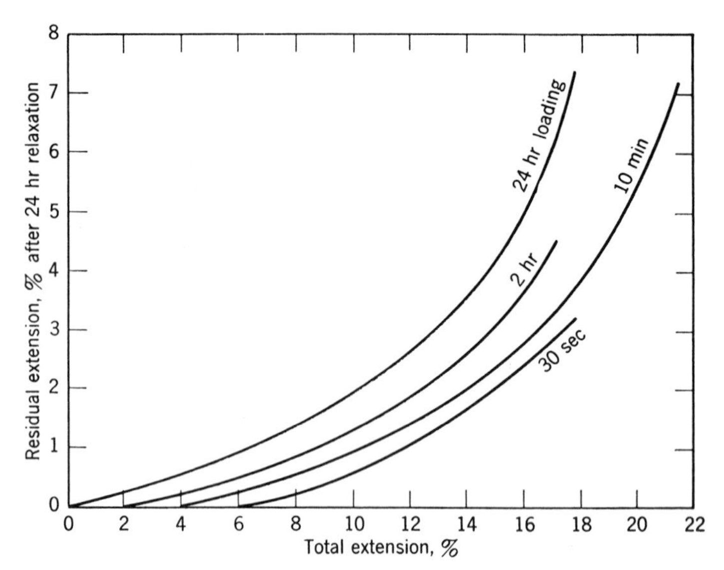

Fig. 25. Effect of total extension after 24 hr recovery and various loading times for nylon 66 yarn.

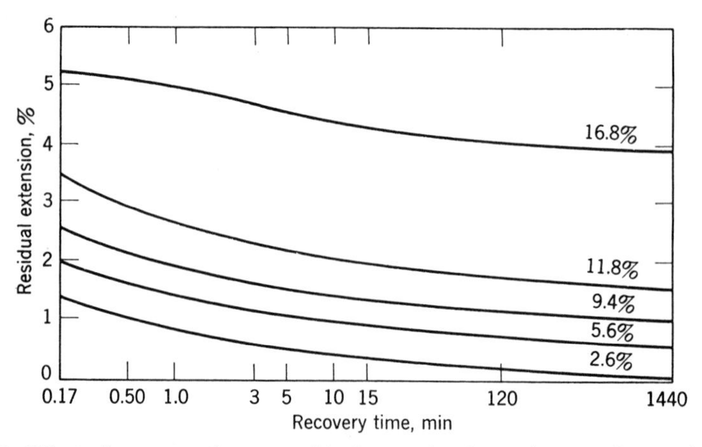

Fig. 26. Effect of recovery time on residual extension for various total extensions of nylon 66.

ably. A 10% increase in cold drawing may increase the tensile strength by 25%.

C. Elastic Recovery

All fibers under stress undergo a delayed extension. The immediate extension of a fiber is immediately recoverable, due to the elasticity. Nylon 66 fibers show an almost complete recovery, even at high loads, as shown by the diagrams in Figs. 23–26. The extent of recovery depends also upon the duration of the load and the time allowed for recovery The cumulative extension in a cyclic loading test is shown in Fig. 27.

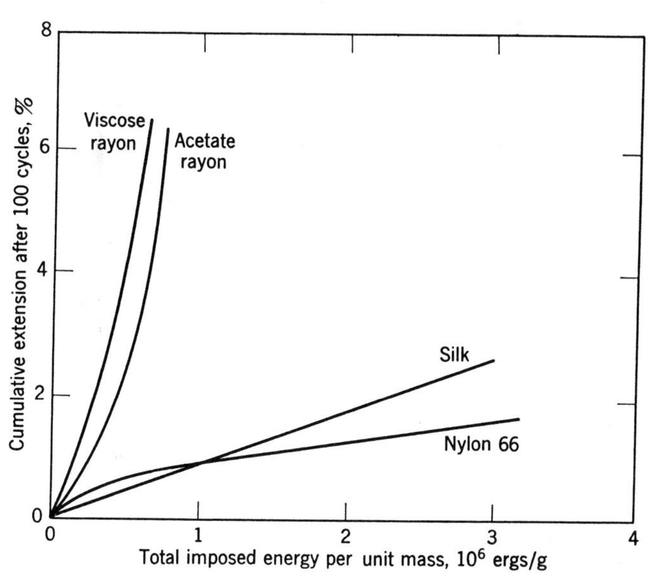

Fig. 27. Cumulative extension of various fibers for the same total imposed energy.

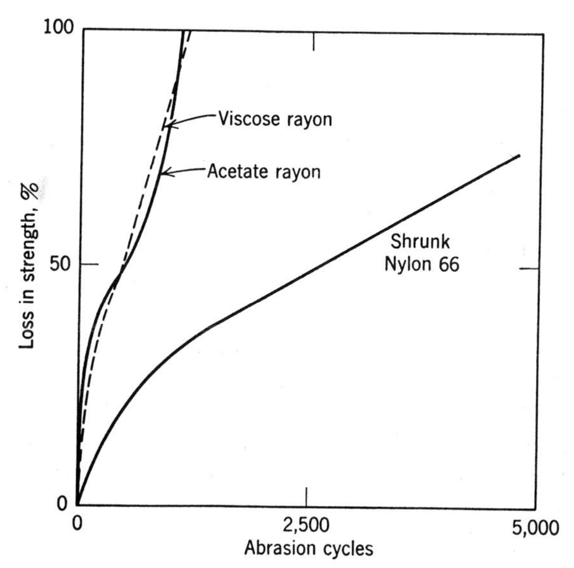

Fig. 28. Loss in strength of fabrics from various fibers on the Taber abrasion tester.

D. Abrasion Resistance

In abrasion resistance nylon 66 and other polyamides surpass nearly all other fibers. The loss in strength of fabrics from various fibers on the Taber abrasion tester is shown in Fig. 28.

E. Moisture Regain

The moisture regain depends, of course, on the relative humidity, as is shown in the diagram (Fig. 29) of Speakman and Saville (59). With increasing molecular orientation and increase in temperature, moisture regain is reduced.

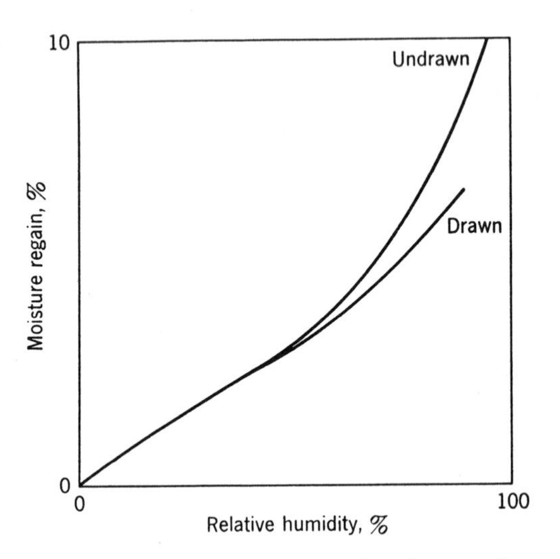

Fig. 29. Moisture regain of drawn and undrawn nylon 66.

F. Dimensional Stability

Nylon 66 will swell in some polar compounds, such as phenols and lower aliphatic acids (especially formic acid), and dissolve in concentrated solution.

Molecular orientation influences the rate of uptake of the swelling agent by polyamide fibers, insofar as the phenol uptake and moisture regain are slightly reduced on cold drawing.

An irreversible change of the fibers is caused when an undrawn nylon 66 yarn is put in water and dried after wash. There occurs a reversible swelling and an irreversible shrinkage. The irreversible shrinkage is shown in Fig. 30. Similar behavior can be caused by heating the yarn,

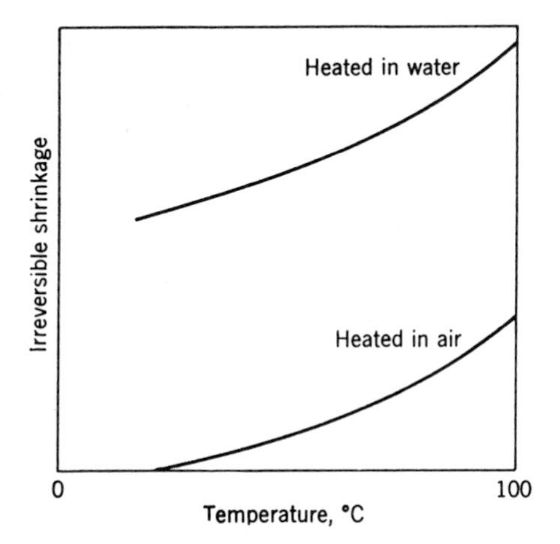

Fig. 30. Irreversible shrinkage of drawn nylon 66 by heating in water and air.

and the combined irreversible effect of water and heat are approximately additive at temperatures below 100°.

If a yarn is set at a certain temperature, it will not undergo further irreversible length changes unless the temperature is exceeded. The same is true for a yarn set in an aqueous phenol solution which will suffer no further irreversible length changes in phenol solution unless the original concentration of phenol is exceeded. The rate of shrinkage depends on the degree of drawing, as shown by Fig. 31.

The set obtained by the removal of irreversible shrinkage is of considerable practical importance for maintaining a fabric in the shape and dimensions to which it is held during treatment.

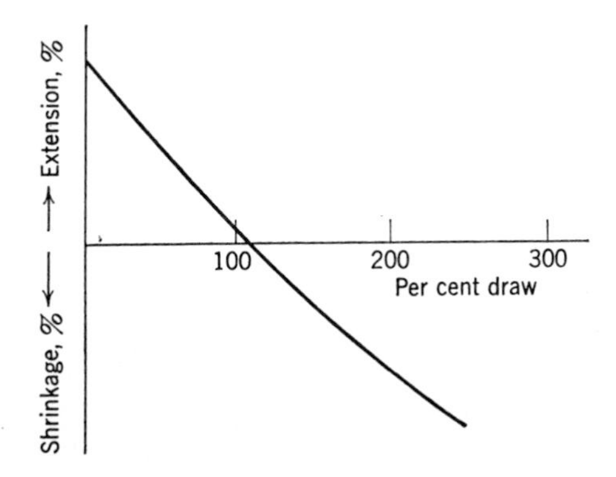

Fig. 31. Change in length, in aqueous phenol, of nylon 66 drawn to various lengths.

G. Optical Properties

The orientation during drawing of the fiber results in positive birefringence. Fully drawn fibers have a refractive index of about 1.58 along the fiber axis and 1.52 laterally. At the lower extents of draw, the birefringence increases more rapidly, as shown by Fig. 32. The cold drawing increases the gloss due to the orientation of the crystallites.

The opacity of nylon 66 varies with the extent of crystallization. According to Hermans and Weidinger (60) it is estimated to be 50–60%

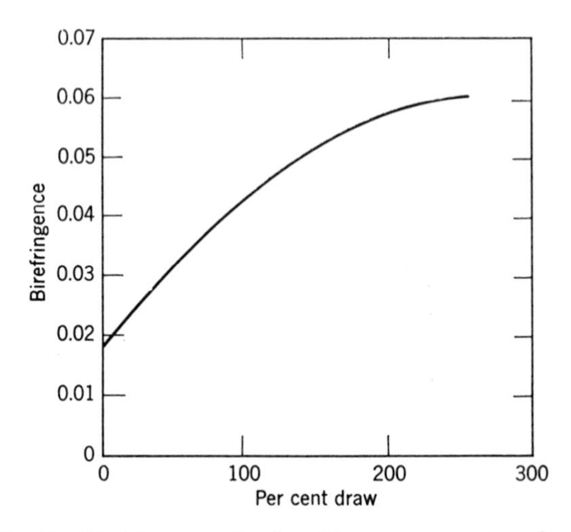

Fig. 32. Birefringence of nylon 66 versus percentage draw.

from x-ray methods in unoriented specimens. By slow cooling of the melt or slow evaporation of the solution of nylon 66, the opaque material shows beautiful spherulites under the polarizing microscope. Rapid cooling or quenching, however, results in a transparent material which is free from visible spherulites.

H. Light Resistance

When nylon 66 is exposed to sunlight, it undergoes degradation manifested by a loss of strength and lower viscosity of the solution. The photodegradation is an oxidative one, because in nitrogen the product is much more stable. Higher temperatures increase the photodegradation; moisture has no great influence. Delustrant increases it, too, especially TiO_2. Many dyestuffs have an influence on the rate of light degradation, some by increasing, others by decreasing it.

I. Heat Resistance

Like irradiation, heat decreases the tensile strength, as is shown in the diagrams in Figs. 33 and 34. Here oxidation is also the reason for the loss in strength.

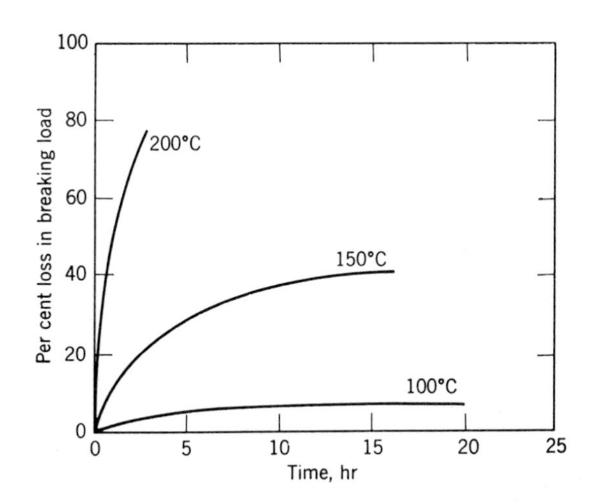

Fig. 33. Thermal degradation of nylon 66 at various temperatures.

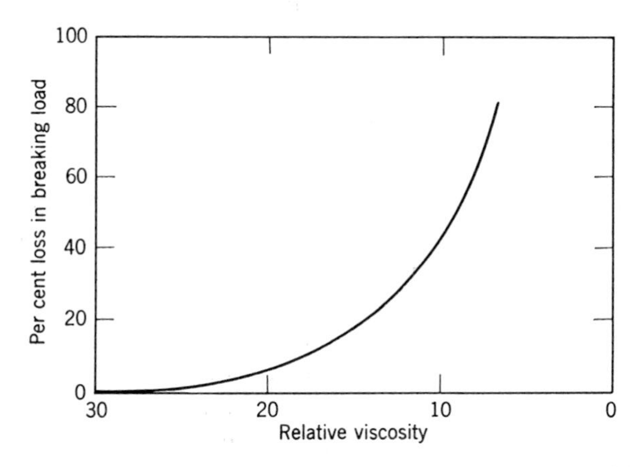

Fig. 34. Loss of strength and relative viscosity of nylon 66 after thermal degradation. (After A. R. Manden.)

J. Electrical Properties

The electrical properties of nylon 66 are rather good. Current conductivity is low. For a 30-den nylon 66 yarn, the value is 5×10^{14}

Ω/cm. With higher moisture regain, the conductivity increases, of course; the surface-absorbed water is responsible for the increase. Higher temperatures increase the current conductivity of polyamides exponentially.

The insulating properties give rise to accumulation of static electrical charges. Positive or negative charges can be generated by yarns during their passage over various surfaces. Humidity and application of conducting finishes will dissipate the static charges.

K. Chemical Properties

The resistance of polyamides to chemicals depends on the end groups and the amide groups, while the hydrocarbon residues are very stable. Water has no influence over long periods at normal temperatures. Water under pressure at temperatures above 150° will cause complete hydrolysis, which is promoted by caustic alkalies. Mineral acids will cause slow hydrolysis in dilute solutions, and stronger organic acids, such as aqueous oxalic or lactic acids, have the same effect. The fiber will be destroyed by strong oxidizing agents, such as nitric acid, potassium permanganate solutions, hydrogen peroxide, and hypochlorites. Formaldehyde will react with the NH_2 and NH groups in the presence of an acid and formation of methylol groups or alkoxymethyl groups in the presence of methanol. By this treatment the fiber will become very elastic.

XVI. APPLICATION OF NYLON 66 FIBERS

The high tensile strength, low modulus, complete but slow recovery, low moisture regain, high abrasion resistance, and ability to acquire a permanent set and low water absorption permit the use of nylon fiber in nearly all fields of the textile industry, including knitting and weaving. Its high tensile strength allows the use of extremely sheer fabric constructions. The low moisture regain and high wet strength result in easy laundering and rapid drying. The high dimensional stability is favorable to the removal of stains by heat treatment, and the high abrasion resistance is conducive to long wear.

The initial coldness to touch is characteristic of a nylon fabric; it is due to its aliphatic chemical nature and water repellance. A special advantage of the fabric lies in the fact that the textiles do not need ironing. Needless to say, nylon can be blended with all types of other fibers, especially wool and rayon, and endows these mixtures with its valuable properties. The improvement of the properties of cotton can be seen in the higher dimensional stability, abrasion, and shock resistance and better crease resistance. The blends with wool give fabrics of higher tensile and wet strength and greatly increased abrasion resistance. A higher nylon content reduces the shrinkage considerably. The high

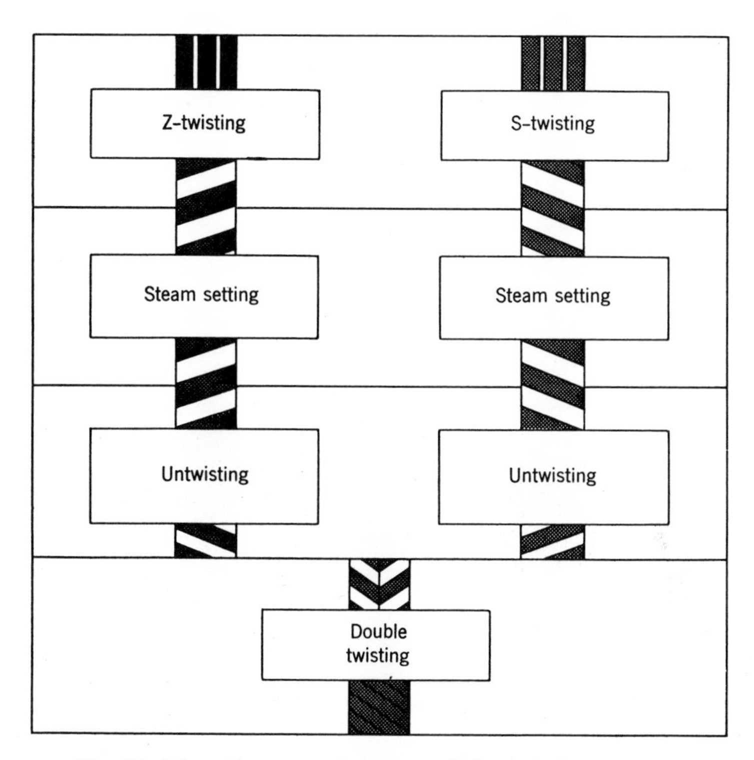

Fig. 34. Discontinuous pretwisting and aftertwisting process.

resilience and crease resistance of the wool greatly improves the properties of these blends.

A. Textured Yarns

One of the factors which have had a great influence on the sharp rise in production of nylon was the invention of the high-elastic-stretch yarns, the principle of which was patented in 1932 by Kaegi (61) for rayon, and which was transferred to nylon by Heberlein. The first process was made in four steps: (*1*) dry twisting at about 3000 rpm of two single yarns in reverse direction; (*2*) fixation of this twist by steam; (*3*) untwisting; and (*4*) retwisting of the two single fibers. This discontinuous process

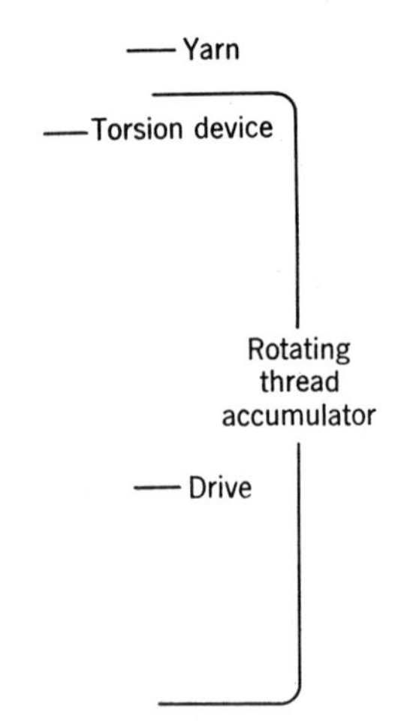

Fig. 36. Scheme for the Helanca process.

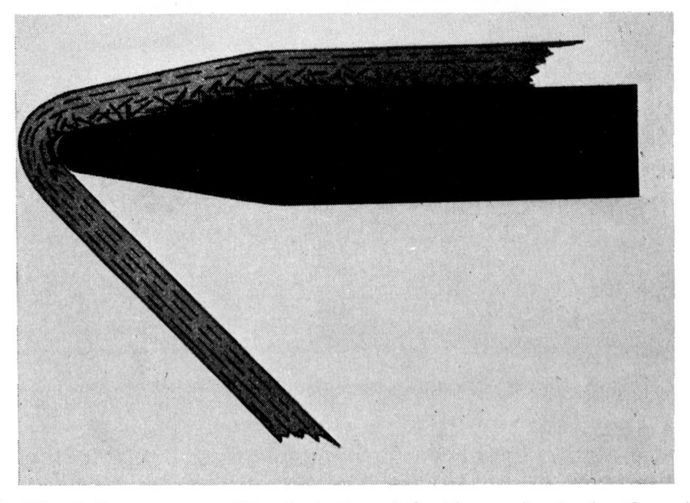

Fig. 37. The Agilon process. Disorientation of the fiber molecules by the point of a metal blade.

leads to a bulky high-elastic yarn with good resilience, but it works only at low speeds.

A much faster three-step process, invented by Finlayson of the British Celanese Corporation (62), works continuously and has had considerable success. The yarn is twisted between two fixed points, then highly twisted at 50,000–350,000 rpm, and then fixed by heating and untwisted to a certain degree at a speed of about 120 m/min. Yarns of this type are Helanca and Fluflon. The articles made from this kind of yarn reduce the number of sizes and have a better wear. The bulky character of these stretch yarns gives a better heat insulation.

Another method, invented by the Deering Milliken Research Corporation, is known as the Agilon process. It consists of leading the yarn over the point of a heated metal blade, whereby a disorientation of the molecules takes place on the metal surface between metal and yarn, leading to a spiral-like curling of the fiber.

The principles of the two processes are shown in Figs. 36 and 37.

XVII. DYEING OF NYLON 66

Nylon can be dyed in all shades by dispersion dyes of the aminoanthraquinone and azo groups as well as by acid dyes. The affinity for dyes decreases with the degree of stretching. A detailed description of this problem is found in Vickerstaff (63). The behavior of nylon with acids is important for the dyeing of nylon with acid dyes (64).

A. Dyeing of Polyamide Fibers with Anionic Dyes

It is well known that the amino groups are essential for the takeup of anionic dyes (acid dyes and metal complex dyes) by wool, silk, and polyamide fibers. As the number of amino groups in commercial polyamide fibers is 20–40 times lower than in wool (20–50 mmoles/kg and 850 mmoles/kg respectively), it is difficult to attain deep hues with simple acid dyes on polyamides. This is particularly true for dyes with more than one sulfonic group (65). Technically this problem can be solved by using acid and complex dyes which have a more hydrophobic (lyophilic) character. It could be shown first (66) for metal complex dyes of the 1:2 chrome type (Irgalan and Cibalan dyes) and later (67) for acid dyes (Carbolan and Milling dyes) that these dyes are taken up by two mechanisms, first by the usual salt formation between the dye anion and the ammonium group of the fiber, and second by a Nernst distribution ("solution mechanism") of the undissociated dye acid. The later mechanism might cause some acid-catalyzed hydrolysis of the carbon–amide linkages in the fiber at high acidities (pH 2) as well as at higher pH values (4–6) at longer dyeing times (more than 2–3 hr) (67,68).

According to Lemin the absorption curve of HCl by nylon shows a sharp inflection in the curve, which was confirmed by Elöd and Fröhlich (69) (see Fig. 38).

Schwemmer (70) used an improved version of Taylor's conductometric titration of amino end groups and obtained the curves shown in Fig. 39. Pure aniline was used as solvent.

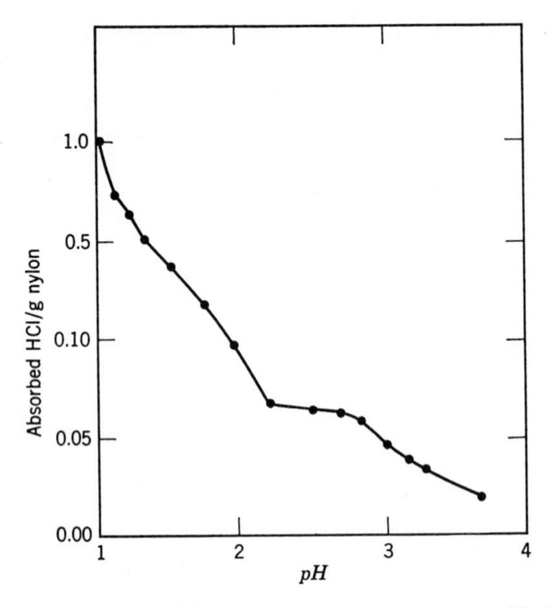

Fig. 38. Absorption of HCl by nylon at room temperature (dilution 1:50).

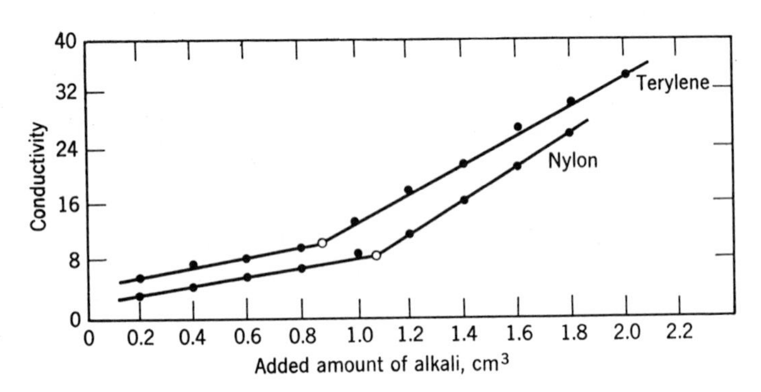

Fig. 39. Titration curves of the conductometric determination of carboxylic end groups in nylon and Terylene.

A very precise chemical method for determination of amino end groups in polyamides was developed by Zahn and Rathgeber (71). It consists of a practical application of the Sanger reagent, 2,4-dinitrofluorobenzene in aqueous alcohol in the presence of $NaHCO_3$. As do all proteins, the polyamides react with this reagent and give a yellow product. By extraction of the colored material, the amino end groups can be determined by colorimetry. The maximum of extinction is already obtained in 8 hr at 20°.

XVIII. ANALYTICAL DETERMINATION

Nylon 66 can be identified easily by saponification with 10% HCl in a sealed tube at 140–150°. The adipic acid will crystallize directly from the mixture after cooling and can be identified by melting point, acid number, and elemental analysis. The amine which is dissolved in the hydrochloric acid can be determined by paper chromatography, according to Zahn and Wolf (72). This method can be used for many polyamides, such as nylon 6, nylon 66, nylon 610, polyurethanes, or mixtures of these products. The hydrolized sample can be separated by a mixture of 75 parts secondary butanol, 15 parts formic acid (88%), and 10 parts water. By this method, the main components (ε-aminocaproic acid and hexamethylene diamine) are separated and can be detected by fluorescence or sprinkling with dinitrofluorobenzene, Pauley reagent, or ninhydrin solution. ε-Aminocaproic acid moves four times faster than hexamethylene diamine. By addition of dinitrofluorobenzene to the hydrolyzed sample, the dinitrophenyl derivatives of the amino components are obtained. The hexamethylene diamine derivative does not move at all in a butanol/formic acid mixture. The aminocaproic acid derivative moves to the front of the solvent.

Cocondensation products of caprolactam and nylon salt can be easily analyzed down to 5%. For the separation of the acid mixture of nylon 66 or Nylon 610, a solvent mixture of 80 parts isobutanol, 15 parts concentrated ammonia, and 5 parts glycol is favorable.

XIX. THE COMPONENTS OF COPOLYAMIDES

Ecochard and Duveau (73) have given a method for the determination of the components if these are known. They use the potentiometric analysis of the hydrolyzed product which contains an excess of HCl, at least one organic dicarboxylic acid, at least one chlorohydrate of a diamine, and at least one ω-amino acid as hydrochloric salt. By potentiometric analysis the total amount of organic acid is determined. For the organic total acidity for a certain amount of the polyamide, the following equation is valid:

$$K = M_1\,(^1/_2 M_2 x - 1)/(M_2 - M_1) \qquad (11)$$

where M_1 is the molecular weight of the monomer of component 1; M_2 is the molecular weight of the monomer of component 2; x is the number of gram-molecules alkali necessary for the neutralization of the organic acids of 1 g of the hydrolyzed copolyamide; and K is the relative content of component 1 in the copolyamide. For mixed copolyamides at least one component of the mixture must be isolated by ion exchange.

REFERENCES

1. E. K. Bolton, *Ind. Eng. Chem.*, **34**, 54 (1942).
2. H. Mark and G. Whitby, *Collected Papers of W. H. Carothers*, Interscience, New York, 1940.
3. *CIOS Report*, File No. 3350, Part 2, p. 571 (1945).
4. Fr. Pat. 913,958 (1943).
5. U.S. Pats. 2,191,786; 2,193,562 (1938).
6. German Pat. 597,973 (1933); U.S. Pat. 2,005,183 (1933).
7. U.S. Pat. 2,228,261, to DuPont (1940).
8. Fr. Pat. 876,620, to Raschig (1941).
9. Fr. Pat. 853,040, to DuPont (1939).
10. Fr. Pat. 898,009 (1941).
11. German Pat. 717,952 to I. G. Farben (1900).
12. U.S. Pat. 2,200,734 (1938); German Pat. 743,967 (1939).
13. Fr. Pat. 866,922 (1940); *CIOS Report*, File No. 3350, Part 2, pp. 584–92 (1945).
14. U.S. Pats. 2,532,311; 2,532,312, to DuPont (1948); Fr. Pat. 962,096 (1947).
15. Fr. Pat. 898,118 (1943).
16. P. Kurtz, *Liebigs Ann. Chem.*, **572**, 31, 49 (1951); **631**, 21 (1960); U.S. Pat. 2,462,388 (1947), 2,583,984 (1950), to DuPont; Brit. Pat. 619,577 (1946), Imperial Chemical Industries.
17. U.S. Pat. 2,439,308, to DuPont (1946).
18. Brit. Pat. 518,697, to I. G. Farbenindustrie AG (1939).
19. I. E. Muskat and H. E. Northrup, *J. Am. Chem. Soc.*, **52**, 4046 (1930).
20. M. W. Farlow, U.S. Pat. 2,518,608, to DuPont (1950).

20a. H. Zahn, P. Miro, and F. Schmidt, *Ber.*, **90**, 1411 (1957).

21. L. Orthner, German Pat., 912,863 (1941).
22. A. Morgan, *Soc. Plastics Engrs. J.*, **15**, 485 (1959).
23. E. L. Wittbecker and A. Morgan, *J. Polymer Sci.*, **40**, 982 (1960).
24. P. W. Morgan, *Condensation Polymers by Interfacial Methods*, Interscience, New York, 1965.
25. G. B. Taylor, *J. Am. Chem. Soc.*, **69**, 635 (1947).
26. H. G. Elias and R. Schumacher, *Makromol. Chem.*, **76**, 23–53 (1964).
27. W. H. Stockmayer and M. Fixman, *J. Polymer Sci. C*, **1**, 137 (1963).
28. W. R. Krigbaum, *J. Polymer Sci.*, **18**, 315 (1955).
29. P. J. Flory, *J. Am. Chem. Soc.*, **62**, 1057, 3032 (1940).
30. T. G Fox and P. J. Flory, *J. Am. Chem. Soc.*, **70**, 2384 (1948).
31. S. R. Rafikow and W. W. Korshak, *Nachr. Akad. Wiss. UdSSR, Abt. Chem. Wiss.*, **1944**, p. 432.
32. J. Boulton, *J. Soc. Dyers Colourists*, **62**, 75 (1946).
33. J. E. Waltz and G. B. Taylor, *Anal. Chem.*, **19**, 448 (1947).
34. W. W. Korshak and W. A. Samjatina, *Nachr. Akad. Wiss. UdSSR, Abt. Chem. Wiss.*, **1948**, p. 412; *Ber. Akad. Wiss. UdSSR*, **59**, 909 (1948).
35. H. Staudinger and G. Schnell, *Makromol. Chem.*, **1**, 44 (1947).
36. W. W. Korshak, *J. Allg. Chem.* (*Russ.*) **14**, 974 (1944); *Nachr. S.*, 144/161-64.
37. L. Mandelkern, *Chem. Rev.*, **56**, 903 (1956).
38. P. Fijolka, I. Lenz, and F. Runge, *Makromol. Chem.*, **23**, 60 (1957).
39. H. Zahn and P. Rathgeber, *Melliand Textilber.*, **34**, 749 (1953).
40. K. Hoshino, *Bull. Chem. Soc. Japan*, **19**, 158 (1944).
41. J. B. Nichols, *Colloid Chem.*, **6**, 1077 (1946).

42. W. Herzog and R. O. Spurlin, *Z. Physik. Chem.* (Bodenstein-Festband), **1931,** 139.
43. R. Schumacher and H. G. Elias, *Makromol. Chem.*, **76,** 12–22 (1964).
44. R. G. Beaman, *J. Polymer Sci.*, **9,** 470 (1952).
45. G. B. Taylor, *J. Am. Chem. Soc.*, **69,** 638 (1947).
46. N. Duveau and A. Piguet, *J. Polymer Sci.*, **57,** 357 (1962).
47. L. H. Cragg and H. Hammerschlag, *Chem. Rev.*, **39,** 79 (1946).
48. D. R. Morey and J. W. Tamblyn, *J. Appl. Phys.*, **16,** 419 (1945).
49. E. J. Ambrose, A. Elliott, and R. B. Temple, *Proc. Roy. Soc. London Ser. A*, **199,** 183 (1949).
50. L. Glatt and J. W. Ellis, *J. Chem. Phys.*, **16,** 551 (1948).
51. G. Schnell, *Ergeb. Exakt. Naturw.*, **31,** 270 (1959).
52. C. G. Cannon, *Spectrochim. Acta,* **16,** 302 (1960).
53. G. Heidemann and H. Zahn, *Makromol. Chem.*, **62,** 123 (1963).
54. R. Brill, *Z. Physik. Chem. B*, **53,** 61 (1943).
55. C. W. Bunn and E. V. Garner, *Proc. Roy. Soc.*, **189,** 39 (1947).
56. A. Elliott, E. J. Ambrose, and R. B. Temple, *J. Chem. Phys.*, **16,** 877 (1948).
57. S. M. Atlas and H. Mark, "Structural Principles of Fiber-Forming Polymers," in *Man-Made Fibers: Science and Technology,* Vol. 1, H. F. Mark, S. M. Atlas, and E. Cernia, Eds., Interscience, New York, 1967.
58. E. K. Bolton, *Chem. Ind.*, **61,** 31 (1941).
59. J. B. Speakman and A. K. Saville, *J. Textile Inst.*, **37,** 271 (1946).
60. P. H. Hermans and A. Weidinger, *J. Polymer Sci.*, **4,** 135, 317, 709 (1949).
61. A. Kaegi, German Pat. 618,050 (1932).
62. D. Finlayson, Brit. Pat. 424,880 (1900), to British Celanese Corp.
63. Th. Vickerstaff, *The Physical Chemistry of Dyeing* (1954), p. 439.
64. P. W. Carlene, A. S. Fern, and Th. Vickerstaff, *J. Soc. Dyers Colourists,* **63,** 388 (1947).
65. R. H. Peters, *J. Soc. Dyers Colourists,* **61,** 325 (1945).
66. G. Back and H. Zollinger, *Helv. Chim. Acta,* **41,** 2242 (1958); **42,** 1526, 1539, 1553 (1959).
67. H. Zollinger, G. Back, B. Milicevic, and A. Roseira, *Melliand Textilber.*, **42,** 73 (1961); M. Greenhalgh, A. Johnson, and R. H. Peters, *J. Soc. Dyers Colourists,* **78,** 315 (1962).
68. B. Ferrini, Ph.D. Thesis, Swiss Federal Institute of Technology, Zurich (1965).
69. E. Elöd and H. G. Fröhlich, *Melliand Textilber.*, **30,** 103 (1949).
70. M. Schwemmer, *Textil-Rundschau,* **11.** 8 (1956).
71. A. Zahn and P. Rathgeber, *Melliand Textilber.*, **34,** 749 (1953).
72. A. Zahn and X. Wolf, *Melliand Textilber.*, **32,** 317 (1951).
73. F. Ecochard and N. Duveau, *Makromol. Chem.*, **1951,** 148.

Nylon 6

Walter Sbrolli
Bombrini Parodi-Delfino, Rome, Italy

CONTENTS

The polymer produced by the polymerization of ε-caprolactam, identical to the polycondensation product of ε-aminocaproic acid, is known in the United States as nylon 6, and in Europe as Perlon or polycaprolactam.

In 1930, Carothers and co-workers (1) examined the possibility of obtaining high polymers from ε-aminocaproic acid, but the products they synthesized had molecular weights of only about 3000, which is too low to produce useful fibers. At the beginning of the century Gabriel (2) and Braun (3) made known the fact that an undistillable polymeric residue is obtained by heating ε-aminocaproic acid.

TABLE I. Nylon 6 Producers and Trademarks

Country	Company	Trademark
Germany (West)	Farbenfabriken Bayer A.G.	Perlon
	Farbwerke Hoechst A.G.	Perlon
	Phrix-Werke A.G.	Perlon
	Spinnstoff-Fabrik Zehlendorf A.G.	Perlon
	Vereinigte Glanzstoff-Fabriken A.G.	Perlon
Germany (East)	VEB Thüringisches Kunstfaserwerk "W. Piek"	Perlon L
	VEB Filmfabrik Agfa Wolfen	Perlon L
	VEB Kunstseidenwerk "F. Engels"	Perlon L
Holland	Algemeine Kunstzijde Unie (AKU)	Enkalon
Italy	ANIC	Nivion
	Bemberg S.A.	Ortalion
	Bombrini Parodi-Delfino	Delfion
	Chatillon S.A.	Helion
	Orsi Mangelli S.A.	Forlion
	Snia Viscosa S.p.A.	Lilion
Japan	Nippon Rayon K.K.	—
	Toyo Rayon K.K.	Amilan
Switzerland	Fibron S.A.	Grilon
	Societé Viscose Suisse	—
Soviet Union	Klin	Kapron
United States	American Enka	Nylenka
	Industrial Rayon Corporation	Nylon 6
	National Aniline Division of Allied Chemical Corporation	Caprolan

In 1938 Paul Schlack (4) of I.G. Farbenindustrie isolated the practical conditions necessary for polymerizing ε-caprolactam with good yields and a molecular weight suitable for textile fiber production.

In 1939 the first fibers were produced on a pilot plant scale, and since World War II the production of nylon 6 from ε-caprolactam has been developed in many countries, particularly in Europe and in Japan, and has reached a very high level of output.

Table I shows a list of the main nylon 6 producers, together with nylon 6 fiber trademarks.

The general characteristics of nylon 6 are very similar to those of nylon 66, the main differences being that the former has a lower melting point, greater moisture absorption, and superior dyeing properties.

Caprolactam is cheaper than the 66 salt, but it must be remembered that during polymerization a certain amount (approximately 8–10%) is not converted to polymer, although caprolactam can easily be recovered with good yields.

The relative development of these two important polyamide fibers, both of which are now used in the textile industry on a large scale, will depend upon the relative availability at low price of the respective monomers.

I. MONOMER

Despite the fact that nylon 6 can be produced both from ε-aminocaproic acid and from its lactam, caprolactam alone is generally used owing to its method of preparation and purification.

Caprolactam (CL), which has the following chemical formula:

$$\begin{array}{lll} CH_2\text{—}CH_2\text{—}CO \\ | \qquad\qquad\quad | \\ CH_2 \qquad\qquad | \\ | \qquad\qquad\quad | \\ CH_2\text{—}CH_2\text{—}NH \end{array} \tag{1}$$

is a white crystalline compound with a melting point of 68–69°C. It can be synthesized by several processes, of which the most classic is that starting from cyclohexanol, which is obtained with high yields from cyclohexane, phenol, or aniline in some cases via benzene.

Cyclohexanol is oxidized to cyclohexanone, which reacts with hydroxylamine to give cyclohexanone oxime, and finally the cyclohexanone oxime is converted to caprolactam in concentrated sulfuric acid by the Beckmann rearrangement.

Other processes which in recent years have reached the stage of industrialization start with the nitration of cyclohexane from which cyclohexanone oxime is obtained by various methods, followed by the usual route to caprolactam.

The last method suggested (5), which is already at the industrial stage, starts from toluene, which is oxidized to benzoic acid, from which hexahydrobenzoic acid is obtained by hydrogenation, which by treatment with nitrosylsulfuric acid gives caprolactam.

It is very important to have an extremely pure caprolactam in order to obtain a good polymer, and it will therefore be useful to comment on purity controls. The melting point must be equal to or above 68.4°C, the humidity 0.2% maximum, the color of a 65% aqueous solution 30 APHA maximum, and water-insoluble compounds must be absent.

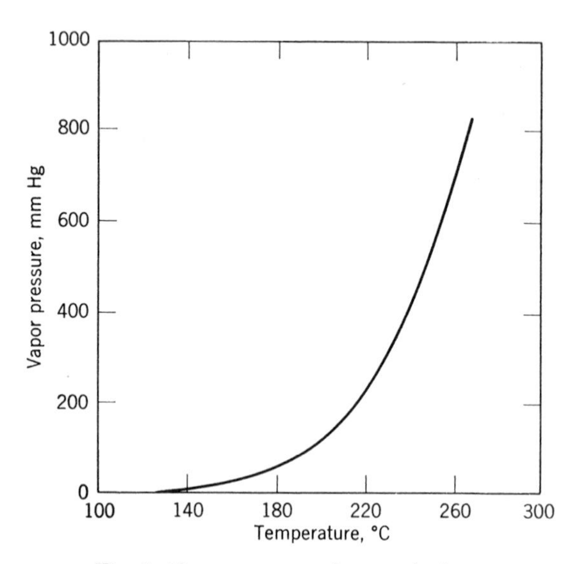

Fig. 1. Vapor pressure of ε-caprolactam.

However, apart from these essential quality requirements it is of the utmost importance to know the amount of basic impurities and reducing agents. The basic impurities are determined in two different ways: as fixed basic compounds by direct titration of an aqueous solution and as volatile substances distilled in the vapor stream from a solution in 1*N* NaOH, in which case the distilled vapors must consume not more than 0.015 ml HCl (0.1 *N*) per 1 g lactam. The reducing agents are estimated from the degree of decolorization of an aqueous solution (1 g/100 ml), to which a small amount of permanganate has been added (1 ml 0.01 *N* solution).

The decolorization is then calibrated by a standard solution containing 0.25 g cobalt nitrate and 0.001 g potassium dichromate in 100 ml water; the time elapsing from the start of the test to the point where an equal color intensity is reached in each solution must exceed 200–300 sec.

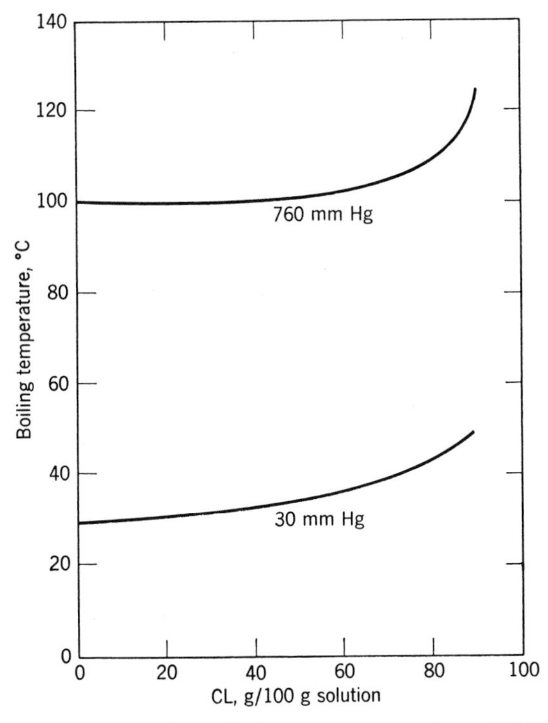

Fig. 2. Boiling temperatures of caprolactam aqueous solutions at different pressures.

Table II shows various physical properties of caprolactam. Figure 1 consists of a vapor pressure diagram, and Fig. 2 the boiling points of aqueous solutions.

TABLE II. Physical Properties of ε-Caprolactam

Viscosity	9 cP at 78°C
Heat of fusion	29 cal/g
Heat of vaporization	116 cal/g
Heat of polymerization	20.000 cal/mole
Refractive index	1.4935 at 40°C.
Specific heat	0.506 at 70°C

II. POLYMERIZATION

A. Theory

1. Experimental Results

Perfectly pure anhydrous caprolactam does not polymerize alone when heated in a closed vessel. This feature was originally demonstrated by

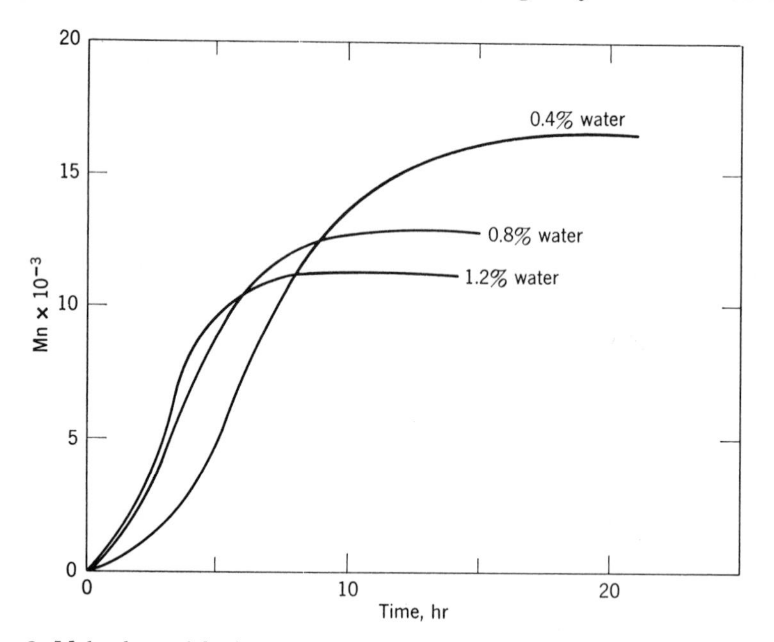

Fig. 3. Molecular weight increase during the polymerization of caprolactam with various amounts of water at 250°C (no stabilizer).

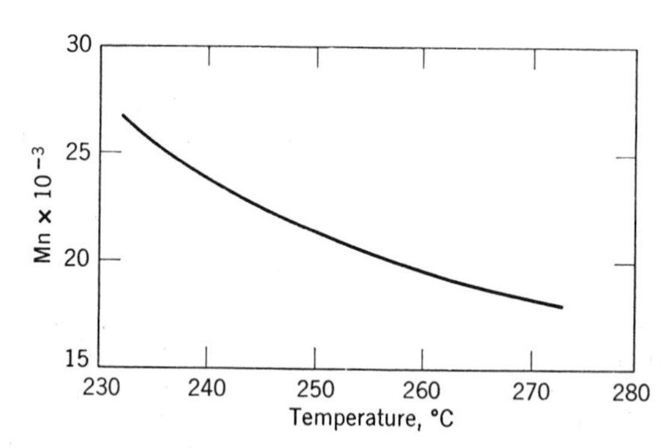

Fig. 4. Equilibrium molecular weight of polycaprolactam, as a function of temperature (water content = 0.3%, no stabilizer); from data of Reimschuessel (30).

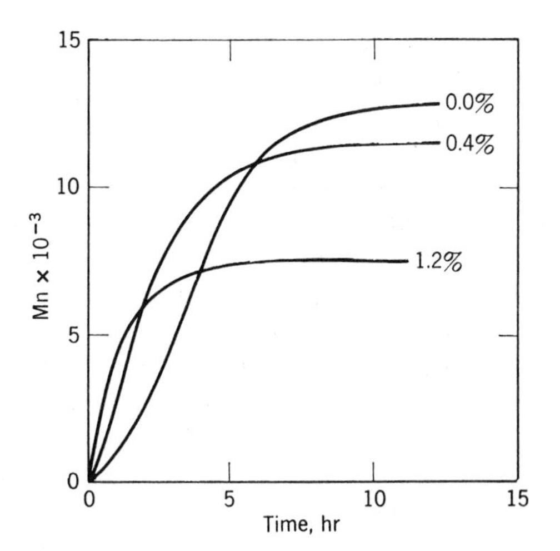

Fig. 5. Molecular weight increase during the polymerization of caprolactam with various amounts of adipic acid (water content = 0.8%, temperature 250°C).

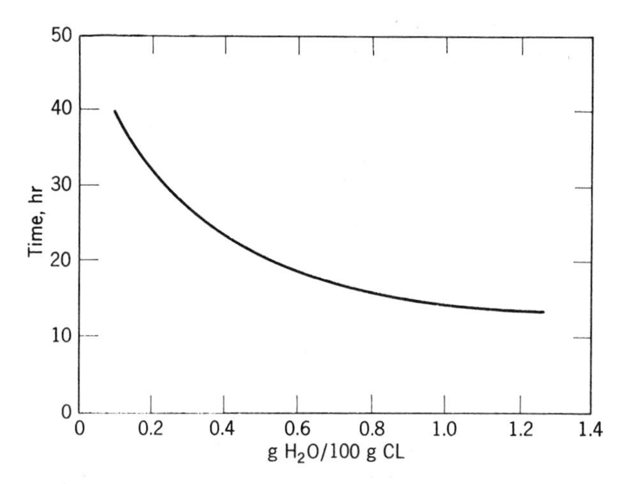

Fig. 6. Time needed to reach equilibrium as a function of water/caprolactam ratio (no stabilizer, temperature 250°); from (30).

Carothers (1), and more recently Hermans (6) and Wiloth (7) confirmed the inability of caprolactam to polymerize alone. According to Hermans, pure anhydrous caprolactam heated at 250°C for 600 hr in a sealed glass tube polymerizes negligibly. The conversion to a linear polymer is made possible by adding small amounts of water; the conversion and degree of polymerization are dependent upon water content, temperature, and time. It is known that caprolactam can also be polymerized by other methods, for instance, by means of sodium hydroxide (8,9), a Grignard reagent (10), hydrochloric acid (11), and by means of amines and their salts (12). However, as these methods have not been adopted in practice for fiber production on a large scale, we shall refer only to polymerization processes with water as the initiating agent.

In the textile fiber field polymer production on an industrial scale involves the addition to caprolactam of water and also of small quantities of acids or amines, which have a double function (see below).

Table III and Figs. 3, 4, and 5 illustrate the typical behavior of caprolactam polymerization relative to the initial caprolactam–water ratio, the temperature, and the stabilizer content. It can easily be seen that molecular weight decreases by increasing the amount of water and stabilizer and also the temperature, while at the same time the conversion rate increases with these factors. This behavior can also be deduced from Fig. 6, where the times needed to reach equilibrium are plotted against the temperature. Moreover, the conversion remains incomplete and some caprolactam is left unconverted at equilibrium, while together with the conversion to a linear polymer, there is at the same time minor conversion to cyclic oligomers.

TABLE III. Polymerization Conditions Necessary for a Molecular Weight of 17,000 and Unconverted Lactam in this Condition, from Data of Reimschuessel (30)

Temperature, °C	Water, %	Unconverted lactam, %
265	0.39	12.4
250	0.46	11.3
235	0.56	10.9
220	0.65	9.8

Thus, the polymerized mixture at equilibrium consists of about 90% polymer, 10% unconverted caprolactam, and small quantities of cyclic oligomers, while the molecular weight of the polymer is dependent upon the amount of water and stabilizer and the polymerization temperature.

2. *Polymerization Mechanism of the Caprolactam–Water System*

In polyamides, which are produced by reacting difunctional acids and amines, the amide-forming reaction alone can explain satisfactorily the polycondensation process, while to polymerize caprolactam two different mechanisms are possible: polycondensation and polyaddition.

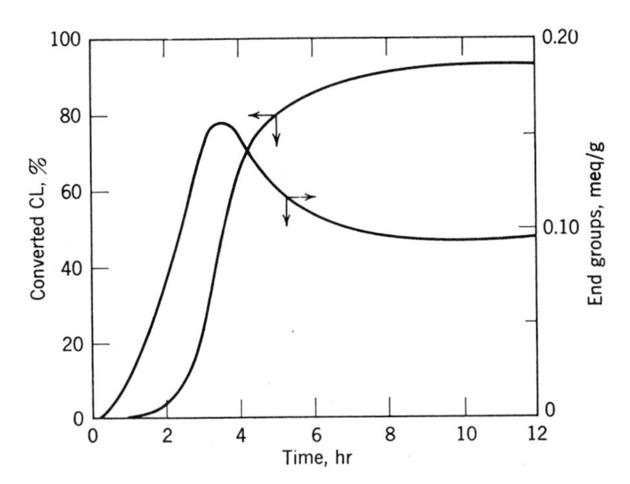

Fig. 7. Caprolactam conversion and corresponding endgroup concentration during polymerization.

In the presence of water or compounds which give off water at polymerization temperature, the caprolactam ring scission is of the hydrolytic type and gives aminocaproic acid, as follows.

$$\overline{NH(CH_2)_5CO} + H_2O \rightleftharpoons NH_2(CH_2)_5COOH \tag{1}$$

which is the first essential step in polymerization.

Subsequently polymerization can proceed either by amino acid polycondensation:

$$\underset{S_1}{NH_2(CH_2)_5COOH} + \underset{S_1}{NH_2(CH_2)_5COOH} \rightleftharpoons \underset{S_2}{NH_2 \text{———} COOH} + H_2O \tag{2}$$

and in general

$$\underset{S_n}{NH_2 \text{———} COOH} + \underset{S_m}{NH_2 \text{———} COOH} \rightleftharpoons \underset{S_{n+m}}{NH_2 \text{———} COOH} + H_2O \tag{2a}$$

or by the polyaddition mechanism

$$S_n + CL \rightleftharpoons S_{n+1} \tag{3}$$

Numerous papers deal with the relative importance of these two reactions in caprolactam polymerization, particularly those by Hermans and coworkers (13–16) in Holland and by Wiloth (17–20) in Germany.

Matthes (21), in the first paper to be published on the polymerization of caprolactam, advanced the hypothesis of a polyaddition mechanism; and subsequently by many careful studies it was possible to reach the conclusion that polyaddition is the prevalent mechanism in the caprolactam. From a chemical point of view, the polyaddition reaction can be defined as an aminolysis of the caprolactam amide bond (NHCO) catalyzed by the carboxylic end groups (22).

The autocatalytic (S-shaped) character of the polymerization is easily deduced from Fig. 7, where the end group concentration is also shown, reaching a maximum which practically coincides with the inflection of the conversion curve.

As far as the polymerization mechanism is concerned, polyaddition is prevalent, and at equilibrium polycaprolactam follows the rules of polycondensation. It is well known (23,24) that the fundamental principle involved in the theory of polycondensation is the equal reactivity of end groups, from which it follows that all the functional groups react with each other at random and are unaffected by the length of the chains. By this principle, either number average degree of polymerization $\bar{n}$ or the molecular weight distribution can easily be deduced from a factor p alone, which represents the probability of a functional group, selected at random, having reacted. Taking as an example the amino acid polycondensation, the factor p is given by

$$p = [\text{—CONH—}]/[\text{—COOH—}] = [\text{—CONH—}]/[\text{—NH}_2] \tag{4}$$

where [—COOH—] ([—NH_2]) is the number of end groups at the beginning of the reaction and [—CONH—] is the number of amide groups formed.

From this theory the following relationships are deduced:

$$\bar{n} = \frac{1}{1 - p} \tag{5}$$

$$w_n = np^{n-1}\,(1 - p)^2 \tag{6}$$

where w_n is the weight fraction of n-mers in the polymer (with n varying from 1 to infinity). Moreover, from Eqs. 5 and 6 the ratio M_w/M_n can be found to be equal to 2.

In order to investigate whether these relationships are applicable to polycaprolactam obtained in the presence of water, Wiloth (25) has proved experimentally that the molecular weight distribution of various polycaprolactam samples follows Eq. 6, and that apparent deviations from this behavior are due to association effects of polycaprolactam at the precipitation point. The determination of the aminocaproic acid content at equilibrium in polycaprolactam is also in accordance with Eq. 6 (15,26) and gives an independent confirmation that the aminocaproic acid is the real monomer for the polycondensation mechanism.

Since the equilibrium state of the caprolactam–water system is defined by the laws of polycondensation, the equilibrium constant, according to the relationship shown in Eq. 2a, will be given by

$$K_2 = [S_{n+m}]\ [H_2O]/([S_n]\ [S_m]) \tag{7}$$

From Eq. 6 we find that the molar concentration of n-mers is

$$[S_n] = w_n/(n \times Mo) = (1/Mo)p^{n-1}(1 - p)^2$$

where Mo is the monomer molecular weight. Therefore Eq. 7 can be rearranged to give

$$K_2 = p \cdot Mo/(1 - p)^2[H_2O] = \bar{n}(\bar{n} - 1)Mo\ [H_2O] \tag{8}$$

From this relationship it follows that at equilibrium an increase in the initial water/caprolactam ratio causes a decrease in the molecular weight, and vice versa.

It has been found experimentally that the constant K_2 is dependent not only upon the temperature but also upon the water–caprolactam ratio; when the water content of the system increases, K_2 decreases. For example, while the K_2 constant is 460 at 253.5°C for a 0.2 caprolactam–water molar ratio, at the same temperature, when the molar ratio is 1.4 K_2 becomes 250 (14). This behavior is not easily explained and it may be tentatively ascribed to an influence of the changing nature of the medium, either as a decrease of water activity or as interactions in the water–caprolactam–polymer system.

Apart from the polycondensation equilibrium, we must also consider a further equilibrium between polymer and caprolactam, as in Eq. 3. The equilibrium constant is given by

$$K_3 = [CL]\ [S_n]/[S_{n+1}] \tag{9}$$

which, rearranged in terms of the corresponding degree of polymerization, becomes

$$K_3 = [CL]/p = [CL]\bar{n}/(\bar{n} - 1) \tag{10}$$

from which we find that the molar concentration of caprolactam at equilibrium increases with the degree of polymerization. The weight concentration tends to decrease, because as the molecular weight increases the molar concentration of the polymer is strongly diminished. The constant K_3 also varies with the water–caprolactam ratio and increases when this ratio becomes higher.

3. *Stabilizer*

Carboxylic acids alone cannot initiate the polymerization of anhydrous caprolactam, and in any case the conversions are very low even after a considerable period of time (16,27); however, on the other hand, the addition of small amounts of carboxylic acids or amines to the water–caprolactam system induces a higher conversion rate and gives a lower molecular weight at the equilibrium.

The decrease in molecular weight is completely accounted for by the polycondensation theory. With difunctional stabilizers, for example dicarboxylic acids, Eq. 5 becomes

$$\bar{n} = (1 + r)/(2r(1 - p) + (1 - r)) \tag{11}$$

where

$$r = [NH_2]/[COOH]$$

which is the ratio between the total number of functional groups, belonging either to the monomer or to the stabilizer (this ratio is inverted when the stabilizer is aminic). With monofunctional stabilizers the form of Eq. 11 is unchanged, but to calculate r the number of functional stabilizer groups must be doubled. Since r is always less than unity, the value of $\bar{n}$ from Eq. 11 is inferior to that calculated from Eq. 5, p being equal.

Consequently, Eq. 6 also becomes

$$w_n = n(pr^{1/2})^{n-1}(1 - pr^{1/2})^2 \tag{12}$$

The action mechanism of the stabilizer is easily understood with reference to the excess of one type of functional group.

The carboxylic and aminic end groups in the polymer are not equal in number, and therefore the probability of polycondensation reaction decreases. As a limiting condition a polymer in which every macromolecule is terminated by a stabilizer molecule remains wholly unaffected by variations in external conditions. On the other hand, since, as far as the conversion is concerned, the prevailing reaction is the aminolysis catalyzed by acidic end groups, the increase in conversion rate is easily explained by the higher carboxylic group concentration. If, instead of organic acids, an aminic compound is used as the molecular weight stabilizer, the higher conversion rate may be attributed to the mechanism of dry caprolactam polymerization initiated by amines (12).

The equilibrium constant K_2 has also been calculated for the water–caprolactam–stabilizer system (28) and has been found to vary with the water–caprolactam ratio, but not with excess of carboxylic or aminic groups.

The theory outlined above is a simplification, since the formation, and therefore the presence, of cyclic oligomers has not been taken into account; however, the reaction rate of these compounds is very low and the amount at equilibrium is also low (2%) and decreases with the number of monomer units in the ring. It has been suggested (29) that the reaction mechanism for cyclic oligomers can be the same as for polymerization.

4. *Semiempirical Relations*

Recently a semiempirical relationship has been advanced (30) by which the degree of polymerization at equilibrium can be calculated from the water concentration and temperature, without using the equilibrium constant.

This relationship, which is a function of functions, is given by

$$\bar{n} = \left[f_1(T) \frac{\lambda(T, w)}{w} \right]^{f_2(T)} \tag{13}$$

where T is the absolute temperature, w the molar ratio between water and caprolactam, and $\lambda(T, w)$ is the caprolactam fraction converted to polymer. The independent functions are given by

$$\lambda(T, w) = 1 - [(T - 392.5)/1345] - 58.24 \times 10^{-2} w[(T - 392.5)/1345] \tag{13a}$$

$$f_1(T) = \exp [(7397/T) - 8.8512] \tag{13b}$$

$$f_2(T) = 0.577 \ln T - 3.0375 \tag{13c}$$

This relationship has been found to be in good agreement with experiments covering a wide range of variations.

Another relationship, which is very simple but which is based on a limited amount of experimental data, has been suggested (31), as follows:

$$\log \bar{n} = 5.97 - 1253 (1/T) - (1/2) \log p \tag{14}$$

where p is the vapor pressure of water, in mm Hg, and T is the absolute temperature.

B. Industrial Polymerization Processes

The processes most widely used on an industrial scale are batch polymerization in autoclaves and the continuous process in a VK tube (from the German, "vereinfacht kontinuerlich," simplified continuous).

Every polymerization process utilizes a heated vessel which melts the caprolactam at about 80°C; in this vessel suitable amounts of water, stabilizer and titanium dioxide which is used as a delusterant can also be added. When all the compounds are well mixed, the melted caprolactam is sent, after filtration, to the polymerization plant. In order to avoid oxidation, the temperature must be kept lower than about 100°C. In some cases certain compounds which give off water at the polymerization temperature are used as hydrolytic agents instead of water. Aminocaproic acid is used for this purpose, without affecting the molecular structuie of the polymer. If, on the other hand, hexamethylenediammonium adipate is used, the polymer obtained is not nylon 6, but more properly a copolymer 6/66. To stabilize the molecular weight, acetic, adipic, and benzoic acids are usually employed rather than aminic compounds, which are seldom used.

1. Discontinuous Autoclave Process

For caprolactam polymerization (Fig. 8) the autoclave must have a top inlet for the melted caprolactam, an inlet for nitrogen, a pipe for connection to the vacuum line, a safety valve, and some kind of pump at the bottom to empty the vessel at the end of the polymerization cycle. Usually the autoclave is provided with a heating jacket, and in order to homogenize the melt an agitator may also be inserted. The capacities of industrial autoclaves in general use range from 1 to 6 m^3, of which only about three-fourths is filled.

The required amounts of caprolactam, water, stabilizer, and delusterant pigment are introduced into the autoclave, which has been previously cleansed with nitrogen, and, after having closed the autoclave, the heating system is started up. The temperature is raised to 220–240°C over several hours, and, during this time, the pressure reaches a value ranging from 12 to 25 kg/cm^2, depending upon the amount of water. Afterwards, the pressure is slowly reduced until a residual pressure of 0.1–0.5 atm is reached and the temperature is increased simultaneously to 250–270°C; this operation lasts from 5 to 10 hr. The pressure is then raised to atmospheric by supplying purified nitrogen, and polymerization is continued under these final conditions for 2–3 hr in order to reach equilibrium.

When the polymerization cycle is complete, the polymer is extruded from the bottom of the vessel across spinnerets so as to form one or more thick threads, which, after cooling in water, are cut into chips and sent for storage in metal containers.

The total time required for one polymerization cycle is dependent upon the initial water and stabilizer content and upon the temperature of the intermediate stage, while the molecular weight of the polymer is dependent upon the residual pressure reached after the evacuation process, the amount of stabilizer, and the temperature of the final stage.

In the first stage under pressure a large amount of water will decrease the induction time and increase the reaction rate, whereas once an adequate degree of conversion has been attained, most of the water must be emptied in order to obtain a sufficiently high degree of polymerization. In the last stage it is very important that the polymer reach equilibrium relative to the water content, the final stabilizer concentration, and the temperature.

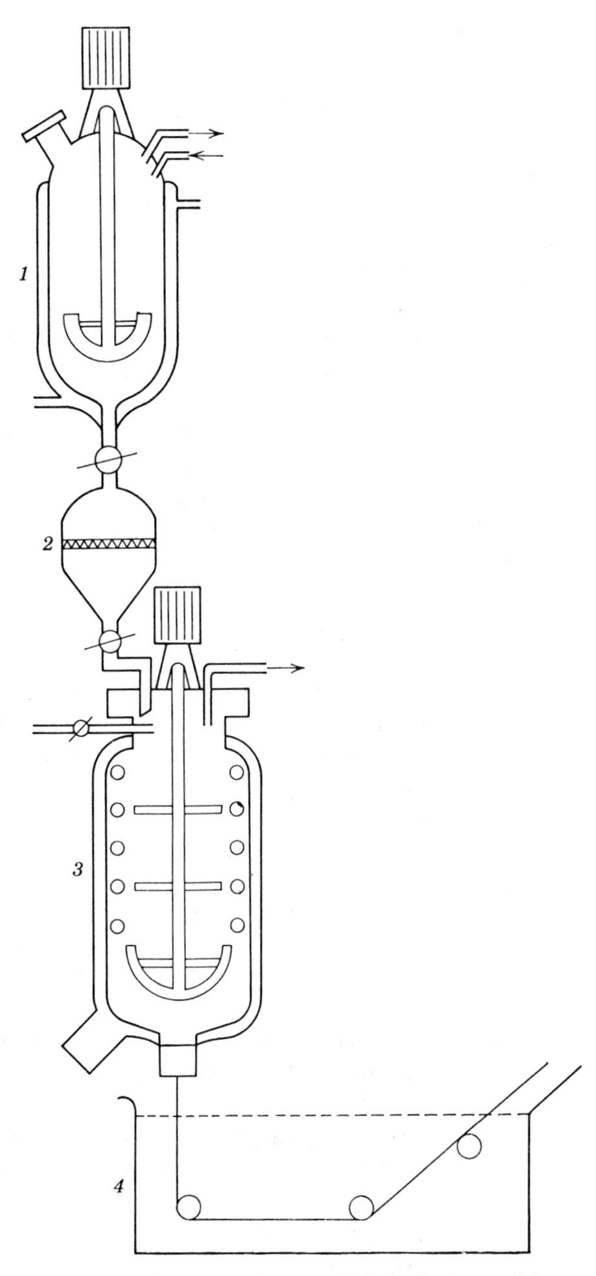

Fig. 8. Schematic diagram of an autoclave. (*1*) Caprolactam melting vessel, (*2*) filter, (*3*) autoclave, (*4*) cooling bath.

2. *VK Tube*

The tube adopted for the continuous polymerization of caprolactam is usually known as the VK tube (32); it is essentially a tube 8–10 m high, the diameter depending upon the production rate; it is also provided with a heating jacket (Fig. 9) which is sometimes divided into several sections (Fig. 10), and a pump is placed at the bottom to extrude the polymer. Feeding of the melted caprolactam together with the stabilizer and the water, which also contains the delusterant, is carried out by metering pumps or by some other kind of nearly continuous device. The inner part of the tube contains certain special fittings, such as perforated plates at varying inclinations, in order to avoid irregular paths of fluxes and to keep the moving flux as flat as possible. The top of the tube is sometimes provided with a heat-exchanger in the form of a grating so as to bring the temperature of the melt rapidly up to the fixed value. The temperature of the polymerizing mixture is maintained between 250 and 270°C; when the tube has several independent heating jackets, the temperature of the central jackets is higher in order to ensure a greater rate of reaction. In addition to the feed pipe, the top of the VK tube is fitted with an inlet for purified nitrogen, which always is kept above the surface of the reacting mixture, and a fractionating column, which may have a dephlegmator to reflux caprolactam alone. The tube dimensions and output per day are regulated so that the retention time of the polymerizing mixture will be longer than 20–24 hr and the speed of its moving front very low.

The quantity of water added to the caprolactam is between 5 and 10% (weight to weight), and, since it is greater than the amount soluble at the operating temperature, it will vaporize, boiling turbulently and causing the upper part of the melt to become agitated.

Moreover, the large amount of water present will reduce the induction time of the polymerization and will carry away most of the volatile impurities in the vapor stream.

Since the degree of polymerization at equilibrium is dependent upon the amount of water remaining in the caprolactam, which, in turn, is regulated only by the temperature at the top of the tube (Henry's law), it follows that the degree of polymerization can be varied not only by the stabilizer content but also by the temperature at the top of the melt.

It is very important, in order to achieve a good homogeneous polymer, that the retention time in the tube be appreciably longer than the time needed to reach the polymerization equilibrium.

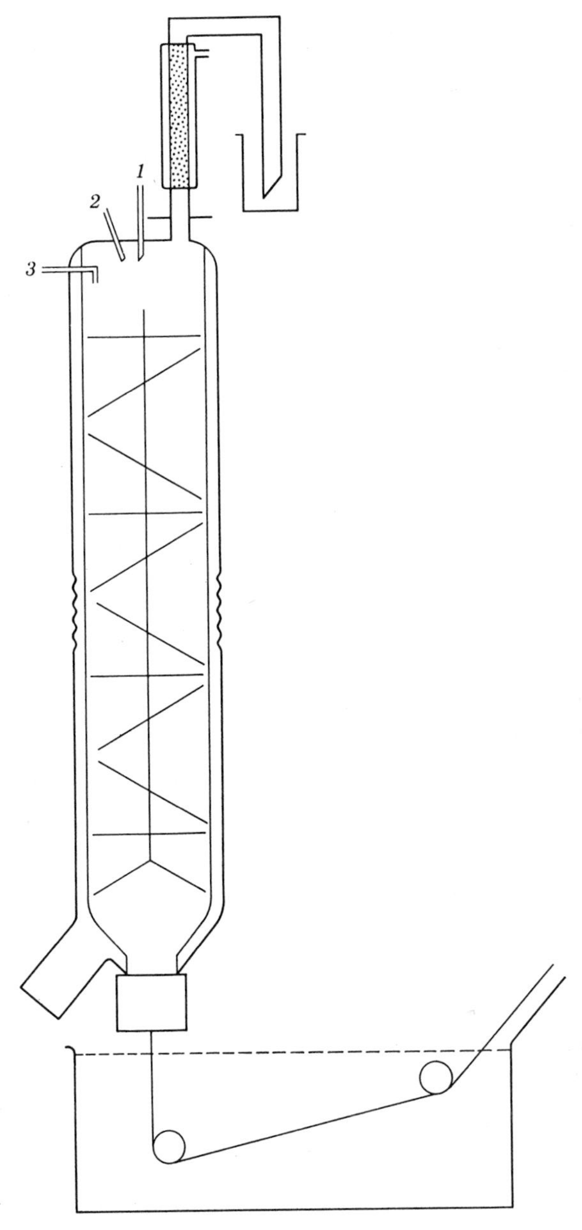

Fig. 9. VK tube with single heating jacket; inlets for (*1*) caprolactam, (*2*) water, and (*3*) nitrogen.

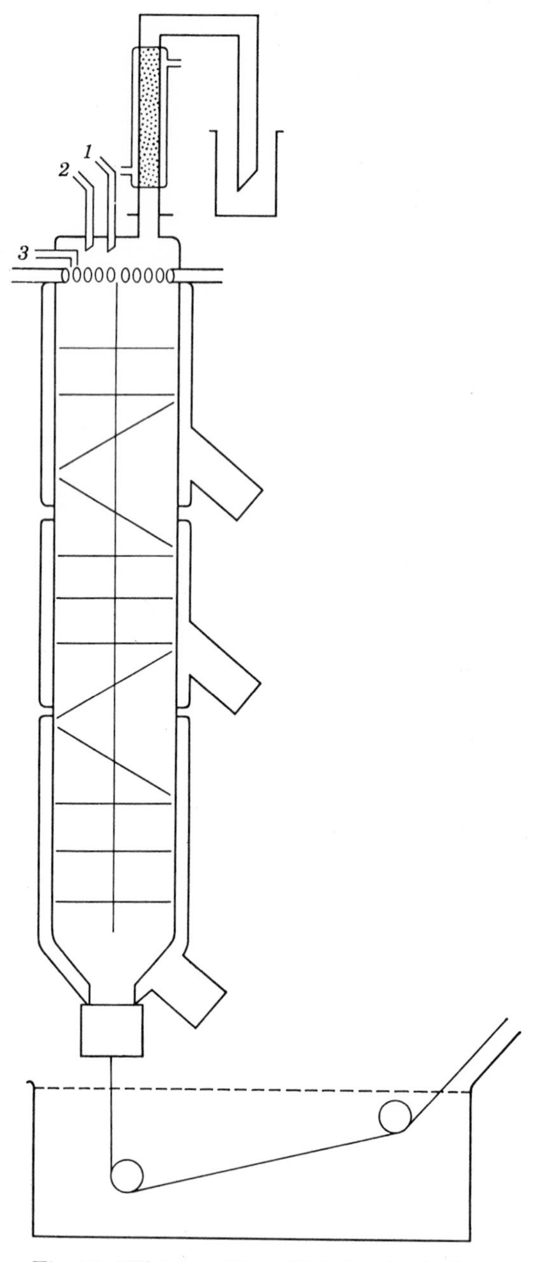

Fig. 10. VK tube with multiple heating jacket.

Some continuous processes have been described which reproduce batch polymerization by autoclave, but their adoption has been insignificant. A final stage under vacuum can remove most of the unconverted caprolactam, but it is very difficult to reach a state of equilibrium.

3. Preparation of Polymer for Spinning

Since at polymerization equilibrium about 10% of caprolactam remains unconverted, it is necessary to remove this amount from the polymer in order to avoid difficulties in the forming and processing of the fiber. In the spinning of continuous filament the caprolactam can give rise to certain defects; moreover, in fiber processing the caprolactam can cause dangerous consequences by migrating to the fiber surface. Usually the removal of the caprolactam is accomplished by washing with hot water. The polymer chips are sent to an extractor (Fig. 11), where they are washed several times with demineralized water at a temperature of 90–100°C. The washing process is so arranged that the last operation is carried out with fresh water while the first operation uses water which has gone through each stage of the cycle in the opposite direction (4°–3°, etc); in this way the water becomes rich in extracted caprolactam for the recovery operation. After the first washing the water-soluble compounds in the polymer are decreased to about 5%, after the second to 2–3%, after the third to 1–1.5% and after the fourth to 0.7–0.4%. These values are only indicative, since they are dependent upon the water/polymer ratio, the water temperature, the specific surface of the chips, the time of each washing operation, and, of course, the efficiency of the process. The final content in the polymer for spinning of compounds which can be extracted will be between 0.5 and 1.0%; within these limits it is of assistance in the spinning process.

After washing, the water which adheres mechanically to the chips is removed—for example, by a gentle stream of warm air of no more than 50°C—and the polymer is then charged, under nitrogen, into a revolving vessel for the drying operation. The drying vessel (Fig. 12) is made from stainless steel and can operate under high vacuum; the heat is supplied by hot water circulating in a jacket. The revolving axis is in line with the diagonal of the drum to assist the mixing of the chips, and the speed is 1–5 rpm. The drying operation lasts from 20 to 50 hr at temperatures of 100–120°C and under a final pressure of 10^{-1} to 10^{-2} torr. After this operation the residual water content in the polymer is below 0.10%, and usually ranged from 0.07 to 0.04%.

The dry polymer is sent to storage containers or to the spinning plant; it is very important at this stage to avoid long exposure of the dry poly-

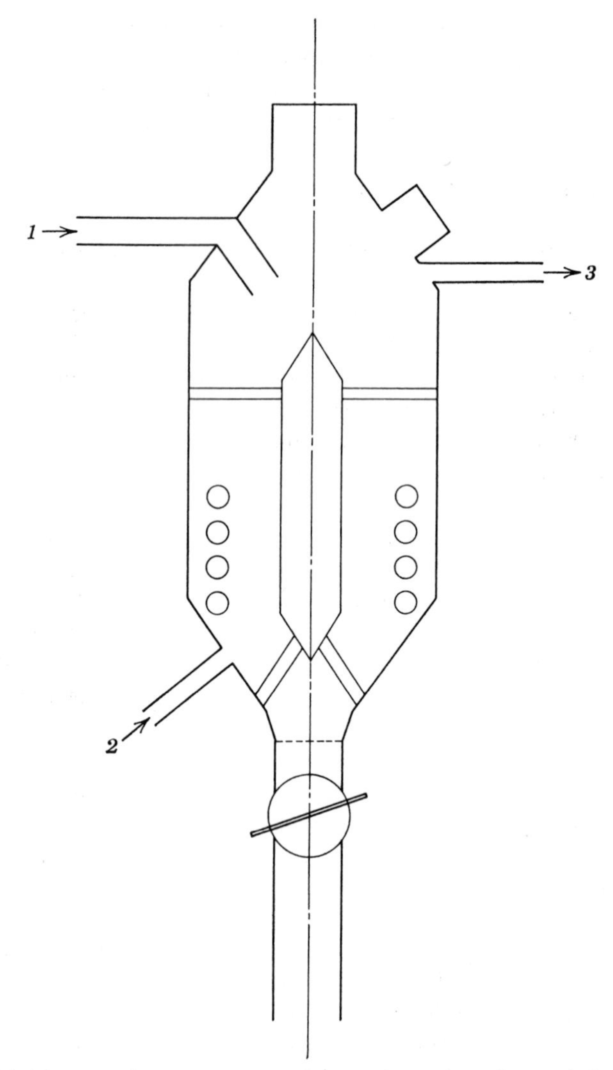

Fig. 11. Washing vessel to remove caprolactam from the polymer (schematic diagram); (*1*) inlet for polymer water suspension, (*2*) water inlet, (*3*) water outlet.

mer to the atmosphere, as water absorption is extremely rapid (see Fig. 13).

C. Depolymerization

The polycaprolactam can be depolymerized hydrolytically in acid solutions; it has been verified (33–35) that its hydrolysis under various

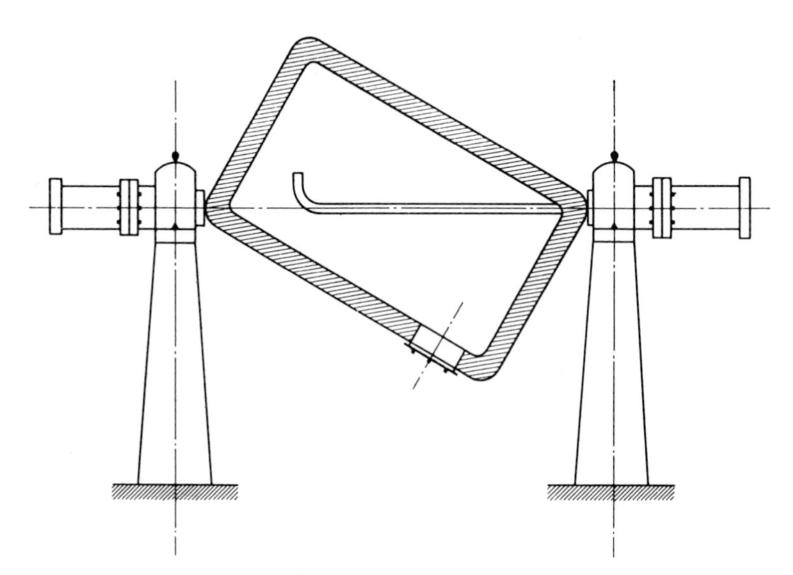

Fig. 12. Drying drum.

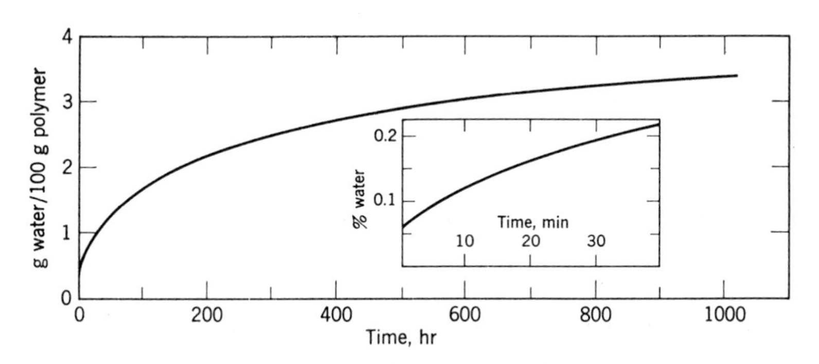

Fig. 13. Water absorption kinetics for dry polymer (room temperature, 65% R.H.).

conditions follows the behavior predicted for polycondensation polymer, i.e., the probability of scission for every amide bond is independent of the bond position in the macromolecule and therefore the degree of polymerization decreases with time, following a first-order reaction.

From a practical point of view polycaprolactam depolymerization is important for caprolactam recovery from waste. Usually the depolymerization process is carried out at high temperature (about 300°C) with acidic or basic catalysts under vacuum in order to remove the caprolactam as soon as it is formed. The yield from this operation may exceed 95%, but the crude caprolactam contains many impurities and its purification is quite complex. The final stage of purification is always

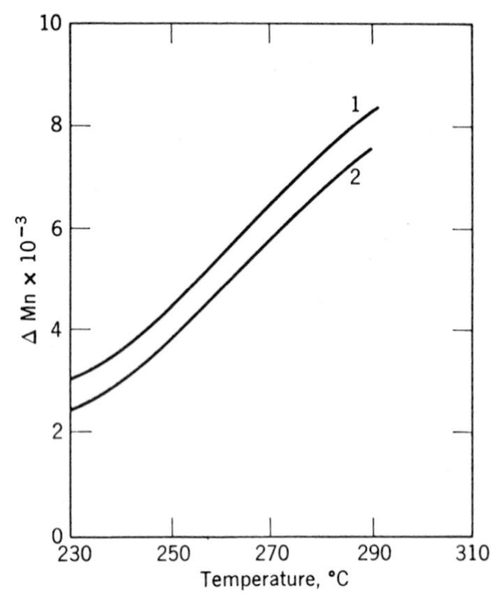

Fig. 14. Molecular weight changes for remelted polymer as a function of remelting temperature (water = 0.45%); (*1*) acetic acid = 0.07%; (*2*) acetic acid = 0.15%; time = 1 hr.

a vacuum distillation to which the caprolactam recovered from the washing of the polymer can be also sent.

III. POLYMER PROPERTIES

A. The Behavior of Melted Polycaprolactam

Since nylon 6 fibers are obtained from polycaprolactam by a melt-spinning process, the behavior of the molten polymer is of the utmost importance.

1. Post-polymerization

When the polycaprolactam is molten and remains in that state some molecular transformation will occur, according to the laws of polycondensation, if the temperature and water content differ from those previously employed to reach equilibrium. If the duration of the new conditions is insufficient to reach a further equilibrium, then the transformation will be controlled by the prevailing kinetic factor. In practice, the fact that the spinning temperature is higher than that usually employed in polymer production should lead to a decrease in the molecular weight. In fact, however, other conditions being equal, if the temperature increases,

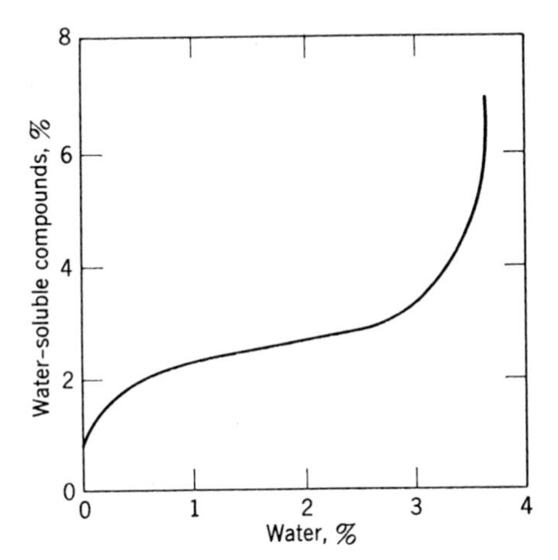

Fig. 15. Increase in water-soluble compounds for remelted polymer as a function of the water content (temperature 270°C; time 1 hr).

the molecular weight will always increase. This apparent contradiction is easily explained when one considers the water repartition between the vapor and liquid phase. Since the spinning environment is essentially dry, time and residual pressure being constant, the amount of water actually remaining in the polymer decreases as the temperature increases; this fact explains the increase in molecular weight.

The change in molecular weight also depends on the amount of stabilizer linked to the polymer; the greater the amount of stabilizer the less is the change in molecular weight, since from Eq. 12 one can see that the effect of p on the degree of polymerization is diminished by the r ratio. Several examples are given in Fig. 14 for remelted polymers under various conditions of water content and temperature in a closed vessel.

The monomer concentration will also change, in accordance with the relationship shown in Eq. 9. The monomer content increases (36,37) with increase in temperature and water content (Fig. 15).

2. *Polycaprolactam–Water Equilibria*

The water content is a predominant factor in the post-polymerization of polycaprolactam; the solubility of water in molten polycaprolactam has been proved experimentally (31) to be proportional to its vapor pressure at constant temperature, as required by Henry's law. With an increase in temperature the amount of water dissolved in the molten polymer decreases (Fig. 16). According to the experimental results of Wiloth and Dietrich (38), the vapor pressure of water in the water–

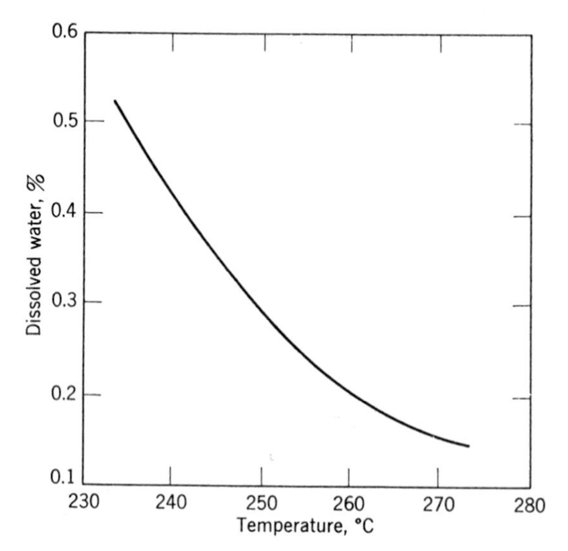

Fig. 16. Water dissolved in the molten polymer as a function of the temperature in saturated atmosphere (from data of Fukumoto (31)).

caprolactam equilibrium polymerizate is considerably lower than the saturated vapor pressure at 220°C, provided the molar ratio of water to caprolactam is lower than 2. With a molar ratio greater than 2 the vapor pressure of water tends asymptotically to the value for the saturated vapor.

3. *Rheological Behavior*

The melt viscosity of the polymer can be represented as a function of molecular weight by the relationship

$$\eta = K(M_w)^{3.4} \tag{15}$$

provided that the molecular weight is superior to a critical value M_c; in Eq. 15 η is the zero shear viscosity, M_w the weight average molecular weight, and K a constant dependent upon the polymer and temperature. This general relation is also valid for polycaprolactam (39). A recent paper (40) deals with the rheological behavior of molten caprolactam over a broad range of molecular weights and shear rates. The rheological behavior of polycaprolactam is non-Newtonian, with a flux index of 0.8 up to shear rates of about 100 sec^{-1}; for higher shear rates the flux index decreases more rapidly the higher the molecular weight. The behavior of concentrated solutions (41) confirms the results obtained on bulk polymer for concentrations above the critical value. Thus, in accordance with this behavior, in spinning when the extrusion rate and therefore also the shear rate are increased, the dependence of viscosity on molecular weight is decreased (Fig. 17).

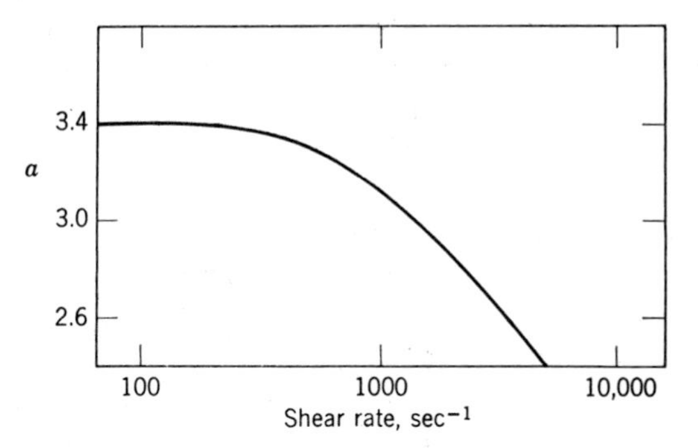

Fig. 17. Dependence of melt viscosity on molecular weight as a function of the shear rate (temperature 230°C); a is the exponent of the relationship $\eta = KM_w^a$ (from data of Pezzin (40)).

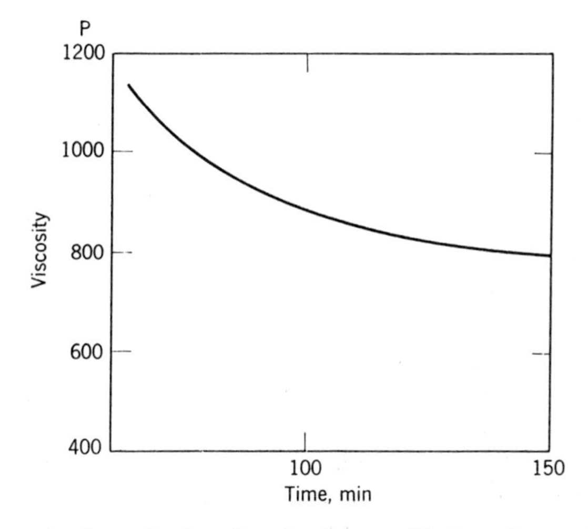

Fig. 18. Change in the melt viscosity of polymer with time (temperature 253°C).

As both molecular weight and monomer content change during the molten stage, the melt viscosity will also change. While the molecular weight affects the viscosity exponentially, as in Eq. 15, the monomer content acts as a plastifier, and thus any increase in this content leads to a decrease in the viscosity. In Fig. 18 various viscosity measurements are plotted against time of duration at 253°C.

B. General Properties and Analytical Methods

1. Molecular Weight

The number-average molecular weight of polymer suitable for textile fiber production ranges from 14,000 to 20,000. Since polycaprolactam can be regarded at equilibrium as a polycondensation polymer, the number-average molecular weight alone is sufficient for its characterization; in fact, the molecular weight distribution is given by Eq. 6 and the ratio M_w/M_n is equal to 2.

The molecular weight value is obtained from viscosity measurements in dilute solutions; the most widely used method in industrial practice is the measurement of relative viscosity in a solution with concentrated sulfuric acid (96%), containing 1 g of polymer per 100 ml of acid; in this solvent the polymer undergoes hardly any degradation (42,43). Many other solvents have been suggested to determine intrinsic viscosity. Several relationships between viscosity in dilute solutions and molecular weight are illustrated in Table IV.

TABLE IV. Relationships between Molecular Weight and Viscosity Measurements in Dilute Solutions

Viscosity	Units	Solvent	Temperature	Equation	Ref.
η_r	—	H_2SO_4 96%	20°C	$\bar{n} = 248(\eta_r^{1/2} - 1)/c - 5$	21
$[\eta]$	dl/g	HCOOH 85%	25°C	$[\eta] = 0.653 \times 10^{-4} M_n^{0.98}$	50
$[\eta]$	dl/g	H_2SO_4 33%	25°C	$[\eta] = 17.3 \times 10^{-4} M_w^{0.50}$	50
$[\eta]$	dl/g	metacresol		$\bar{n} = 136.7[\eta]^{1.309}$	51

c is concentration of solution in g/100 ml.

Another interesting method of calculating the degree of polymerization is based on the titration of end groups. The end groups present in the polycaprolactam are carboxylic, aminic, and acetylic groups, provided the stabilizer is acetic acid. The titration of aminic groups is also of importance in testing the affinity of the polymer for dyes. The carboxylic end groups are titrated in benzyl alcohol solution with alcoholic potassium hydroxide, the aminic groups in phenol–alcohol solution with hydrochloric acid, and the acetylic groups by hydrolysis of the polymer in phosphoric acid followed by distillations in the vapor stream of the acetic acid formed and its subsequent titration (44).

2. Monomer and Oligomers

The cyclic oligomers of caprolactam up to the monamer have been found in polycaprolactam (45–48), but since the cyclic oligomer concentration decreases very rapidly as the number of monomer units in the ring increases, the most important oligomers are the dimer, the trimer, and the tetramer, the main characteristics of which are shown in Table V. All the cyclic oligomers are soluble in boiling benzene and insoluble in petroleum ether. The most used methods for determining monomer and oligomers quantitatively (14) are based on extraction with boiling anhydrous methanol; the extract is eluted on exchange resins in order to separate the linear oligomers and is then fractionated by sublimation under vacuum at different temperatures. The sublimation temperature for monomer under a residual pressure of 2 mm Hg is 110°C, for dimer 210–230°C, and for trimer 260°C. A direct method for monomer determination has been proposed (49) based on the sublimation of polymer, but in industrial practice the method adopted is the measurement of the amount extractable in boiling water. By this method, the relative percentage of monomer and oligomers in the extract are of course unknown, and the nitrogen titrated by the Kjeldahl method is usually expressed entirely as caprolactam. In Table VI typical compositions of various polycaprolactam extracts are shown.

TABLE V. Caprolactam Cyclic Oligomers

	Melting point, °C	Molecular weight (56)		Solubility in H_2O (47), % at room temperature
		Theoretical	Experimental	
Dimer	348	226.3	225	0.1
Trimer	248	339.5	336	0.9
Tetramer	242	452.6	439	0.04
ε-Caprolactam	69	—	—	320

TABLE VI. Content of Water and Methanol Extracts

	Water extract, % on polymer	Methanol extract, % on polymer
Caprolactam	6.1	6.5
Linear oligomers	0.4	0.7
Dimer	0.7	0.8
Higher cyclic oligomers	1.6	1.7

3. *Moisture Content*

Chemical methods for the determination of the moisture content of polycaprolactam all incorporate the titration of water with Karl Fisher reagent, but they differ as to type of water extraction method used. The water can be extracted with anhydrous methanol, or the whole polymer can be dissolved in anhydrous solvents, or the removal of the water can be accomplished by a stream of dry inert gas flowing along the surface of the melted polymer. A relatively simple physical method involves the measurement of the vapor pressure of water in a flask of known capacity, previously prepared at about 10^{-2} mm Hg residual pressure. In order to remove the water the polymer is kept in a molten state. Every method which involves molten polymer contains some systematic errors, as during the melting process polycondensation takes place and therefore water is produced.

4. *Melting Point*

The melting point of polycaprolactam is 215°C and that of nylon 66 270°C. This difference is very considerable, despite the similar structure of the two polymers. Many papers deal with this difference, but thus far no theory can be regarded as completely satisfactory. The hypothesis of a lower degree of hydrogen bonding (52) has been disproved by accurate x-ray studies (55). Some authors (53,54) suggest that the difference may be due to a greater melting entropy, whereas others (55) refer to some general law concerning the odd number of carbon atoms between amide groups.

5. *Chemical Properties*

The most widely used solvents for polycaprolactam are reported in Table VII; this polymer, like other polyamides, is generally soluble in organic and mineral acids and in their aqueous concentrated solutions, in phenols, and in some alcohols, especially at elevated temperatures. It has been seen that polycaprolactam is hydrolyzed in dilute acid solutions, while in concentrated acid solutions at room temperature the polymer is soluble but the hydrolysis rates are very low or practically zero, as in 96% sulfuric acid; for instance, in polymer solutions prepared with this solvent viscosity changes cannot be detected 20 days after the preparation (43) of the solution.

The polycaprolactam is very resistant to basic agents; for example, the nylon 6 fiber immersed in a boiling 10% solution of NaOH loses only about 10% of its tenacity. The effect of oxidizing agents (hydrogen peroxide, sodium hypochlorite) is more noticeable, while reducing agents have no effect. The more usual organic solvents have at most a swelling action on polycaprolactam; more specifically, those compounds, which have groups suitable for hydrogen bond formation are strong swelling agents (see Table VII).

TABLE VII. Solvents and Swelling Agents

Compound	Solvent: Room temp.	Solvent: Hot	Swelling agent
Sulfuric acid (>33% conc.)	+		
Phosphoric acid	+		
Formic acid	+		
Hydrochloric acid	+		
Phenol (>6% conc.)	+		
Acetic acid	+		
Chloroacetic acid			+
Thioglycolic acid			+
Benzyl alcohol		(120°)	+
Butyl alcohol		(120°)	
Methanol saturated with $CaCl_2$	+		
Resorcinol			+
Metacresol	+		
Trifluoroethanol	+		
Water			+
Chloroform			+
Methanol			+

IV. SPINNING AND DRAWING

A. Continuous Filament

1. Spinning

The melt-spinning process for the production of textile fibers from nylon 6 is very similar to that for nylon 66. A spinning assembly consists schematically of a type of grid for melting the polymer, a small well to collect the molten polymer, a filter pack, and a spinneret. The various kinds of spinning assemblies differ from one another (*1*) in the system of heating which may be electrical or by fluid circulation; (*2*) in the method of keeping the molten polymer level constant (self-regulating or by servocontrol); (*3*) in the fluid used to prevent oxidation of the polymer during and after the melting (by purified nitrogen ($O_2 < 5$ ppm) or superheated steam). Figure 19 shows some schematic designs of spinning assemblies; each individual melting element can feed several spinnerets, each supplied with its metering pump. In some very recent spinning assemblies the molten polymer feed is carried out by a screw-extruder in order to obtain a higher output and to ensure that the molten polymer is properly homogeneous.

The spinnerets (see Fig. 20) are made from a stainless steel block and are circular in form; the capillary is provided with an entrance cylinder

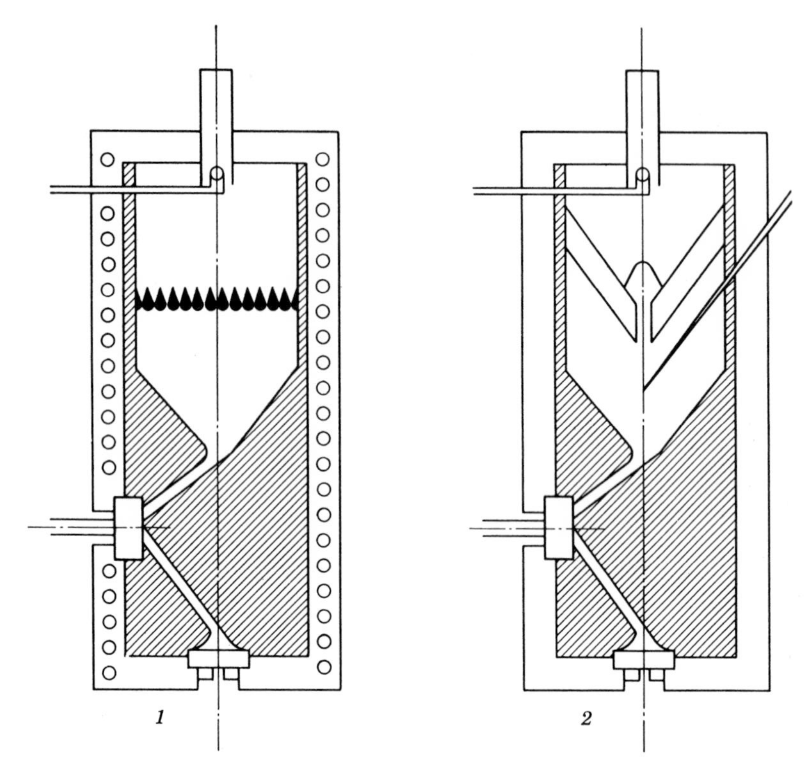

Fig. 19. Schematic diagram of spinning assembly. (*1*) Fluid heating, (*2*) electric heating.

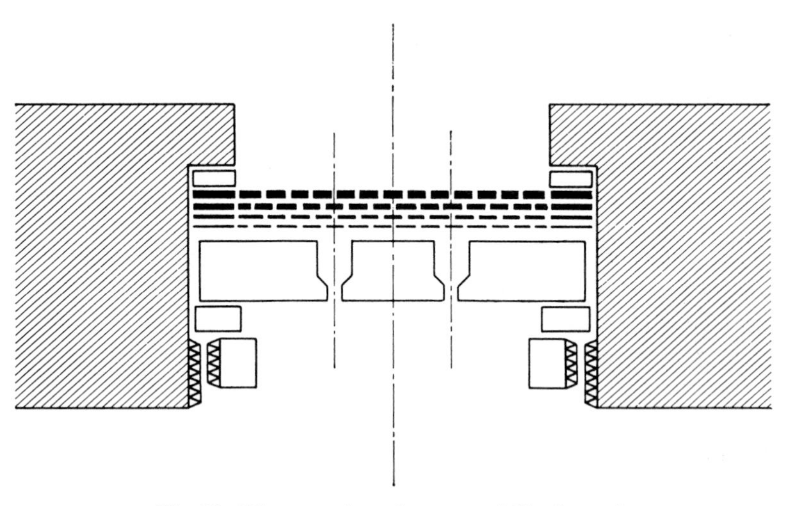

Fig. 20. Diagram of a spinneret and filtering unit.

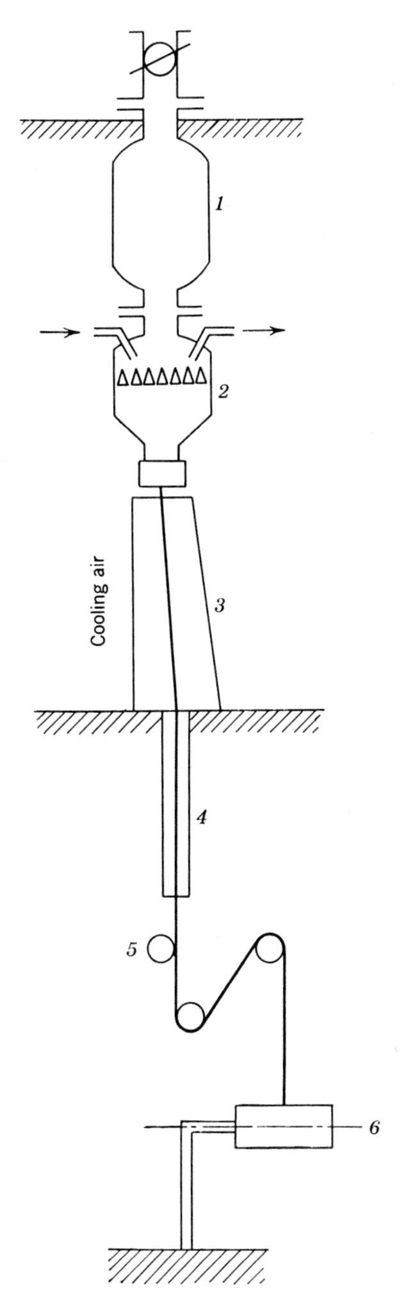

Fig. 21. Schematic diagram of a spinning line; (*1*) polymer container, (*2*) melt grid, (*3*) blowing chimney, (*4*) conditioning chamber, (*5*) finishing roll, (*6*) yarn package.

and a cone-shaped connection. The capillary diameters usually range from 0.2 to 0.3 mm and their height ranges from 1 to 3 times the diameter. From the rheological point of view the spinnerets must be properly considered as holes in a plate. A noncircular section of the spinneret holes can be employed to produce filaments with special sections (triangular, multilobal, or indented).

The melting temperature is about 260–280°C and the retention time must be long enough to obtain a molten polymer which is completely homogeneous, but must not allow the formation of an excessive amount (>3%) of caprolactam so as to avoid difficulties at the fiber processing stage.

The thin stream of molten polymer emerging from the lower face of the spinneret is usually cooled by a cross air blast and, after solidification, it is wetted with an emulsion of antistatic and lubricating agents (spinning finish). The purpose of the finishing application is not only to form a surface layer so as to avoid difficulties arising from static electricity and high friction coefficients, but also to facilitate moisture absorption from the dry filament and then hygrothermic equilibrium of the fiber. After the finishing application the yarn is wound onto bobbins at speeds ranging from 600 to 1100 m/min.

The general layout of a spinning line is shown in Fig. 21. The cross air blast which is freed from dust and conditioned is passed through an adequate blowing chimney, supplied with an equalizing filter. In order to obtain a good even yarn the output of the cross air blast must be perfectly constant and uniform throughout, without creating whirling motions around the yarns, possibly leading to variances in their diameters.

The mechanical and rheological aspects of melt spinning have been thoroughly studied (57–65) and several papers have been published dealing with polycaprolactam spinning. These studies show that the fundamental factor for fiber formation is the velocity gradient parallel to the spinning axis. This gradient is a function of the extrusion speed (V_e), of the winding speed (V_f) and of the distance from the spinneret (l) at which the fiber cross section becomes constant. This latter, in turn, is a function of the cooling gradient, and hence depends on the specific surface of the fiber and on thermal exchanges with the surrounding atmosphere. The average velocity gradient, parallel to the spinning axis, is given by

$$(V_f - V_e)/l$$

and has a much greater effect upon fiber formation than the ratio between winding speed and extrusion speed, which is known incorrectly as "draw ratio at the spinneret."

Changes in the fiber cross section take place up to a distance of usually less than 1.5 m from the spinneret. This stage gives rise to the first orientation of the fiber and is followed by the orientation which results from the difference in speed between the first godet and the windup unit. The overall undrawn fiber orientation is known as "preorientation" and depends on the difference between the winding speed and the extrusion speed and also on the quantity and humidity of the blowing air, increasing together with these factors and decreasing as the temperature of the blown air increases.

The effect of the velocity gradient parallel to the spinning axis on the undrawn fiber preorientation is easily seen from Table VIII.

TABLE VIII. Preorientation of Fiber as Function of Winding Speed

Winding speed, m/min	Titer, den	Birefringence
1000	68	0.0164
900	73	0.0154
800	72	0.0133

The quality of the bobbins of undrawn yarn depends not only on mechanical factors but especially on water absorption, which exerts its influence by two different mechanisms. The water absorption causes an elongation of the undrawn fiber, in accordance with the isotherms of Fig. 22, and on the other hand it influences the rate of crystallization,

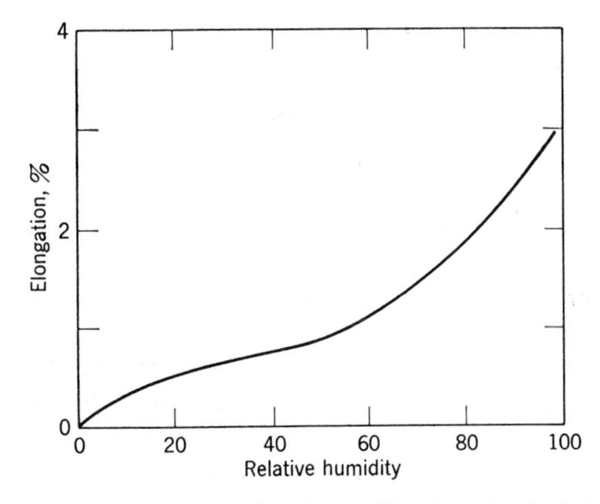

Fig. 22. Longitudinal deformations of undrawn fiber, previously dried, conditioned at various relative humidities at room temperature.

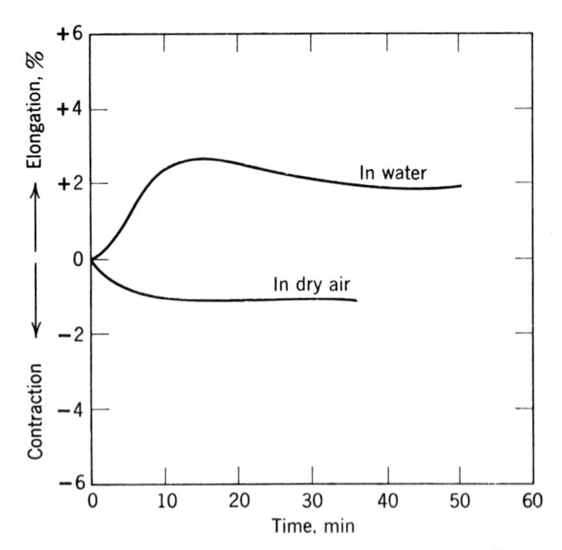

Fig. 23. Longitudinal deformations of undrawn fiber immersed, immediately after spinning, in water or in dry air at room temperature.

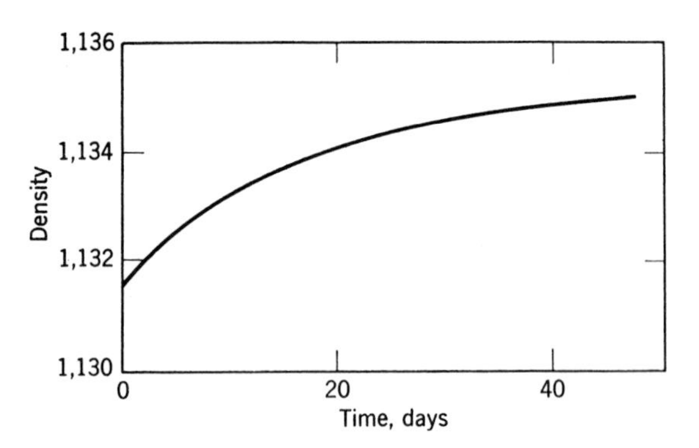

Fig. 24. Changes in density of undrawn fiber with time at room temperature.

causing the fiber to contract. This behavior is evident from Fig. 23, where the dimensional changes of an undrawn fiber without finish are plotted against time; the newly spun fiber is either kept in dry air or immersed in water.

Before moving on to the drawing operation, the fiber bobbin must be kept for a short period in a conditioned atmosphere in order to achieve a near-equilibrium of crystallization; actually the undrawn yarn tends asymptotically to reach this equilibrium (Fig. 24), but after a few hours equilibrium is almost reached (66), and it should be remembered that it is undesirable to draw yarns which have crystallized too far.

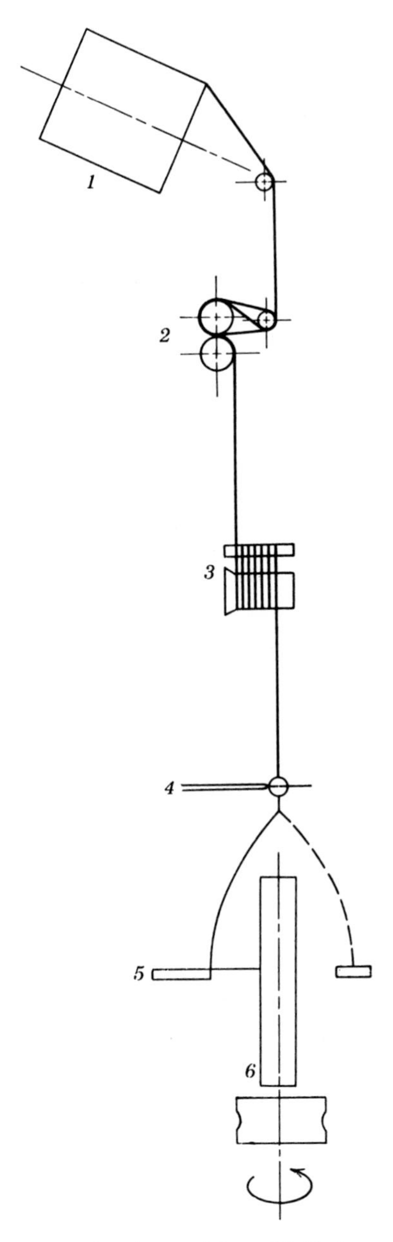

Fig. 25. Schematic diagram of a draw-twister. (*1*) Undrawn yarn package, (*2*) feed roller, (*3*) draw roller, (*4*) lappet, (*5*) ring holder, (*6*) drawn yarn bobbin.

2. *Drawing*

In order to achieve final properties which are suitable for textile applications, the undrawn nylon 6 fiber must be drawn to 3.5–4 times its undrawn length (250–300% elongation). This operation is carried

TABLE IX. Recovery after Drawing

Retention time in the drawn state (hr)	Recovery, %	
	Draw ratio 1:4	Draw ratio 1:5
0	14.5	16.0
3	11.3	12.6
30	10.0	12.0
60	9.0	11.0

out on a draw-twisting unit, a general layout of which is shown in Fig. 25. The most important parts of the draw twister are the feed and draw rolls, which have different peripheral speeds, thus determining the machine draw ratios. This differs from the true draw ratio, since between draw roll and the packaging unit the yarn recovers a small amount of the imposed elongation (see Table IX). The recovery obviously depends upon the drawing speed and upon the distance between the draw roll and the bobbin, which determines the relaxation

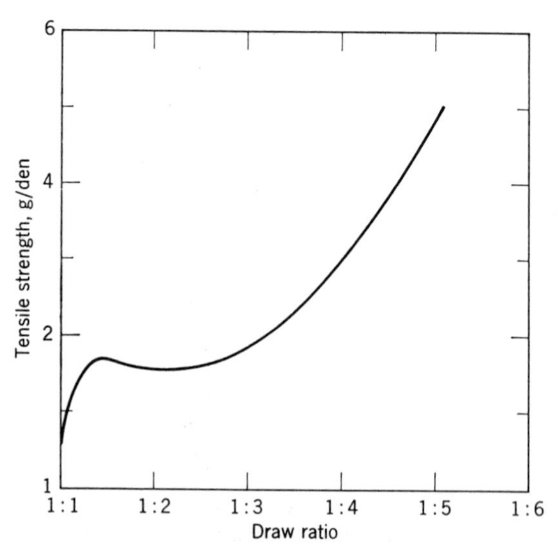

Fig. 26. Stress–strain diagram of undrawn fiber; the stresses correspond to final titer.

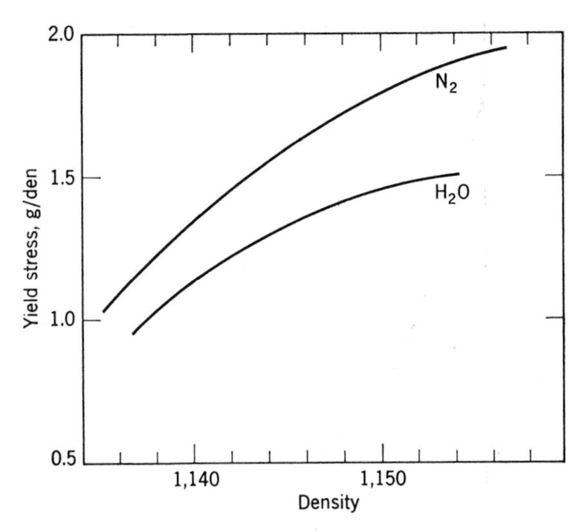

Fig. 27. Changes in the yield stress for undrawn fibers conditioned in nitrogen or water at various temperatures (at very low drawing speed).

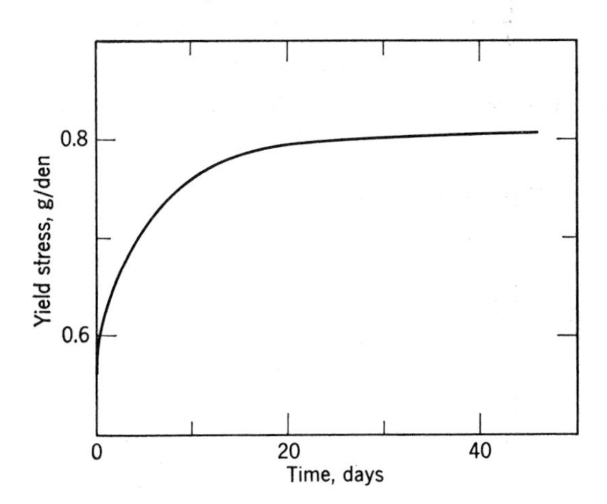

Fig. 28. Changes in the yield stress for undrawn fibers as a function of time elapsed after spinning (at very low drawing speed).

time, and also on the tension acting on the fiber before the winding up operation.

From the stress–strain diagram of an undrawn nylon 6 fiber (Fig. 26) three fundamental stages can be recognized: the first is from zero stress up to yield stress, the second is characterized by elongation without an increase in tension (this is also called "natural draw ratio" (67)), and the third shows an increase in the elastic modulus. The actual values of

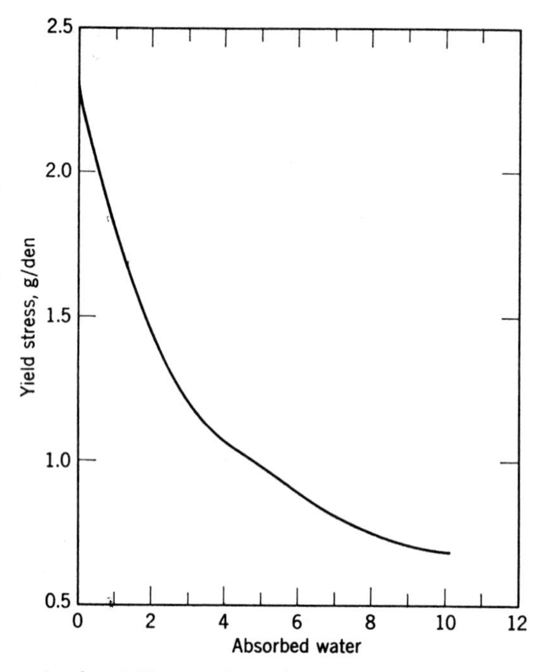

Fig. 29. Decrease in the yield stress for undrawn fibers related to increase in wate absorbed by the fiber.

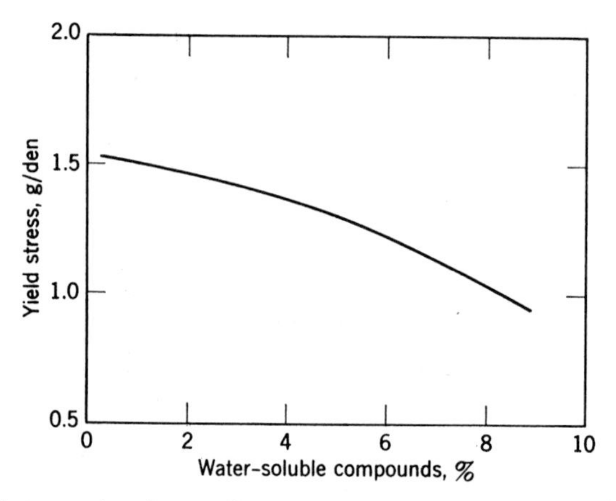

Fig. 30. Yield stress of undrawn fibers as function of the content of water-soluble compounds (from data of Roth and Schroth (69)).

these quantities are dependent on several factors related to the structure of the undrawn fiber. By increasing the crystallinity or, more accurately, the structural regularity of the fiber, the yield stress is in-

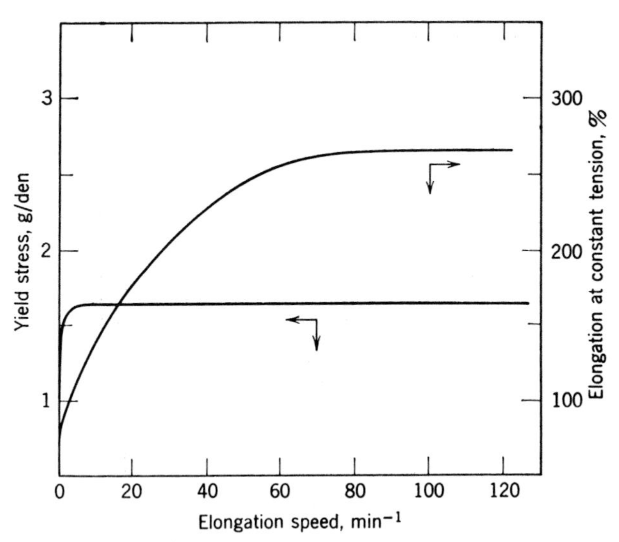

Fig. 31. Changes in the yield stress and elongation at constant tension related to variations in elongation speed.

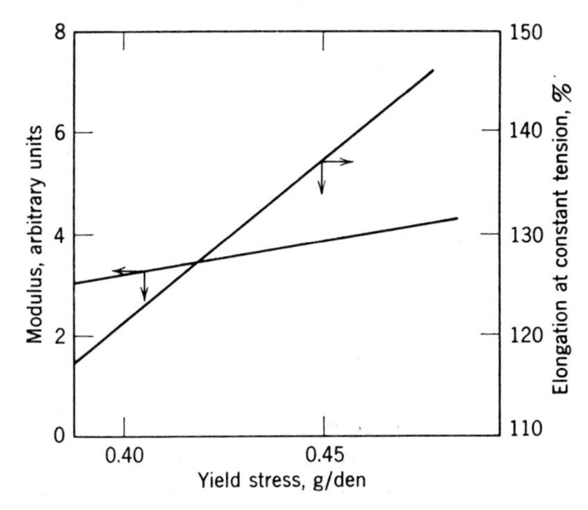

Fig. 32. Correlations between elastic modulus, yield stress, and elongation at constant tension for undrawn fibers with the same titer and elongation speed.

creased; however, this increase is not univocal because it also depends on the method used to improve the structure. For example the yield stresses of fibers treated in dry heat in an atmosphere of nitrogen are superior to these of fiber of the same density treated in hot water (Fig. 27); moreover, the increase in density with time will result in higher yield stresses (Fig. 28). By increasing the amount of adsorbed water the

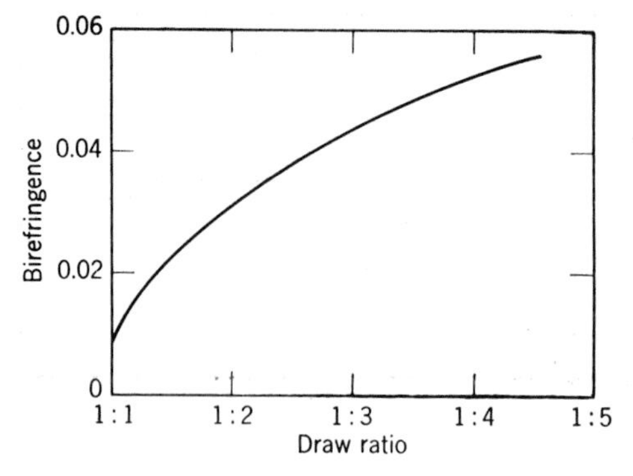

Fig. 33. Increase in birefringence with the draw ratio for 20-den monofilament.

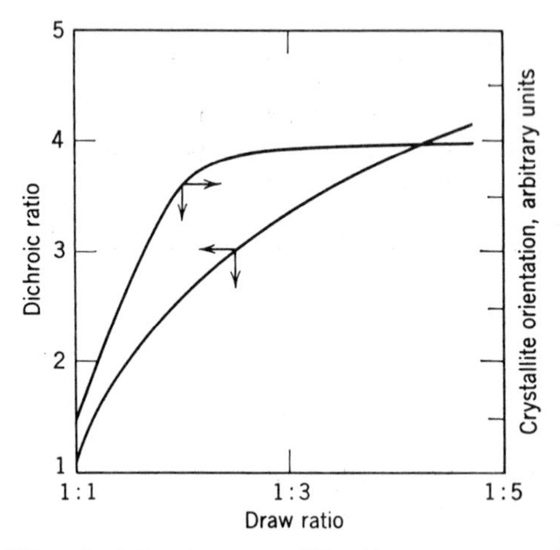

Fig. 34. Crystallite orientation by x-ray diffraction measurements and amorphous part orientation by dichroic ratio of an absorbed dye as a function of the draw ratio.

yield stress decreases (Fig. 29), hence it is desirable to keep the storage and drawing at a relatively high level of humidity. Moreover, the extractable compounds which act as plastifiers reduce the yield stress (Fig. 30). The qualitative behavior of the various stages of the drawing diagram is shown in Fig. 31 as a function of the deformation speed; while the yield stress rapidly reaches a maximum value, the elongation at constant tension tends to its limit very slowly. The initial elastic modulus, the yield stress, and the elongation at constant tension are also intercorrelated (Fig. 32) when they are measured at the same elongation speed on filaments obtained under different conditions. All these results are evidence of the relationship between the drawing behavior and the order regularity (crystallinity) of the fiber, and also between the elongation speed and relaxation times. The change in crystallinity, as deduced from density and x-ray measurements (68), is not very high and reaches a maximum increase of 20–25% compared with that of undrawn fiber. The orientation increases with the draw ratio and this can be deduced from the increase in birefringence (Fig. 33), which is an integrated measure of the overall order of the fiber. The orientation of the crystalline phase can be followed by x-ray diffraction and that of the amorphous phase by dichroic ratio developed by drawing an undrawn fiber dyed with a dichroic dye (see Fig. 34). From the results of these measurements, it is possible to arrive at a first approximation, namely, that in the first and second zones of the drawing diagram and until the natural draw ratio is reached, the orientation of the crystalline phase is dominant, while in the third zone both the overall arrangement of the amorphous phase and the perfecting of crystallites are improved.

The draw ratios commonly used in practice range from 1:3.5 to 1:3.9, depending upon the preorientation at spinning; the winding speeds can reach as high as 700 m/min. In order to ensure certain desirable final properties it is important that the spinning history of the fiber be taken into consideration, and particularly the preorientation and crystallinity. By increasing the draw ratio the tensile strength and elasticity modulus are increased, while the elongation at break and titer decrease. Typical values for drawn nylon 6 monofilament at various draw ratios are shown in Table X.

TABLE X. Properties of Yarns as Function of Draw Ratio

Draw ratio	Titer, den	Tenacity, g/den	Final elongation, %	Elastic modulus, kg/mm^2
1:3.2	17.5	4.8	62	14
1:3.5	15.8	5.3	41	23
1:3.8	14.8	5.7	30	34
1:4.2	13.5	6.5	22	39

3. *Hot-Drawing*

To obtain very high tensile strength it is necessary to have high molecular weight, orientation, and crystallinity. Since the drawing tensions increase both with crystallinity and with the draw ratio adopted, hot-drawing is used with fibers with molecular weights of 20,000–25,000 in order to avoid this difficulty. Hot-drawing facilitates the drawing process since, due to the higher molecular mobility, the drawing tensions decrease and the crystallinity is increased. Hot-drawing usually follows a normal cold-drawing with a low draw ratio; both operations can be carried out either on one machine or on two different machines (Fig. 35). The heating area is provided by a heater plate, the temperature of which must be carefully controlled and kept constant. The temperature of

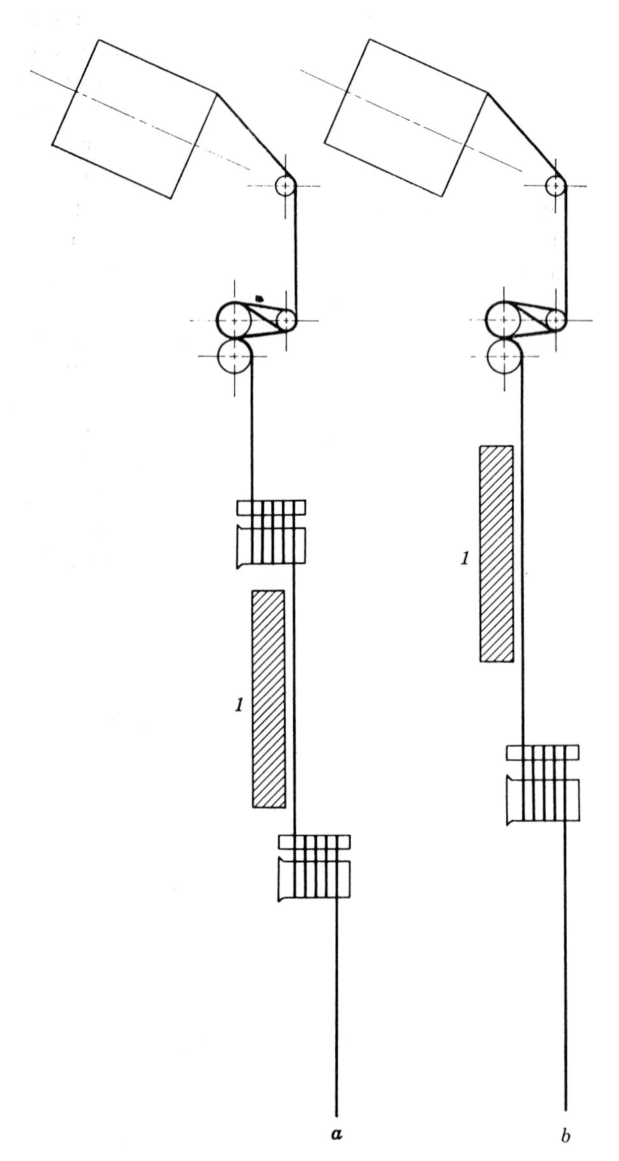

Fig. 35. Schematic diagram of hot-drawing units. (*a*) Cold- and hot-drawing unit, (*b*) hot-drawing alone, (*1*) heating plate.

the plate must be below the limit at which the fiber properties are adversely affected and the probability of fiber breakage during the drawing begins to increase. This limit depends on the actual temperature reached by the fiber, and hence upon the structural characteristics of the machine. In Table XI a set of values is given for fibers drawn at various temperatures in a silicon oil bath.

TABLE XI. Properties of Yarns, Drawn at Various Temperatures (Draw Ratio 1:5; in Silicone Oil Bath)

Bath temperature, °C	Tenacity, g/den	Final elongation, %
140	9.9	14.0
150	9.8	13.4
160	9.7	13.0

Tenacities above 8 g/den and elongations at break below 12% can be obtained by correct hot-drawing.

B. Staple

Nylon 6 staple production is not very dissimilar in principle from that of continuous filament, but in practice the two processes are quite different. In the case of staple the polymer obtained from continuous polymerization plant is usually spun directly without any preparation, but sometimes, before spinning a final stage is added under vacuum so as to remove most of the uncoverted caprolactam from the polymerizing mixture. After spinning and storage several bobbins of undrawn yarns are gathered together in one large thread and processed simultaneously.

The fundamental operations for staple production from undrawn thread are as follows: drawing, crimping, monomer removal, setting, finishing, drying, cutting. The sequence of these operations is varied in several different ways after drawing, and sometimes the setting and monomer removal are combined into one stage. Figure 36 gives two general diagrams of staple-producing lines. Sometimes the overall draw ratio is divided into two parts, one of which can also be heated by infrared sources or by steam; it can be seen that the aim of this operation is to increase tenacity and elastic modulus of the fiber. Another very important part of a staple production line is the crimping, which can be carried out either on the line, provided the caprolactam is removed with boiling water after crimping, or alternatively after cutting in a steam-box on the pressed staple. The crimp, together

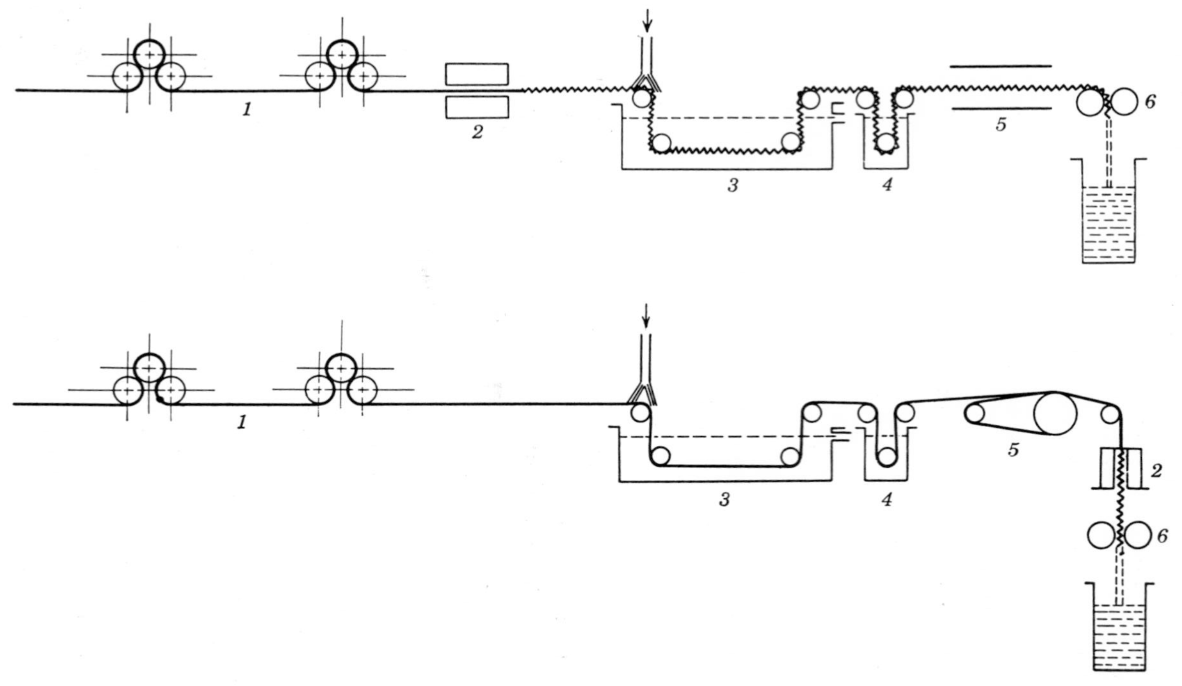

Fig. 36. Diagrams for staple production: (*1*) drawing, (*2*) crimping, (*3*) washing, (*4*) finishing, (*5*) drying, (*6*) cutting.

with the frictional and antistatic properties, which obviously depend on the quality and amount of finish given to the fiber, are the most important features of the staple for processing purposes.

In some plants the carding of the staple is avoided and the tow is obtained on one machine direct from the thread, which has been drawn, crimped, washed, and dried.

V. STRUCTURE AND PROPERTIES OF THE FIBER

A. Structure

The structure of nylon 6 is very complex compared with other polyamides; the following different phases have been discovered by x-ray diffraction (55,71–74): amorphous; γ, pseudohexagonal; β, hexagonal; α, paracrystalline monoclinic; α, Bunn's monoclinic.

The relative amount of the various phases depends on the thermal and processing history of the sample.

The most stable form is Bunn's α, the dimensions assigned to its elementary cell being a = 9.56 Å, b = 17.24 Å, c = 8.01 Å, and $\beta = 67^1/_2°$ (55), which agrees closely with Brill's first indexing (75). This structure is defined by a three-dimensional order and by the configuration of the macromolecular chains which are fully extended planar zigzag, in order to reach complete hydrogen bonding neighboring chains must be antiparallel; the distance between two chains is fixed by the length of hydrogen bond and is equal to 4.8 Å. The paracrystalline α form is an imperfect crystal, in accordance with Hosemann, and the β and γ forms are characterized by the absence of reticular planes. The unstable forms tend to transform in the α form as a result of the various treatments which improve the overall orientation and crystallinity of the fiber, namely drawing and heating in air or in water. In the undrawn fiber, immediately after spinning, there is no crystallinity at all, but after a short time (about 10–30 min) crystallization begins with a large amount of γ phase and a small amount of α and β phases. After drawing, and especially after hot-drawing, the more stable α form is prevalent. In so-called "direct spinning," where drawing is directly coupled with spinning, the predominant crystalline phase is the γ form.

A very interesting α–γ transition can be obtained chemically (76,77), immersing the fiber in an aqueous solution of iodine–potassium iodide, and then removing the iodine with an aqueous solution of sodium thiosulphate. The most likely mechanism for this transition is iodine absorption in the crystalline part of the fiber by the formation of a coordination complex of oxygen in the amide group, resulting in the dissociation of the hydrogen bond, followed by the formation of a halogen bond between the amide groups of two adjacent planes. During the iodine removal the hydrogen bonds are reformed in the positions previously occupied by the halogen bonds. The γ form can be changed back to the α form by drawing and annealing the fiber or by treating it with an aqueous solution of phenol.

The most recent calculations of density from x-ray data give the following values (74): α, Bunn = 1.230 g/cm^3; α, paracrystalline = 1.174 g/cm^3; β = 1.150 g/cm^3; γ = 1.159 g/cm^3; and amorphous 1.084 g/cm^3.

From this picture of the structure of nylon 6 it is clear that the simplified model of two phases, amorphous and crystalline, for obtaining crystallinity values from density measurements is very inaccurate and uncertain; one can merely say that higher values of density correspond to better overall order in the fiber; exhaustive information can be obtained from x-ray measurements using the methods published by Reichle and Prietzchk (71) or by Roldan, Rahl, and Paterson (74).

As far as fiber orientation is concerned, it is possible to obtain excellent information from x-ray and birefringence data. An empirical relation (78,79) has been established between fiber birefringence (Δn) and draw ratio (λ), related to a hypothetical fiber with no real drawing at all, i.e., without any orientation; the mathematical expression for nylon 6 is

$$d\Delta/d \ln \lambda = 51 \times 10^{-3} - 0.54\, \Delta n \qquad (16)$$

The infrared spectrum of nylon 6 has been studied by several authors (77,80–83) and the absorption bands at 935, 970, and 1030 cm^{-1} have been attributed to crystalline vibrations (80). Figure 37 shows the infrared spectrum and Table XII gives the assignment of the main absorption bands.

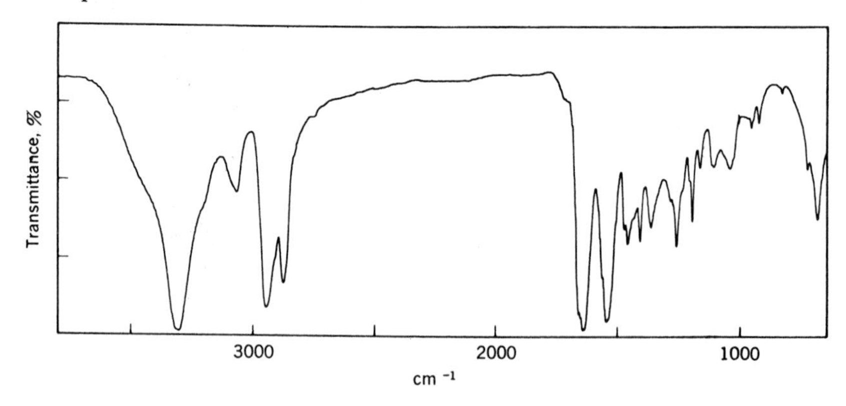

Fig. 37. Infrared spectrum of nylon 6.

B. Mechanical Properties

The ultimate mechanical properties of nylon 6 fiber are strongly dependent upon the overall orientation and degree of order and on the molecular weight of the polymer. They are also dependent upon the nature of the predominant crystalline phase; for example, fibers with a prevalent γ structure have a lower tenacity than those with an α structure (Fig. 38). The usual textile fibers have tensile strengths ranging from 5 to 7 g/den and elongation at break from 25–40% of the initial length, if tested at room temperature and 65% R.H. As the temperature increases the tenacity and initial elastic modulus decrease, while the elongation at break increases (Fig. 39). An increase in water absorbed

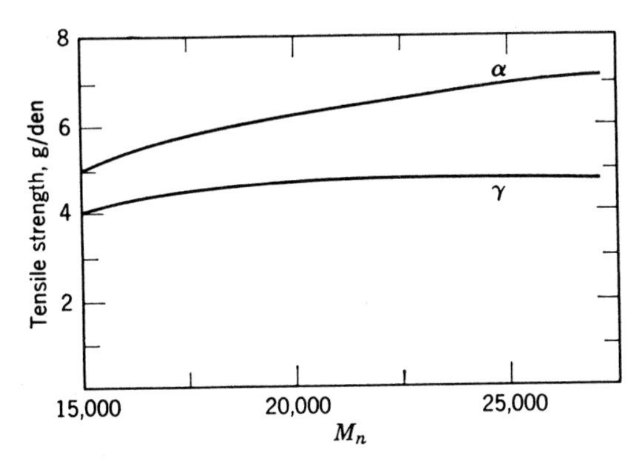

Fig. 38. Tenacity of fibers with prevalent α or γ crystalline phase, as a function of molecular weight (from data of Reichle and Prietzschk (71)).

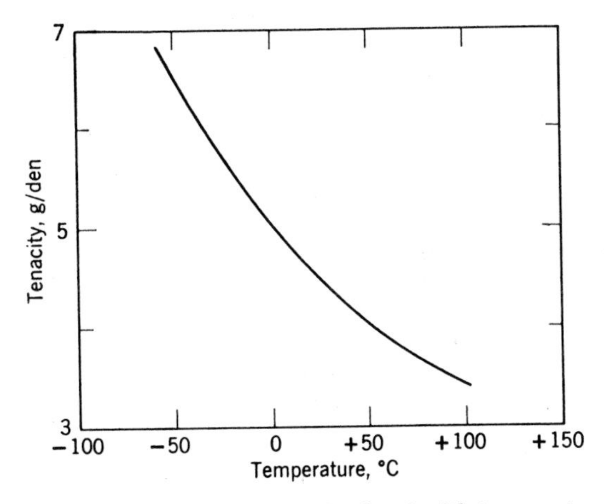

Fig. 39. Changes in tenacity of nylon 6 with temperature.

TABLE XII. Assignment of Some Absorption Bands of Nylon 6 in the Infrared

Wave number,[a] cm^{-1}				Intensity	Assignment
a	b	c	d		
	3420				
	3280	3290	3290	vs	Hydrogen bonded NH stretching
	3200				
	3080	3070	3090	m	Hydrogen bonded NH stretching
		2930	2930	vs	CH_2 asym stretching
	2910				
	2860	2865	2860		CH_2 sym stretching
	1650	1642	1642	ws	Amide I
	1560		1562	vvs	Amide II
		1545		ws	
	1480	1480			
	1465	1465	1464		CH_2 deformation
	1440	1438	1441		
	1420	1417			
1370	1370	1373	1368		CH_2 twisting
1305	1305	1305	1306		CH_2 wagging
1290		1295			
	1280		1284		
1270		1271	1274	m	Amide III
	1265				
1250		1247			
	1240		1238	m	CH_2 wagging
1220					
	1215	1214	1214		
1214					Amide III
	1205	1202		m	
1175	1170	1171	1171	m	
1130					
1120	1115	1121	1120	m	CC stretching
1080	1075	(1076–1074)	(1081–1074)	m	Skeletal motion
1040	1040	1041			CC stretching
1030		1029	1029	m	CONH in plane
990			1000		
970	977		977	m	Related to γ-form
965	962	960			
		952			CONH in plane
935					
	926	928		m	
835	832	833	776		CH_2 rocking
	730	731	728	s	
	690	692	708	s	Amide V

[a] a from Sandeman and Keller (80); b from Tobin and Carrano (82); c and d from Arimoto (77).

TABLE XIII. Properties of Yarns, Set in Boiling Water for 2 hr

Treatment state	Strength, kg/mm²	Elongation, %	Elastic modulus, kg/mm²
Free	51.3	43.6	9.6
Held at constant length	60.0	37.7	19.9
Elongated 5%	60.0	38.3	30.5
Elongated 15%	68.0	30.0	35.9
No treatment	59.9	34.5	25.0

by the fiber changes the shape of the stress–strain diagram (Fig. 40); the tenacity and the moduli are lowered since the water loses some hydrogen bonds.

In comparison with natural fibers the stress–strain diagram of nylon 6 lies between cotton and wool (Fig. 41); it shows an initial elastic modulus, a yield point, a second zone where tension and elongation are almost proportional to each other, and a second yield point. Their relative

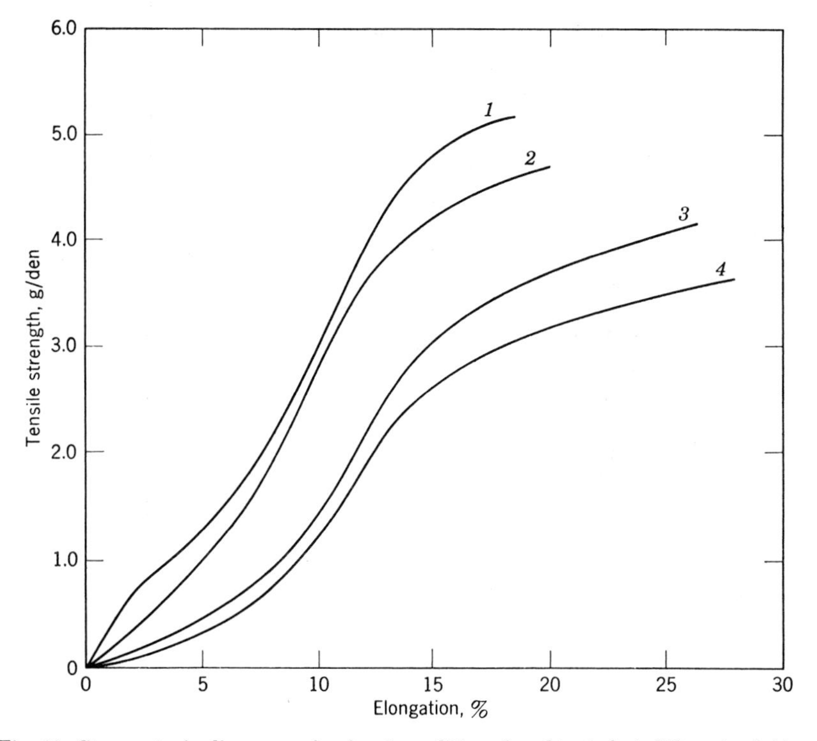

Fig. 40. Stress–strain diagrams of nylon 6 conditioned and tested at different relative humidities. (*1*) Dry, (*2*) 60% RH, (*3*) 95% RH, (*4*) in water (room temperature).

values depend on the draw ratio given to the sample and on its overall order. The most important factor in this respect is an increase in orientated crystallinity on the already formed fiber, such as can be ob-

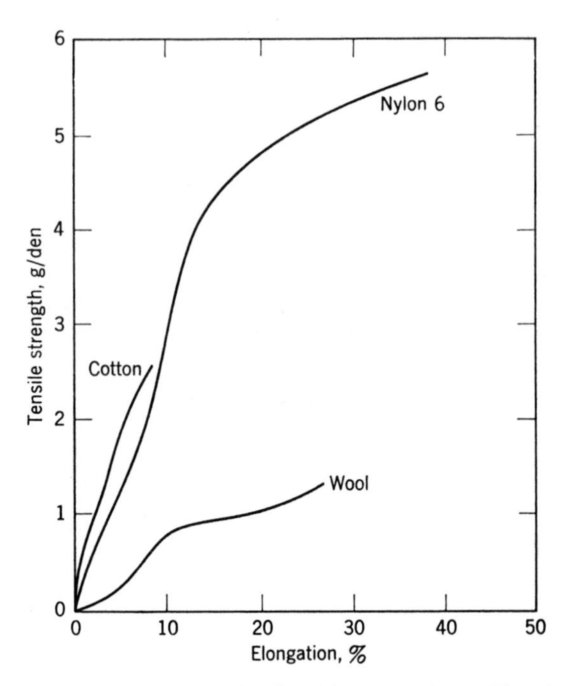

Fig. 41. Stress–strain diagram of nylon 6 in comparison with natural fibers.

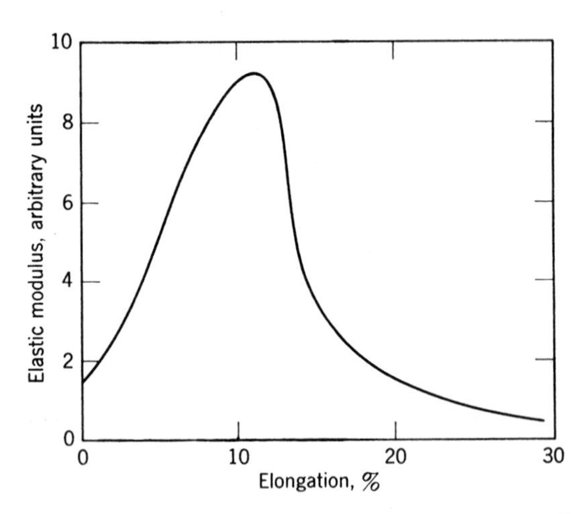

Fig. 42. Tangent elastic modulus as a function of percentage elongation.

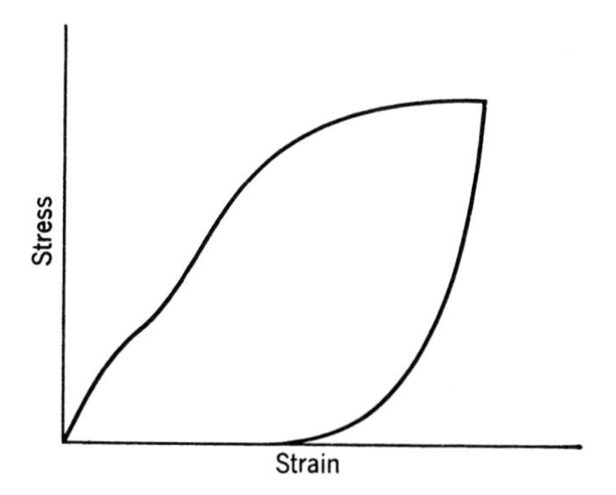

Fig. 43. Elastic recovery from high deformation.

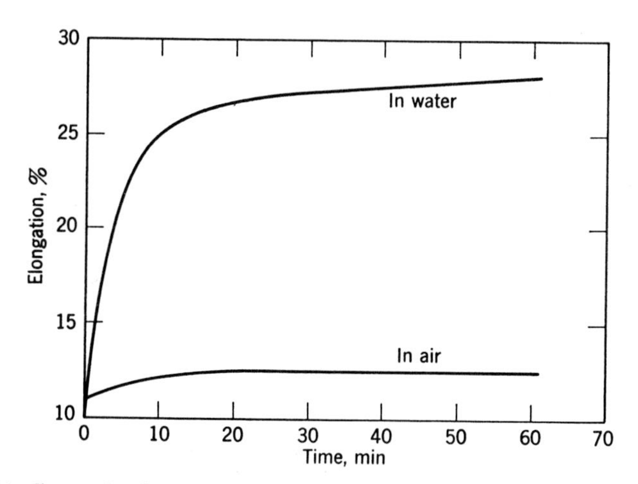

Fig. 44. Creep of nylon 6 fiber in air and in water (tension equal to 3 g/den).

tained by treating the fiber under tension at high temperatures in presence of water (see Table XIII).

From the practical standpoint, the elastic modulus at various elongations is of much greater importance than the ultimate properties of the fiber. The tangent elastic modulus is plotted against the elongation in Fig. 42; the increase in the elastic modulus with the elongation up to a maximum value is quite unusual and counterbalances the effect of the quite low initial modulus.

As with other polymers, the mechanical behavior of nylon 6 can only be completely understood if time dependence is taken into account. Its viscoelastic properties are evident from the incomplete elastic recovery (Fig. 43) and from creep and stress relaxation experiments (Figs. 44 and 45), in which, moreover, the presence of a swelling agent greatly enhances

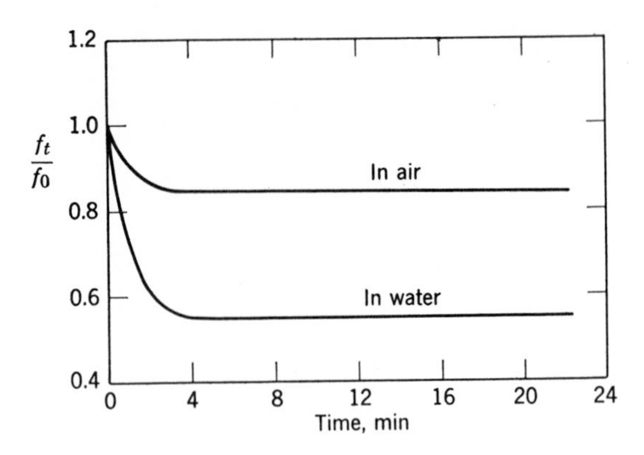

Fig. 45. Stress relaxation of nylon 6 fiber in air and in water; f_0 = initial stress; f_t = stress at time t, deformation 5%.

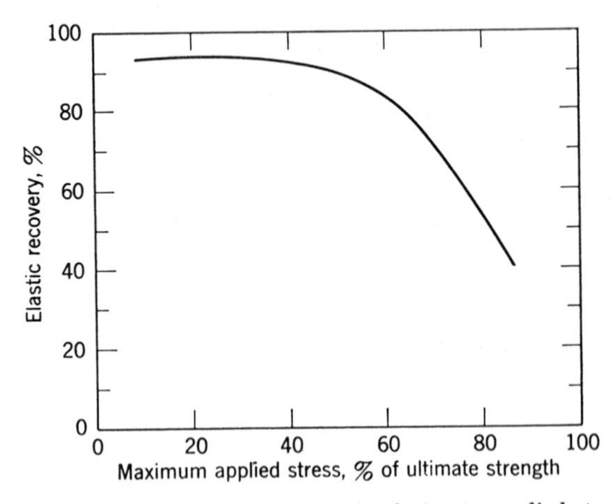

Fig. 46. Elastic recovery (per cent) relative to applied stress.

the viscoelastic behavior. The elastic recovery is high with only minor deformation, but it rapidly decreases as the strain increases (Fig. 46), and it is also dependent upon the number of cycles occurring between the maximum and minimum stresses (Fig. 47).

The dynamic behavior of nylon 6 has been studied over quite a large frequency range (84). In the case of the undrawn fiber an increase in the frequency results in an increase of Young's modulus which, however, at above 10^5 Hz reaches a near constant value of 2.2×10^{10} dynes/cm^2 and becomes independent of the crystallinity of the sample. The relaxation time spectrum shows a tendency to parallel shift toward longer times with the increase in crystallinity and orientation. The dynamic Young's modulus also increases considerably with draw ratio.

In conclusion, elastic modulus, tensile strength, and elongation at break are closely dependent upon the nature and rate of deformation upon environmental conditions and also upon the processing and thermal "history" of the sample.

The resistance to abrasion of nylon 6 compared with other textile fibers is very high; while the crease resistance of wool is 25,000 cycles and of cotton 35,000, that of nylon 6 reaches 300,000 cycles. The abrasion values are 10,000 for wool, 18,000 for cotton, and 200,000 for

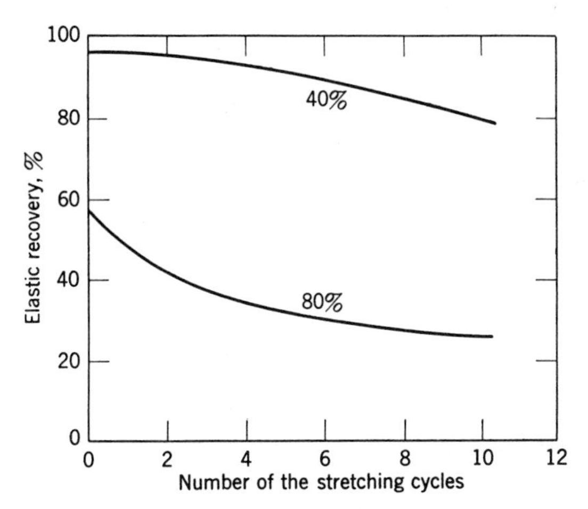

Fig. 47. Elastic recovery (per cent) as a function of the number of consecutive stretching cycles for applied stresses equal to 40% and 80% of final strength.

nylon 6 (85). The very high abrasion resistance of nylon 6 can be explained by the quite low elastic modulus and by its high elastic recovery for small deformations. From a practical standpoint, the nylon 6 filament can cause rapid wear of the guiding mechanism in textile machines.

C. Friction

In each processing stage a filament comes into contact with various materials at a certain displacement speed. The frictional forces, which develop during these contacts, increase the tension acting on the fiber, and hence it is important for the fiber to have a low friction coefficient. In order to obtain good friction coefficients the fiber is coated with a thin continuous film of lubricating agents.

The nylon 6, which has not been treated with a lubricating agent, follows the general laws of friction; particularly in the case of fringes

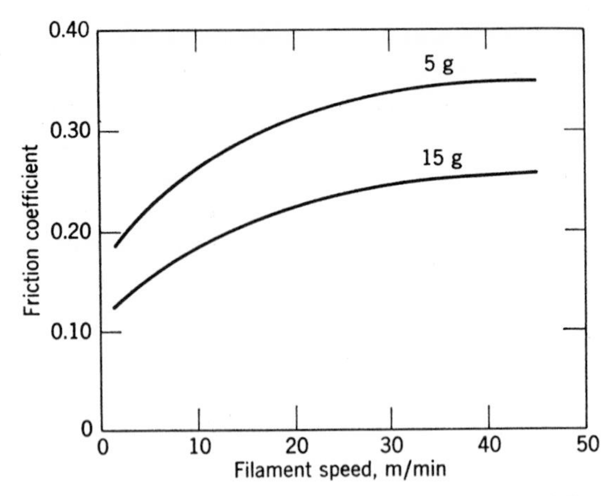

Fig. 48. Friction coefficients of untreated nylon 6 as a function of filament speed and of tension acting on filament before reaching the pin of chrome-plated brass.

of fibers the friction force is not dependent upon the contact area between the fringes but upon the applied load (86), as given by

$$F_s = 2.33\, P^{0.81} \tag{17}$$

where F_s is the friction force and P is the applied load. The frictional behavior is considerably modified by the presence of lubricating agents. For example, although in nylon 6 the static frictional force is greater than the dynamic frictional force, some lubricating agents can invert this behavior. As far as friction with other materials is concerned the most frequent case is friction around a pivot; in general this friction coefficient depends on the type of materials (see Table XIV), on the radius of pivot, and on the torsion number of the multifilament; it decreases as the tension acting on the filament before the pivot increases (87), whereas the faster the gliding speed, the higher the friction coefficient (see Fig. 48).

D. Static Electrification

The capacity of nylon 6 to undergo static electrification is due to the quite low moisture regain and to the high electrical resistivity. The dielectric constant of dry nylon 6 is 3.7 at 10^5 Hz and 20°C, and tang $\delta = 0.31$ (88); both increase with an increase in water absorption. The opposite occurs in the case of electrical resistivity, which from a value of 6×10^{14} Ω-cm for dry fiber reaches a value of 2×10^8, for fiber conditioned in an atmosphere of 100% relative humidity at 20°C. Figure 49 shows the changes in electrical resistance during the conditioning time in such an atmosphere.

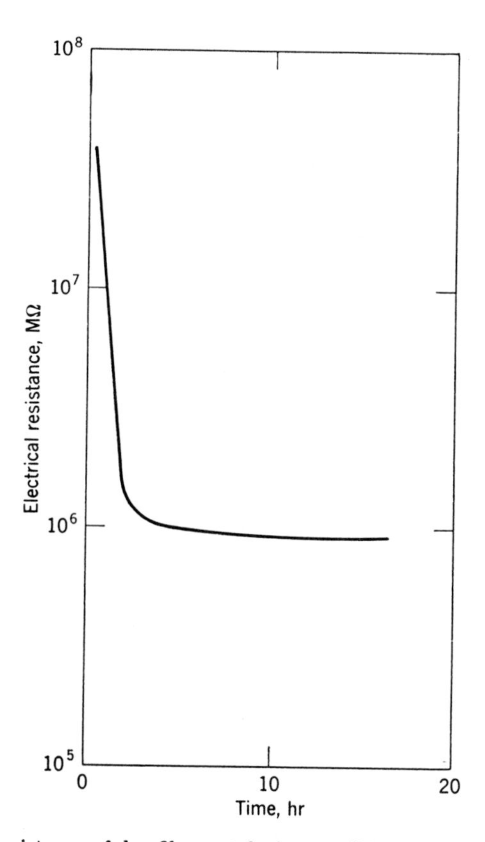

Fig. 49. Electric resistance of dry filament during conditioning at 100% RH at room temperature; filament length, 10 cm.

To avoid processing difficulties the fibers are coated with antistatic agents; the very high changes in electrical resistivity obtained with antistatics can be seen from the data in Table XV. The antistatics and lubricating agents are applied to the fiber during the spinning as components of the finishing emulsion; it is of the utmost importance that the film deposited on the surface of the fiber be completely uniform.

TABLE XIV. Friction Coefficient for Pins of Various Materials

Material	Yarn speed		
	10 m/min	100 m/min	300 m/min
Chrome-plated	0.21	0.38	0.46
Glass	0.22	0.31	0.31
Porcelain	0.22	0.32	0.29

E. Moisture Regain

The moisture regain of nylon 6 depends on the crystallinity of the fiber, the vapor pressure of the water, and the temperature; at room temperature and at normal relative humidity the water absorbed by nylon 6 is

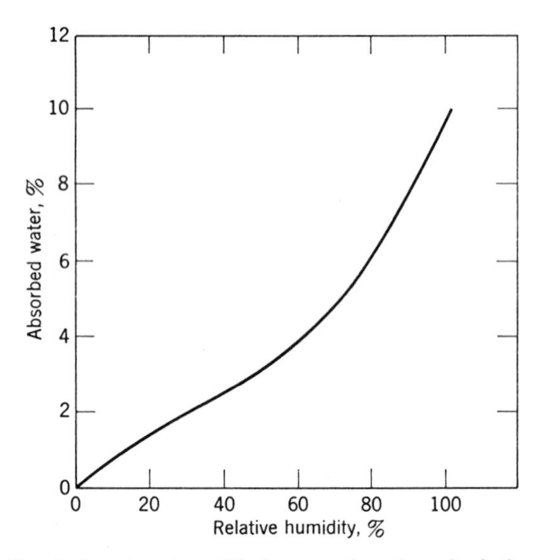

Fig. 50. Absorbed water at equilibrium as a function of relative humidity.

about 4.5–5.0%; in Fig. 50 the absorption isotherm for the fiber is plotted against the relative humidity. The adsorption velocity is dependent not only upon these factors but also upon the specific surface of the fiber.

TABLE XV. Effect of Antistatics on Electric Resistance of Yarn at 65% RH and 25°C

Antistatic	Amount on yarn, %	Electric resistance, Ω
A	0.63	5.5×10^{11}
B	0.61	1.7×10^{12}
C	0.63	2.8×10^{9}
—	—	10^{14}

The water absorbed by the fiber loses some of its hydrogen bonds between the amide groups in the amorphous phase. On the drawn fiber this leads to contraction (Fig. 51), while in the undrawn fiber, as seen in Figs. 22 and 23, the result is an elongation.

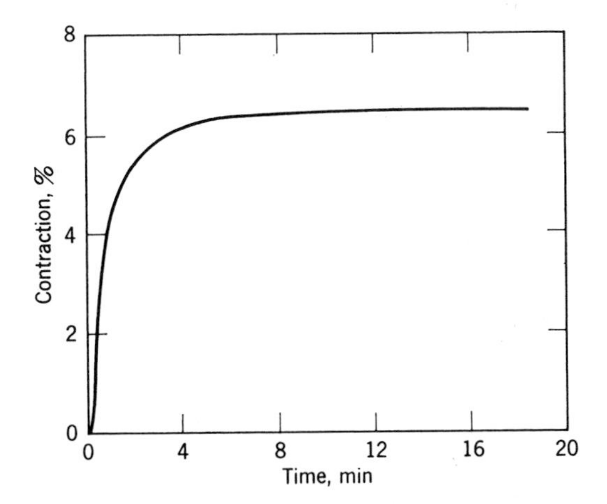

Fig. 51. Shrinkage of drawn fiber in water (room temperature).

VI. DEGRADATIONS

A. Thermal Oxidation

When heated in the presence of oxygen, nylon 6 fiber decreases in tensile strength and assumes a yellowish coloration; however, before the yellowing is visible to the naked eye, a strong ultraviolet absorption band develops (89), extended in shape and with an inflection at about 2400 Å, which can be correlated with the oxygen consumption. In Fig. 52 some examples of the ultraviolet absorption band are shown, measured in sulfuric acid solution, and in Fig. 53 the consumption of oxygen is

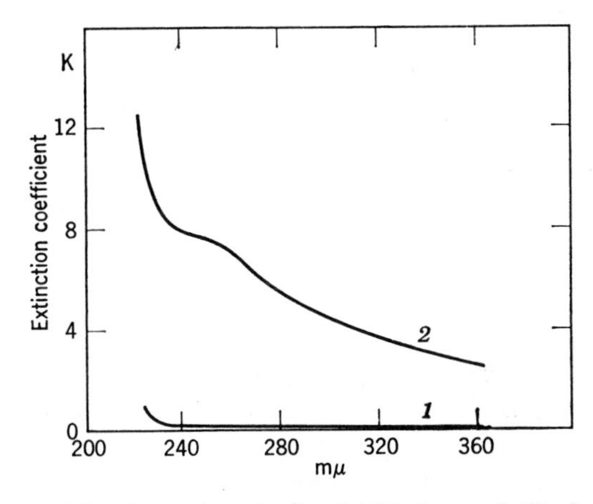

Fig. 52. Ultraviolet absorption of nylon 6 (*1*) before and (*2*) after oxidation.

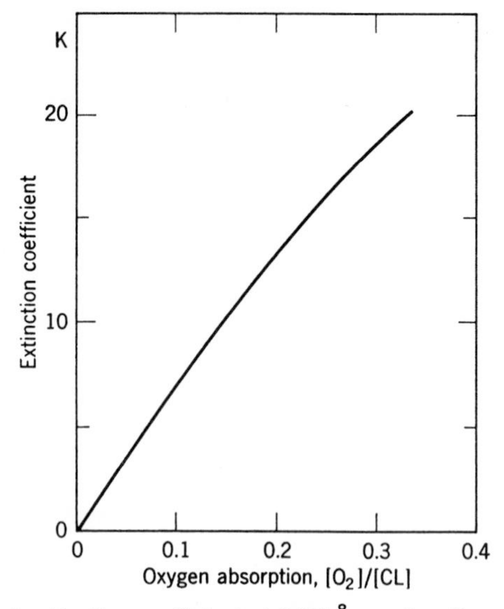

Fig. 53. Ultraviolet extinction coefficient at 2400 Å as a function of absorbed oxygen.

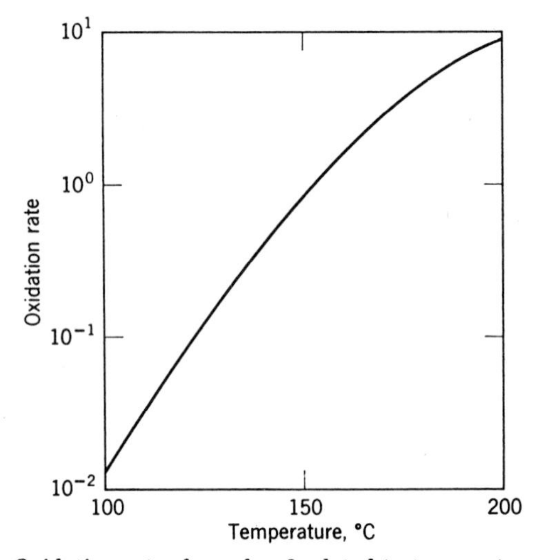

Fig. 54. Oxidation rates for nylon 6 related to temperature (dk/dt).

plotted against the extinction coefficient of oxidized nylon 6. From the experimental results it can be concluded that there is real oxidation, which therefore depends on the partial pressure of oxygen, the specific surface of the sample, and the temperature. In oxidized nylon 6 pyrrole groups, double bonds, immidic groups, and some hydrophilic groups have been found (90); at the same time the molecular weight decreases, while the typical polyamide end groups diminish more than the molecular weight. The reaction kinetics has the sigma shape typical of autoxidation; when the temperature and the partial pressure of oxygen are increased a black compound is eventually formed which is insoluble in hot concentrated acids.

Elemental analysis has shown this compound to have less hydrogen and more oxygen than polycaprolactam, but a carbon/nitrogen ratio very close to the original. It is a strongly crosslinked polycaprolactam derivative, originating from polymerizable groups created by oxidation of linear chains.

In air, oxidation becomes effective only at temperatures above 50°C, and the oxidation rate increases considerably with temperature (Fig. 54), and the initial induction time is greatly decreased (see Table XVI).

TABLE XVI. Induction Time in Oxidation

Temperature, °C	Oxygen pressure, mm Hg	Induction time, min
150	156 (air)	10
100	156 (air)	2100
200	6	15
200	4	30

The reaction mechanism seems to consist of the attack on an α carbon atom (91), with the consequent formation of hydroperoxide, oxidrile, carbonile, and possible chain scission. A decrease in tensile strength accompanies the decrease in molecular weight (see Table XVII).

TABLE XVII. Properties of Yarns Oxidized at Various Temperatures in Air

Temperature, °C	Time, hr	Tenacity,[a] g/den	Molecular weight
100	—	8.35	15,800
100	48	7.40	14,000
100	96	6.75	13,400
100	400	4.30	11,000
125	24	4.00	10,700
125	48	3.10	9,700
150	8	2.30	6,700
150	48	1.40	3,800

[a] Referred to cross section at break.

The autocatalytic character of the oxidation is more evident in oxidation with ozone; the oxidative attack is so localized that it is possible to observe a very high decay in tensile strength due to the formation of a small but very weak defective zone, marked by strong yellowing. The decrease in molecular weight is not so great also because the sample needed for molecular weight measurement is large compared with the oxidized zone (see Table XVIII).

B. Photochemical and Photolytic Degradation

The degradation produced by radiation must be divided into photolysis and photosensitization; in the first case the quanta of radiation must have sufficient energy to initiate a chain scission, and moreover they must be directly absorbed by the polymer, whereas in the second case the radiant energy is absorbed by a compound other than the polymer, and this compound must be capable, by self-excitation, of promoting the polymer attack either directly or indirectly.

In the absorption spectrum of polycaprolactam the absorption bands are below 2400 Å, and photolysis can thus occur with far ultraviolet radiations. On the other hand, the presence of the TiO_2 anatase, used in powder form as a delustering agent, can act as a photosensitizing agent in the near ultraviolet, i.e., at wavelengths which are also present in solar radiations reaching the earth. From the practical point of view this kind of light degradation is by far the most important.

TABLE XVIII. Properties of Yarns Degraded with Ozone at 100°C

O_3 concentration, %	Time, hr	Final strength, kg/mm²	Molecular weight
—	—	66.8	17,500
—	8	65.3	17,600
0.5	4	65.0	17,400
0.5	8	46.4	15,000
0.5	32	12.4	12,400

It now seems well established (92,93) that the radiation quanta absorbed by TiO_2 cause the removal of atomic oxygen with the consequent formation of metastable Ti_2O_3, which on reaction with molecular oxygen reverts to TiO_2. The presence of humidity increases the photosensitizing activity, since hydrogen peroxide is formed by a similar mechanism.

Because of the TiO_2 activity the molecular weight and tensile strength of the fiber decrease; the loss of tensile strength (F), in terms of the cross section at break, is related to the actual degree of polymerization (P) by Sippel's general relationship (94), which has been verified (95)

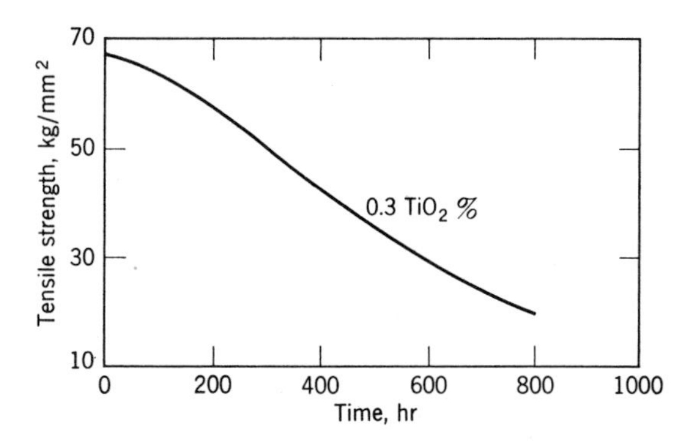

Fig. 55. Decrease in tensile strength of nylon 6 exposed to near ultraviolet radiations.

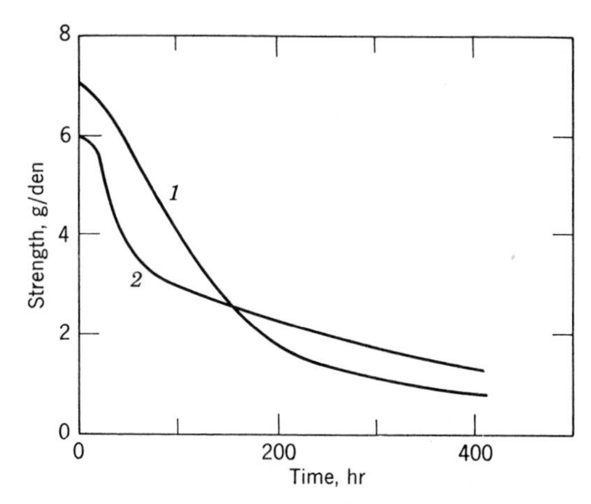

Fig. 56. Decrease in tensile strength of nylon 6 without (*1*) and with (*2*) titanium dioxide exposed to far ultraviolet radiations.

under various conditions of photochemical and photolytic degradation:

$$\ln F = \text{const} - m_0/P \qquad (18)$$

where m_0 depends on the penetrating power of the degrading agent.

Apart from the time and nature of the irradiation, the degradation value also depends on the titer of the single fiber, the fiber with the higher cross section having a lower degradation.

Again, in radiation-induced degradation a change appears in the absorption spectrum of degraded nylon 6, and pyrrole groups have been found; in this case the absorption band is more distinct than in the oxidized fiber and has a maximum at 2850 Å (96) which can be ascribed to CO groups.

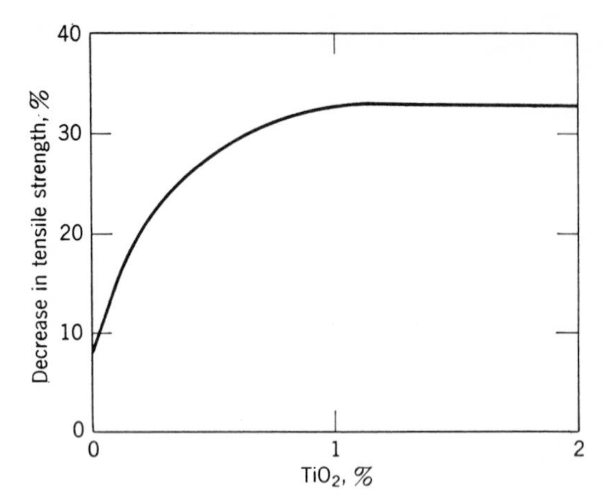

Fig. 57. Tensile strength decrease of nylon 6, containing various amounts of titanium dioxide, after 400 hr exposure to near ultraviolet radiations.

With regard to the TiO_2 activity, it has been found that in the far ultraviolet, in the presence of oxygen, delustered fibers have a lower degradation than bright fibers (96); the probable explanation for this is a deactivation of the oxidation reaction, initiated by radicals produced by photolysis; this deactivation is probably due to an increase in the termination processes from atomic oxygen released from the TiO_2.

Some examples of losses in tensile strength are plotted against exposure time in the near and far ultraviolet in Figs. 55 and 56, while in Fig. 57 the behavior of degradation as a function of the amount of delustering pigment (times of exposure being equal) is shown.

VII. SETTING

Setting is a treatment given to the fiber, usually after making up, in order to improve its dimensional stability, wear, and washing resistance.

The feasibility of such a treatment is related to the stress relaxation, which is increased by swelling agents and temperature, and to an increase in ordered crystallinity. To achieve this some of the existing hydrogen bonds in the amorphous zones must be loosened. This can easily be carried out by swelling agents and/or by heating. New hydrogen bonds are then formed in the shape taken up by the fiber once the swelling agent or the heat source has been removed. In addition, this type of treatment increases the crystallinity.

The most important setting methods are (*1*) swelling agents at room temperature; (*2*) swelling agents at high temperature; (*3*) saturated steam; (*4*) dry heat.

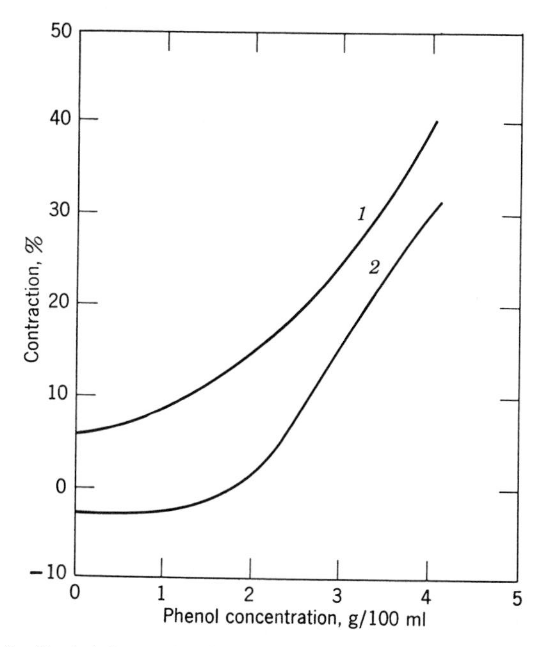

Fig. 58. Longitudinal deformation in aqueous phenol solutions of unwashed (*1*) and washed (*2*) fibers.

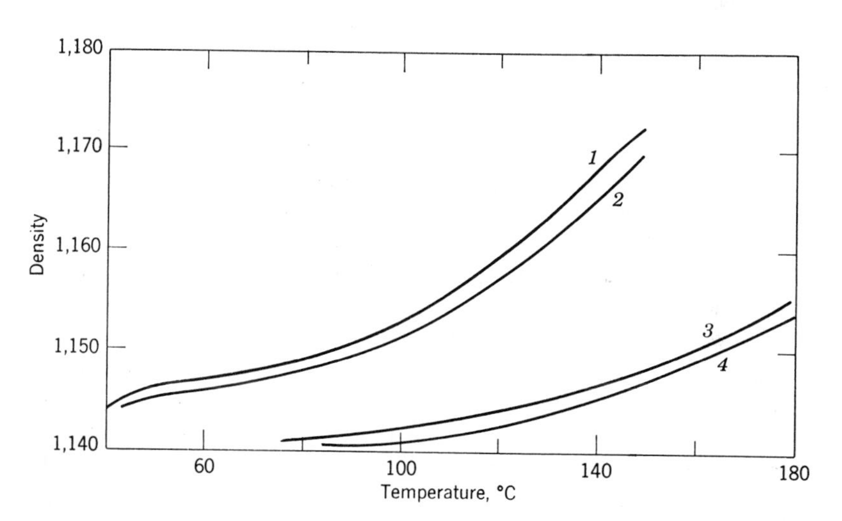

Fig. 59. Changes in density of fibers set at different temperatures: (*1*) free in water, (*2*) held at constant length in water, (*3*) free in nitrogen, (*4*) held at constant length in nitrogen.

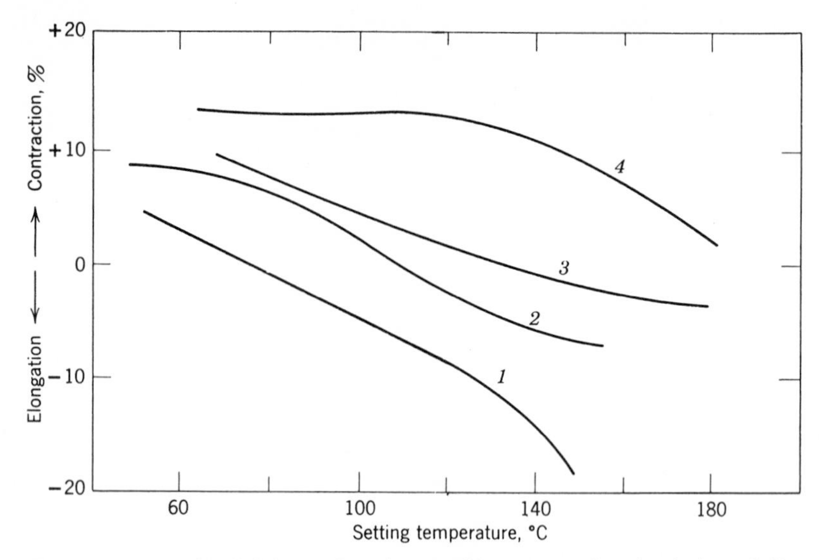

Fig. 60. Longitudinal deformations in a 2.5% aqueous phenol solution of fibers set at different temperatures: (*1*) free in water, (*2*) held at constant length in water, (*3*) free in nitrogen, (*4*) held at constant length in nitrogen.

Of the various room-temperature swelling agents, dilute aqueous solutions of phenol have been widely studied and are effective, as can be seen from Fig. 58, where the longitudinal deformation of the fiber is plotted against the phenol concentration. In untreated fibers this deformation is usually in the form of a shrinkage, but in treated fibers it may take the form of an elongation; it is important to note that a correlation has been found between deformation and stress relaxation (97) in the same swelling agent. This correlation permits a simple measurement of longitudinal deformation in order to test the degree of setting.

However, for practical applications, by far the most commonly used methods are those which combine the effects of heating and of water as swelling agent. The best conditions for nylon 6 are water at 105°C, saturated steam at 130°C, or dry heat at 180–190°C. Due to the importance of setting processes in the textile industry, many studies have been made (85,98,99) which examine both the mechanism and degree of setting under various conditions. During the treatment the fiber can be free, held at constant length, or elongated. In each case the density (overall order) increases considerably, while the orientation increases for fibers set under elongation or at constant length and decreases for free set fibers. The increase in density is higher in the presence of water (Fig. 59), but the elastic modulus decreases and dye affinity and dye diffusion rate increase. These apparent contradictions can be explained by the less perfect crystalline order (69) of the fiber in the presence of water, which also facilitates crystallization; it is interesting to note that nylon 6 melts in saturated steam at about 150°C (98).

The increase in oriented crystallinity obtained in fibers set under tension will also increase the tenacity and modulus and decrease the elongation at break. A comparison between various setting treatments is given in Fig. 60, in which the dimensional changes of various set fibers in an aqueous solution of phenol are shown.

Sometimes a setting treatment is also carried out on multifilaments in order to stabilize the twists, and setting is widely used in the texturized fiber production. The basic principle of this kind of texturizing is to set a multifilament twisted in one direction and then to twist the set yarn again in the opposite direction. In most machines the texturizing is carried out continuously by a false torsion assembly and by dry heat setting.

In setting yarns already wound onto bobbins, it is important to take into account the contraction of the yarn as a result of the setting treatment, and also to ensure that the setting agent penetrates the whole bobbin, which is essential for obtaining complete homogeneity in the various fiber layers. The yarn is normally wonnd on a non-rigid perforated core.

VIII. DYEING

Nylon 6 is easily dyed with various types of dye since its chains contain several hydrophilic groups. The most commonly used dyes are acidic dyes, dispersed dyes, chrome dyes, and vat dyes. In general, the dyeing mechanism is related to the diffusion of the dye into the fiber and to the successive formation of some bond between the dye molecules and particular groups present in the fiber. These groups are more or less accessible according to the fiber structure and swelling. The equilibrium dye absorption depends on the number of accessible groups that can form a bond with the dye molecules, and on dyeing conditions, i.e. temperature, bath pH, and dye concentration, while the absorption rate is also dependent on the specific surface of the fiber.

In industrial processes the absorption rate is extremely important, since the dyeing is continued until the bath is exhausted and variations in shade can occur in the fiber due to differences in structure, titer, and molecular weight (100). These dyeing defects depend largely on the type of dye and therefore on the dyeing mechanism.

Both acidic dyes, and generally speaking also the anionic dyes, if the bath pH is greater than about 2–3, are absorbed mainly by the aminic end groups of the polycaprolactam (101,102). Below this pH value, the

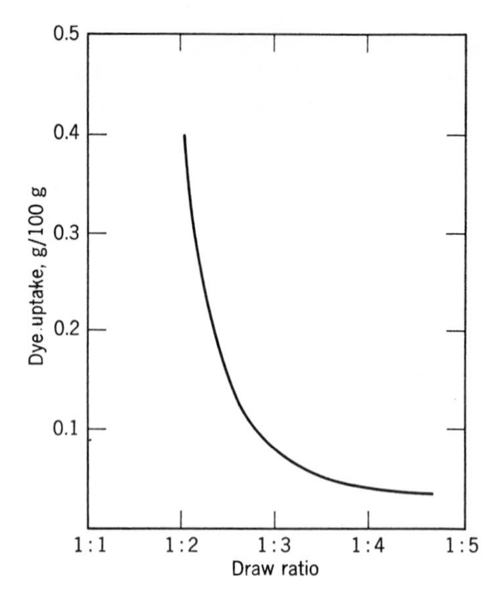

Fig. 61. Dye uptake of nylon 6 as a function of the draw ratio.

amidic groups are also protonized and may cause absorption of the dye molecules; however at this very low pH the tenacity of the fiber decreases (103), owing to the hydrolysis of the amide group.

Dispersed dyes are absorbed by the formation of hydrogen bonds with amide groups. Obviously this class of dye is much less sensitive to the concentration of aminic end groups and also to the fiber structure, while the acidic dyes are very sensitive to changes in the aminic end group concentration.

Chrome dyes must be used in acid solutions, and the dyed fiber must then be treated with an acid dichromate; the absorption mechanism is similar to that of acid dyes, while vat dyes are probably absorbed by means of the dispersed dye mechanism.

The dependence of dye uptake on overall fiber orientation can easily

TABLE XIX. Absorbed Dye (Solway Blue BN from ICI) as Function of Aminic End Group Content

Absorbed dye, mg/g	$—NH_2$, μeq/g
5.12	20.2
6.93	29.3
6.95	29.6
6.30	31.3
7.58	31.8

be seen from Fig. 61, where the amount of dye absorbed is plotted against the draw ratio of the fiber. In Table XIX various examples of differences in dyeing due to different aminic end group concentrations are shown.

General References

R. Hill, *Fibres from Synthetic Polymers*, Elsevier, Amsterdam, 1953.

R. Pummerer, *Chemische Textilfasern Filme und Folien,* Ferdinand Euke, Stuttgart, 1953.

H. Hopff, A. Müller, and F. Wenger, *Die Polyamide*, Springer, Berlin, 1954.

H. Klare, *Technologie und Chemie der syntetischen Fasern aus Polyamiden,* VEB Verlag Technik, Berlin, 1954.

F. Fourné, *Synthetische Fasern,* Wissenschaftlige Verlagsgesellschaft, Stuttgart, 1964.

I. I. Press, *Man-Made Textile Encyclopedia,* Textile Book Publishers, Inc., New York, 1959.

W. N. Dawydoff, *Bestimmung des Molekulargewichts von Polyamiden,* VEB Verlag Technik, Berlin, 1954.

REFERENCES*

1. W. H. Carothers and J. Berebet, *J. Am. Chem. Soc.*, **52,** 5289 (1930).
2. S. Gabriel and T. A. Maas, *Chem. Ber.*, **32,** 1266 (1899).
3. I. V. Braun, *Chem. Ber.*, **40,** 1840 (1907).
4. P. Schlack, German Pat. 748,253 (1938); U.S. Pat. 2,241,321 (1941).
5. Belg. Pat. 582,793 (to Snia Viscosa).
6. P. H. Hermans, *J. Appl. Chem.*, **5,** 493 (1955).
7. F. Wiloth, *Makromol. Chem.*, **15,** 106 (1955).
8. W. E. Hanford and K. M. Joyce, *J. Polymer Sci.*, **3,** 167 (1948).
9. D. Heikens, *Makromol. Chem.*, **18,** 62 (1956).
10. S. Schaaf, *Faserforsch. Textiltech.*, **10,** 257 (1959).
11. G. M. van der Want and C. A. Kruissink, *J. Polymer Sci.*, **35,** 119 (1959).
12. G. M. Burnett, I. N. Hay, and A. J. McArthur, Symposium on the Chemistry of Polymerization Process (April 1965) Soc. Chem. Ind. (London).
13. P. H. Hermans, *Rec. Trav. Chim.*, **72,** 998 (1953).
14. P. F. van Velden, G. M. van der Want, D. Heikens, C. A. Kruissink, P. H. Hermans, and A. J. Staverman, *Rec. Trav. Chim.*, **74,** 1376 (1955).
15. P. H. Hermans, D. Heikens, and P. F. van Velden, *J. Polymer Sci.*, **26,** 451 (1955).
16. P. H. Hermans, D. Heikens, and P. F. van Velden, *J. Polymer Sci.*, **30,** 81 (1958).
17. F. Wiloth, *Z. Physik. Chem.* (*Frankfurt*), **5,** 66 (1955).
18. F. Wiloth, *Kolloid Z.*, **143,** 129 (1955).

* Many of the experimental results reported in the text have been derived from the unpublished data of the author's co-workers to whom the author wishes to express his gratitude.

19. F. Wiloth, *Z. Physik. Chem. (Frankfurt)*, **11,** 78 (1957).
20. F. Wiloth, *Makromol. Chem.*, **30,** 189 (1959).
21. A. Matthes, *Makromol. Chem.*, **5,** 197 (1951).
22. K. G. Wyness, *Makromol. Chem.*, **38,** 189 (1960).
23. P. J. Flory, *Principles of Polymer Chemistry* (Cornell University Press, Ithaca, New York, 1953).
24. G. V. Schulz, *Z. Physik. Chem. (Leipzig)*, **182,** 127 (1938).
25. F. Wiloth, *Makromol. Chem.*, **14,** 156 (1954).
26. D. Heikens and P. H. Hermans, *Makromol. Chem.*, **39,** 246 (1958).
27. T. G. Majury, *J. Polymer Sci.*, **31,** 383 (1958).
28. D. Heikens, P. H. Hermans, and G. M. van der Want, *J. Polymer Sci.*, **64,** 437 (1960).
29. D. Heikens, P. H. Hermans, and G. M. van der Want, *J. Polymer Sci.*, **64,** 429 (1960).
30. H. K. Reimschuessel, *J. Polymer Sci.*, **41,** 457 (1959).
31. O. Fukumoto, *J. Polymer Sci.*, **22,** 263 (1956).
32. H. Ludewig, *Chem. Tech. (Berlin)*, **4,** 523 (1952).
33. A. Matthes, *J. Prakt. Chem.*, **162,** 245 (1943).
34. E. Montroll and R. Simha, *J. Chem. Phys.*, **8,** 721 (1940).
35. K. Hoshino and M. Watanabe, *J. Am. Chem. Soc.*, **73,** 4816 (1951).
36. S. Smith, *J. Polymer Sci.*, **30,** 459 (1958).
37. D. Heikens, P. H. Hermans, and S. Smith, *J. Polymer Sci.*, **38,** 265 (1959).
38. F. Wiloth and W. Dietrich, *Makromol. Chem.*, **21,** 50 (1956).
39. T. G Fox, S. Gratch, and S. Loshaek, *Rheology*, Vol. I (F. R. Eirich, Ed.) (Academic Press, New York, 1956).
40. G. Pezzin and G. B. Gechele, *J. Appl. Polymer Sci.*, **8,** 2195 (1964).
41. W. Sbrolli and C. Meneghini, *Chim. Ind. (Milan)*, **46,** 1322 (1964).
42. W. Dawydoff, *Faserforsch. Textiltech.*, **8,** 267 (1957).
43. W. Sbrolli and C. Meneghini, *Ann. Chim. (Rome)*, **53,** 1199 (1963).
44. P. W. Allen, *Techniques of Polymer Characterization* (Butterworths, London, 1959).
45. M. Rothe, *J. Polymer Sci.*, **30,** 227 (1958).
46. P. H. Hermans, *Rev. Trav. Chim.*, **72,** 798 (1953).
47. I. Rothe and M. Rothe, *Chem. Ber.*, **88,** 284 (1955).
48. D. Heikens, *Rec. Trav. Chim.*, **75,** 1199 (1956).
49. H. H. Schenker, C. C. Casto, and P. W. Mullen, *Anal. Chem.*, **29,** 825 (1957).
50. W. Sbrolli and T. Capaccioli, *Chim. Ind. (Milan)*, **42,** 243 (1960).
51. J. R. Schaefgen and P. J. Flory, *J. Am. Chem. Soc.*, **70,** 2709 (1948).
52. R. Hill and E. E. Walker, *J. Polymer Sci.*, **3,** 609 (1948).
53. A. M. Liquori and A. Mele, *Chim. Ind. (Milan)*, **35,** 799 (1953).
54. R. Brill, *Makromol. Chem.*, **18/19,** 294 (1956).
55. D. R. Holmes, C. W. Bunn, and D. J. Smith, *J. Polymer Sci.*, **17,** 159 (1955).
56. P. Hermans, *Nature*, **177,** 126 (1956).
57. A. Ziabicki and K. Kędzierska, *Kolloid Z.*, **171,** 51 (1960).
58. A. Ziabicki and K. Kędzierska, *Kolloid-Z.*, **171,** 111 (1960).
59. A. Ziabicki, *Kolloid Z.*, **175,** 14 (1961).
60. A. Ziabicki and K. Kędzierska, *J. Appl. Polymer Sci.*, **2,** 14 (1959).
61. A. Ziabicki, *J. Appl. Polymer Sci.*, **2,** 24 (1959).
62. A. Ziabicki and K. Kędzierska, *J. Appl. Polymer Sci.*, **6,** 111 (1962).
63. A. Ziabicki and K. Kędzierska, *J. Appl. Polymer Sci.*, **6,** 361 (1962).

64. V. Gröbe and H. Versäumer, *Faserforsch. Textiltech.*, **14,** 249 (1963).
65. S. Kase and T. Matsuo, *J. Polymer Sci. A*, **3,** 2541 (1965).
66. G. Bodor, Z. Holly, and A. Kallò, *Symposium über makromolecule in Wiesbaden*, Part I, Vol. 13 (1959).
67. I. Marhall and A. B. Thompson, *Proc. Roy. Soc.* (*London*), *Ser. A*, **221,** 541 (1954).
68. G. W. Urbanczyk, *J. Polymer Sci.*, **59,** 245 (1962).
69. W. Roth and R. Schroth, *Faserforsch. Textiltech.*, **11,** 312 (1960).
70. W. Roth and R. Schroth, *Faserforsch. Textiltech.*, **11,** 365 (1960).
71. A. Reichle and A. Prietzschk, *Angew. Chem.*, **74,** 562 (1962).
72. L. G. Roldan and H. S. Kaufman, *J. Polymer Sci. B*, **1,** 603 (1963).
73. W. Ruland, *Polymer*, **5,** 89 (1964).
74. L. G. Roldan, F. Rahl, and A. R. Paterson, *J. Polymer Sci. C*, **8,** 145 (1965).
75. R. Brill, *Z. Physik. Chem.* (*Leipzig*), **B53,** 61 (1943).
76. Y. Kinoshita, *Makromol. Chem.*, **33,** 1 (1959).
77. H. Arimoto, *J. Polymer Sci. A*, **2,** 2283 (1964).
78. E. Kordes, F. Günther, L. Büchs, and W. Göltner, *Kolloid Z.*, **119,** 23 (1950).
79. H. de Vries, *J. Polymer Sci.*, **34,** 761 (1959).
80. I. Sandeman and A. Keller, *J. Polymer Sci.*, **19,** 401 (1956).
81. A. Miyake, *J. Polymer Sci.*, **64,** 223 (1960).
82. M. C. Tobin and M. J. Carrano, *J. Chem. Phys.*, **25,** 1044 (1956).
83. C. G. Cannon, *Spectrochim. Acta*, **16,** 302 (1960).
84. N. Tokita, *J. Polymer Sci.*, **20,** 515 (1956).
85. F. Fourné, *Melliand Textilber.*, **33,** 639 (1952).
86. W. Sbrolli and E. Rottenbacher, *Riv. Tessile*, **3,** 247 (1959).
87. H. G. Howell, *J. Text. Inst.*, **44,** T 359 (1953).
88. A. Müller and R. Pflüger, *Kunststoffe*, **50,** 203 (1960).
89. W. Sbrolli, T. Capaccioli, and E. Bertotti, *Chim. Ind.* (*Milan*), **42,** 37 (1960).
90. W. Sbrolli and T. Capaccioli, *Chim. Ind.* (*Milan*), **42,** 1325 (1960).
91. N. Grassie, *The Chemistry of High-Polymer Degradation Processes*, Butterworths, London, 1956.
92. W. A. Weyl and T. Förland, *Ind. Eng. Chem.*, **42,** 259.
93. W. Sbrolli and E. Bertotti, *Ann. Chim.* (*Rome*), **49,** 1143 (1959).
94. A. Sippel, *Melliand Textilber.*, **33,** 645 (1952).
95. G. Prati, *Ann. Chim.* (*Rome*), **48,** 15 (1958).
96. W. Sbrolli and T. Capaccioli, *Ann. Chim.* (*Rome*), **53,** 1184 (1963).
97. E. Rottenbacher and W. Sbrolli, *Simp. Intern. Chim. Macromolec. Torino–Milano* (1954).
98. M. Tsuruta, A. Koshimo, T. Tagawa, and T. Karishita, *J. Appl. Polymer Sci.*, **9,** 3, 11, 25, 31, 39, 45, 55, 69, 81, 91 (1965).
99. A. Koshimo, T. Tagawa, M. Tsuruta, and T. Shimoyama, *J. Appl. Polymer Sci.*, **9,** 117, 129, 139 (1965).
100. H. W. Peters and J. C. Turner, *J. Soc. Dyers Colourists*, **74,** 252 (1958).
101. H. W. Peters, *J. Soc. Dyers Colourists*, **61,** 95 (1945).
102. P. W. Carlene, A. S. Fern, and T. Wickerstaff, *J. Soc. Dyers Colourists*, **63,** 388 (1947).
103. W. R. Remington and E. K. Gladding, *J. Am. Chem. Soc.*, **72,** 2553 (1950).

Fiber-Forming Aromatic Polyamides

W. B. Black and J. Preston
Chemstrand Research Center, Inc., Durham, North Carolina

CONTENTS

I. INTRODUCTION

The commercially important fiber-forming polyamides or nylons have until very recently been restricted to those polyamides prepared from aliphatic dibasic acids and aliphatic diamines, aliphatic α,ω-amino acids, and caprolactam. Fibers of poly(hexamethylene adipamide) (nylon 66) and polycaprolactam (nylon 6) are of major worldwide commercial importance, and they are produced in very great tonnages (1). Although these two aliphatic polyamide fibers have properties which make them suitable for a large number of end uses, both textile and industrial, they do have limitations. Some of these limitations are the result of low modulus and relatively low dimensional stability or a propensity to creep under load. As a consequence of creep, automobile tires made with nylon 66 or nylon 6 tire cord develop a flat area at the point of contact of the tire with the road surface when the vehicle is motionless. This problem, however, is one of aesthetics; for tire cord performance, nylons 66 and 6 are still the fibers of choice because of their outstanding toughness and durability. Nevertheless, even though a very large market for nylon tires has developed, it would undoubtedly be still larger were it not for this tendency of aliphatic polyamides to flatspot. The aliphatic polyamide fibers are also limited in their chemical resistance and physical properties at temperatures above 150–200°C. These limitations are, however, shared by all natural organic fibers and all commercially available synthetic fibers (except for the recently commercialized wholly aromatic polyamide fiber, Nomex* (2,3)).

It has long been known that the incorporation of aromatic rings in linear polymers yields higher-melting, stiffer, and more dimensionally stable polymers than does the incorporation of comparable amounts of aliphatic units (4). The pronounced effect of aromatic units on the melting point is most noteworthy in the case of the commercially important polyethylene terephthalate fibers: whereas polyethylene terephthalate melts at 265°C, the comparable aliphatic polymer, polyethylene suberate, melts at about 45°C (5), over 200°C lower. That a comparable difference in melting point results from incorporation of the *para*-phenylene unit in polyamides was also reported long ago (1948), when it was noted that polyhexamethylene terephthalamide melts at about 350°C (with decomposition) (4); by comparison, polyhexamethylene adipamide (nylon 66) melts at 265°C.

Unfortunately, the high-melting aliphatic-aromatic polyamides such as polyhexamethylene terephthalamide could not be melted without

* Du Pont Company trademark.

decomposition, and consequently, could neither be prepared by melt polycondensation nor melt-spun to fiber in the same manner as nylon 66. Spinning fiber from solutions of these polymers was, of course, a possibility, but solution spinning of condensation polymers until recently has not been an area of research marked with success. Moreover, the aliphatic-aromatic polyamides are so much less soluble than the already difficultly soluble aliphatic polyamides that obtaining solutions suitable for solution spinning is difficult. Owing to the combination of synthesis and fabrication difficulties encountered with the aliphatic-aromatic polyamides coupled with the fact that aliphatic polyamides (unlike aliphatic polyesters) perform adequately for most end uses, research and development in the field of aliphatic-aromatic polyamides lagged far behind that for the aliphatic polyamides.

It was apparent from the physical properties of the aliphatic-aromatic polyamides that the replacement of all the aliphatic units in polyamides by aromatic units would lead to very high-melting polyamides which in all probability would be much more resistant to thermal degradation than any known fiber-forming polymers. In addition, it was recognized during the 1950's that space-age technology would require such thermally resistant fibers. This need, in fact, provided considerable stimulus for research in the area of fiber-forming wholly aromatic polyamides. The synthesis and fabrication of the wholly aromatic polyamides, however, faced formidable barriers, since these polymers were certain to be very insoluble and also very unstable in the melt, if meltable at all.

Clearly, for progress in the field of aromatic polyamides some technological breakthroughs were necessary. These came in the late 1950's and early 1960's, when it was demonstrated that high-molecular-weight wholly aromatic polyamides could be prepared by two nonbulk, low-temperature polymerization processes—interfacial and low-temperature solution polycondensation. These polymerization techniques are discussed in the next section. Equally important was the discovery of nondegrading solvents for many of the aromatic polyamides, rendering solution spinning feasible. It has turned out that progress in the field of the wholly aromatic polyamides has been far more dramatic than in the case of the aliphatic-aromatic polyamides.

In addition to sections which discuss aliphatic-aromatic and wholly aromatic polyamides which are thermally stable, a section (Section V) has been included which deals with soluble aromatic polyamides which are themselves thermally unstable, but which are precursors to more thermally stable polymers. In general, thermally stable polymers derived from the soluble polyamide precursors either cannot be prepared by any direct route, or, if they can be prepared directly, are too intractable to allow fabrication to useful articles.

II. POLYMER PREPARATION AND CHARACTERIZATION

A. Low-Temperature Polycondensation

The usual melt methods for the preparation of aliphatic polyamides are unsuited to the preparation of high-molecular-weight, wholly aromatic polyamides both because of their high melting points (almost always with decomposition) and because of the low reactivity of aromatic amines. The melt methods are also frequently useless for the preparation of aliphatic-aromatic polyamides for the same reasons. Low-temperature (i.e., below about 100°C) polycondensation procedures developed during the past decade, however, have led to the preparation of very many high-molecular-weight polyamides which would be otherwise unobtainable. Morgan in an excellent text (6a), has reviewed the literature on low-temperature polycondensation methods up to 1965. The principle low-temperature methods are liquid–liquid interfacial polycondensation and solution polycondensation.*

1. Interfacial Polymerization

The interfacial method for the preparation of polyamides is an adaptation of the well-known Schotten-Baumann reaction: the diacid chloride is dissolved or dispersed in an inert, water-immiscible organic solvent which is preferably a swelling agent for the polymer, and the diamine is dissolved or dispersed along with a proton acceptor in the aqueous phase. The two-phase system may be stirred or unstirred, but higher-molecular-weight polymers are generally obtained when the system is stirred rapidly. In the latter process, the use of an emulsifying agent is usually helpful. The polymer is collected and dried; it can then be dissolved in a suitable solvent and fabricated.

2. Solution Polymerization

Solution polycondensation of diacid chlorides and diamines is often more convenient to carry out than interfacial polycondensation and has the further advantage of usually providing a solution of polymer amenable to direct fabrication of fibers, films, and coatings. Another distinct advantage of solution polycondensation over the interfacial method results from the peculiar solubility characteristics of certain wholly aromatic polyamides: while such polymers are soluble when made in

* The numerous references to this subject which might be cited are omitted; the interested reader will find these in Morgan's book. Some of the leading references are given, where appropriate, under other headings in this chapter.

solution, they cannot be redissolved in solvents (other than strong acids) once precipitated (7). Since interfacial polymerization yields a precipitated product, polymers of the above type cannot be readily fabricated when made by the interfacial technique.

In solution polycondensation the polymerization medium is a solvent for at least one of the reactants and is a solvent or swelling agent for the polymer, preferably a solvent. The solvent must be inert to the reactants. To ensure completeness of the reaction, an acid acceptor, usually a tertiary amine, is used unless the solvent itself is such an acceptor. The better solvents are amides such as dimethylacetamide, *N*-methylpyrrolidone, and hexamethylphosphoramide. Dimethylformamide is not useful because of its rapid and irreversible reaction with acid chlorides (8–10). For the solution polymerization of many aromatic polyamides there is no known organic solvent sufficiently powerful to keep the polymer in solution as its molecular weight builds up. The solvating power of many organic solvents is greatly increased, however, by the addition of inorganic salts such as lithium chloride and calcium chloride (11). Use of these mixed solvents has permitted preparation in solution of many high-molecular-weight polymers which have not been obtainable using organic solvents alone. Also, mixtures of the basic amide solvents such as dimethylacetamide with a minor amount of their hydrochloride salts are much better solvents for aromatic polyamides than are the amide solvents alone (9). This is turned to great advantage, since hydrogen chloride is produced in the condensation of aromatic diamines with diacid chlorides, and, consequently, when amide solvents are used the desired salt–solvent combination is produced. Moreover, the quantity of the hydrochloride salt increases as the polycondensation proceeds, thereby increasing the solvating power of the solvent at the same time that the molecular weight of the polymer is building up.

Although the solution technique is not useful for the direct preparation of aromatic polyimides, it is used advantageously in the preparation of polyamic-acids (polyamides with free carboxyl groups) which are soluble precursors to aromatic polyimides (12). In fact, this type of polymerization is the cornerstone for almost the whole field of wholly aromatic polyimides.

B. Physical Characterization of Polymers, Fibers, and Films

1. Thermal Properties

Since aromatic polyamides and polyimides are high-melting, thermally stable materials developed chiefly for use at elevated temperatures, it is necessary to characterize these materials by tests carried out at elevated temperatures and by tests on the materials after they have been exposed to elevated temperatures either in oxidative atmospheres or in inert atmospheres.

The term thermal stability (or thermal resistance) as used in this chapter does not mean resistance of the polymer to homolytic rupture of covalent bonds as a result of thermal energy alone, but has to do rather with the resistance of bulk polymer to changes in properties in a given environment at elevated temperatures, whether the changes are due to physical changes such as melting or to chemical changes including oxidation. Indeed, when tests are conducted in air at elevated temperatures, the polymer almost always undergoes thermally induced oxidative degradation.* The effects of an oxidative atmosphere are usually more pronounced the slower the test; they are always quite pronounced in the case of isothermal tests run at intermediately elevated temperatures. Neverthless, thermal stability evaluations of aromatic polyamides and polyimides are frequently made in air, since most such polymers are expected to find wider applicability in products to be used in air rather than in inert atmospheres or *in vacuo*.

There is no one test which provides sufficient information for an adequate description of the behavior of the aromatic polyamides and polyimides at elevated temperatures. Two tests, thermogravimetric analysis (TGA) and differential thermal analysis (DTA), are the most important ones, and the combined information obtainable from them is usually sufficient for screening purposes. TGA and DTA are not adequate, however, to determine how well fibers and films will retain strength and flexibility upon undergoing various thermal treatments. Consequently, tests of fibers and film properties must also be made where such information is required.

a. Thermogravimetric Analysis (TGA). Thermogravimetric analysis is the measurement of the retention (or loss) in weight of a polymer sample at elevated temperatures. Although techniques and equipment have been developed which detect small changes in weight, TGA is a relatively crude way to determine thermal stability, since polymers can degrade substantially by random chain scission without an appreciable loss in weight. TGA is nevertheless a rapid and very effective way to screen polymers believed to be thermally stable. In this test, the sample is heated on a thermobalance at a uniform rate or isothermally at some

* In this chapter the nature of the atmosphere—nitrogen, argon, air, etc.—under which a given test was conducted will be given if it was reported. In the last several years researchers have usually reported such information, but this is still far from universal practice.

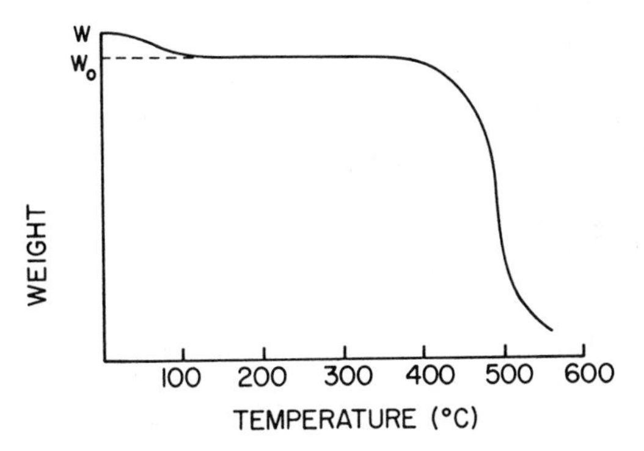

Fig. 1. Programmed thermogravimetric analysis (TGA) showing weight (or weight per cent) retention versus temperature.

elevated temperature either under vacuum or in a selected atmosphere, such as air, nitrogen, or argon. The results can be presented by several methods—primarily weight versus temperature (Fig. 1) and rate of loss of weight versus temperature (Fig. 2). The weight axis may be scaled to show true weight or a percentage of the original; the latter method is preferred when TGA curves are to be compared as to overall shape.

The temperature at which the polymer is said to decompose is taken either as the temperature at which there is an arbitrary per cent loss of weight, frequently 10–15%, or more often as the temperature at which there is an inflection in the TGA curve, i.e., the temperature of maximum rate of weight loss. When the arbitrary weight loss method is used, a correction is often necessary for the small initial weight loss, $W - W_0$, due to desorption of water or solvent.

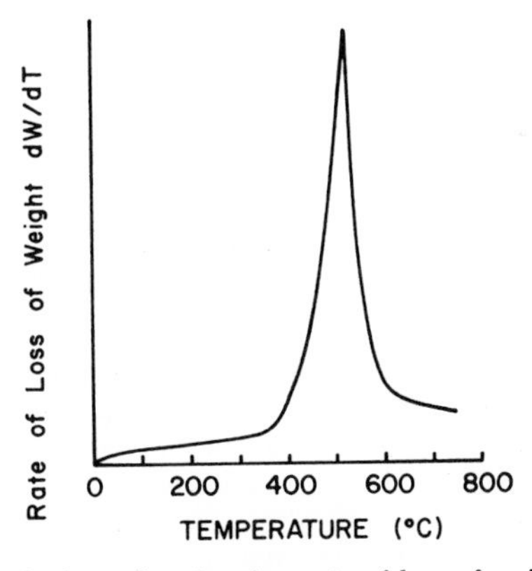

Fig. 2. Differential weight loss plot showing rate of loss of weight with temperature.

For meaningful comparison of the decomposition temperatures of different polymer samples, it is important that the samples be tested in the same atmosphere or a comparable one, and that the samples be heated at the same rate or nearly so.

b. Differential Thermal Analysis (DTA). By differential thermal analysis one measures changes in enthalpy. In many respects DTA is a companion test to TGA; indeed, in some recent work simultaneous determinations of the DTA and TGA curves have been made.

A typical DTA thermogram is shown in Fig. 3. For meaningful comparison of DTA data, such as glass transition temperatures of different polymers or of different samples of the same polymer, the DTA's must be made under comparable test conditions; in particular, the atmosphere must be the same or comparable, and the rate of heating should be the same or nearly so. Normally DTA's are made in an inert atmosphere.

c. Melting Point. Giving the melting point of a condensation polymer has usually been the accepted and most convenient way to indicate

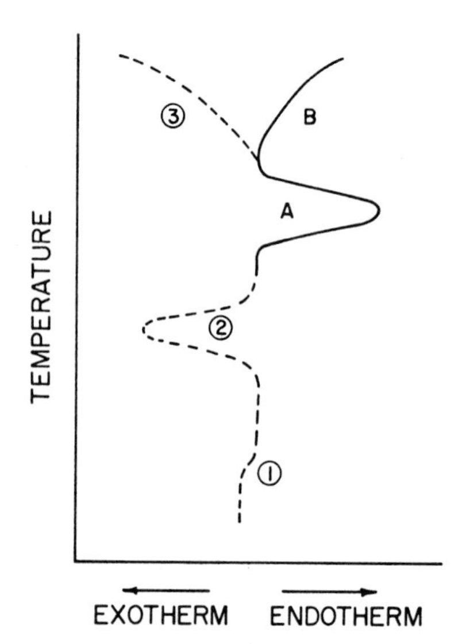

Fig. 3. A typical DTA thermogram. The endothermal band *A* indicates the taking up of heat by the sample; this suggests melting, volatilization of a component, or a chemical reaction. The portion of the curve *B* at very high temperatures indicates thermal degradation. Other phenomena that can be detected by means of DTA are shown by broken lines. They are: (*1*) the second-order or glass transition temperature; (*2*) crystallization, or an intercrystalline transition; and (*3*) oxidation or other chemical reaction.

the upper limit of usefulness of a polymer in the solid state. In the case of aromatic polyamides and polyimides this has led to considerable confusion, since most such polymers with high aromatic content do not melt below 325°C, and in general polymers which do not melt up to this temperature do not melt in the conventional sense, but decompose, sometimes without softening. Although it is obvious that the melting point is not the most important property in determining the overall usefulness of these polymers at elevated temperatures, where obtainable the melting point is still a valuable indicator of the upper limit of utility of the polymer.

By use of DTA one can often determine the melting point even when the melting process is accompanied by decomposition. The DTA melting point is generally accepted as the most reliable one obtainable for polymers which show no evidence of melting below about 375°C.

d. Tensile Testing of Fibers and Films During and After Thermal Treatment. The most sensitive tests for thermal effects are those which are made on fibers and films. One can determine the effect of a given thermal treatment by measuring changes in tensile strength, elongation, and flexibility; changes in tensile strength and elongation can be measured very accurately by use of tensile testing devices such as the Instron Tester. Tensile testing of fibers to determine the thermal stability of polymers is usually resorted to, however, only for polymers of exceptional interest.

Two distinctly different types of tests are made on fibers to evaluate their thermal stability: measurement of the tensile properties of the fiber at a series of elevated temperatures, usually up to the temperature where the fiber no longer has any strength, and secondly, measurement of the tensile properties of the fiber at room temperature after heat-aging the fiber at some elevated temperature for an extended period of time, usually hours to months. The former test is the more common one.* In this test, failure of the filament near the upper limit of test temperatures is sometimes due to softening of the polymer as well as due to chemical degradation, and failure is occasionally due primarily to softening.

From a practical point of view, the heat-aging test is frequently the more important one because information is obtained with regard to the long-term performance that can be expected of the fiber. In the heat-aging test, use of air as the test atmosphere almost always results in a

* This test is made by mounting the fiber in the jaws of the tensile tester, the fiber is enclosed by an oven, the temperature is raised to that desired, the specimen is held at this temperature for a specified time (usually 1 min) and the sample is then broken.

much more rapid degradation than use of an inert atmosphere, showing that the effects of oxidative degradation are very pronounced in heat-aging.

While the tensile testing of fibers to determine their thermostabilities is simple in principle, actual testing and evaluation require of the researcher a degree of sophistication not readily apparent.

2. *Miscellaneous Tests*

Other useful characterization tests for polyamides and polyimides include general polymer characterization (13–15), softening and melting behavior determined by the use of the penetrometer (16), electrical properties and special tests (17).

III. ALIPHATIC-AROMATIC POLYAMIDES

A very large number of aliphatic-aromatic polyamides have been prepared, most of them in recent years. This chapter is concerned primarily with those aliphatic-aromatic polyamides having distinctive properties due to the presence of aromatic units. A large number of polymers which have properties primarily characteristic of the aliphatic polyamides (due to high aliphatic content) are as a consequence not discussed. Further, discussion is largely concerned with those classes of aliphatic-aromatic polyamides from which one or more members have been spun to fiber; some classes of polymers which could be expected to be fiber-forming on the basis of other properties are also considered.

A. Structure–Property Relationships

The incorporation of aromatic units such as the phenylene moiety into polymers in place of aliphatic units affects the properties in quite complex ways. Although difficult, it is profitable for the polymer chemist to unravel these effects as best he can in order to design polymers to meet specific end-use requirements.

Certainly one of the most general effects resulting from incorporation of aromatic units in polyamides is to greatly increase the glass transition temperature, T_g (Table I); the polymers containing aromatic units are accordingly more dimensionally stable at conventional use temperatures than aliphatic polyamides. There is, however, no direct relationship between the glass transition temperatures and the melting points of the polymers: substitution of a phenylene unit in place of six

TABLE I. Glass Transitions and Melting Points of Selected Polyamides

No.	Structure	Glass transition, °C[a]	Melting point, °C	Refs.
1	$-NH(CH_2)_6-NH-C(=O)-(CH_2)_4-C(=O)-$	80	265	—
2	$-NH(CH_2)_5-C(=O)-$	75	220	—
3	$-NH-CH_2-C_6H_4-CH_2-NH-C(=O)-(CH_2)_4-C(=O)-$ (meta-phenylene)	115	243	20
4	$-C(=O)-C_6H_4-C(=O)-NH-(CH_2)_6-NH-$ (meta-phenylene)	142	198	27, 28
5	$-NH-C_6H_4-NH-C(=O)-(CH_2)_4-C(=O)-$ (meta-phenylene)	160	250	27

[a] The glass transitions (T_g) in this table are taken from a du Pont patent (26); all were determined in the same way, by measuring the temperature at which maximum work loss occurred. T_g values are highly dependent on the particular test method used; the values given here are considerably higher than they would be if determined by the penetrometer method; for example, the T_g for polyamide 3 determined by the penetrometer method is 68°C (20).

methylene units can increase the T_g even when it results in a melting point lowering (cf. polymers 1 and 5, Table I). This is of great practical importance with respect to developing a polyamide which is both dimensionably stable and melt-spinnable for end uses such as tire cord.

Another general effect of the incorporation of aromatic units in polyamides is increased modulus or stiffness. *Para*-oriented aromatic units give rise to a higher modulus than do *meta*-oriented units. (The relationship between tensile modulus and the orientation of the arylene unit, e.g., *meta*- versus *para*-phenylene, is considered in the section on fiber properties.)

The substitution of *para*-phenylene units for hexamethylene segments in a polyamide greatly increases the melting point—by almost 200°C in the case of polytetramethylene suberamide (Table II). The very high-melting nature of the polyterephthalamides in general is shown by the DTA melting points of the members of a homologous series (Table III). The melting point of a polyamide, unlike the glass

TABLE II. Melting Point Comparisons

Group	Structure	Melting point, °C	Refs.
A	$-NH-(CH_2)_6-NH-C(=O)-(CH_2)_4-C(=O)-$	265	—
	$-NH-(p\text{-}C_6H_4)-NH-C(=O)-(CH_2)_4-C(=O)-$	340	27
	$-NH-(m\text{-}C_6H_4)-NH-C(=O)-(CH_2)_4-C(=O)-$	250	27
B	$-C(=O)-(CH_2)_6-C(=O)-NH-(CH_2)_4-NH-$	250(247)	29(30)
	$-C(=O)-(p\text{-}C_6H_4)-C(=O)-NH-(CH_2)_4-NH-$	436	18
	$-C(=O)-(m\text{-}C_6H_4)-C(=O)-NH-(CH_2)_4-NH-$	250	—
C	$-NH-(CH_2)_8-NH-C(=O)-(CH_2)_8-C(=O)-$	197	31
	$-NH-CH_2-(p\text{-}C_6H_4)-CH_2-NH-C(=O)-(CH_2)_8-C(=O)-$	268	29
	$-NH-CH_2-(m\text{-}C_6H_4)-CH_2-NH-C(=O)-(CH_2)_8-C(=O)-$	193	20
D	$-NH-(CH_2)_8-NH-C(=O)-(CH_2)_4-C(=O)-$	235	31
	$-NH-(CH_2)_{10}-NH-C(=O)-CH_2-(p\text{-}C_6H_4)-CH_2-C(=O)-$	242	29
	$-NH-(CH_2)_{10}-NH-C(=O)-(CH_2)_8-C(=O)-$	194	31
	$-NH-CH_2-(m\text{-}C_6H_4)-CH_2-NH-C(=O)-(CH_2)_4-C(=O)-$	243	20

TABLE III. Melting Points of Polyterephthalamides of Straight Chain Diamines[a]

Polymer from:	Code	T_m, °C[b]
1,2-Ethylenediamine	2-T	455 (400)[c]
Trimethylenediamine	3-T	399 (305)[c]
Tetramethylenediamine	4-T	436 (315)[c]
N,N'-Dimethyltetramethylene-diamine	Me4-T	~275
Pentamethylenediamine	5-T	353 (310)[c]
Hexamethylenediamine	6-T	371
N,N'-Dimethylhexamethylene-diamine	Me6-T	~260
Heptamethylenediamine	7-T	341

[a] From work of Shashoua and Eareckson (18). [b] Determined by differential thermal analysis (DTA). [c] Determined by x-ray analysis.

transition temperature and the modulus, is not, however, necessarily raised by replacement of an aliphatic segment by an aromatic unit. The symmetry of the aromatic unit plays a large role with respect to the effect of the substituted unit on the melting point. Whereas arylenes oriented *para* greatly increase the melting point, arylenes oriented *meta* frequently lower the melting point slightly (Table II). Further, in every comparison of a polyamide containing a *para*-phenylene unit with the *meta*-phenylene containing isomeric polyamide, it is seen that the melting point difference is large (Tables IV and V); the difference in melting point between polytetramethylene terephthalamide and its isomeric isophthalamide is almost 200°C. The difference in melting point between a given polyamide containing *meta*-phenylene units and its *ortho*-phenylene-containing isomer, however, is generally somewhat smaller than that between a given *para* polyamide and its *meta* counterpart (Table V). Separation of the phenylene unit from the amide linkage by interposition of a methylene unit does not eliminate the strong symmetry effect on the melting point (Table II).

These melting point data indicate that the *para*-phenylene unit in the polymer chain permits much better molecular organization than does either the *meta*- or *ortho*-phenylene unit and, presumably, *para*-phenylene units allow better intermolecular registration of amide groups for hydrogen bonding. Consistent with these suppositions is the observation that those polyamides with *para*-arylenes are more easily crystallized than ones with *meta*-arylenes.* The effects of symmetry of aromatic units on polymer properties will be dealt with more extensively in the section on wholly aromatic polyamides.

* The apparent discrepancies in melting points of certain polymers in Table V may be due to crystallinity in the case of the higher melting polymers.

TABLE IV. Melting Point Comparisons of Polyisophthalamides with Polyterephthalamides

Diacid	Diamine	M.P., °C	Ref.
HO—CO—(p-C6H4)—CO—OH	$NH_2(CH_2)_4NH_2$	436	18
HO—CO—(m-C6H4)—CO—OH	$NH_2(CH_2)_4NH_2$	250	33
HO—CO—(p-C6H4)—CO—OH	$NH_2(CH_2)_6NH_2$	370–371	18, 32
HO—CO—(m-C6H4)—CO—OH	$NH_2(CH_2)_6NH_2$	198	27, 28
HO—CO—(p-C6H4)—CO—OH	$NH_2(CH_2)_8NH_2$	186	27
HO—CO—(m-C6H4)—CO—OH	$NH_2(CH_2)_8NH_2$	123	27

TABLE V. Melting Points of Polyamides Derived from *o*-, *m*-, and *p*-Phenylenediamines[a,b]

Diacid segment	Softening temperature,[c] °C, with various ring structures of complementary diacid segment		
	—NH—(p-C6H4)—NH—	—NH—(m-C6H4)—NH—	—NH—(o-C6H4)—NH—
—C(=O)—$(CH_2)_4$—C(=O)—	>340	250[d]	179
—$(CH_2)_6$—	>340	196[d]	150
—$(CH_2)_8$—	319	184[d,e]	125

[a] From work of Hopff and Krieger (27).

[b] Polymers were prepared by the stirred interfacial method.

[c] The softening point in most cases is the polymer melt temperature determined on a gradient temperature bar.

[d] Kwolek and Morgan (27a) have recently reported melting point values for the polyamides derived from *m*-phenylenediamine which are considerably higher than the corresponding values observed by Hopff and Krieger. These values for the adipamide, suberamide, and sebacamide polymers were: 344, 302, and 258°C, respectively.

[e] 205°C (28).

Studies of the crystallinity or crystallizability could shed considerable light on molecular organization of aliphatic-aromatic polyamides. Such studies, however, are difficult due to complexities not encountered in the case of polyamides such as nylon 66. For example, although it has been reported that the polyterephthalamides from straight-chain diamines, C_4 through C_7, are crystalline (18), Statton (19) has shown that those polyterephthalamides derived from the odd-carbon diamines have longitudinal order only, rather than the three-dimensional order characteristic of polymers such as nylon 66.

Another effect of the incorporation of aromatic units into polyamides that deserves comment if only for its subtlety, is conjugation of the amide linkage with the aromatic unit. Although poly-*m*-xylylene adipamide and polyhexamethylene isophthalamide, polyamides 3 and 4, respectively (Table I), are isomeric, poly-*m*-xylylene adipamide is crystalline while polyhexamethylene isophthalamide is amorphous (20). In the polyisophthalamide the carbonyl groups are in conjugation with the phenylene ring, probably resulting in planarity of a longer segment of the repeat unit than is the case for the poly-*m*-xylylene adipamide. The amorphous nature of the isophthalamide has been attributed to limited hydrogen bonding resulting from poor registration of amide units due to the restricted rotation of polymer segments imposed by the rigid conjugated segments (20). Conjugation of the amide linkages with a phenylene unit, however, does not *a priori* preclude crystallinity, as was seen in the case of the crystalline polyterephthalamides derived from the linear aliphatic diamines (18).

As in the case of aliphatic polyamides (21), the melting points of a homologous series of aliphatic-aromatic polyamides alternate with odd–even alternation of the number of methylenes in either the diamino moiety (Table III) or the diacyl moiety (20).*

N-Alkyl substitution of aliphatic-aromatic polyamides has two very marked effects on their properties: it increases their solubilities very greatly (18) and lowers their melting points markedly (Table III); the longer the alkyl group the greater the effect. Whereas polyalkylene terephthalamides are soluble only in such solvents as concentrated sulfuric and trifluoroacetic acids, their *N*,*N'*-dimethyl derivatives are readily soluble in such solvents as chloroform and acetone (18). This increased solubility is very largely the result of completely eliminating internal hydrogen bonding by the alkyl substitution. Although *N*-methyl substitution results in lowering of the melting points up to

* This odd–even alternation effect also appears in the tensile properties of alphatic-aromatic polyamide fibers. Figure 4 shows the alternation of elongation and tensile modulus of an homologous series of polyterephthalamides.

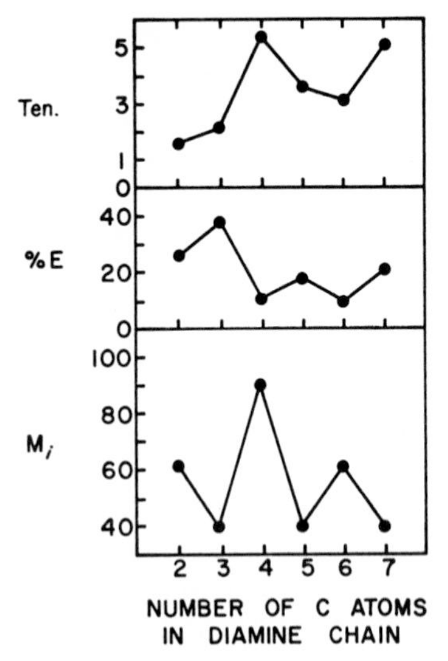

Fig. 4. Tensile properties of fibers from primary aliphatic terephthalamides: T = tenacity, g/den; $\% E$ = elongation, %; M_i = initial modulus, g/den. (Taken from the work of Shashoua and Eareckson (18).)

almost 200°C, it does not appear to disrupt the molecular organization greatly, since it has been observed that all of the *N*-methylated polyterephthalamides based on straight-chain diamines up to C_7 can be crystallized (18). The *N*-ethylated polymers on the other hand were amorphous, indicating substantial disruption of molecular organization (18).

Aromatic polyamides based on piperazines can be viewed as a special class of *N*-alkylated aliphatic-aromatic polyamides. As in the case of the *N*-alkylated polyalkylene terephthalamides discussed above, no internal hydrogen bonding is possible; in contrast, however, the piperazine polymers are more symmetrical along the chain axis. The polyamides based on piperazine, 2-methyl-piperazine, and 2,5-dimethylpiperazine with terephthalic, isophthalic, and *o*-phthalic acid have been studied (Table VI). Although these polymers in general have softening temperatures well over 300°C, they are readily soluble at room temperature in such solvents as chloroform and chloroform–methanol (22). (These data when considered with the solubility and melting point data for aliphatic-aromatic polyamides derived from *N*-alkylated diamines show that there is no direct relationship between solubility and melting point for aliphatic-aromatic polyamides.) The readily soluble nature of these polymers is a consequence of the lack of internal hydrogen bonding. The high-melting nature of these polymers is attributable to the

TABLE VI. Melting Points of Piperazine Polyamides[a]

Diamine segment	Softening temperature,[b] °C with various ring structures of complementary diamine segment		
	o-phthaloyl (—CO—C$_6$H$_4$—CO—, ortho)	isophthaloyl (—CO—C$_6$H$_4$—CO—, meta)	terephthaloyl (—CO—C$_6$H$_4$—CO—, para)
piperazine (—N(C$_4$H$_8$)N—)	325	340	350
2-methylpiperazine (CH_3)	350	280	350
2,5-dimethylpiperazine (CH_3, CH_3)	350	315	350

[a] From work of Katz (22).
[b] The polymers melt with decomposition; the "maximum decomposition points" (DTA) range between 449 and 483°C (22).

rigidity of the aliphatic ring and the fact that rotation of the aliphatic ring is much more difficult than rotation of a straight-chain aliphatic segment. In contrast to the great reduction in melting point that results from *N*-methyl substitution in polyterephthalamides derived from straight-chain diamines (Table III), an increase in melting point results from 2-methyl and 2,5-dimethyl substitution of piperazine in poly-*o*-phthalamides, but no change in melting point results from the same substitution in corresponding polyterephthalamides (Table VI). Evidently, any disruption in chain packing caused by methyl substitution is offset by an increased hindrance to rotation of the piperazine segment.

A very noteworthy feature of the poly-*o*-phthalamides and polyisophthalamides of piperazine and the alkyl-substituted piperazines is that their softening points are very high; they are about the same as the softening points of the corresponding polyterephthalamides (Table VI). This is in striking contrast to the melting point differences of the polyterephthalamides and poly-*o*-phthalamides or polyisophthalamides of straight chain diamines (Table IV). In keeping with the melting point observations, differential thermal analysis indicates little difference in the decomposition temperatures of the polypiperazine-*o*-phthalamides and the corresponding polypiperazine terephthalamides (22). The reason for the similarities in the high-temperature behavior of the terephthalamides, isophthalamides, and phthalamides can only be surmised at this point, but an unusual and highly specific chain packing as well as hindered rotation would seem to be involved.

Poly-2,5-dimethylpiperazine terephthalamide has a glass transition temperature characteristic of those for wholly aromatic polyamides; it is in fact appreciably higher than that for poly-*m*-phenylene isophthalamide, 292 versus 273°C (23).

Aliphatic-aromatic polyamides have moisture regain values as high as or higher than comparable wholly aliphatic polyamides (18, 24–25). Under a given set of test conditions polyhexamethylene terephthalamide and nylon 66 were each found to have a regain value of 4.5% (24). In contrast, under the same conditions polyethylene terephthalate had a regain of only 0.6% (24). Even more striking is the fact that under conditions where polyethylene terephthalate fiber had a moisture regain of only 1%, drawn fibers of the corresponding aliphatic-aromatic polyamide, polyethylene terephthalamide, had a regain of 17.7% (18). Obviously, the nature of the polar linkage is far more important than the aromatic units with regard to moisture absorption. That the high moisture regain of aliphatic-aromatic polyamides is not due to the presence of *N*-hydrogen is shown by comparison of moisture regain values of polyamides derived from piperazines and hexamethylene diamine each with a given aromatic diacyl moiety: the piperazinepolymers had higher moisture regain values (25) (the piperazine-derived polymers were also the higher-melting polymers).

B. Synthesis of Selected Classes of Fiber-Forming Aliphatic-Aromatic Polyamides

Of the large number of aliphatic-aromatic polyamides, most were prepared in recent years using low-temperature polycondensation techniques. In his recent review of polyamides prepared by low-temperature polycondensation, Morgan (6b) listed approximately two hundred aliphatic-aromatic polyamides thus prepared, attesting to the relative ease of preparing aliphatic-aromatic polymers by the low-temperature methods.

For convenience polyamides derived from diamines and diacyl compounds are referred to as AA-BB polymers, and polyamides derived from a monomer containing both the acyl and amino groups are called A-B polyamides.

1. AA-BB Polyamides

a. Polyamides from Aromatic Diacyl Compounds. ***(1) Polyterephthalamides.*** The polyterephthalamides of straight chain primary aliphatic diamines have probably received more attention than any other class of aliphatic-aromatic polyamides (18,24,34–36) (Table III). Polymers derived from diamines with six or fewer methylenes are so high melting that they are degraded either at temperatures below their melting points or at their melting points (18), and for this reason cannot be prepared by conventional melt condensation methods. Melt condensation is possible, however, if there are eight or more methylenes in the diamine (18,34–36). Polyhexamethylene terephthalamide, the most studied polymer in the series, has been prepared by a modified bulk polymerization method in which the salt of hexamethylenediamine and terephthalic acid is heated just below its melt temperature (37). Polyterephthalamides derived from straight-chain primary diamines can in general be prepared, however, by interfacial polycondensation (18,38). Even so, obtaining high-molecular-weight polymers in the case of the lower homologs is difficult due to the very insoluble nature of these polymers. Polyhexamethylene terephthalamide, for example, is readily soluble only in strongly acidic solvents such as cold concentrated sulfuric and trifluoroacetic acids.

(2) Polyisophthalamides. The polyisophthalamides of straight-chain primary diamines present much less of a problem in synthesis than do the polyterephthalamides. They are readily prepared by low-temperature polymerization, and due to their much lower melting points they can in general be readily prepared by melt polymerization as well (Table IV). To prepare the polyisophthalamides of cyclic diamines such as piperazine, however, low-temperature polycondensation is apparently required.

(3) Poly-o-phthalamides. Poly-*o*-phthalamides cannot be prepared as high-molecular-weight polymers from primary diamines presumably because of chain termination resulting from imide formation (22).

$$C_6H_4(COX)_2 + NH_2\text{—}R\text{—}NH_2 \longrightarrow C_6H_4(CO)_2N\text{—}R\text{—}\sim\sim \qquad (1)$$

Since imide formation is, however, not possible with secondary amines, high-molecular-weight poly-*o*-phthalamides can be prepared with such amines. A series of very high-melting polypiperazine-*o*-phthalamides have been prepared by interfacial polymerization (Table VI). Clear, flexible films were prepared from solution, and although no fibers were reported, it is likely that fibers could be spun from solutions of these compositions.

(4) Polyamides from 4,4′-Sulfonyldibenzoyl Dichloride. Two series of high-melting fiber-forming polyamides have been prepared by interfacial polymerization of 4,4′-sulfonyldibenzoyl dichloride with straight-chain primary diamines and with piperazine and its 2-methyl- and 2,5-dimethyl derivatives (25). In the first series the melting points range up to 380°C for the polyamide derived from ethylenediamine, and in the piperazine series up to above 380° for the polymer based on piperazine.

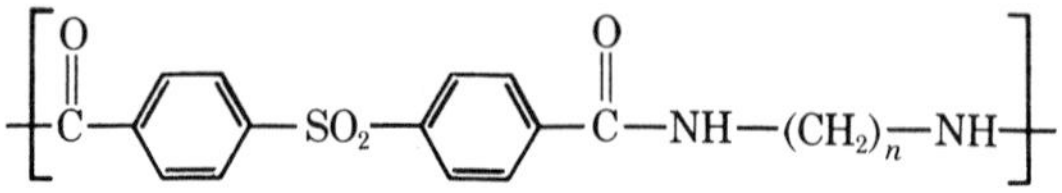

$$\left[-\overset{\overset{O}{\|}}{C}-C_6H_4-SO_2-C_6H_4-\overset{\overset{O}{\|}}{C}-NH-(CH_2)_n-NH- \right]$$

($n = 2,3,4,$ and 6)

$$\left[-\overset{\overset{O}{\|}}{C}-C_6H_4-SO_2-C_6H_4-\overset{\overset{O}{\|}}{C}-N\langle C_4H_8 \rangle N- \right]$$

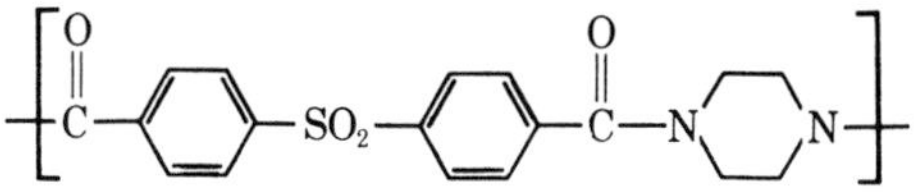

The polymers based on straight-chain diamines are lower melting than the corresponding terephthalamides, and they are more soluble, the greater solubility presumably being due to the polar sulfone group (39). The hexamethylene-derived polymer has a melting point (310°C) low enough to permit melt-spinning; the polymer was also solution-spun from trifluoroacetic acid solution. Fibers of the composition, however, were not of high quality.

b. Polyamides from Diamines Containing Arylene Units. High-molecular-weight aliphatic-aromatic polyamides cannot be prepared by melt condensation of arylene diamines with aliphatic diacids due to the low reactivity of the aromatic amino group (40,41). Polymers based on phenylene diamines can, however, be prepared by low-temperature poly-condensation using diacid chlorides, and a large number of polyamides have now been made in this manner.*

Diamines in which the amino groups are separated from the aromatic nucleus by an aliphatic unit have the characteristic reactivity of aliphatic diamines. They can be polymerized with aliphatic diacids by conven-

* Fibers of some polymers based on these diamines have been reported (27a) since this chapter was completed. Unfortunately, it was not possible to include these in the section on fibers.

tional melt polymerization of the salt when the resultant polymer is not too high melting (20). A number of polyamides based on *m*-xylylenediamine have been melt-polymerized (20,24,42,43), and fiber of one of these, poly-*m*-xylylene adipamide, has been studied extensively (24,42,42a).

2. *A-B Polyamides*

Polyamides from monomers having both the amino and acyl groups on the same molecule (A-B polyamides) have received little attention, even though stoichiometric balance is inherent in such cases. By masking the amine group with hydrogen chloride, Schaefgen (44) was able to prepare a very low-molecular-weight polyamide from *p*-aminomethylbenzoyl chloride by interfacial polymerization. The lack of research in this area has been due largely to difficulties in synthesis. In order to polymerize any A-B monomer by low-temperature solution polycondensation one must first obtain a monomer with both an amino group and a reactive acyl function such as the acid chloride. Prevention of premature condensation in the synthesis of such monomers remains a difficult problem.

$$HCl{\cdot}NH_2{-}CH_2{-}C_6H_4{-}\overset{O}{\overset{\|}{C}}{-}Cl \longrightarrow \left[NH{-}CH_2{-}C_6H_4{-}\overset{O}{\overset{\|}{C}} \right] \qquad (2)$$

In the case of amino acids where the amino group is attached directly to the aromatic nucleus, low reactivity of the amino group and complicating reactions preclude satisfactory polycondensation by melt methods.

3. *Polyoxamides*

The oxamides of aromatic diamines constitute a special class of aromatic polyamides. Although they are included here under aliphatic-aromatic polyamides, it would be equally appropriate to classify them as wholly aromatic polyamides. The polymers are very high melting and their solubility characteristics also strongly support a wholly aromatic classification: the polymers are surprisingly soluble in those amide solvents such as *N*-methylpyrrolidone and tetramethylurea which are characteristically useful for wholly aromatic polyamides.

The polymers are too high melting to be made by melt condensation, but a number of them have recently been prepared by solution polycondensation of the reactive diphenylthiol oxalate with aromatic diamines at 130–200°C (45), and by the interfacial reaction of gaseous oxalyl chloride with aqueous solutions of the diamines (46–47). Tough, clear, flexible films were prepared from solutions of two of these polymers (I and II below; mp > 400°C and 376°C, respectively) (45); although nothing was reported about it, there appears to be no reason why fibers could not be spun from solutions of these polymers.

$$\left[-NH-C_6H_4-C(CH_3)_2-C_6H_4-NH-\overset{O}{\overset{\|}{C}}-\overset{O}{\overset{\|}{C}}- \right]$$

I

$$\left[-NH-C_6H_4-SO_2-C_6H_4-NH-\overset{O}{\overset{\|}{C}}-\overset{O}{\overset{\|}{C}}- \right]$$

II

C. Fibers of Aliphatic-Aromatic Polyamides

1. Polyhexamethylene Terephthalamide (Nylon 6-T) and Poly-m-xylylene Adipamide (MXD-6) Fibers

Although fibers have been spun from quite a few aliphatic-aromatic polyamides, it appears that fibers of only two polymers have been studied extensively, namely, fibers of polyhexamethylene terephthalamide (18,24,48) and poly-*m*-xylylene adipamide (20,24,42). These are often referred to as nylon 6-T and MXD-6 fibers, respectively.

Nylon 6-T fibers have been wet-spun from cold concentrated sulfuric acid (24) and dry-spun from trifluoroacetic acid (18). The properties of fiber spun from sulfuric acid have been studied in considerable detail, and in Table VII they are compared with fiber properties of nylon 66 and polyethylene terephthalate. The superiority of nylon 6-T to either nylon 66 or polyethylene terephthalate in thermal resistance properties is clearly evident.

The high thermal resistance of nylon 6-T fiber in comparison with that of nylon 66 and polyethylene terephthalate fibers could well result in the use of this fiber for high-temperature applications too demanding for nylon 66 and polyethylene terephthalate but which do not require the outstanding thermal resistance of the more expensive wholly aromatic polyamide fibers. Both hexamethylene diamine and terephthalic acid are commercially available and are relatively inexpensive.

In addition to its thermal resistance, nylon 6-T fiber has a high dimensional stability, indicating possible utility for tire cord with a low

TABLE VII. Fiber Properties of Various Aliphatic-Aromatic Polymers[a]

	Nylon 6-T	Polyester[b] 2 GT	Nylon MXD-6	Nylon 66
Melting point, °C	370	265	243	265
Density, g/cc	1.21	1.38	—	1.14
Glass transition temp., °C	180	115	90	60
Moisture regain, %	4.5	0.6	—	4.5
Tensile properties				
Tenacity, g/den	4.5	4.8	4.3	4.9
Elongation, %	35	54	29	57
Modulus, g/den	45	40	50	40
Strength retained, %, after 5 hr				
at 150°C	100	100	—	85
at 185°C	100	95	—	40
at 220°C	60	—	—	0

[a] From work of Sprague and Singleton (24).
[b] Polyethylene terephthalate.

TABLE VIII. Laboratory Flat-Spotting Performance of Fibers[a]

	Set,[b] %
Nylon 66	1.36
Polyethylene terephthalate	0.25
Nylon 6-T	0.25

[a] From work of Sprague and Singleton (24).
[b] Level of perceptible flatspotting corresponds to a set value of ~0.6%.

flatspotting propensity. Its set value is the same as that of polyethylene terephthalate fiber (Table VIII). (The set value of a fiber is a viscoelastic property which can be related to the flatspotting tendency of the fiber.)

In contrast to nylon 6-T, MXD-6 is relatively low melting (mp 243°C), permitting spinning by the conventional grid melt-spinning technique (24). It has a glass transition temperature greater than that of polyethylene terephthalate and a modulus well above that of nylon 66. Properties of melt-spun fiber are given in Table VII, where they can be compared with the properties of nylon 66, nylon 6-T, and polyethylene terephthalate fibers. For a time this fiber appeared to be quite promising, but despite the several good properties of MXD-6 fibers, wide use of these fibers in textile applications is precluded by its excessive sensitivity to moisture and, to a lesser degree, heat. The modulus, for example, undergoes a severe reduction in the presence of water at temperatures only slightly above room temperature.

2. Miscellaneous Fibers of Aliphatic-Aromatic Polyamides

a. Fibers from Polymers Based on Primary Diamines. Fibers of the polyterephthalamides of the straight chain diamines, C_2 through C_7 (nylons 2-T–7-T) have been dry-spun from trifluoroacetic acid solutions of the respective polymers; the tensile properties of these fibers are plotted in Fig. 4. Of particular interest are the relatively lower initial tensile moduli and higher elongations for the fibers based on odd carbon diamines. (See Table III for polymer melt temperatures.)

Crystalline fiber of polyhexamethylene-4,4′-sulfonyldibenzamide has been prepared both by melt-spinning and by spinning a trifluoroacetic acid solution of the polymer. The tensile properties of the fiber were relatively poor. This is directly attributable to poor drawability, which is in turn indirectly most likely due to the sulfone linkage between two phenylene units (25). The sulfone unit is tetrahedral (25), and consequently *p*-phenylene units separated by the sulfone linkage cannot be both in a straight line and coplanar at the same time. This explanation for the poor drawability is supported by the poor drawability and relatively poor tensile properties of fibers from piperazine-containing polymers also based on the 4,4′-sulfonyldibenzoyl unit (to be discussed later); it is, however, not the only explanation that could be advanced.

b. Fibers from Polymers Based on Piperazine and Related Diamines. Aliphatic-aromatic polyamides based on piperazines are attractive for fibers because they are very high melting and have high glass transition temperatures, while at the same time they are sufficiently soluble to permit them to be spun from solutions of the polymer in solvents other than strong acids (Section III-A). The polymers are soluble, for example, in such solvents as dimethylformamide (25), acetic acid (22), chloroform (22), chloroform–methanol (22), and formic acid (23,38).

(1) Polyterephthalamides of 2,5-Dimethylpiperazine and 1,2-Di(4-piperidyl)ethane. The fiber from the polyterephthalamide of 2,5-dimethylpiperazine is particularly significant because of the high tenacity obtained—7.7 g/den (23). This demonstrates that neither the nonplanarity of the piperazine ring nor the pendent methyl groups necessarily prevents the molecular organization necessary for high strength. Other tensile properties of this fiber were 8% elongation and an initial modulus of 150 g/den. The initial tensile modulus was strikingly high, but it is consistent with the very high T_g of 292°C that has been reported for the polymer.

Fibers having only relatively low tenacity (2.8 g/den) were reported for the polyterephthalamide of 1,2(di-4-piperidyl)ethane (38). The low tenacity of these fibers is probably due to the method of spinning, however, rather than to the polymer structure.

(2) ***Polyamides from 4,4′-Sulfonyldibenzoyl Dichloride with 2-Methyl- and 2,5-Dimethylpiperazine.*** The tensile properties of the fibers from these polymers are not outstanding (Table IX). The polymers were not crystalline and could not be induced to crystallize. In each case the fibers were difficult to draw. In view of the excellent tensile strength obtainable with fibers of the polyterephthalamide of 2,5-dimethylpiperazine, it would appear that the sulfone link between the phenylene units of the diacyl moiety is once again the source of the difficulty.

TABLE IX. Fiber Properties of Polyamides Based on 4,4′-Sulfonyldibenzoic Acid[a]

	2-Methylpiperazine polymer, drawn 300% at 290°C	2,5-Dimethylpiperazine polymer, drawn 325% at 325°C
Tenacity, g/den	3.0	2.5
Elongation, %	25	20
Initial modulus, g/den	40	45
Shrinkage, %	4	2
Zero strength temp, °C[b]	355	340

[a] From work of C. W. Stephens (25).
[b] The temperature at which the fiber will break under a load of 0.1 g/den.

3. *Fibers from Blends of Aliphatic-Aromatic Polyamides with Aliphatic Polyamides*

One of the most important uses of aliphatic-aromatic polyamides may be as admixtures with aliphatic polyamides to obtain fibers with a lower creep propensity than is characteristic of wholly aliphatic polyamides such as nylon 66. Fibers have been spun from melt-blended mixtures of nylon 66 with a number of aliphatic-aromatic polyamides (26). Since amide interchange takes place at the melt temperature, it is believed that melt blending first leads to block copolymer formation. The degree of randomization of the two polymers which takes place as a result of the interchange is presumably a direct function of time, temperature, and intimacy of blending.

The flatspotting tendency of these fibers has been estimated, as in the case of nylon 6-T, by comparison of the set value of the fiber with that of nylon 66 or nylon 6 (Table X). Fibers with set values of 1.0 or less (as determined by the particular method used for the fibers listed in Table X) are considered to be "non-flatspotting." It is seen that

TABLE X. Set Values of Block Copolyamides[a]

No.	Aromatic Polymer	Wt. %	Nylon 66, wt. %	Nylon 6, wt. %	Set,[c] %	Tenacity, g/den
1	— —		100		1.7	8.5
2	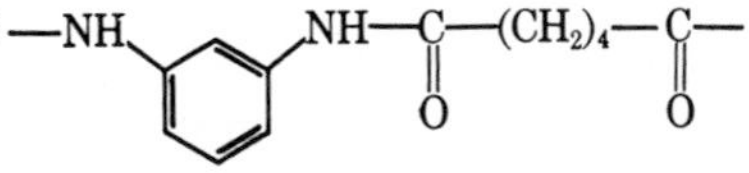 $-NH-C_6H_4-NH-C(=O)-(CH_2)_4-C(=O)-$ (m-phenylene)	30	70		0.56	8.7
3	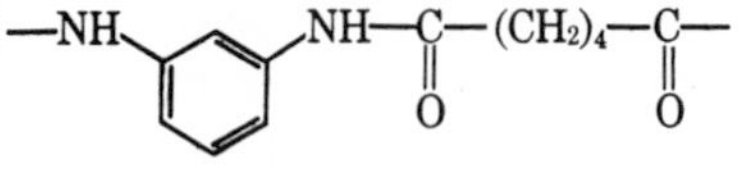 $-NH-C_6H_4-NH-C(=O)-(CH_2)_4-C(=O)-$ (m-phenylene)	20	80		1.04	7.6
4	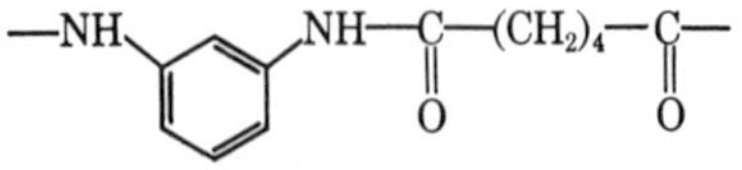 $-NH-C_6H_4-NH-C(=O)-(CH_2)_4-C(=O)-$ (m-phenylene)	20[b]	80[b]		2.3[b]	3.1
5	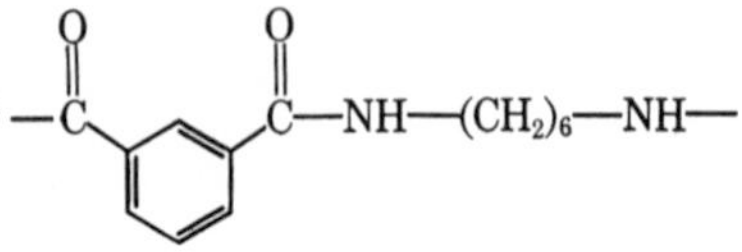 $-C(=O)-C_6H_4-C(=O)-NH-(CH_2)_6-NH-$ (m-phenylene)	30	70		0.86	5.4
6	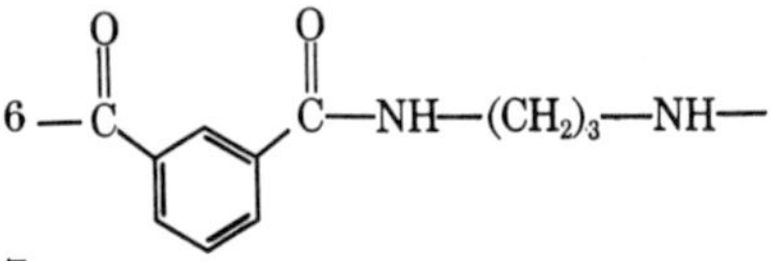 $-C(=O)-C_6H_4-C(=O)-NH-(CH_2)_3-NH-$ (m-phenylene)	20	80		0.64	4.7
7	— —			100	2.1	
8	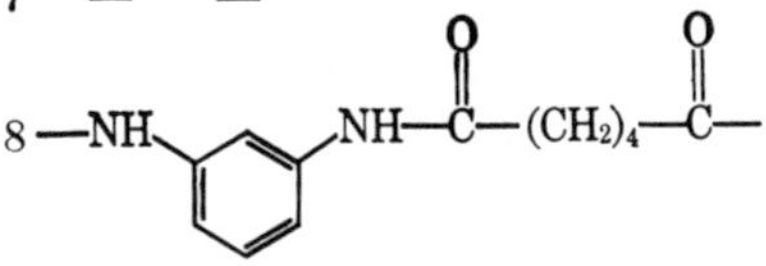 $-NH-C_6H_4-NH-C(=O)-(CH_2)_4-C(=O)-$ (m-phenylene)	30		70	0.79	
9	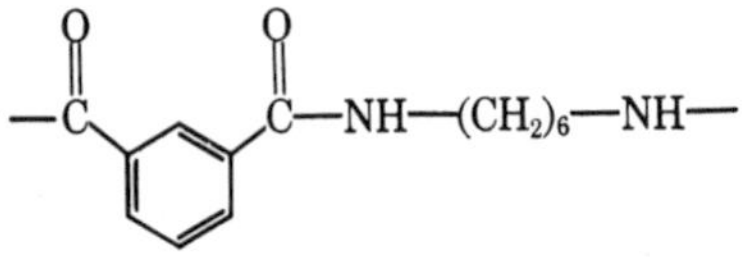 $-C(=O)-C_6H_4-C(=O)-NH-(CH_2)_6-NH-$ (m-phenylene)	35		65	1.07	

[a] From du Pont patent (26).
[b] Random copolymer.
[c] Determined at a relative humidity of less than 10%.

the set value is highly sensitive to the aromatic content of the polymer: the presence of as little as 10 wt. % phenylene units is sufficient for obtaining the required set value (Table X).

IV. WHOLLY AROMATIC POLYAMIDES

Since the replacement of some of the aliphatic segments of polyamides with aromatic units resulted in a class of polymers having thermal properties substantially superior to those of wholly aliphatic polyamides such as nylon 66 (Section III), it was almost obvious that replacement of all aliphatic segments with aromatic units would result in polymers having even higher melting points and greater resistance to thermal degradation. Nevertheless, that such would be the case was not *a priori* a certainty, since the limit of thermal stability of the amide linkage itself was not known. In short, however, it has been found that the wholly aromatic polyamides are indeed much higher melting and are far more resistant to thermal degradation.

Wholly aromatic polyamide polymers appear to have great potential for thermally stable fibers and related products such as paper. One such fiber, Nomex, presumed to be poly-*m*-phenylene isophthalamide, is in commercial production, and another, the polyterephthalamide of *N*,*N′*-*m*-phenylene-bis-*m*-aminobenzamide, has undergone extensive evaluation (7,49,50); both fibers are discussed in detail in this section. (Nomex was known as HT-1 while still an experimental fiber (2).)

The number of wholly aromatic polyamides that have been reported is not as great as the number of aliphatic-aromatic polyamides. On the other hand, the wholly aromatic ones as a class have been characterized as well as, and perhaps even better than, the aliphatic-aromatic polyamides.

The order of discussion in this section will be the same as in the previous one: A, polymer structure–property relationships; B, general synthesis considerations; and C, fiber properties and end uses.

A. Structure–Property Relationships

In the section on aliphatic-aromatic polyamides the polymers were considered from the point of view of their being a special kind of polyamide as a consequence of their containing arylene units. While it is necessary to view the wholly aromatic polyamides as modified polyamides, it is desirable to consider them in a different perspective as well: namely, as modified polyphenylenes (51–54), i.e., polyphenylenes with amide groups inserted between the phenylene units.

Table XI lists the more important wholly aromatic polyamides that have been reported along with pertinent polymerization and thermal property data. Polyamides having phenylene units bridged by a single methylene unit have been placed here instead of in the aliphatic-aromatic polyamide section because from a property point of view they more closely approach the wholly aromatic polymers and, also, because most of the literature concerning these polymers is interwoven with that of the wholly aromatic polymers. Only representative examples of polymers with aliphatic substituents on either the nitrogen of the amide link

TABLE XI. Some Physical Properties of Wholly Aromatic Polyamides

No.	Polymer	Viscosity[a] η_{inh}, dl/g	Sol-vent	Thermal properties T_g, °C	T_m, °C[b]	T_{dec}, °C[c]	Ref
AB Polymers							
1	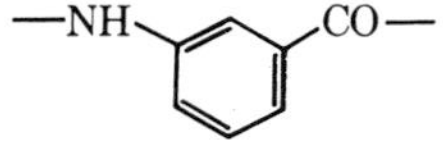 —NH— —CO—	0.46[d]	A		424[e]		65
2	 —NH— —CO—	0.76[d]	B		503[b]	~500	66
3	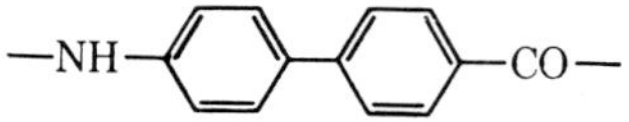 —NH— —CO—				>500[f]	~650	67
AA-BB Polymers							
4	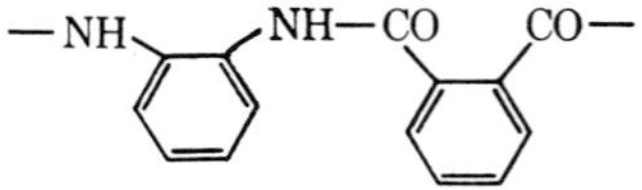 —NH— NH—CO CO—				~185[g]		68
5	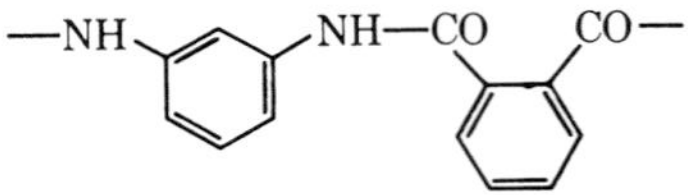 —NH— NH—CO CO—				~200[g]		68
6	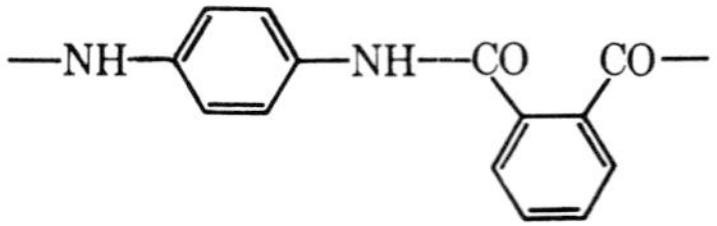 —NH— —NH—CO CO—				~240[g]		68
7	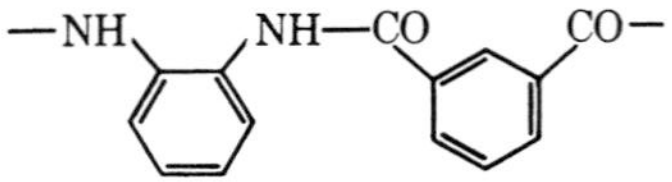 —NH— NH—CO CO—				~240[g]		68

8	—NH—(o-phenylene)—NH—CO—(p-phenylene)—CO—			~295[g]	68
9	—NH—(m-phenylene)—NH—CO—(m-phenylene)—CO—	0.72	B (273)[h]	365[i]	69 (23)
10	—NH—(m-phenylene)—NH—CO—(5-Cl-m-phenylene)—CO—	0.84	B	305[i]	9
11	—NH—(m-phenylene)—NH—CO—(p-phenylene)—CO—	1.04	B	>400[i]	9
12	—NH—(p-phenylene)—NH—CO—(m-phenylene)—CO—	0.39[d]	B	>400[e]	70
13	—NH—(p-phenylene)—NH—CO—(p-phenylene)—CO—	0.96[j]	B	(500)[e]	71 (70)
14	—NH—(4,4'-biphenylene)—NH—CO—(p-phenylene)—CO—	0.28[d]	B	>350[i] (>500)[e]	72 (73)
14a	(m-phenylene)	0.51	B	>400[e]	73
15	—NH—(3,3'-dimethyl-4,4'-biphenylene, CH_3, CH_3)—NH—CO—(m-phenylene)—CO—	1.70	B (253)[h]	365[i]	69 (23)

(continued)

TABLE XI (*continued*)

No.	Polymer	Viscosity[a] η_{inh}, dl/g	Viscosity[a] Solvent	Thermal properties T_g, °C	Thermal properties T_m, °C[b]	Thermal properties T_{dec}, °C[c]	Ref.
16	—NH—(p-C₆H₄)—S(O)(O)—(p-C₆H₄)—NH—CO—(m-C₆H₄)—CO—	1.53	B		>400[k]		60
17	—NH—(p-C₆H₄)—S(O)(O)—(p-C₆H₄)—NH—CO—(p-C₆H₄)—CO—	1.88	B		>360[k]		60
18	—NH—(m-C₆H₄)—P(O)(CH₃)—(m-C₆H₄)—NH—CO—(p-C₆H₄)—CO—	0.28[l]	C		325–330[i]		74
19	—NH—(p-C₆H₄)—O—(p-C₆H₄)—NH—CO—(p-C₆H₄)—CO—	0.54[j] (0.57)			(>340)[i]		71 (75, 76)
Copolymers of Limited Order							
20	—NH—(m-C₆H₄)—CO—NH—(p-C₆H₄)—NH—CO—(m-C₆H₄)—CO—	0.67	B		365[e]		55
21	—(p-C₆H₄)— —(p-C₆H₄)— —(p-C₆H₄)—	0.64	B		570[f,m]		55
Ordered Copolymers							
22	—NH—(m-C₆H₄)—CO—NH—(m-C₆H₄)—NH—CO—(m-C₆H₄)—NH—CO—(m-C₆H₄)—CO—	1.48	A	290[n]	410[f]	(450)	7 (53)

23	$-(p\text{-}C_6H_4)-$	1.92	A		450[f]		7
24	$-(p\text{-}C_6H_4)-(p\text{-}C_6H_4)-$	2.38	A		420[f]	490	53
25	$-(2,6\text{-}C_{10}H_6)-$	2.42	A		430[f]	490	53
26	$-(m\text{-}C_6H_4)-\ -(p\text{-}C_6H_4)-\ -(m\text{-}C_6H_4)-\ -(m\text{-}C_6H_4)-$	1.30	A	305[f]	460[f]		7
27	$-(p\text{-}C_6H_4)-$	1.31	A	295[f]	467[f]		7
28	$-NH-(m\text{-}C_6H_4)-CO-N(CH_3)-(p\text{-}C_6H_4)-N(CH_3)-CO-(m\text{-}C_6H_4)-NH-CO-(m\text{-}C_6H_4)-CO-$	0.42	A		265[o,p]		7
29	$-NH-(m\text{-}C_6H_4)-CO-N(CH_3)-(p\text{-}C_6H_4)-N(CH_3)-CO-(m\text{-}C_6H_4)-NH-CO-(p\text{-}C_6H_4)-CO-$	0.65	A		300[o,p]		7
30	$-NH-(p\text{-}C_6H_4)-CO-NH-(m\text{-}C_6H_4)-NH-CO-(p\text{-}C_6H_4)-NH-CO-(m\text{-}C_6H_4)-CO-$	1.27	A	335[n]	475[f]	(485)	7 (53)
31	$-(p\text{-}C_6H_4)-$	1.42	A		490[f]		7

(*continued*)

TABLE XI (*continued*)

No.	Polymer	Viscosity[a]		Thermal properties			Ref.
		η_{inh}, dl/g	Solvent	T_g, °C	T_m, °C[b]	T_{dec}, °C[c]	
32		1.20	A		490[f]	490	53
33		1.38	A		>500[f]	500	53
34		0.99	A		480[f]		7
35		1.98[d]	B		555[f]		7
36		0.58	A		470[f]	500	53
37		0.60	A		480[f]	>500	53
38		0.57	A		>500[f]	500	53
39		0.72	A		>500[f]	>600	53
40		1.13	A		400[f]	430	53
41		0.99	A		>500[f]	480	53

42		0.62	A	>500[f]	490	53
43		0.85	A	>500[f]	450	53
44		0.75	A	475[f]	475	53
45	—NH—⟨ring⟩—NH—CO—⟨ring⟩—CO—NH—⟨ring⟩—NH—CO—⟨ring⟩—CO—					54
Polymers Containing Methylene Bridges in the Chain						
46	—NH—⟨ring⟩—CH_2—⟨ring⟩—NH—CO—⟨ring⟩—CO—	1.4	B	400[k]		60
47	—NH—⟨ring⟩—C(CH_3)$_2$—⟨ring⟩—NH—CO—⟨ring⟩—CO—	1.2	C	375[k]		60, 69

[a] Viscosity values given, unless otherwise indicated, are inherent viscosities determined at 0.5 g/100-ml. at 30°C. Solvents were: A, dimethylacetamide containing 5% dissolved lithium chloride; B, sulfuric acid; C, *m*-cresol. [b] Melting or softening point. [c] Determined by means of thermogravimetric analysis (TGA) in nitrogen. [d] Determined at 25°C. [e] Capillary melting or softening point. [f] Determined by means of differential thermal analysis (DTA) in nitrogen. [g] Softening point determined on a Kofler hot-stage microscope. [h] Determined on fiber from sonic modulus as a function of temperature. [i] Method of determination not indicated. [j] Intrinsic viscosity. [k] Minimum temperature at which polymer leaves a wet, molten trail as it is stroked on a heated block. [l] Reduced specific viscosity. [m] Visual m.p., 490°C. [n] Determined by means of the penetrometer. [o] Softening point of film. [p] The m.p. for the polyterephthalamide of *N,N′*-dimethylhexamethylenediamine is 260°C (18).

or on the phenylene units have been listed. The data reported for the melting or softening point frequently means no more than the fact that the polymer did not melt at a temperature less than that given. Since almost every wholly aromatic polyamide which contains neither *N*-substitution nor *ortho*-phenylene units begins to decompose near its melting point, determination of the melting point is usually very difficult. The use of differential thermal analysis for the determination of the melting point of such high-melting polymers has now become generally accepted as the best technique; even here interpretation of the data is frequently not unequivocal.

Since decomposition has frequently been found by thermogravimetric analysis to begin at a temperature below that of polymer melting, the decomposition temperature in such instances is a better guide to the thermal stability than is the melting point. However, since there is a relationship between the melting points of polyamides and their decomposition temperatures, knowledge of the temperatures at which polymers would melt if decomposition were not a complicating factor is of value as a guide to the polymer chemist in molecular engineering. This is so because melting is related to polymer rigidity, chain packing, and intermolecular forces, all of which can be varied by structural modifications.

Further discussion of the thermal decomposition of wholly aromatic polyamides is reserved for the section on fiber properties (Section IV-C).

The melting points of aromatic polyamides are directly related to the orientation (i.e., *ortho, meta, para*) of the arylene units in the polymer repeat units (Table XI). For example, replacement of all of the *meta*-phenylenes by *para*-phenylenes in a given all-*meta* wholly aromatic polymer results in a melting point elevation on the order of 100°C (cf. 1 versus 2; 9 versus 13; 22 versus 35, Table XI). This increase is of the same order of magnitude as found in the case of the same substitution in the aliphatic-aromatic series (Tables IV and V, Section II-A). There is, however, one major difference between the two classes of polymers: whereas it was found for the aliphatic-aromatic polymers that exchange of an *ortho*-phenylene unit for a *meta*-phenylene unit resulted in little difference in the melting point, it is seen in the case of the wholly aromatic polymers that the same exchange results in a drastic lowering of the melting point.

The melting points of polyamides containing the 4,4′-biphenylene unit and naphthalene units of various orientations generally lie somewhere between those of polymers having *meta*- and *para*-phenylene units substituted in their places as shown in one study of thirteen ordered, wholly aromatic copolyamides (53) (Table XI). In general, incorporation of symmetrical naphthalene units and the 4,4′-biphenylene unit in

TABLE XII. Melting Points of Some Polyamides and Polyesters

No.	Structure	M.P., °C	Ref.
Polyesters			
1	$-O-\overset{O}{\overset{\|}{C}}-C_6H_4-\overset{O}{\overset{\|}{C}}-O-CH_2-CH_2-$	264	4
2	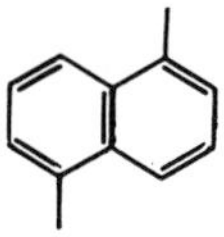 (1,5-naphthylene)	226–230	4
3	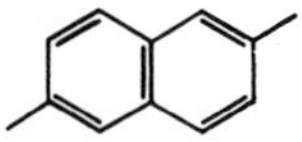 (2,6-naphthylene)	255–260	4
4	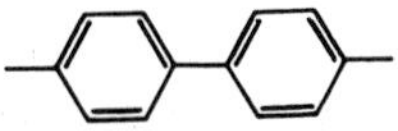 (4,4′-biphenylene)	346	77
Polyamides			
5	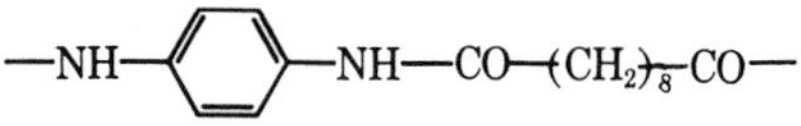 $-NH-C_6H_4-NH-CO-(CH_2)_8-CO-$	319 (320–325)	27 (78)
6	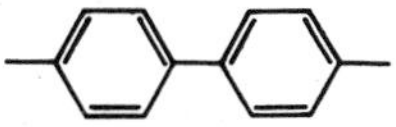 (4,4′-biphenylene)	398–408	78

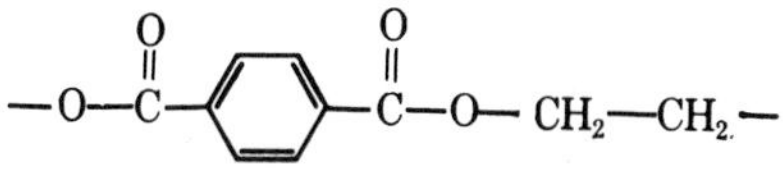

place of a *para*-phenylene unit produces no significant change in polymer melting point. This effect is markedly different from those observed for such substitutions for *para*-phenylene in polyethylene terephthalate (Table XII).

N-Methyl substitution, as in the case of the aliphatic-aromatic polyamides, results in very substantial lowering of the melting point. *N*-methyl substitution of only half of the amide linkages of the polyisophthalamide of *p*-phenylene-*N*,*N*′-bis-*m*-aminobenzamide (structure I, below, mp 265°C) resulted in a melting point lowering of 195°C (7) (see also polymers 27 and 29, Table XI).

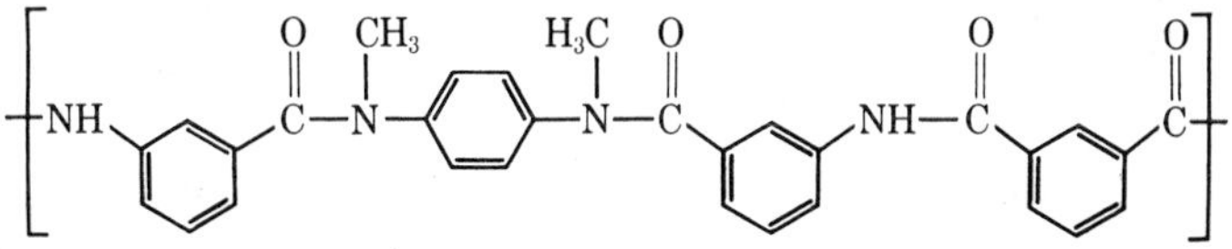

$$\left[-NH-C_6H_4-\overset{O}{\overset{\|}{C}}-\underset{}{\overset{CH_3}{\overset{|}{N}}}-C_6H_4-\overset{H_3C}{\overset{|}{N}}-\overset{O}{\overset{\|}{C}}-C_6H_4-NH-\overset{O}{\overset{\|}{C}}-C_6H_4-\overset{O}{\overset{\|}{C}}-\right]$$

I

Such a great melting point depression in wholly aromatic polyamides seems to be attributable as much to disruption of orderly packing as to reduction of hydrogen bonding (7), since complete *N*-methyl substitution of the *N*-hydrogens of polyhexamethylene terephthalamide yields a polymer which melts at 260°C, only 110°C below the melting point of the parent polymer (18). Also indicating that the lack of hydrogen bonding does not necessarily result in a low-melting polyamide is the fact that poly-2,5-dimethylpiperazine terephthalamide, a polymer in which there can be no hydrogen bonding, has a melting point of 350°C (22).

Although either most of the wholly aromatic polyamides reported have been prepared as high molecular weight polymers, or it appears that high-molecular-weight polymers could be prepared based on present technology, fabrication of certain of these polymers to useful products has, however, been difficult or impossible due to poor solubility. In general, the higher the *para*-phenylene content, the poorer the solubility and hence the greater the difficulty in preparing high-molecular-weight polymer; the simple all-*para* polyamides, for example, are readily soluble only in strong acids such as concentrated sulfuric acid. As is seen in Table XI, the thermal stability is higher the higher the *para*-phenylene content in the polymer. Since most researchers have sought the most thermostable polymer that can be fabricated to useful products, the problem has been largely one of incorporating *para*-phenylene units in the polymers and still retaining adequate solubility to allow fabrication. Several approaches have been employed: (*a*) copolymerization of simple aromatic diacids and aromatic diamines (polymers 11 and 12); (*b*) incorporation of heteroelement units such as the sulfonyl group in the polymer backbone (polymers 16–19); and (*c*) the synthesis of ordered copolymers (polymers 20–45). The most versatile method has been the ordered copolymer approach.

Several classes of ordered copolyamides have been investigated. The eight possible isomeric ordered copolymers of the type represented by structure II have all been prepared (polymers 22–23, 26–27, 30–31, 34–35; Table XI). The importance of the ordered sequence of the units

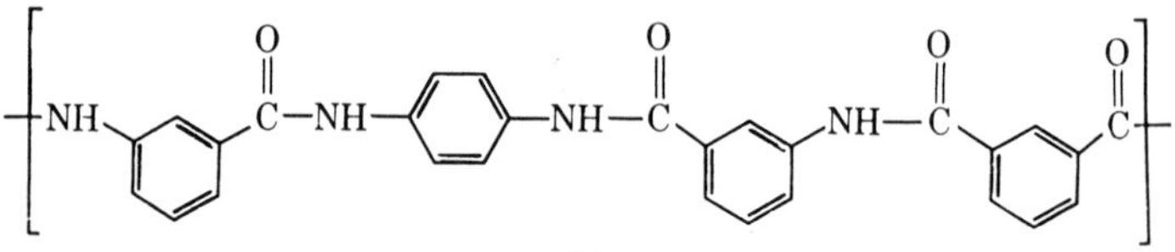

$$\left[-NH-C_6H_4-\overset{O}{\overset{\|}{C}}-NH-C_6H_4-NH-\overset{O}{\overset{\|}{C}}-C_6H_4-NH-\overset{O}{\overset{\|}{C}}-C_6H_4-\overset{O}{\overset{\|}{C}}-\right]$$

II

was shown by the fact that a random copolymer composed of proper proportions of the three units required to make the all-*meta* ordered copolymer (polymer 22, Table XI) had a melting point 60–110°C lower than that of the all-*meta* ordered copolymer (7).

One member, III, of a related ordered copolyamide series has been studied (54); structure–property data are scanty.

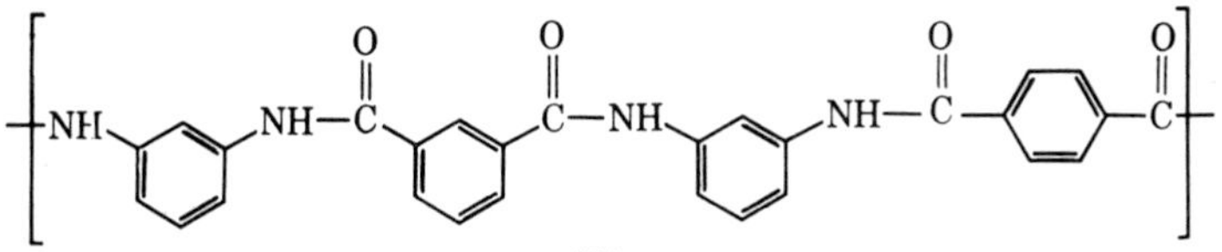

$$\left[-NH-C_6H_4-NH-\overset{O}{\overset{\|}{C}}-C_6H_4-\overset{O}{\overset{\|}{C}}-NH-C_6H_4-NH-\overset{O}{\overset{\|}{C}}-C_6H_4-\overset{O}{\overset{\|}{C}}- \right]$$

III

In this series, unlike in the preceding series, there are no arylene units to which are attached both a carbonyl group and an amide nitrogen.

Ordered copolyamides in which the units are less ordered than in the preceding classes have also been studied (polymers 20 and 21, Table XI). As is seen in formula V, the unsymmetrical diamine IV can enter the polymer chain in two ways. To the extent that there is a preferential reaction of one of the amine groups of diamines such as IV with the diacid chloride, there will be directional ordering of the diamine units along the chain (55) as a result of the formation of blocks such as VI; this effect could be expected to be more pronounced in the case of interfacial polymerization (6b). The thermal stabilities of polymers in this class are good (Table XI); however, they are in general poorer than those of polymers containing the same units in a more ordered arrangement.

Since tractability is a problem in the field of thermostable wholly aromatic polyamides, particularly in the case of polyamides with high *para*-phenylene content, certain thermally stable, aromatic heterocycles, which impart greater solubility to polymers than phenylene units (57–59), have been used in conjunction with phenylene units in the backbone of polymer chains to obtain thermostable wholly aromatic polyamides of increased solubility. Both 5- and 6-membered aromatic heterocyclic units, such as oxadiazole, thiazole, bithiazole, and pyridine have been incorporated in aromatic polyamides. (It has recently been shown conclusively that the oxadiazole ring is electronically and spectrally equivalent to the *para*-phenylene unit (56).)

The use of 5-membered aromatic heterocycles in ordered copolyamides has indeed led to very thermally stable amide–heterocycle copolymers (Table XIII) which are sufficiently soluble for fabrication to high-strength fibers. In fact, it was found that by the incorporation of certain 5-membered aromatic heterocycles in polyamides, one can make polyamides having melting points above 500°C which are at the same time soluble in organic solvents (polymers 4, 8, and 11, Table XIII); this has not been possible in the case of polyamides containing only phenylene units.

In the series of heterocycle–amide copolymers listed in Table XIII, the heterocycle (as shown in VII) in effect replaces two amide linkages

$$H_2N-C_6H_4-\overset{O}{\overset{\|}{C}}-NH-C_6H_4-NH_2 \quad \xrightarrow{Cl-\overset{O}{\overset{\|}{C}}-C_6H_4-\overset{O}{\overset{\|}{C}}-Cl}$$

IV

$$\left[\left(NH-C_6H_4-\overset{O}{\overset{\|}{C}}-NH-C_6H_4-NH-\overset{O}{\overset{\|}{C}}-C_6H_4-\overset{O}{\overset{\|}{C}}\right)_x\left(NH-C_6H_4-NH-\overset{O}{\overset{\|}{C}}-C_6H_4-NH-\overset{O}{\overset{\|}{C}}-C_6H_4-\overset{O}{\overset{\|}{C}}\right)_y\right] \quad (3)$$

V

$$NH_2-C_6H_4-\overset{O}{\overset{\|}{C}}-NH-C_6H_4-NH-\overset{O}{\overset{\|}{C}}-C_6H_4-\overset{O}{\overset{\|}{C}}-NH-C_6H_4-NH-\overset{O}{\overset{\|}{C}}-C_6H_4-NH_2$$

VI

TABLE XIII. Aromatic Ordered Amide–Heterocycle Copolymers

No.	R	**H**[a]	R′	η_{inh}[c]	Melt transition temperature, °C[d]	Decomposition temperature, °C[e]
		⸺NH—R—**H**—R—NH—CO—R′—CO⸺				
1	*m*-Phenylene	1,3,4-Oxadiazole	*m*-Phenylene	1.46	320[f]	420
2	*m*-Phenylene	1,3,4-Oxadiazole	*p*-Phenylene	2.18	345	425
3	*p*-Phenylene	1,3,4-Oxadiazole	*m*-Phenylene	1.65	465	440
4	*p*-Phenylene	1,3,4-Oxadiazole	*p*-Phenylene	2.58[g]	515	480
5	*m*-Phenylen	4-Phenyl-1,2,4-triazole	2,6-Naphthalene	0.50	450	455
6	*m*-Phenylene	Thiazolo[5,4-d]thiazole	*m*-Phenylene		345	465
7	*m*-Phenylene	5,5′-2,2′-bis-1,3,4-Oxadiazole	*m*-Phenylene	1.03	370	490
8	*p*-Phenylene	2,2′-Bithiazole	*m*-Phenylene	2.36	535	490
9	*m*-Phenylene	5,5′-Bibenzimidazole	*m*-Phenylene	1.86	370	410
10	*p*-Phenylene	*m*-bis-Thiazol-2-yl-benzene	*m*-Phenylene	1.20	475	475
11	*p*-Phenylene	*m*-bis-Thiazol-2-yl-benzene	*p*-Phenylene	1.95	525	520
		⸺CO—R—**H**—R—CO—NH—R′—NH⸺				
12	*m*-Phenylene	1,3,4-Oxadiazole	*m*-Phenylene	0.81	325[g]	430

[a] Names given refer to the parent heterocyclic ring systems from which the radical, **H,** is derived.
[b] From work of Preston and Black (62).
[c] Determined at 30°C for a solution of 0.5 g of polymer dissolved in 100 ml of dimethylacetamide containing 5% dissolved lithium chloride.
[d] Endothermic transition observed by differential thermal analysis (DTA) in nitrogen (rate = 20°C/min).
[e] Decomposition temperatures observed by thermogravimetric analysis (TGA) in nitrogen (rate = 15°C/min).
[f] Softening point observed by heating film.
[g] Determined at 30°C for a solution of 0.5 g of polymer dissolved in 100 ml of concentrated sulfuric acid.

TABLE XIV. Comparison of Properties of Poly-2,6-pyridinedicarbonamides[a] with Polyisophthalamides

No.	Diamine segment	Diacid segment: –CO–C$_6$H$_4$–CO– (isophthaloyl) Viscosity[b]	M.P., °C	Diacid segment: –CO–C$_5$H$_3$N–CO– (2,6-pyridinedicarbonyl) Viscosity[c]	M.P., °C[d]	Ref.
1	–NH–C$_6$H$_4$–C$_6$H$_4$–NH–	—	348–350 (dec.)	0.51	400	73
2	–NH–C$_6$H$_3$(CH$_3$)–C$_6$H$_3$(CH$_3$)–NH–	0.14[e]	370 (dec.)	1.70	365	69
3	–NH–C$_6$H$_4$–CH$_2$–C$_6$H$_4$–NH–	0.41[f]	318	1.40	400	79
4	–NH–C$_6$H$_4$–CO–C$_6$H$_4$–NH–	0.17[g]	312	—	—	—
5	–NH–C$_6$H$_4$–SO$_2$–C$_6$H$_4$–NH–	0.15[h]	297	1.53	400	60

[a] From work of Terent'yev et al. (80).
[b] The viscosity numbers are the reduced specific viscosities, $\eta_{sp/c}$, determined at 20°C.
[c] Inherent viscosities determined at 30°C for 0.5 g of polymer per 100 ml concentrated sulfuric acid.
[d] Capillary m.p.
[e] 0.3% solution in sulfuric acid.
[f] 0.32% solution in dimethylformamide.
[g] 0.41% solution in dimethylformamide.
[h] 0.4% solution in dimethylformamide.

and a phenylene unit of the ordered copolyamides exemplified by III. By varying the orientation of the phenylene units in VII, a series of polymers having considerable variation in properties has been prepared (polymers 1–4, Table XIII).

$$\left[-NH-C_6H_4-(C_2N_2O)-C_6H_4-NH-CO-C_6H_4-CO-\right]$$

VII

The effect of 6-membered heterocycles in aromatic polyamides has been little studied, and on the basis of work done to date it is difficult to evaluate their potential importance. One would expect, however, that as a class their value would be greater than that of 2,6-pyridine. The substitution of 2,6-pyridine units for *meta*-phenylene units surprisingly resulted in substantial lowering of the melting point (Table XIV).

Glass transition temperatures, T_g, have not been reported for many wholly aromatic polyamides, but all of those reported have been above 250°C and have ranged up to 335°C (Table XI). Although no glass transition temperatures have been reported for all-*para* polyamides, they can be expected to be above 335°C.

Wholly aromatic polyamides have moisture regain values somewhat higher than those of nylon 66. For example, Nomex (2) and the polyterephthalamide of *N*,*N*′-*m*-phenylenebis-*m*-aminobenzamide (7) have regain values of approximately 5% and 5.2%, respectively, at 70°F and 65% relative humidity.

No study of the crystallinity of wholly aromatic polyamides has been made of a comprehensiveness equal to that by Statton on aliphatic-aromatic polymers (19). In general, the wholly aromatic polyamides as prepared are amorphous (60); many of the polymers, however, are crystallizable (7,23,61–63). They can be crystallized particularly effectively while being oriented (i.e., while being drawn) at a temperature above the glass transition temperature, or less effectively by various treatments after having been oriented. Three after-treatments have proven effective: (*a*) treatment of fiber (presumably oriented) with high-pressure steam, e.g., for 1 hr at 100 psi (60); (*b*) treatment of fiber with solvents or solvent mixtures such as 99% formic acid at 95°C for 1 hr, or 50/50 water/dimethylacetamide at the boiling point for 12 hr (60); and (*c*) heat crystallization of oriented fiber (7,23,50,61–63). Heat treatment of the fiber under tension at 300°C or higher is without question the preferred method, since crystallization can be effected in a fraction of a second (61), making possible the production of the finished fiber an in-line spinning process. Although it does not appear that being crystalline (as determined by x-ray diffraction patterns) is nearly so critical for wholly aromatic polyamide fibers as it is for aliphatic polyamide fibers in order for them to have useful properties (23), it does seem that the wholly aromatic polyamide fibers should be crystalline for maximum properties (60–61). The degree of orientation, however, appears to be at least as important as the degree of crystallinity with regard to maximizing fiber properties. To what extent this is the consequence of considerable alignment of planar units into protocrystallites upon orientation cannot yet be answered.

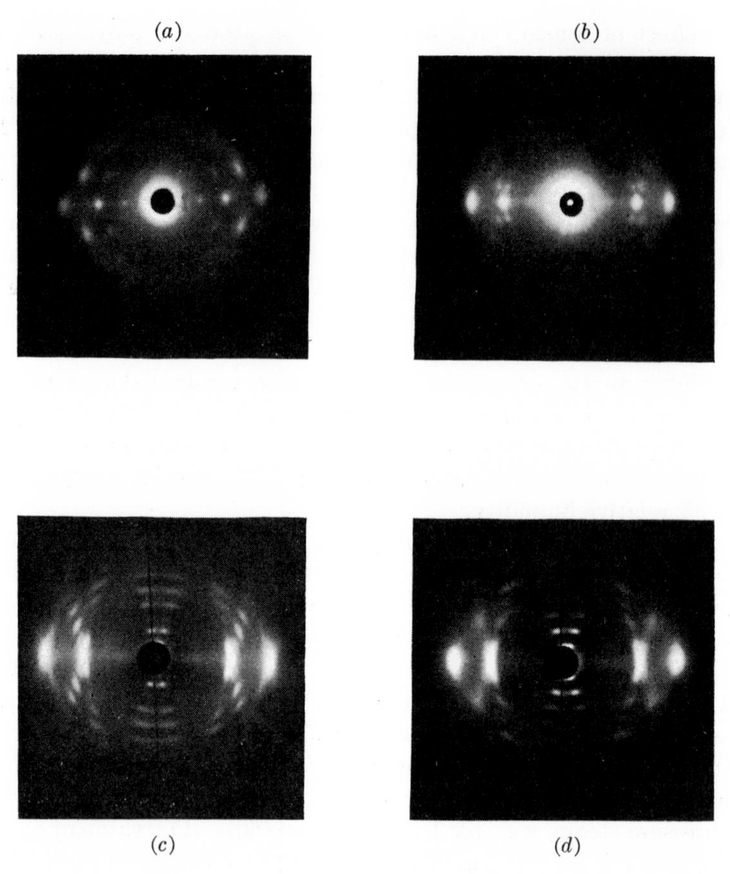

Fig. 5. X-ray diffraction patterns of selected aromatic polyamide fibers. (*a*) Wholly aromatic ordered copolyamide (polymer 33, Table XI). (*b*) Ordered oxadiazole-amide copolymer (polymer 1, Table XVI). (*c*) Ordered thiazole–amide copolymer (polymer 3, Table XVI). (*d*) Ordered bithiazole–amide copolymer (polymer 4, Table XVI).

A study of the density of unoriented-amorphous, oriented-amorphous, and oriented-crystalline polymers should shed some light on the relationship between molecular organization and properties. In the one instance where data of this nature have been reported, the oriented-amorphous fiber has a density of 1.288 g/cc compared with 1.36 g/cc for the same fiber after crystallization (60). It is of interest to note that the crystalline polymer had considerably superior elongation properties above 150°C.

Densities have been reported for five crystalline fibers of wholly aromatic polyamides derived from carbocyclic rings; the range of densities was remarkably narrow, 1.35–1.36 g/cc, considering that the polymers ranged from those with all *meta*-phenylene units to one in which three-fourths of the units were *para* (7,49,60). Densities for crystalline fibers of four wholly aromatic polyamides based in part on heterocycles fall again into a narrow range, 1.37–1.40 g/cc (63). Thus, the variation in density for all crystalline fibers of wholly aromatic polyamides whose density has been reported is less than 4%.

X-ray diffraction patterns of fibers of one ordered polyamide and several ordered heterocycle–amide copolymers are shown in Figure 5. It is apparent that there is a high degree of order in the heterocycle–amide fibers.

It would also be desirable to make an x-ray diffraction study of unstretched films of wholly aromatic polyamides which have been cast from solution. Ikeda (64) has observed that unstretched films of the polypyromellitimide of oxydianiline (made indirectly by solution casting) show no preferential organization when viewed perpendicular to the plane of the film, but that the film viewed edge-on, i.e., parallel to the plane of the film, shows that there is a preferential ordering of the polymer parallel to the plane of the film. Presumably, the aromatic rings tend to lie in the plane parallel to the plane of the film. Although the polyimide film studied by Ikeda was derived from a precursor polyamide film, there was no mention of a study of the precursor polyamide film.

B. Synthesis of Selected Classes of Fiber-Forming Polymers

Several classes of fiber-forming wholly aromatic polyamides have been prepared. In addition to the conventional AB and AA-BB classes, certain classes of AA-BB polymers of more complex structure have been made. Synthesis of the latter types involves the use of diamines or diacids containing preformed amide or heterocycle units, or ones having pendent functional groups which do not participate in the polycondensation.

1. Simple AA-BB Polyamides

Although there are many references in the literature to the preparation of AA-BB wholly aromatic polyamides by thermal condensation processes such as the thermal condensation of diamines with diesters (148), none of these processes have proven to be satisfactory. Only the low-temperature polycondensation of diacid chlorides with diamines appears to yield high-molecular-weight polymers, i.e., $\eta_{inh} \geqq 0.5$ (0.5 g polymer per 100 ml solvent). The interfacial polycondensation technique was the first low-temperature process to yield high-molecular-weight wholly aromatic polyamides (60,69,71,75,78,81–83). Earlier work (72) in which low-molecular-weight polybenzidine terephthalamide had been made interfacially had demonstrated that this low temperature route to the wholly aromatic polyamides was feasible. Copolyamides (mixed diamines with a diacid or vice versa) have also been readily prepared (70). Although high-molecular-weight polymer can usually be prepared by interfacial polycondensation, doing so frequently involves considerable difficulty (6b). The use of polar cycloaliphatic solvents such as tetramethylene sulfone, tetrahydrofuran, and cyclohexanone has led to the most generally useful two-phase process (6b,69–70). These solvents are either miscible or partially miscible with the aqueous phase, and consequently weak acid acceptors are preferred to minimize hydrolysis of the acid chloride. The ability of these cycloaliphatic solvents to keep the polymer partially swollen during the polymerization process is probably more important than their water-miscibility for the excellent results obtained.

In general, high-molecular-weight wholly aromatic polyamides can be obtained more consistently by the low-temperature solution polycondensation (9,84). The great value of this polymerization method has been shown amply by the numerous reports of high-molecular-weight, fiber-forming polymers of widely varying structure. In general, however, wholly aromatic polyamides which are sufficiently high melting to be useful for very thermally stable fibers will not remain in solution when prepared by solution polymerization unless either (*a*) inorganic salts such as lithium chloride (11) are present or (*b*) a basic organic solvent, such as dimethylacetamide, which forms a salt with hydrogen chloride is used (9). With but one exception (7), high-molecular-weight polymers in which all the phenylenes have *para* orientation do not remain in the polymerization medium even when a salt is present. As stated earlier, low-temperature solution polycondensation is also particularly attractive since the polymer solutions that result can be used directly for any solution spinning process.

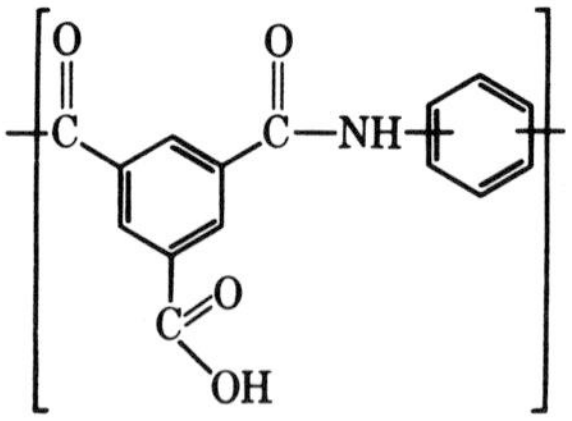

In addition to polyamides of the types found in Table XI, polymers having reactive substituents on the rings can be prepared provided the reactive substituent is either masked during the polycondensation or is unreactive under the conditions of the polycondensation (85). The carboxyl group is a substituent of the latter type, and two polymers having pendent carboxyl groups of the type shown have been prepared. Aromatic polyamides having pendent groups *ortho* to the amide linkage are discussed in Section V.

2. *AA-BB Polyamides from Intermediates Containing Preformed Amide Linkages*

Ordered copolyamides are readily prepared by low-temperature polycondensation from diamines or diacid chlorides which contain preformed amide linkages, since under the conditions of polymerization no reorganization of the structural units is possible (7,53–54,86) (Table XI). Such copolymerization is shown by the following examples. Polymers of the type exemplified by II (see also Table XI) were prepared by both the interfacial and the solution methods, but more consistent results and higher inherent viscosities were obtained by the solution technique (7,86).

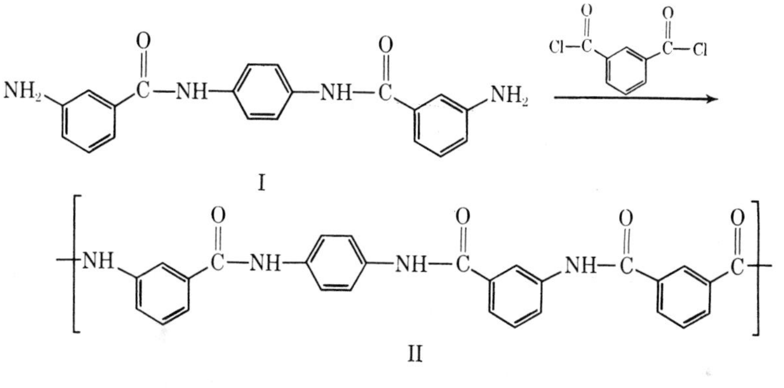

I

II

(4)

Diamines such as I were prepared by reaction of aromatic diamines with nitroaroylchlorides followed by reduction of the dinitro intermediate. Diamines of the type represented by diamine III were prepared by the Shotten-Bauman reaction using a large excess of diamine with the diacid chloride (54); a more convenient synthesis of these diamines is the reaction of the nitroaniline with the diacid chloride followed by reduction (87).

A series of copolyamides (polymers 20 and 21, Table VI) having somewhat less order was prepared by the low-temperature polymerization of diaminobenzanilides with diacid chlorides; both interfacial and solution

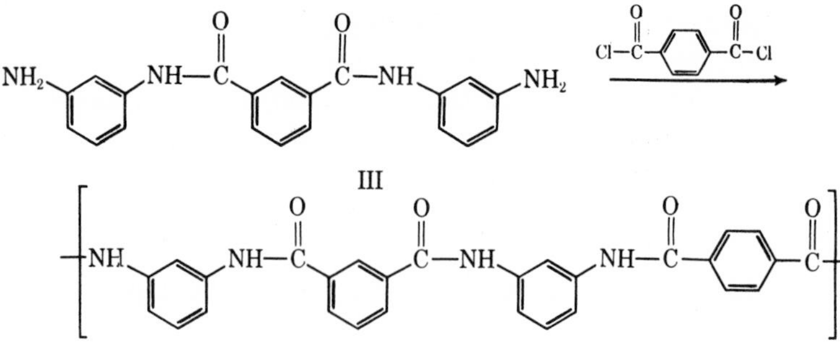

III

IV

(5)

methods were investigated (55). Since the diamines are not symmetrical, polymer having a simple repeat unit, such as VI, is improbable. (See Section IV-A.)

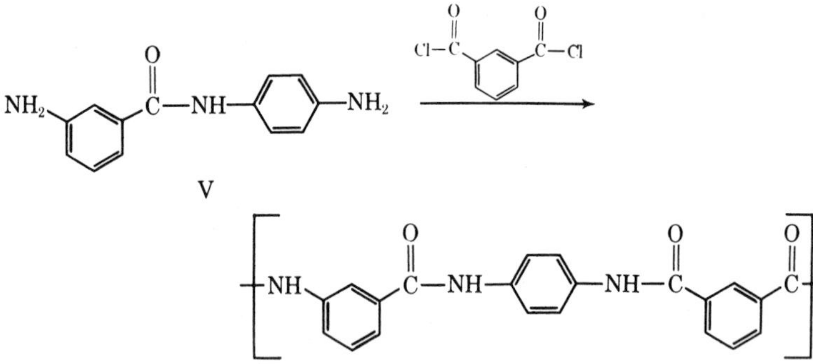

V

VI

(6)

3. AA-BB Polyamides from Intermediates Containing Preformed Heterocyclic Units

Polymers characterized structurally by an ordered sequence of amide and heterocyclic units in the polymer chain were prepared by low-temperature solution polycondensation of an aromatic diacid chloride and an aromatic diamine, one of which contains a heterocyclic unit (62) (Table XIII). The reaction scheme is as follows:

$$NH_2-R-\mathbf{H}-R-NH_2 + Cl-CO-R'-CO-Cl \longrightarrow -[NH-R-\mathbf{H}-R-NH-CO-R'-CO]-$$

where R = or and R′ = R or

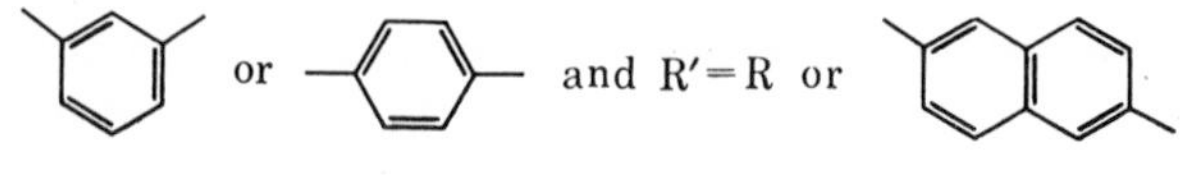

H =

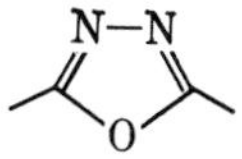

1,3,4-Oxadiazole* 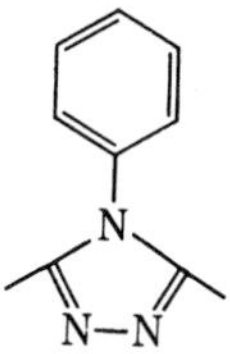 4-Phenyl-1,2,4-triazole* 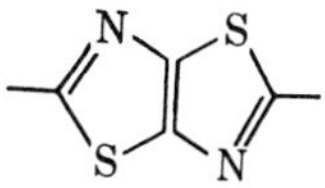 Thiazolo[5,4-d]thiazole*

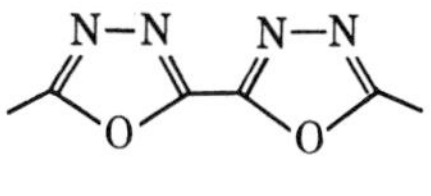

2,2′-Bis-1,3,4-Oxadiazole* 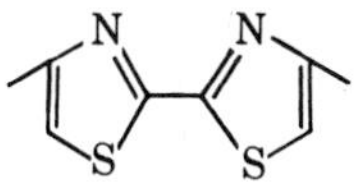 2,2′-Bithiazole*

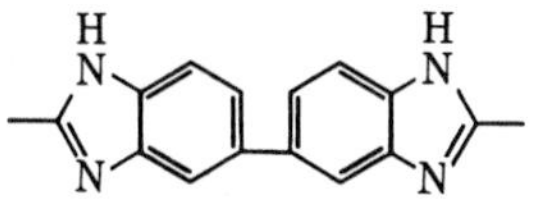

5,5′-Bibenzimidazole* 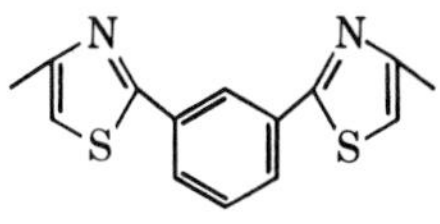 *m*-bis-Thiazol-2-yl-benzene*

* Names given refer to the parent heterocyclic ring systems from which the radical, **H**, is derived.

In general, solvents containing either organic salts or inorganic salts were found to be necessary in order to obtain high-molecular-weight polymer and to keep the polymer in solution so that it could be spun directly from the polymerization mixture.

Polyamides containing benzimidazole rings have been reported which illustrate two methods of preparing such polymers. The first method employs the technique of using a preformed heterocyclic group as above, in this case a benzimidazole group (87a); the second method employs the technique of using a preformed amide group and forming the benzimidazole group during polycondensation (87b).

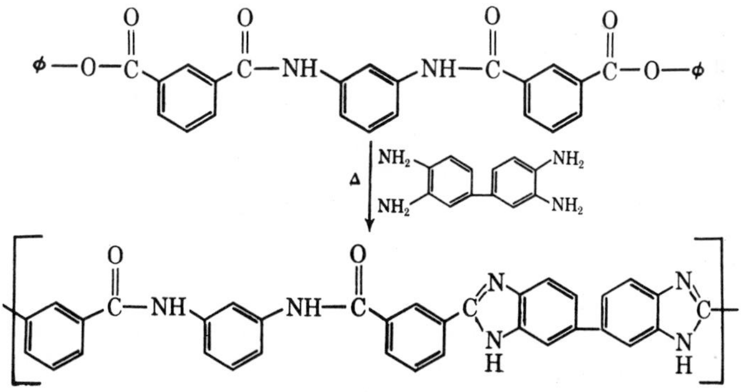

(7)

4. A-B Polyamides

Few references are made in the literature to wholly aromatic polyamides prepared by the homopolymerization of aminocarboxylic acids or their equivalents. Only a few of these polymers appear to be of high molecular weight or are well characterized. Several polymers were prepared by thermal condensations of the free amino acid or amino ester (88).

$$NH_2-C_6H_4-\overset{O}{\overset{\|}{C}}-O-CH_3 \xrightarrow{240°C} \left[NH-C_6H_4-\overset{O}{\overset{\|}{C}} \right] \quad (8)$$

$$NH_2-C_6H_4-C_6H_4-\overset{O}{\overset{\|}{C}}-OH \xrightarrow{260°C} \left[NH-C_6H_4-C_6H_4-\overset{O}{\overset{\|}{C}} \right] \quad (9)$$

Heating of the *N*-acetyl derivatives of *o*-, *m*-, and *p*-benzoic acid is claimed (89–90) to yield the corresponding polyamides.

$$CH_3-\overset{O}{\overset{\|}{C}}-NH-C_6H_4-\overset{O}{\overset{\|}{C}}-OH \xrightarrow[-CH_3-CO-OH]{\Delta} \left[NH-C_6H_4-\overset{O}{\overset{\|}{C}} \right] \quad (10)$$

Polymer was reported to be obtained by heating 4-(3-aminobenzoyl)-benzoic acid, but no experimental conditions and no polymer properties were given (91).

Considerably better results have been obtained by low-temperature polycondensation of reactive AB-monomers. High-molecular-weight polyamides derived from *m*- or *p*-aminobenzoic acids have been prepared from an aminobenzoyl chloride hydrochloride by the addition of a base under special conditions (66–67,92).

$$NH_2-C_6H_4-\overset{O}{\overset{\|}{C}}-OH \xrightarrow[-HCl]{SOCl_2} O{=}S{=}N-C_6H_4-\overset{O}{\overset{\|}{C}}-Cl \xrightarrow[\phi\text{-H or }Et_2O]{\text{dry HCl}}$$

$$HCl\cdot NH_2-C_6H_4-\overset{O}{\overset{\|}{C}}-Cl \xrightarrow[-HCl]{\text{base}} \left[NH-C_6H_4-\overset{O}{\overset{\|}{C}} \right] \quad (11)$$

It is interesting to note that in the polymerization of poly-*m*-benzamide one worker (92) reported that interfacial polymerization of *m*-aminobenzoyl chloride hydrochloride yielded a polymer of η_{inh} 0.7 while another (65) reported a polymer of η_{inh} 2.36; on the other hand, the use of solution techniques by the same workers gave polymers of η_{inh} 1.37 and η_{inh} 0.3, respectively.

When the interfacial technique was used with *p*-aminobenzoyl chloride hydrochloride, no polymer was obtained and only *p*-aminobenzoic acid and its dimer were recovered. High-molecular-weight polymer, η_{inh} 0.7, was obtained, however, upon the addition of a tertiary organic base—for example, pyridine—to a slurry of *p*-aminobenzoyl chloride hydrochloride in dry dioxane (66). In contrast, 4-amino-4′-biphenylcarboxyl chloride hydrochloride yielded polymer when reacted under interfacial conditions (67).

$$HCl \cdot NH_2-C_6H_4-C_6H_4-\overset{O}{\overset{\|}{C}}-Cl \xrightarrow[-HCl]{base} \left[NH-C_6H_4-C_6H_4-\overset{O}{\overset{\|}{C}}\right] \quad (12)$$

The polyamide from anthranilic acid is reported to have been prepared from isatoic anhydride in dioxane with basic initiators at room temperature (93).

$$\text{isatoic anhydride} \xrightarrow[-CO_2]{base} \left[NH-C_6H_4-\overset{O}{\overset{\|}{C}}\right] \quad (13)$$

C. Fibers of Wholly Aromatic Polyamides

1. Spinning and Fiber Tensile Properties

All wholly aromatic polyamide fibers reported have been spun from solutions of the polymers. Both dry-spinning and wet-spinning techniques appear to be equally satisfactory (54,61–62,86,94–96). Polyamides prepared by solution polycondensation can be spun very conveniently from the resulting polymer solution, circumventing isolating and redissolving of the polymer. The ability to spin directly is crucial for those polymers which do not redissolve or redissolve only with difficulty after isolation in the dry state (7). Polymers prepared by interfacial polymerization must necessarily be dissolved prior to spinning since solutions are never produced directly by this polymerization method (11,61,69,94–95,97).

As pointed out in an earlier section, almost all wholly aromatic polyamides require the presence of a salt, either organic or inorganic, in the solvent to dissolve them or to prevent them from precipitating from

TABLE XV. Fiber Properties of Wholly Aromatic Polyamides

No.	Polymers	R.T. $T/E/M_i$[a]	$T/E/M_i$[a] at 250°C	$T/E/M_i$[a] at 300°C	Zero strength temp.,[b] °C	Ref.
1	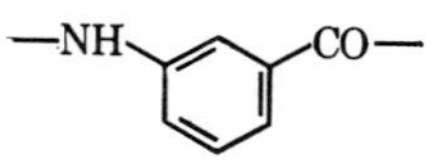 —NH— —CO—	5.8/10/118		3.0/7.5/89	480–550	92
2	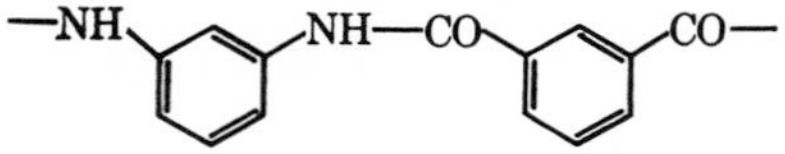 —NH— —NH—CO— —CO—	5.5/28/113	3.1/22/63	1.2/23/75	440	54
3	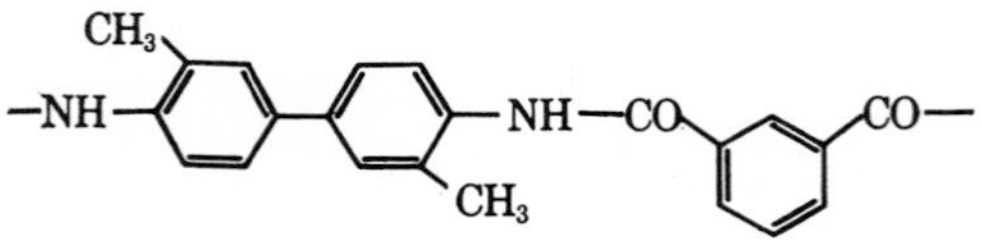 CH_3 —NH— — —NH—CO— —CO— CH_3	9.2/6.8/182		2.6/12/33		23
4	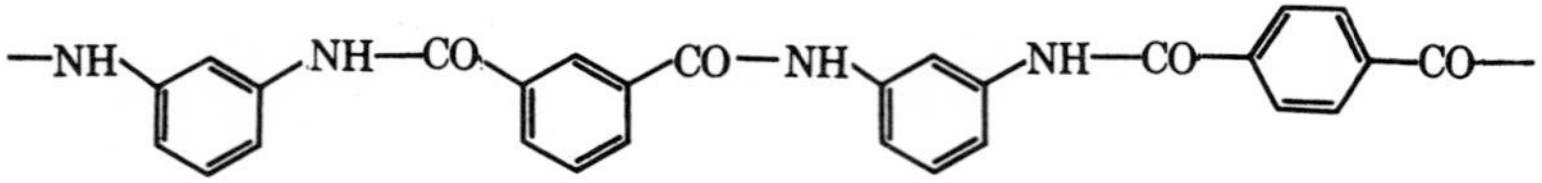 —NH— —NH—CO— —CO—NH— —NH—CO— —CO—	4.1/33/89	2.7/48/38	1.6/51/26	490	54
5	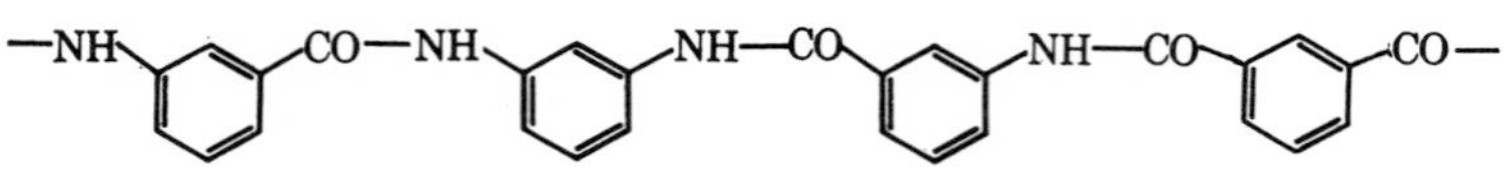 —NH— —CO—NH— —NH—CO— —NH—CO— —CO—	5.1/37/89		1.5/22/11	(>400)	7(49)

6		6.0/23/101		2.0/11/50	485	49
7	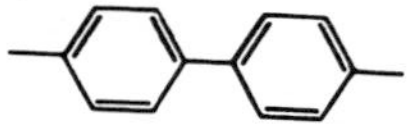	5.9/16/93	1.6/15/58		>450	53,49
8	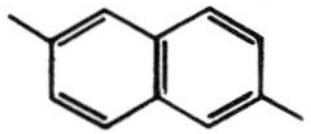	6.3/19/94		2.0/19/—	455	49
9	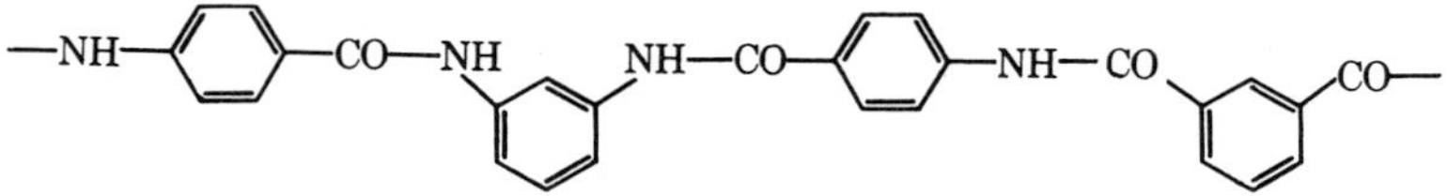 —NH— —CO—NH NH—CO— —NH—CO CO—	6.2/20/70	3.3/21/46	2.3/19/36	470	49
10	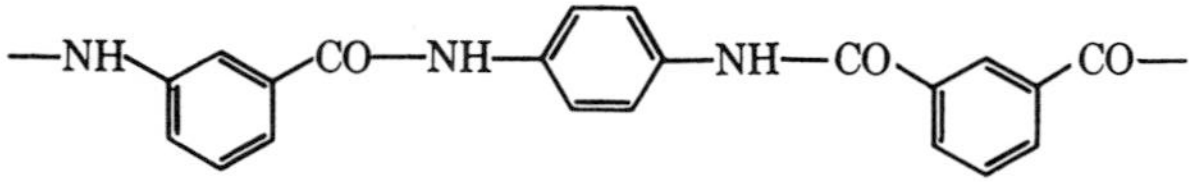 —NH CO—NH— —NH—CO CO—	4.8/27/72[c] (8.6/28/—)	2.4/41/28			55

[a] $T/E/M_i$ = tenacity in grams per denier, elongation in per cent, initial modulus in grams per denier.
[b] Temperature at which the fiber breaks under a load of 0.1 g/den.
[c] Tensile properties of polymer of η_{inh} 1.1; fibers prepared by dry spinning.
[d] Tensile properties of polymer of η_{inh} 2.8; fibers prepared by wet spinning.

TABLE XVI. Fibers of Ordered Aromatic Amide–Heterocyclic Copolymers[a,b]

No.	Structural formula	η_{inh}[c]	Tensile Properties: Tenacity, g/den	Tensile Properties: Elong. to break, %	Tensile Properties: Initial modulus, g/den	Density, g/cc	Color
1	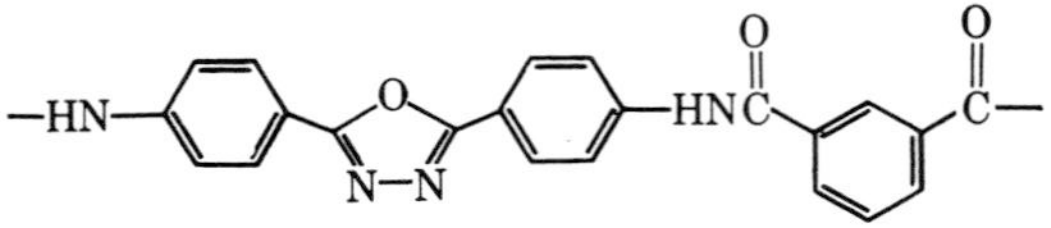	1.65	6.7	11.0	114	1.37	off-white
2	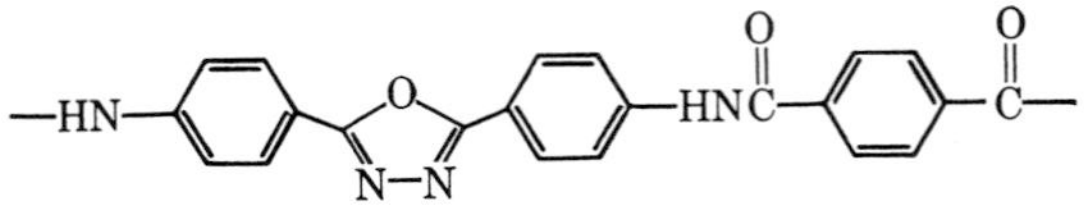	2.58[d]	6.5	7.5	126	1.40	yellow
3	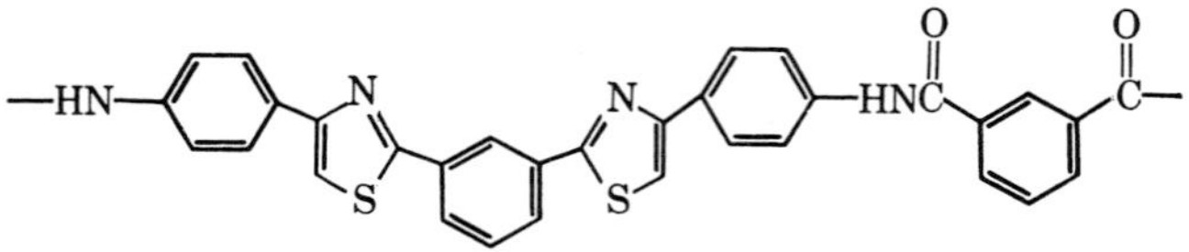	1.20	3.4	12.8	88	1.39	straw
4	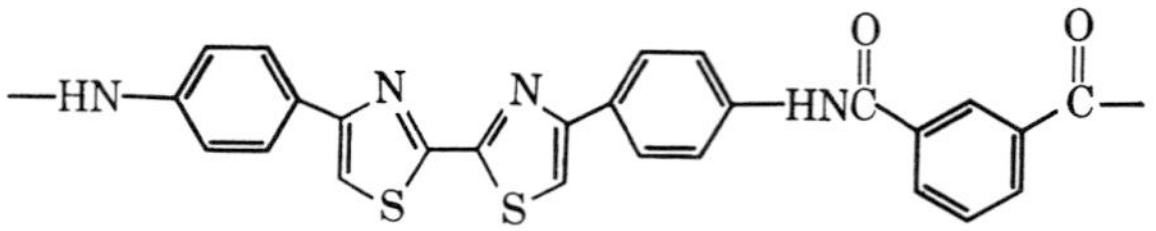	2.36	7.8	6.6	168	1.40	yellow-green

[a] From work of Preston and Black (49).

[b] All of the fibers possessed high orientation and crystallinity (determined from x-ray diffraction patterns).

[c] Determined at 30°C for a solution of 0.5 g of polymer dissolved in 100 ml dimethylacetamide containing 5% dissolved lithium chloride.

[d] Determined at 30°C for a solution of 0.5 g of polymer dissolved in 100 ml concentrated sulfuric acid.

solution if prepared by solution polycondensation; this is the case even for the best solvents. If organic salts such as dimethylacetamide hydrochloride are the solvating salts, it is common practice to neutralize the hydrogen chloride with an inorganic base such as lithium hydroxide prior to spinning to prevent corrosion of spinning equipment. In the case of dry spinning, this salt remains in the spun fiber and must subsequently be leached in order to obtain fiber with optimum mechanical properties. Fiber containing salt also has poorer thermal stability (98) and poorer electrical properties. In wet spinning most of the salt diffuses from the fiber during spinning (96).

In Tables XV and XVI fiber properties of aromatic polyamides at room temperature are given. These fibers are characterized by medium to very high tensile strength, medium to low elongation—somewhat lower than for most polymers containing aliphatic segments—and unusually high tensile modulus. Fibers from heterocycle-containing polyamides (Table XVI) as a class show a higher tensile modulus than polyamides containing only arylene and amide units, probably because of the high *para*-phenylene content of these polymers. Most of the arylene-amide fibers (Table XV) have been reported to be either highly crystalline (7,53,86) or crystallizable (60–61,86) when oriented; none have been reported to be noncrystallizable. All of the amide–heterocycle fibers are highly crystalline (Table XVI).

2. Fiber Properties with Respect to End Uses

Since most of the work on wholly aromatic polyamides has been directed toward the development of temperature-resistant fibers, most of the fiber data in the literature is concerned with their resistance to thermal and thermooxidative degradation. Fibers and films of these polymers have properties, however, that should make them more broadly useful than for high-temperature applications alone. Low elongation and high tensile modulus have already been mentioned; these and other properties such as high resistance to ionizing irradiation, excellent chemical resistance, and high dielectric strength are discussed in terms of end use potential of these fibers.

a. Thermal Stability of Fibers. The reader is referred to Section II of this chapter for a discussion of the techniques and significance of measurements of the thermal stability of fibers.

(1) Fiber Tensile Properties at Elevated Temperatures. The tensile properties of the fibers at elevated temperatures are given in Table XV and XVII. The arylene–amide fibers (Table XV) have tensile strengths at 250°C which are characteristic of conventional textile fibers

TABLE XVII. Tenacity of Fibers at Elevated Temperatures[a]

No.	Structural formula	Tenacity[b] (g/den) in air at: R. T.	200	300	350	400	450	500°C	Zero strength temp. in N_2,[c] °C
1	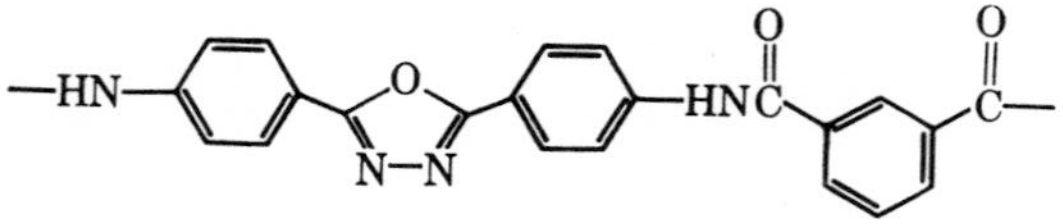	6.7	3.8	2.5	1.3	0.64	0.23		535
2	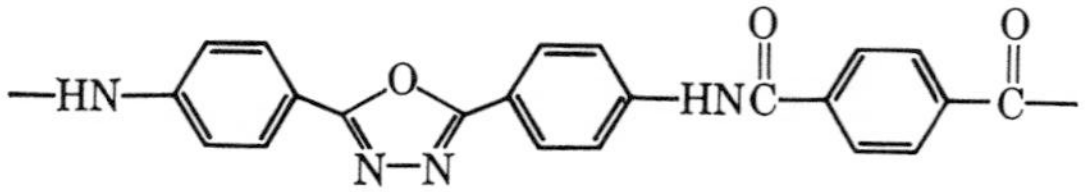	6.5	4.1	2.2		1.5	1.4	0.44	520
3	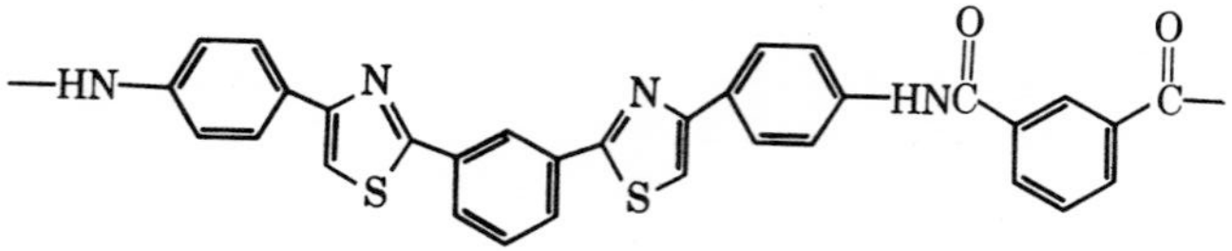	3.4	2.1	1.6	0.97	0.66	0.6		520
4	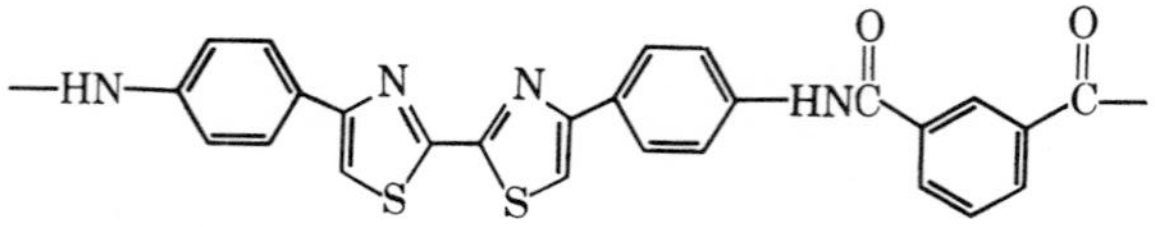	7.8	4.5	3.1	2.4	2.3	2.1	0.36	580

[a] From work of Preston and Black (49).

[b] The fiber is held in an oven at the indicated temperature for 1 min and then tested at that temperature.

[c] Temperature at which fiber breaks under a load of 0.1 g/den when being heated at the rate of 5°C/min in nitrogen.

at room temperature, and have useful tenacities up to above 300°C. By way of contrast, nylon 66 fiber loses almost all of its strength at about 205°C. The heterocycle–amide fibers are more thermally stable than the arylene–amide fibers at greatly elevated temperatures; they have tenacities at 400°C in air (Table XVII) which are roughly comparable to those of the arylene–amide fibers at 300°C. Consistent with this are higher zero strength temperatures for the heterocycle–amide fibers.

The tensile modulus of the arylene amide fibers falls off considerably at 300–350°C; it is still substantial, however, even at these temperatures (Table XV). Surprisingly, the elongation in general tends to be less at 300°C than at room temperature.

(2) *Fiber Tensile Properties after Prolonged Aging at Elevated Temperatures.* For determining the long-term usefulness of fibers at elevated temperatures, evaluation of the tensile properties after heat-aging at intermediately elevated temperatures is more meaningful than determining the tensile properties at greatly elevated temperatures. If the fibers are to be used in air, the heat-aging should be done in air; the need to do this is particularly great in the case of fibers because of their high surface-to-volume ratio.

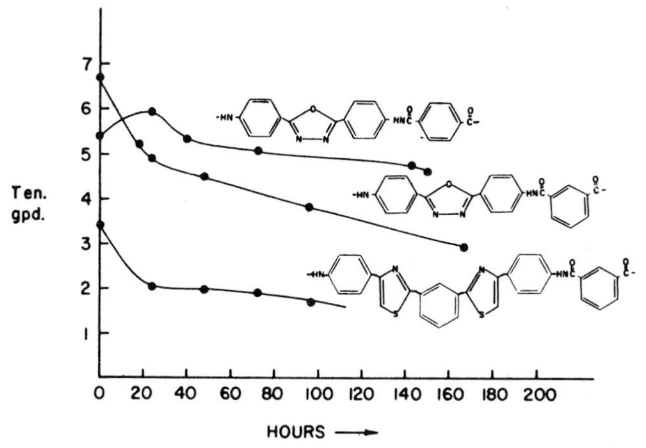

Fig. 6. Effect on tenacity of heat-aging fibers of ordered heterocycle-amide copolymers in air at 300°C.

The effect of heat-aging at 300°C in air on the fibers is shown in Table XVIII and Figure 6. In general, the arylene–amides retain useful tensile properties for 1–2 weeks; the heterocycle–amide fibers, on the other hand, perform considerably better. The heat-aging conditions of 300°C in air are severe; for example, whereas Nomex in the form of

TABLE XVIII. Effect of Physical Properties of Wholly Aromatic Polyamides after Prolonged Exposure in Air at 300°C

No.	Polymers	$T/E/M_i$[a] for: 0	1	7	14	35 days	Ref.
1	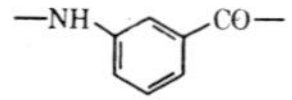 —NH CO—	5.8/10/118	—	—	—	3.5/4/130	92
2	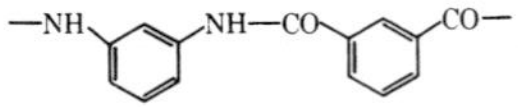 —NH NH—CO CO—	5.5/28/113	2.9/9.9/97	1.7/5.7/77	0.71/1.6/46	—	54
3	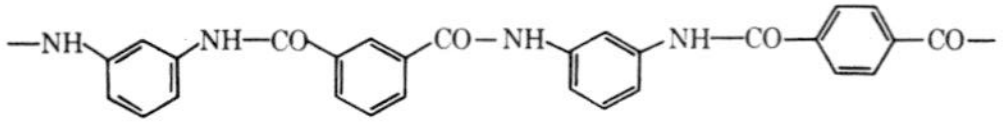 —NH NH—CO CO—NH NH—CO— —CO—	4.1/33/89	3.4/32/71	1.0/3.1/50	0.71/1.4/58	—	54
4	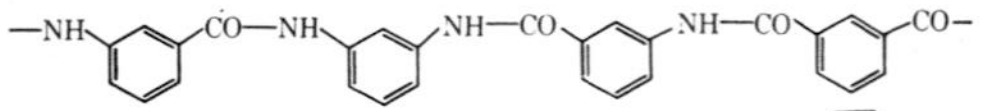 —NH CO—NH NH—CO NH—CO CO—	5.1/37/89	3.3/25/94	2.6/13/89	—	—	7
5		6.0/23/101	3.5/9.0/74	2.0/3.0/75	—	—	7
		(5.4/15/130)	(3.3/14/100)	—	(1.8/5/100)	—	(50)
6	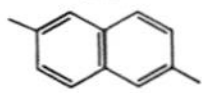	5.5/25/90	—	1.2/2.5/53[b]	—	—	53
7	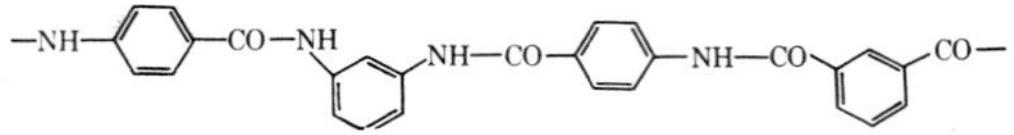 —NH— —CO—NH NH—CO— —NH—CO CO—	6.5/20/78	4.5/17/67	1.4/16/—	—	—	49

[a] $T/E/M_i$ = tenacity in grams per denier, elongation in per cent, initial modulus in grams per denier.
[b] Determined after nine days.

paper was reported to have a useful lifetime of around 40 hr at 300° for a certain electrical application, it had a useful lifetime of about 1400 hr at 250°C for the same application (3). This same fiber retained 80% of its strength after exposure to air for several thousand hours at 177°C, a temperature at which nylon 66 retained only 50% of its original strength after only 50 hr (3).

Heat-aging almost always results in a decrease in the elongation of the fibers, the loss being roughly proportional to the decrease in tenacity. Frequently the limit of usefulness of a fiber is even more dependent on elongation than tenacity, so that loss of elongation is of greater concern than loss of tenacity. Where the fibers are to be used in flexible products retention of elongation is particularly important.

(3) Behavior on Ignition and Pyrolysis. Wholly aromatic polyamide fibers characteristically burn only with difficulty (2,50), and they do not melt as do nylon 66 and polyethylene terephthalate fibers, so that they are very useful for protective clothing.

b. Electrical Properties. Wholly aromatic polyamides have high volume resistivities and high dielectric strengths and, significantly, they retain these properties at elevated temperatures to a high degree (3,53). Accordingly, they have considerable potential as high-temperature dielectrics, particularly for use in motors and transformers. The high-temperature electrical properties of aromatic polyamides are exemplified by those of two-ordered copolymers; these polymers have breakdown voltages of 3000 V/mil at temperatures up to 180°C (Table XIX). By comparison, the breakdown voltage for polytetrafluoroethylene is only 2250 V/mil at 150°C.

TABLE XIX. Breakdown Voltage of Aromatic Polyamide Films at Elevated Temperatures

No.	Composition	Temp., °C	Breakdown[a] voltage, V/mil	Ref.
1	MMM-P[b]	23	3000	50
		150	3000	50
2	MMM-N6[c]	180	3000	53
3	Polytetrafluoro-ethylene	150	2250	53
4	Nylon 66	150	120	53
5	Polyethylene	23	900	53

[a] Measured according to ASTM-D149-55.
[b] Polymer 23, Table XI.
[c] Polymer 25, Table XI.

Paper of HT-1 (Nomex) has almost twice the dielectric strength of high-quality rag paper and retains its useful electrical properties at higher operating temperatures than the upper limit for the rag paper (about 105°C) (3). It is believed that the production of Nomex in the form of paper rivals the production of Nomex to be used in the form of fiber.

c. Resistance to Change by Chemical Agents, UV Light, and Ionizing Radiation. The chemical resistance of aromatic polyamide fibers is in general very good (Tables XX and XXI). Although the polymers are much more resistant to acid than nylon 66, they are not as acid resistant as polyethylene terephthalate. Their resistance to strong base is comparable to that of nylon 66 (2,50,53). The hydrolytic stability of the aromatic polyamides is greatly superior to that of nylon 66 (2,50).

Aromatic polyamide fibers are quite akin to their aliphatic counterparts with regard to susceptibility to degradation by ultraviolet light; flanking the amide bond on each side by an arylene unit confers no special immunity of the amide linkage to degradation by UV light (21,53–54,63. 49–50).

TABLE XX. Chemical Resistance of Fibers of Aromatic Ordered Copolyamides[a]

Reagent	Strength	Temp., °C	Time, hr	% Strength retained	
				MMM-P[b]	MMM-N6[c]
Dimethylacetamide	100%	21	264	81	99.5
Sodium hypochlorite	0.5%	21	8	96	89
			264	55	44
Sodium hydroxide	16N	21	8	100	84
			264	71	74
	4N	100	8	33	38
			22	—[d]	19
Sulfuric acid	20N	21	8	95	70
			264	76	70
	4N	100	8	51	51
			96	—[e]	—[f]

[a] From work of Dobinson and Preston (53).
[b] Polymer 23, Table XI.
[c] Polymer 25, Table XI.
[d] Too weak to test.
[e] Disintegrated.
[f] Weak, but still in fiber form.

TABLE XXI. Chemical Resistance of Nomex[a] High-Temperature-Resistant Nylon Fiber[b]

Chemical	Concentration, %	T, °C	Time, hr	Effect on breaking strength[c]
Acids				
Formic	90	21	10	none
Hydrochloric	10	95	8	none
	35	21	10	appreciable
	35	21	100	appreciable
Sulfuric	10	21	100	none
	10	60	1,000	moderate
	70	21	100	none
	70	95	8	appreciable
Alkalis				
Ammonium hydroxide	28	21	100	none
Sodium hydroxide	10	21	100	none
	10	60	100	slight
	10	95	8	appreciable
	40	21	10	none
	50	60	100	degraded
Miscellaneous chemicals				
Dimethylformamide	100	70	168	none
Perchloroethylene	100	70	168	none
Phenol	100	21	10	none
Sodium chlorite	0.5	21	10	none
" "	0.5	60	100	moderate

[a] Du Pont registered trademark. [b] Taken from du Pont literature (2). [c] None, 0–9% strength loss; slight, 10–24% strength loss; moderate, 25–44% strength loss; appreciable, 45–79% strength loss; degraded, 80–100% strength loss.

TABLE XXII. Resistance of Fibers to Ionizing Radiation Degradation[a]

	% Tenacity retained	
	Nomex	Nylon 66
Beta radiation (Van de Graaff)		
200 megareps	81	29
600 megareps	76	0
Gamma radiation (Brookhaven Pile)		
200 megareps	70	32
2000 megareps	45	0
X-rays (50 kv)		
50 hr	85	22
100 hr	73	0

[a] Taken from du Pont literature (2).

The resistance of wholly aromatic amides to ionizing radiation is greatly superior to that of nylon 66 (Table XXII). Nomex fiber retained 76% of its original strength after exposure to 600 megareps in a Van de Graaff generator, whereas the strength of nylon 66 fiber was reduced to zero after the same exposure (2). The greater resistance of Nomex fibers to degradation in comparison with nylon 66 fiber is just as marked upon exposure to gamma radiation and x-rays. That

TABLE XXIII.

No.	Polyamide intermediate
1	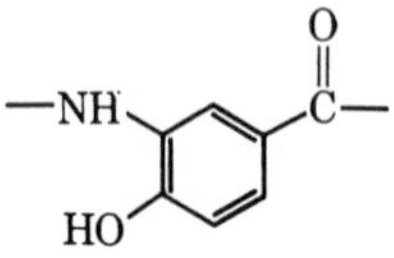 —NH, HO, O, C—
2	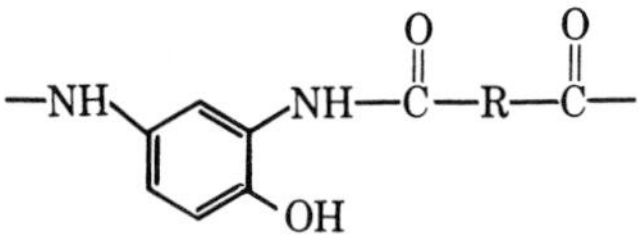 —NH, NH—C—R—C—, O, O, OH
3	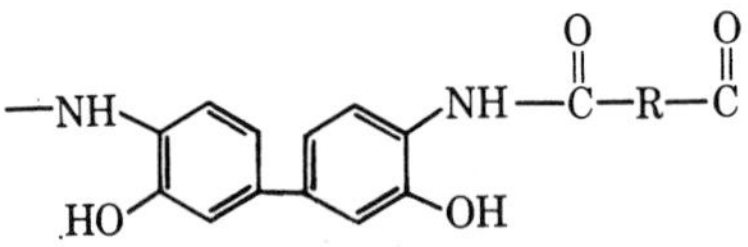 —NH, HO, NH—C—R—C, O, O, OH
4	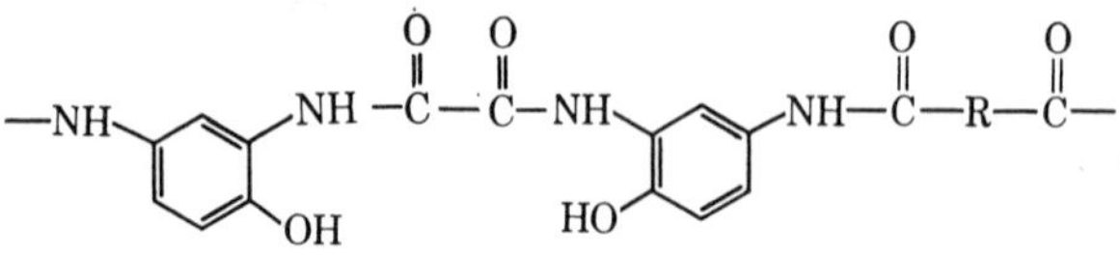 —NH, OH, NH —C—C—NH, O, O, HO, NH—C—R—C—, O, O
5	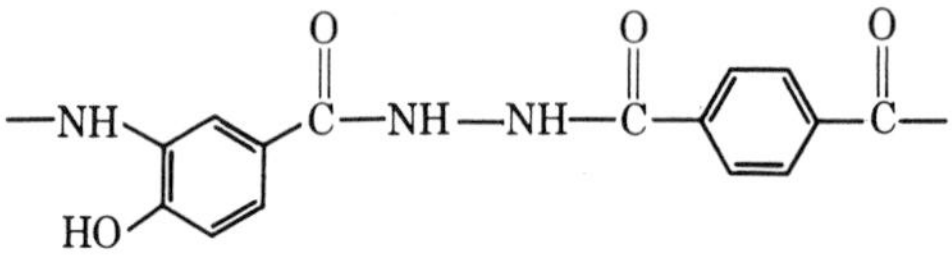 —NH, HO, C—NH—NH—C, O, O, C—, O
6	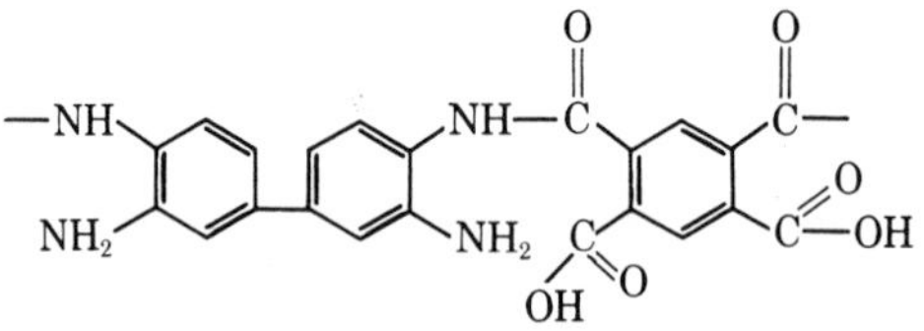 —NH, NH_2, NH—C, O, NH_2, C, OH, O, C—, O, C—OH, O

excellent radiation resistance is a characteristic property of the wholly aromatic polyamides is evidenced by the fact that two amide–oxadiazole fibers (fibers 1 and 2, Table XVI) retained 99 and 97% of their strength respectively (63) after exposure to 15 megarads of gamma radiation. Fibers of two ordered aromatic polyamides (fibers 6 and 8, Table XV) actually gained about 10% in strength after exposure to a dose of 3 megarads of gamma radiation (49).

Derived polymer	Ref.
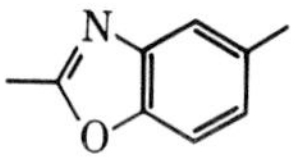 N, O	100
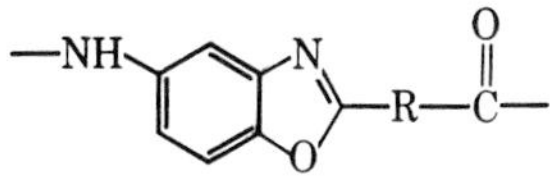 —NH— N, O —R—C(=O)—	101
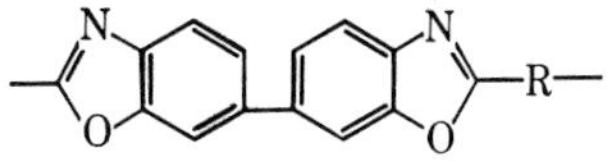 N, O N, O —R—	102, 103, 103a
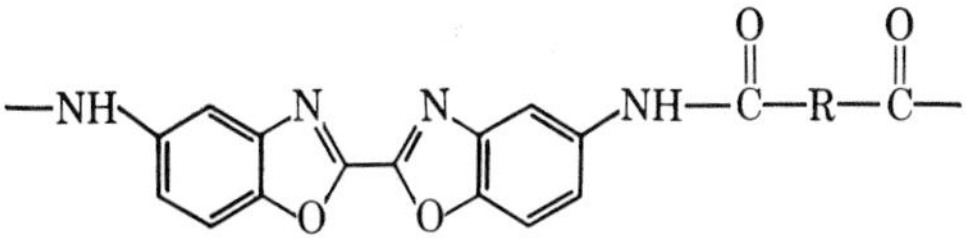 —NH— N, O N, O NH—C(=O)—R—C(=O)—	104
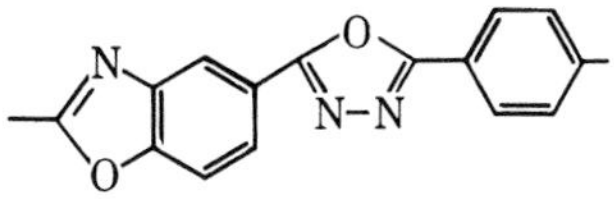 N, O O, N–N	105
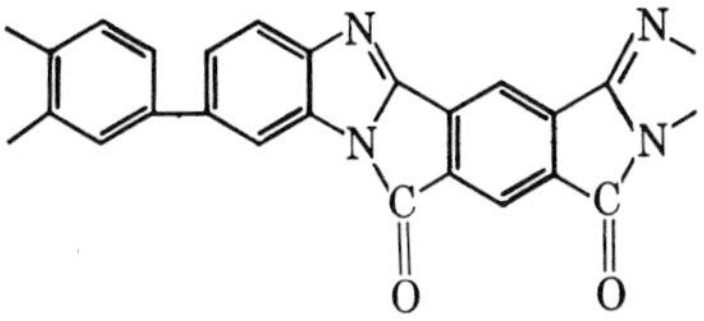 N N N N C=O C=O	106–109

(*continued*)

TABLE XXIII (*continued*)

No.	Polyamide intermediate
7	O O ‖ ‖ —NH NH—C—NH— —NH—C— HO—C C—OH ‖ ‖ O O
8	O O ‖ ‖ —NH NH—C— —C— HO—C C—OH ‖ ‖ O O
9	—Ar—C(=O)—NH—NH—C(=O)—R—C(=O)—NH—NH—C(=O)—
10	—Ar—C(=O)—NH—NH—C(=O)—C(=O)—NH—NH—C(=O)—R—C(=O)—NH—NH—C(=O)—
11	—Ar—C(=O)—NH—NH—C(=O)—Ar′—C(=O)—NH—NH—C(=O)—
12	O O O O O O ‖ ‖ ‖ ‖ ‖ ‖ —NH— —C—NHNH—C—C—NHNH—C— —NH—C C—
13	O O ‖ ‖ —C CNH NH— O O | | CO CO | | O—CH_3 O—CH_3

Derived polymer	Ref.
HN NH O=C C=O —N N— C C O O	110
—N N— O C C O O O	111
—O—Ar—O—R— N–N N–N	112
—Ar—O O R O— N–N N–N N–N	112
—Ar—O—Ar′—O— N–N N–N	113
—NH O O NH—C C— N–N N–N O O	104
O O —N–C C–N C–O O–C O O	114

V. AROMATIC POLYAMIDES USEFUL AS PRECURSORS FOR THERMOSTABLE POLYHETEROCYCLES

Aromatic polyamides which are soluble precursors to intractable, thermally stable polymers constitute an increasingly important class of aromatic polyamides. Their importance lies in the fact that they can easily be fabricated into fibers and films prior to conversion to the desired intractable polymer, thereby providing a route to otherwise unobtainable fibers and films of such polymers. The condensation product of *m*-phenylene diamine and pyromellitic anhydride, the very soluble polyamic acid I, is a typical example of this class of polyamides.

NH_2 NH_2 O O C C O O C C O O

O O NH—C C—NH HO—C C—OH O O $\xrightarrow{-H_2O}$ O O C C N N C C O O (14)

I II

Conversion to the intractable, ring-closed product—as for example the polyimide II—is accomplished by either thermal or chemical dehydration. (The polyamic-acid precursors to polyimides and their conversion to the polyimides are discussed more fully in the following chapter, "Wholly Aromatic and Aliphatic-Aromatic Polyimides.")

In Table XXIII a number of other types of soluble precursor polyamides along with the derived intractable polymers are also given. Although not isolated as such, polyamides are suspected intermediates in the preparation of a number of heterocycle polymers such as polybenzimidazoles (57), polybenzothiazoles (99), and certain polybenzoxazoles (100,100a,100b).

REFERENCES

1. International Textile Bulletin, World Edition Spinning, No. 3, 4 (1965).
2. *Properties of Nomex High Temperature Resistant Nylon Fiber*, NP-33 Bulletin, du Pont Co., Wilmington 98, Delaware.
3. L. K. McCune, *Textile Res. J.*, **32** (9), 762 (1962).
4. R. Hill and E. E. Walker, *J. Polymer Sci.*, **3,** 609 (1948).
5. C. S. Fuller and C. L. Erickson, *J. Am. Chem. Soc.*, **59,** 344 (1937).

6a. P. W. Morgan, *Condensation Polymers: By Interfacial and Solution Methods*, Interscience, New York, 1965.

6b. P. W. Morgan, *Op. cit.*, Chapter V.

7. J. Preston, *J. Polymer Sci., A-1*, **4,** 529 (1966); J. Preston, U.S. Pat. 3,232,910 (1966) (to Monsanto).
8. G. M. Coppinger, *J. Am. Chem. Soc.*, **76,** 1372 (1954).
9. S. L. Kwolek, P. W. Morgan, and W. R. Sorenson, U.S. Pat. 3,063,966 (1962) (to du Pont).
10. V. M. Savinov and L. B. Sokolov, *Polymer Sci. USSR English Transl.*, **7,** 851 (1966).
11. L. F. Beste and C. W. Stephens, U.S. Pat. 3,068,188 (1962) (to du Pont).
12. W. M. Edwards, U.S. Pat. 3,179,614 (1965), (to du Pont).
13. W. R. Sorenson and T. W. Campbell, *Preparative Methods of Polymer Chemistry*, Interscience, New York, 1961.
14. B. Ke, *Newer Methods of Polymer Characterization*, Interscience, New York, 1964.
15. P. E. Slade and L. T. Jenkins, *Polymer Thermal Analysis*, Vol. 1, Part 1, Marcel Dekker, Inc., New York, 1966.
16. L. E. Nielsen, *Mechanical Properties of Polymers*, Reinhold, New York, 1962.
17. J. V. Schmitz, Ed., *Testing of Polymers*, Vol. I, Interscience, New York, 1965.
18. V. E. Shashoua and W. M. Eareckson, III, *J. Polymer Sci.*, **40,** 343 (1959).
19. W. O. Statton, *Ann. N.Y. Acad. Sci.*, **83,** 27 (1959).
20. E. F. Carlston and F. G. Lum, *Ind. Eng. Chem.*, **49,** 1239 (1957).
21. D. D. Coffman, G. F. Berchet, W. R. Peterson, and E. W. Spanagel, *J. Polymer Sci.*, **2,** 306 (1947).
22. M. Katz, *J. Polymer Sci.*, **40,** 337 (1959); M. Katz, U.S. Pat. 2,949,440 (1960) (to du Pont).
23. Belg. Pat. 569,760 (1958) (to du Pont).
24. B. S. Sprague and R. W. Singleton, *Textile Res. J.*, **35** (11), 999 (1965).
25. C. W. Stephens, *J. Polymer Sci.*, **40,** 359 (1959).
26. Brit. Pat. 918,637 (1963) (to du Pont).
27. H. Hopff and A. Krieger, *Makromol. Chem.*, **47,** 93 (1961).

27a. S. L. Kwolek and P. W. Morgan, U. S. Pat. 3,287,323 (1966) (to du Pont).

28. R. G. Beaman, P. W. Morgan, C. R. Koller, E. L. Wittbecker, and E. E. Magat, *J. Polymer Sci.*, **40,** 329 (1959).
29. Brit. Pat. 506,125 (to du Pont).
30. P. W. Morgan and S. L. Kwolek, *J. Polymer Sci.*, **40,** 299 (1959).
31. W. W. Triggs, Brit. Pat. 474,999 (1937).
32. J. E. Kirby, U.S. Pat. 2,625,356 (1953) (to du Pont).
33. J. Preston, data from Chemstrand Research Center, Inc.
34. S. Akiyoshi, S. Hashimoto, and K. Takami, *J. Chem. Soc. Japan, Ind. Chem. Sect.*, **57,** 212 (1954).

35. Brit. Pat. 794,365 (1958) (to British Nylon Spinners, Ltd.).
36. O. B. Edgar and R. Hill, *J. Polymer Sci.*, **8,** 1 (1952).
37. A. C. Werner, U.S. Pat. 3,232,909 (1966) (to American Celanese), Fr. Pat. 1,351,588 (1965) (to American Celanese).
38. J. Preston and R. W. Smith, publication in progress; Belg. Pat. 629,358 (1963) (to Monsanto).
39. C. F. Horn, *Makromol. Chem.*, **30,** 123 (1959).
40. R. Hill, Ed., *Fibers from Synthetic Polymers* (Elsevier, New York, 1953), p. 136.
41. W. W. Triggs, Brit. Pat. 525,516 (1940).
42. N. Yoda, *Bull. Chem. Soc. Japan*, **35,** 1349 (1962).
42a. T. Ōta, M. Yamashita, O. Yoshizaki, and E. Nagai, *J. Polymer Sci. A*, **4,** 959 (1966).
43. N. Yoda and I. Matsubara, *J. Polymer Sci. A*, **2,** 253 (1964).
44. J. R. Schaefgen, F. H. Koontz, and R. F. Tietz, *J. Polymer Sci.*, **40,** 377 (1959).
45. H. K. Hall, Jr. and J. W. Berge, *J. Polymer Sci. B*, **1,** 277 (1963).
46. L. B. Sokolov, L. V. Turetskiĭ, and T. V. Kudim, *Vysokomol. Soed.*, **2,** 1744 (1960).
47. L. B. Sokolov, L. V. Turetskiĭ, and L. I. Tugova. *Vysokomol. Soed.*, **4,** 1817 (1962).
48. C. Cipriani, U.S. Pat. 3,227,793 (1966) (to American Celanese).
49. J. Preston, R. W. Smith, and C. J. Stehman, *J. Polymer Sci. C*, **19,** 7 (1967).
50. J. O. Weiss, H. S. Morgan, and M. R. Lilyquist, *J. Polymer Sci. C*, **19,** 29 (1967).
51. D. A. Frey, H. Hasegawa, and C. S. Marvel, *J. Polymer Sci. A*, **1,** 2057 (1963).
52. P. Kovacic and F. W. Koch, *J. Org. Chem.*, **28,** 1864 (1963).
53. F. Dobinson and J. Preston, *J. Polymer Sci. A*, **1, 4,** 2093 (1966); J. Preston and F. Dobinson, U.S. Pats. 3,240,760 (1966) (and 3,242,213 (1966) (to Monsanto).
54. C. W. Stephens, U.S. Pat. 3,049,518 (1962) (to du Pont).
55. J. Preston and R. W. Smith, *J. Polymer Sci. B*, **4,** 1033 (1966); Belg. Pat. 651,-149 (1965) (to Monsanto).
56. J. Sauer, R. Huisgen, and H. J. Sturm, *Tetrahedron*, **11,** 214 (1960).
57. H. Vogel and C. S. Marvel, *J. Polymer Sci.*, **50,** 511 (1961).
58. J. R. Holsten and M. R. Lilyquist, *J. Polymer Sci. A*, **3,** 3905 (1965).
59. J. R. Holsten and M. R. Lilyquist, *J. Polymer Sci. C*, **19,** 77 (1967).
60. H. W. Hill, Jr., S. L. Kwolek, and W. Sweeny, U.S. Pat. 3,094,511 (1963) (to du Pont).
61. E. L. Alexander, Jr., U.S. Pat. 3,133,138 (1964) (to du Pont).
61a. W. Sweeny, U. S. Pat. 3,287,324 (1966) (to du Pont).
62. J. Preston and W. B. Black, *J. Polymer Sci. B*, **4,** 267 (1966); Belg. Pat. 660,339 (1965) (to Monsanto).
63. J. Preston and W. B. Black, *J. Polymer Sci. C*, **19,** 17 (1967).
64. R. M. Ikeda, *J. Polymer Sci. B*, **4,** 353 (1966).
65. W. A. H. Huffman, R. W. Smith, and W. T. Dye, Jr., U.S. Pat. 3,203,933 (1965), (to Monsanto).
66. J. Preston and R. W. Smith, U.S. Pat. 3,225,011 (1965) (to Monsanto).
67. R. W. Smith, W. A. H. Huffman, and W. T. Dye, Jr., U.S. Pat. 3,240,758 (1966) (to Monsanto).
68. R. A. Dine-Hart, B. J. C. Moore, and W. W. Wright, *J. Polymer Sci. B*, **2,** 369 (1964).
69. H. W. Hill, Jr. and S. L. Kwolek, U.S. Pat. 3,006,899 (1961) (to du Pont).

70. H. Mark, S. M. Atlas, and N. Ogata, *J. Polymer Sci.*, **61**, S49 (1962).
71. L. B. Sokolov and T. V. Kudim, *Vysokomol. Soed.*, **2**, 698 (1960).
72. E. E. Magat, U.S. Pat. 2,831,834 (1958) (to du Pont).
73. W. B. Black and J. Preston, data from Chemstrand Research Center, Inc.
74. T. Ya. Medved, T. M. Frunze, C. M. Hu, V. V. Kurashev, V. V. Korshak, and M. I. Kobachnik, *Vysokomol. Soed.*, **5**, 1309 (1963).
75. L. B. Sokolov and L. V. Turetskiĭ, *Vysokomol. Soed.*, **2**, 710 (1960).
76. V. M. Savinov and L. B. Sokolov, *J. Appl. Chem. USSR English Transl.*, **34**, 2021 (1961).
77. Brit. Pat. 588,497 (1947) (to Imperial Chemical Industries).
78. O. Ya. Fedotova, M. L. Kerber, and I. P. Losev, *Vysokomol. Soed.*, **2**, 1020 (1960).
79. M. A. Dahlen, U.S. Pat. 2,001,526 (1935) (to du Pont).
80. A. P. Terent'yev, YE. G. Rukhadze, I. G. Mochalina, and G. V. Panova, *Vysokomol. Soed.*, **5**, 837 (1963); *Polymer Sci. USSR English Transl.*, **4**, 1556 (1963).
81. L. V. Turetskiĭ and L. B. Sokolov, *Vysokomol. Soed.*, **3**, 1449 (1961).
82. O. Ya. Fedotova, M. L. Kerber, I. P. Losev, G. K. Genkina, and L. B. Dynina, *Vysokomol. Soed.*, **3**, 1524 (1961).
83. O. Ya. Fedotova, M. L. Kerber, and I. P. Losev, *Vysokomol. Soed.*, **3**, 1528 (1961).
84. P. W. Morgan, *J. Polymer Sci. C*, **4**, 1075 (1963).
85. M. N. Bogdanov, S. N. Kharkov, I. A. Spirina, A. U. Leshiner, and L. A. Plyashkevich, *Vysokomol. Soed.*, **7**, 813 (1965); *Pol. Sci. USSR English Transl.*, **7**, 898 (1966).
86. J. Preston and F. Dobinson, *J. Polymer Sci. B*, **2**, 1171 (1964).
87. M. A. Dahlen, U.S. Pat. 2,001,526 (1935) (to du Pont).
87a. Y. Iwakura, K. Uno, Y. Imai, and M. Fukui, *Makromol. Chem.*, **77**, 41 (1964).
87b. G. Rabilloud, B. Sillion, and G. de Gaudemaris, *Bull. Soc. Chim. France*, 926 (1966).
88. J. Colonge and E. Fichet, *Bull. Soc. Chim. France*, 412 (1955).
89. H. Hasegawa, *Bull. Chem. Soc. Japan*, **27**, 327 (1954); *Chem. Abstr.*, **49**, 8665 (1955).
90. D. A. Berry, U.S. Pat. 3,109,836 (1963) (to Esso Research).
91. R. A. Jacobson, U.S. Pat. 2,279,752 (1942) (to du Pont).
92. Brit. Pat. 901,159 (1962) (to du Pont).
93. N. E. Boyer, *Technikas Apskats*, **31**, 13 (1961); *Chem. Abstr.*, **59**, 1526 (1965).
94. F. W. King, U.S. Pat. 3,079,219 (1963) (to du Pont).
95. C. Boyer, U.S. Pat. 2,955,017 (1961) (to du Pont).
96. Belg. Pat. 665,638 (1965) (to Monsanto).
97. W. A. Hare and H. L. White, U.S. Pat. 2,989,495 (1961) (to du Pont).
98. W. R. Clay, U. S. Pat. 3,300,450 (1967) (to du Pont); Belg. Pat. 624,182 (1962).
99. P. M. Hergenrother, W. Wrasidlo, and H. H. Levine, *J. Polymer Sci. A*, **3**, 1665 (1965).
100. W. W. Moyer, Jr., C. Cole, and T. Anyos, *J. Polymer Sci. A*, **3**, 2107 (1965); W. W. Moyer, Jr., U.S. Pat. 3,230,196 (1966) (to Borg-Warner).
100a. Y. Imai, I. Taoka, K. Uno, and Y. Iwakura, *Makromol. Chem.*, **83**, 167 (1965).
100b. Y. Imai, I. Taoka, K. Uno, and Y. Iwakura, *Makromol. Chem.*, **83**, 179 (1965).
101. R. J. Angelo, U. S. Pat. 3,322,723 (1967) (to du Pont); Belg. Pat. 649,334 (1965) (to du Pont).
102. T. Kubota and R. Nakanishi, *J. Polymer Sci. B*, **2**, 1171 (1964).

103. Belg. Pat. 649,333 (1965) (to du Pont).
103a. V. S. Yakubovich, G. V. Myasnikova, G. I. Braz, and A. Ya. Yakubovich, *Dokl. Akad. Nauk SSSR*, **159,** 630 (1964); English transl., **159,** 1251 (1964).
104. H. C. Bach and J. Preston, U. S. Pat. 3,354,120 (1967) (to Monsanto); Belg. Pat. 660,339 (1965) (to Monsanto).
105. B. M. Culbertson and R. Murphy, *J. Polymer Sci. B*, **4,** 249 (1966).
106. F. Dawans and C. S. Marvel, *J. Polymer Sci. A*, **3,** 3549 (1965).
107. J. G. Colson, R. H. Michel, and R. M. Paufler, *J. Polymer Sci. A*, **4,** 59 (1966); Belg. Pat. 658,494 (1965) (to du Pont).
108. V. L. Bell and G. F. Pezdirtz, *J. Polymer Sci. B*, **3,** 977 (1965); V. L. Bell and G. F. Pezdirtz, *ACS Polymer Preprints*, **6** (2), 747 (1965).
109. R. L. Van Deusen, *J. Polymer Sci. B*, **4,** 211 (1966).
110. N. Yoda, R. Nakanishi, M. Kurihara, Y. Bamba, S. Tokyama, and K. Ikeda, *J. Polymer Sci. B*, **4,** 11 (1966).
111. N. Yoda, M. Kurihara, K. Ikeda, S. Tohyama, and R. Nakanishi, *J. Polymer Sci. B*, **4,** 551 (1966); Fr. Pat. 1,448,897 (1965) (to Toyo Rayon Co., Ltd.).
112. A. H. Frazer and F. T. Wallenberger, *J. Polymer Sci. A*, **2,** 1137 (1964).
113. A. H. Frazer and F. T. Wallenberger, *J. Polymer Sci. A*, **2,** 1147 (1964).
114. R. J. Angelo, U.S. Pat. 3,244,675 (1966) (to du Pont).

Wholly Aromatic and Aliphatic–Aromatic Polyimides

J. Preston and W. B. Black
Chemstrand Research Center, Inc., Durham, North Carolina

CONTENTS

I. INTRODUCTION

Wholly aromatic polyimides are already attaining considerable importance even though the first such polymer was not reported until 1955 by Edwards (1). The aromatic polyimides, like their aromatic polyamide counterparts, are of interest primarily because of their great thermal stability, particularly in air. Indeed, as a class, the wholly aromatic polyimides are substantially superior to the best wholly aromatic polyamides and are among the most thermally stable organic polymers known. In addition, aromatic polyimides have outstanding dielectric and mechanical properties at high temperatures, and outstanding resistance to ionizing radiation and to solvent attack.

Of the substantial amount of aromatic polyimide research that has been done in the last decade, a large part has been directed toward the investigation of products other than fibers, namely, films, coatings, varnishes, and laminating resins—i.e., toward those products which are in general best suited for taking advantage of the high-temperature dielectric properties of polyimides. For applications of this kind a number of products have already reached the commercial stage: Kapton* film† (known experimentally as H-film), Pyre-ML* wire enamel and Skybond‡ 700 laminating resins.§ Shaped objects from Vespel* molding resins also have been introduced recently.

Despite the fact that aliphatic–aromatic polyimides (1) have been known as long as have been the wholly aromatic polyimides, they have received relatively little attention, no doubt owing to the fact that the wholly aromatic polyimides appear to have considerably greater commercial potential as a consequence of their greater thermal stability.

Sroog (2) has recently reviewed the polymerization chemistry and properties of both aliphatic–aromatic and wholly aromatic polyimides, particularly with regard to those wholly aromatic polymers useful for films; no data on fibers, however, were given. Even though no fibers of wholly aromatic or aliphatic–aromatic polyimides have reached the stage of commercialization, it is known that excellent polyimide fibers can be made; an outstanding one, presumably the polypyromellitimide of bis(4-aminophenyl) ether, is now in the research stage (3,4). There appears to be no property inherent in aromatic polyimides that would limit them as a class to products other than fibers, and one can expect to hear more of aromatic polyimide fibers in the near future.

Since both the polymerization chemistry and the characterization of the resultant polymers is far more complete in the case of the wholly aromatic polyimides, these will be discussed first. The properties of the aliphatic–aromatic polyimides, and to a degree the polymerization

* Du Pont Company registered trademark.
† H-4 Technical Bulletin, du Pont, Wilmington, Del.
‡ Monsanto Company registered trademark.
§ Technical Bulletin No. 5042B, Monsanto Co., St. Louis, Mo.

chemistry as well, will be discussed within the framework of the properties and polymerization chemistry of the wholly aromatic polyimides.

II. WHOLLY AROMATIC POLYIMIDES

Wholly aromatic polyimides are derived from aromatic dianhydrides and aromatic diamines (AA-BB polyimides) or from aromatic compounds containing both an amine and an anhydride group (A-B polyimides). The polymers are not meltable and are soluble only in strong acids such as fuming nitric acid. The highly intractable nature of these polyimides has precluded both their direct synthesis (with but very few exceptions) and their direct fabrication to useful articles. The recent successes in wholly aromatic polyimide synthesis and fabrication have been due (*a*) to the discovery that polyimides can be prepared stepwise by way of a soluble and fabricatable polyamic-acid precursor, and (*b*) to the fact that high-molecular-weight polyamic-acid precursors can be prepared by low-temperature solution polycondensation (5–16). (Low-temperature solution polycondensation is discussed in Section II of previous chapter.) Films, fibers, and coatings, etc., are made from the polyamic-acid solution; the shaped polyamic-acid is then readily converted to the polyimide.

In addition to aromatic polyimides of the A-B and AA-BB types, other classes of polyimides more complex in structure have also been prepared. Syntheses of the latter are accomplished by condensation of a simple dianhydride with a diamine containing preformed heterocycle, amide, or ester units, or vice versa. Each type is discussed in turn.

A. Synthesis of Wholly Aromatic Polyimides

1. Simple AA-BB Polyimides

Soluble polyamic-acids (also called poly-*o*-carboxy-aromatic amides or aromatic polyamide acids) are produced by low-temperature polycondensation of aromatic dianhydrides with diamines in polar solvents, e.g., dimethylformamide, dimethylacetamide, dimethyl sulfoxide, *N*-methylpyrrolidone, or *m*-cresol (6,8,11,22); for optimum polymerization, a temperature of around 50°C should not be exceeded (2,6), with the possible exception of conditions under which *m*-cresol is used. It has been reported (17) that *m*-cresol solutions of polyamic-acids can be heated safely to 125–160°C. Attainment of high molecular weight depends on extremely pure monomers, rigorous exclusion of moisture, solvent used, and the maintenance of a low to moderate polymerization temperature (7). Although polyamic-acids do show some variation in solubility with variation in structure (8,17a), solubility is apparently adequate in all cases for the preparation of high-molecular-weight polymer suitable for fabrication.

Polyamic-acid synthesis and conversion to the corresponding polyimide are shown in Eq. 1. The 1,4-diamide structure of the polyamic-acid is presumed to be the predominate one (5), but the isomeric 1,3-

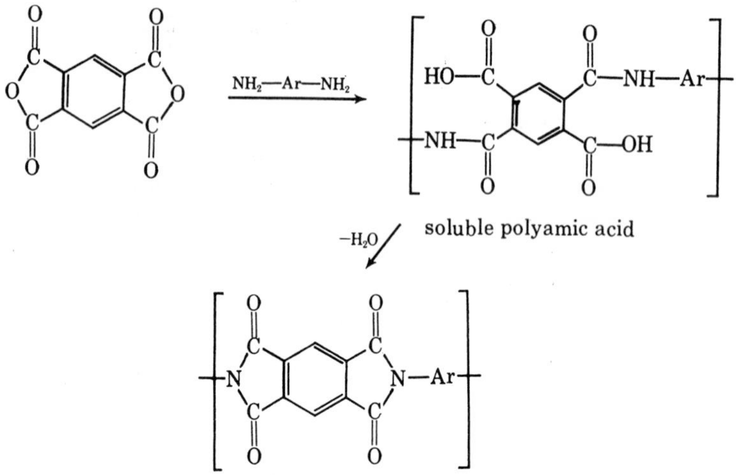

$$\xrightarrow{NH_2—Ar—NH_2} \text{soluble polyamic acid} \xrightarrow{-H_2O} \qquad (1)$$

Ar = (m-phenylene), (p-phenylene), (4,4'-biphenylene), —C₆H₄—X—C₆H₄—

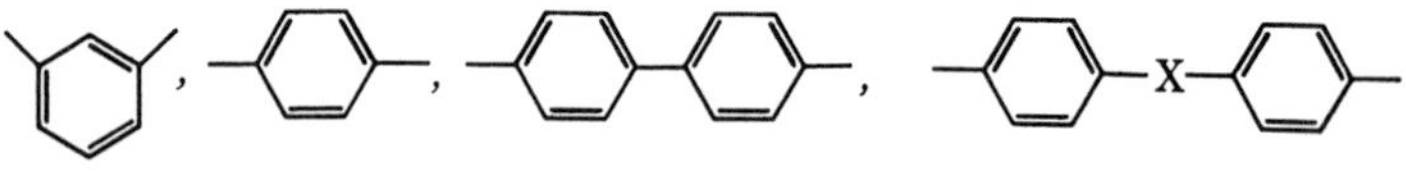

$X = —O—, —S—, —SO_2—$; etc.

diamide structure undoubtedly is present to some extent. The polyamic-acids, after fabrication to fiber, film, coatings, etc., from the solution of the polymer, are dehydrated by thermal or chemical means to yield the polyimides (17b).

The polyamic-acid derived from pyromellitic dianhydride and bis(4-aminophenyl) ether has been characterized rather thoroughly (18). This polyamic-acid is reported to be unstable in solution and to degrade slowly upon aging (19). The cause, apparently, is the water formed by the inadvertent reaction of some amic-acid groups to form imide groups; the water so produced presumably brings about hydrolysis of some of the amide groups linking the units of the polymer chain. Similar reactions have been shown for monomeric carboxyamides (20). Bower and Frost (8) reported that the amide groups of the polymer chain undergo an interchange with amine and anhydride end-groups, making stoichiometric equivalence most important. Although addition of excess diamine or dianhydride can cause rapid lowering of the viscosity, recovery can be effected by introduction of an equivalent of the complementary reactant (8).

Salts of polyamic-acids, unlike the acid polymers themselves, are quite resistant to hydrolysis, and films can be cast from aqueous solutions of such polyamic-acid salts (21). These films in turn can be dried and converted to polyimides by the usual thermal treatments. The highly viscous solutions of these polyelectrolytes are rendered considerably less viscous by the addition of solvents such as isopropanol (21).

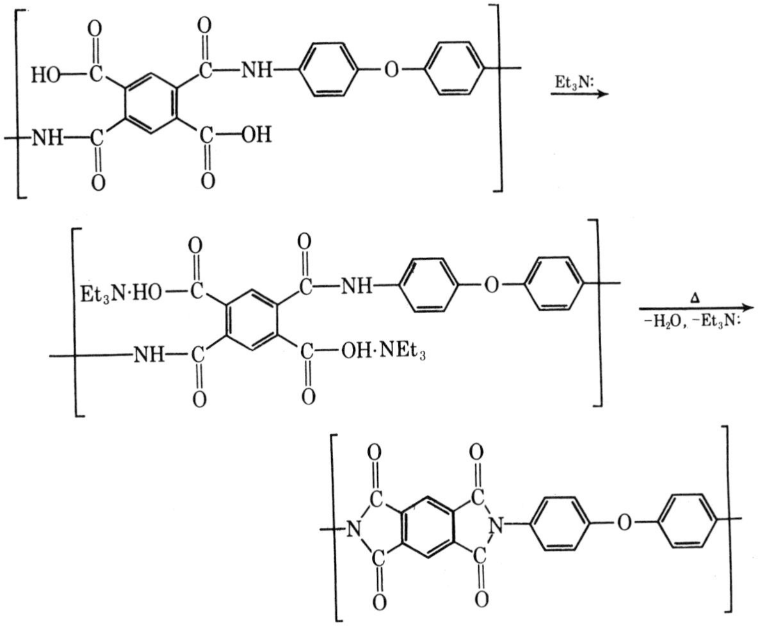

HO—C(=O)— ... —C(=O)—NH—C₆H₄—O—C₆H₄— ; —NH—C(=O)— ... —C(=O)—OH $\xrightarrow{Et_3N:}$

$Et_3N \cdot HO$—C(=O)— ... —C(=O)—NH—C₆H₄—O—C₆H₄— ; —NH—C(=O)— ... —C(=O)—$OH \cdot NEt_3$ $\xrightarrow[-H_2O,\ -Et_3N:]{\Delta}$

—N(C=O)₂C₆H₂(C=O)₂N—C₆H₄—O—C₆H₄— (2)

At present the only dianhydride of importance other than pyromellitic dianhydride for the preparation of polyimides is 3,4,3′,4′-benzophenone tetracarboxylic dianhydride, compound **I** below (13,16–17,22a,23). The products derived from this dianhydride and aromatic diamines are

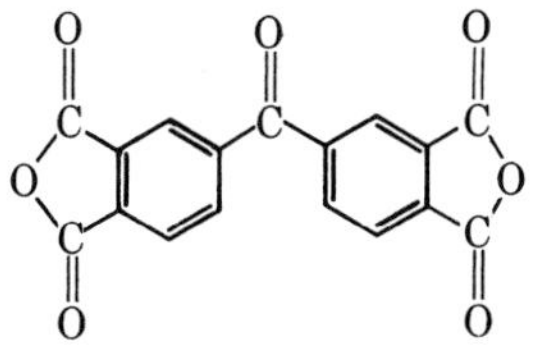

I

stated to be crosslinked (22); also, patents have been issued which state that copolyimides containing benzophenone moieties indeed crosslink more readily. Crosslinking is thought to occur through the reaction of the carbonyl bridge with amine groups. Copolymers from diamines and mixtures of dianhydrides containing at least 20 mol. % **I** are claimed (24) to yield films with mechanical properties superior to those of polyimide homopolymers.

When polyamic-acids are heated above 150°C, conversion to the polyimide is rapid; heating in the range of 300°C, however, is necessary for complete conversion (7). It has been pointed out (8) that those polyimides high in imide content, e.g., polyimides derived from *m*- or *p*-phenylenediamine and pyromellitic dianhydride, are more apt to be brittle when heated at 150°C for only an hour or two than are polymers lower in imide content. Toughness and flexibility of films high in imide content can be improved markedly by heating the partially converted films to a temperature of about 300°C for a few minutes (8). The good flexibility of the films of polyamic-acids is probably attributable to the high order that exists in these polymers, as is the case in other aromatic polyamides (previous chapter, Sections III-A and IV-A). On the other hand, the poor flexibility of polyamic-acid films after heating to temperatures too low to effect complete cyclodehydration (150–225°C) can probably be ascribed to disorder introduced into the polymer, i.e., to the random occurrence of amic-acid and imide groups. Good flexibility of the film is achieved once more when order has been restored upon conversion of the remaining amic-acid groups to imide groups by heating the film to 300°C or higher. Incorporation of some linkages which are known to provide high flexibility in polymers, such as —O— and —S—, results in films which are fairly flexible during conversion from polyamic-acid to polyimide.

In addition to thermal processes for conversion of polyamic acids to polyimides, low-temperature chemical processes employing dehydrating agents such as acetic anhydride in pyridine (25) also cause conversion to the imide structure. In practice the temperature employed is usually room temperature. The kinetics of this reaction have been reported (26).

In addition to the simple imide linkage that has been discussed (Eq. 1), the iminolactone linkage is also detected (12–16) in the dianhydride–

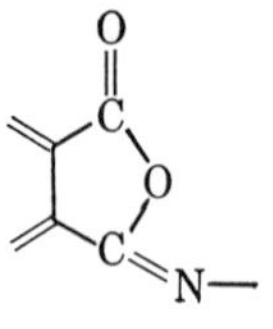

diamine condensation product. Patents have disclosed procedures for making polymers in which the iminolactone linkage is the predominant one (14,27–35). This can be done, for example, by heating the polyamic acid with acetyl chloride, trifluoroacetic anhydride, or *N*,*N′*-dicyclohexylcarbodiimide. Reaction of the polyiminolactone with alcohols (Eq. 3), *N*-alkyl amines, or ammonia leads to *ortho*-carboxy esters, **II**,

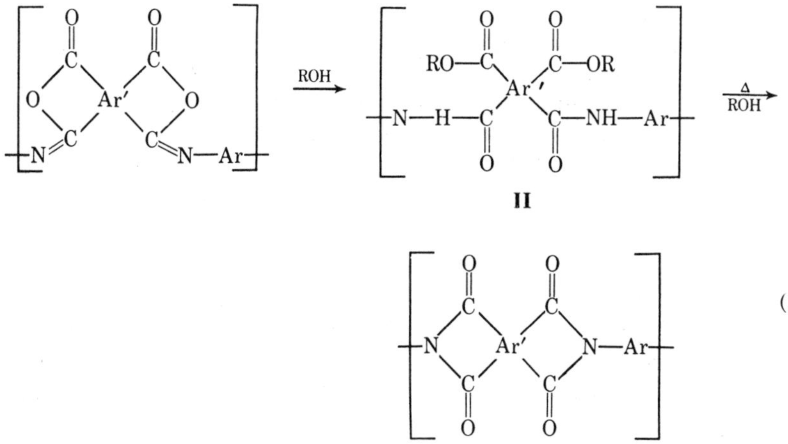

$$\xrightarrow{\text{ROH}} \quad \textbf{II} \quad \xrightarrow[\text{ROH}]{\Delta} \qquad (3)$$

and *ortho*-carboxamide polymers which can in turn be converted thermally to the corresponding polyimide (27).

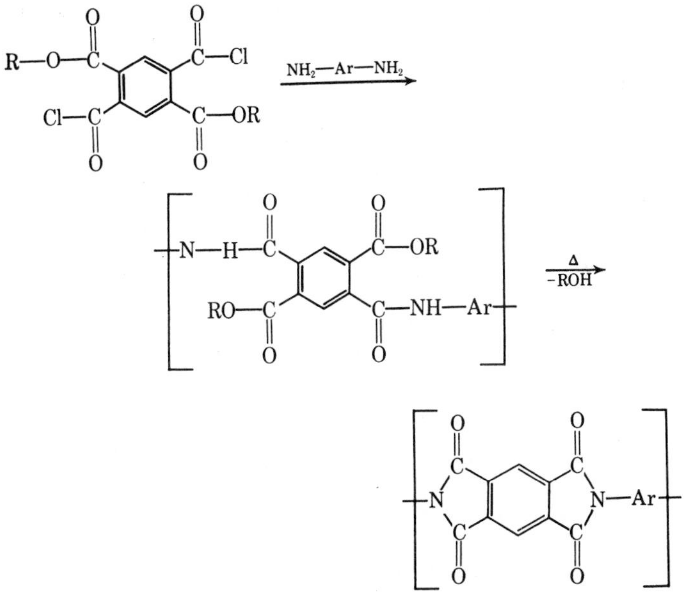

$$\xrightarrow{\text{NH}_2\text{—Ar—NH}_2} \quad \xrightarrow[\text{-ROH}]{\Delta} \qquad (4)$$

Polyimides can also be prepared indirectly by the condensation of diamines with diester/diacid chlorides (36) (Eq. 4), diacid/diesters (22, 31), or tetraesters. The reaction of an ester with a diamine may be used to produce low-molecular-weight materials which are particularly suitable for use as laminating resins.

2. *Simple A-B Polyimides*

Jones (6) has pointed out that probably the first recorded synthesis of a polyimide was made by Bogert and Renshaw (37), who observed that heating 4-aminophthalic anhydride or dimethyl-4-aminophthalate yielded an insoluble, infusible gray material, which they called "a polymolecular imide"; their product was not characterized further. More recently, in the course of the development of experimental procedures for the preparation of pure 4-aminophthalic anhydride by Brandt (38), it was also indicated that the product of Bogert and Renshaw apparently contained some polyimide. Brandt also showed that reduction of 4-nitrophthalic anhydride, if not carefully controlled, yields the polyamic-acid, **III**, with a degree of polymerization of 8–10. Brandt thus appears to be the first to report an aromatic poly-*o*-carboxyamide, i.e., an aromatic polyamic-acid.

An interesting finding by Jones (39) was that a solid state polymerization of 4-aminophthalic anhydride can be carried out to yield a polyamic-acid, **III**, which can then be dissolved in dimethylformamide, dimethylacetamide, or dimethyl sulfoxide, and cast into film (compare solution polymerization of the AA-BB type above). This film can be converted to the polyimide, **IV**, by thermal or chemical dehydration in the same manner as AA-BB polyamic-acids.

Polyimides of the A-B type, in addition to being difficult to prepare, possess rather poor mechanical properties (39); they are quite brittle in general compared with polyimides of the AA-BB type.

NH_2–C₆H₃(CO)₂O $\xrightarrow{\text{solid state polymerization}}$

$$\left[\text{C}_6\text{H}_3(\text{C(=O)–NH})(\text{C(=O)–OH}) \right]_n \xrightarrow[-H_2O]{\Delta} \left[\text{C}_6\text{H}_3(\text{C(=O)})_2\text{N} \right] \qquad (5)$$

III **IV**

3. *Heterocycle–imide Copolymers*

An ordered heterocycle–imide copolymer (9,10,40,41) is produced when a diamine containing a heterocyclic unit is polymerized with a dianhydride followed by cyclodehydration of the intermediate polyamic acid, as in the case of other AA-BB polyimides.

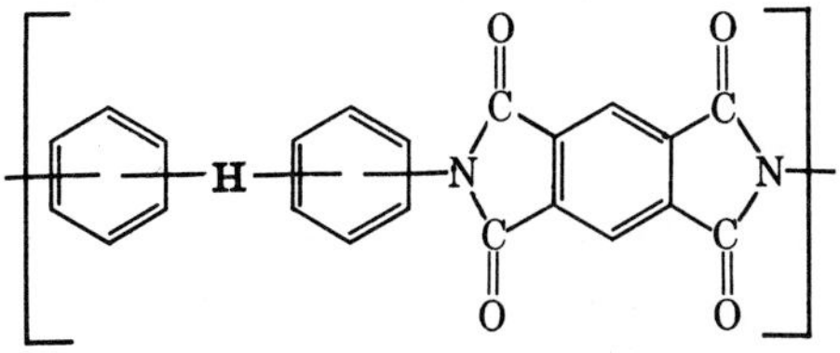

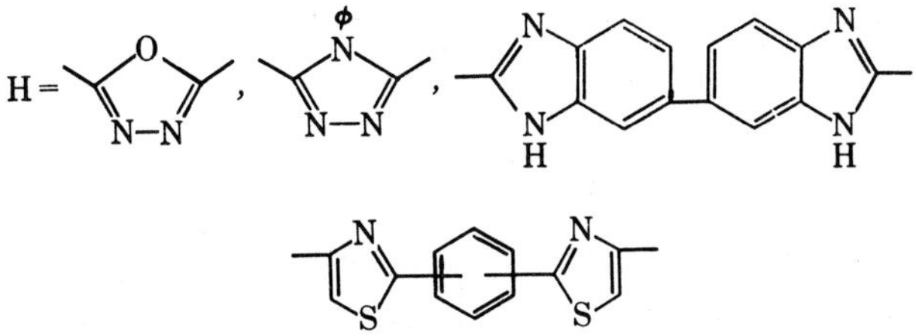

Benzheterocycle-imide copolymers, e.g., benzimidazole-imide copoly-

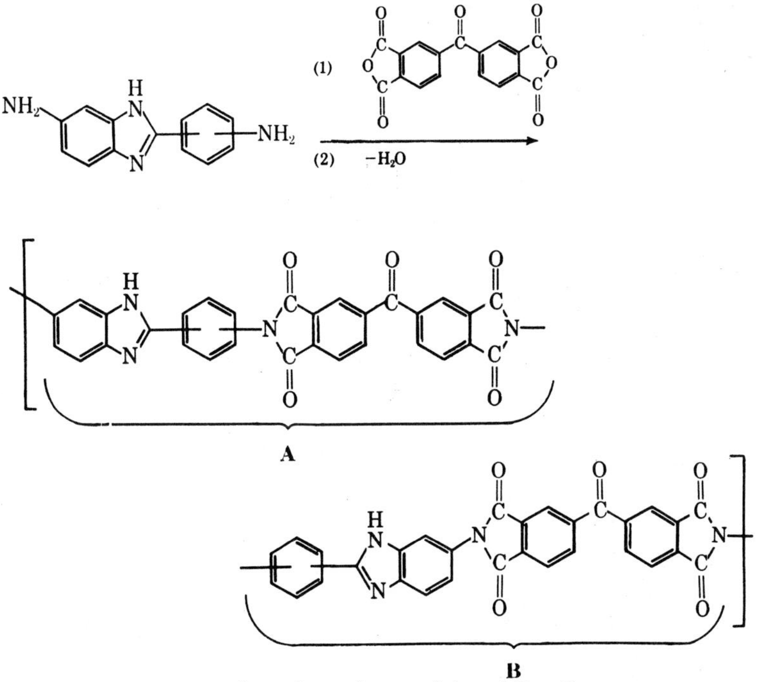

(1) (2) $-H_2O$

A

(6)

B

A random mixture of A and B units

mers (eq. 6), have also been prepared (42). Although the thermal stabilities of the latter polymers are reported to be good, they undoubtedly would be better if the same units occurred in a more ordered arrangement.

4. *Polyamide-imides*

Polyamide-imides can be prepared by the reaction of dianhydrides with diamines containing preformed amide groups (8,43–45), by the reaction of trimellitic anhydride acid chloride with diamines (46,47), or by the reaction of a diamine with a dianhydride containing a pre-

NH_2 NH—C(O) C(O)—NH NH_2 $\xrightarrow[-H_2O]{\text{pyromellitic dianhydride}}$

[NH—C(O) C(O)—NH N(C=O)(C=O) N] (7)

Cl—C(O) C(O)OC(O) $\xrightarrow[-H_2O]{NH_2—Ar—NH_2}$ [NH—Ar—N(C=O)(C=O) C(O)] (8)

C(O)OC(O) C(O)—NH NH—C(O) C(O)OC(O) $\xrightarrow{NH_2—Ar—NH_2}$

[N(C=O)(C=O) C(O)—NH NH—C(O) C(O)N(C=O)—Ar] (9)

formed amide group (48). Also, a low-molecular-weight aromatic polyamide with amine end-groups can be reacted with an aromatic dianhydride to yield a polyamide-imide (44,45).

5. *Polyester–imides*

Polyester-imides have been prepared by the reaction of diamines containing preformed ester linkages with a simple dianhydride (8), by the reaction of a diamine (48) or a diisocyanate (49) with a dianhydride containing a preformed ester group (50), and by the reaction of diols with diacids containing preformed imide groups (51).

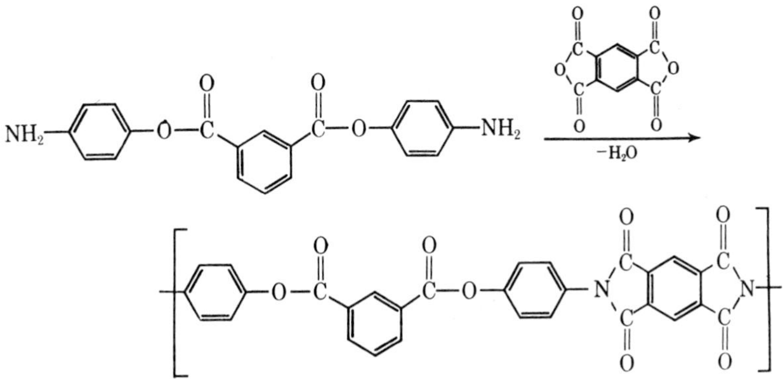

NH_2—C₆H₄—O—C(=O)—C₆H₄—C(=O)—O—C₆H₄—NH_2 + pyromellitic dianhydride $\xrightarrow{-H_2O}$

[—C₆H₄—O—C(=O)—C₆H₄—C(=O)—O—C₆H₄—N(CO)₂C₆H₂(CO)₂N—] (10)

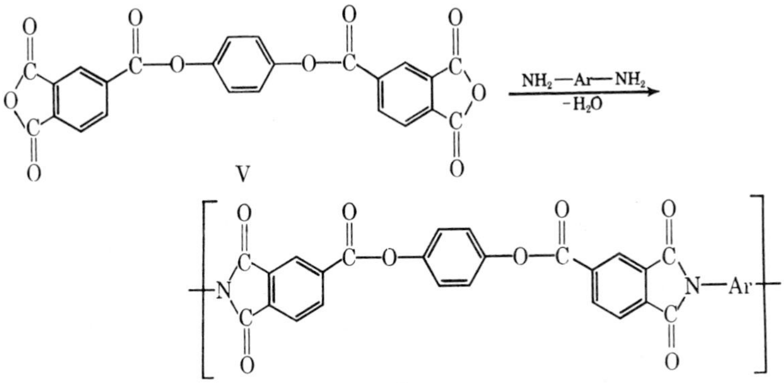

V

$\xrightarrow[-H_2O]{NH_2—Ar—NH_2}$

[—N(CO)₂C₆H₃—C(=O)—O—C₆H₄—O—C(=O)—C₆H₃(CO)₂N—Ar—] (11)

A related polymer, a so-called polyester-amide-imide, has been reported as the product of **V** with an aromatic dihydrazide, **VI** (52). Aromatic

$$\mathbf{V} + NH_2{-}NH{-}\overset{O}{\overset{\|}{C}}{-}C_6H_4{-}\overset{O}{\overset{\|}{C}}{-}NH{-}NH_2 \xrightarrow[-H_2O]{\Delta}$$

VI

$$\left[\overset{O}{\overset{\|}{C}}{-}C_6H_4{-}\overset{O}{\overset{\|}{C}}{-}NH{-}N\langle(CO)_2\rangle C_6H_3{-}\overset{O}{\overset{\|}{C}}{-}O{-}C_6H_4{-}O{-}\overset{O}{\overset{\|}{C}}{-}C_6H_3\langle(CO)_2\rangle N{-}NH\right] \qquad (12)$$

dihydrazides have also been reacted with pyromellitic dianhydride to give polymers containing pyromellitimide units (53,54).

$$\mathbf{VI} \xrightarrow[(2)\ \Delta,\ -H_2O]{(1)\ \text{pyromellitic dianhydride}} \left[NH{-}N\langle(CO)_2\rangle C_6H_2\langle(CO)_2\rangle N{-}NH{-}\overset{O}{\overset{\|}{C}}{-}C_6H_4{-}\overset{O}{\overset{\|}{C}}\right] \qquad (13)$$

6. *Miscellaneous Aromatic Polyimides*

Heterocyclic dianhydrides, heterocyclic diamines, and a heterocyclic tetraacid (55) are included in patents (11–14,55) among the monomers which, it is claimed, can be polymerized to yield polyimides. All such polymers, except for that from the tetraacid, would be prepared via soluble precursor polyamic acids; no examples were given, however.*

In addition to the polyimides already discussed, noncyclic polyimides also have been reported (56); **VII**, an example of this type of polymer, results from the reaction of *N,N'*-dimethyl terephthalamide and terephthaloyl chloride in refluxing *o*-dichlorobenzene (56).

* Recently the preparation and properties of one such polymer was reported (55a).

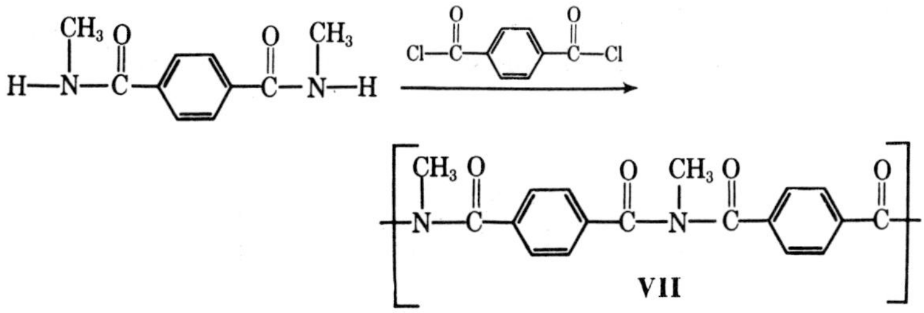

(14)

VII

The reaction of aromatic dianhydrides with tetraamines (Chapter XIX, Section V) is reported (57–60) to yield polymers which, after thermal treatments, contain imide-like linkages fused to imidazole linkages.

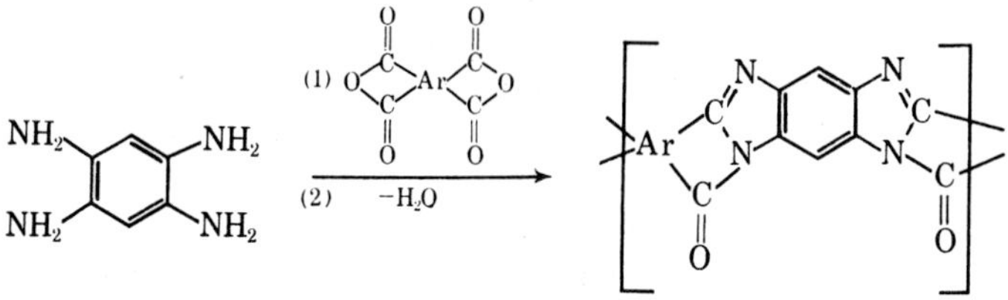

(15)

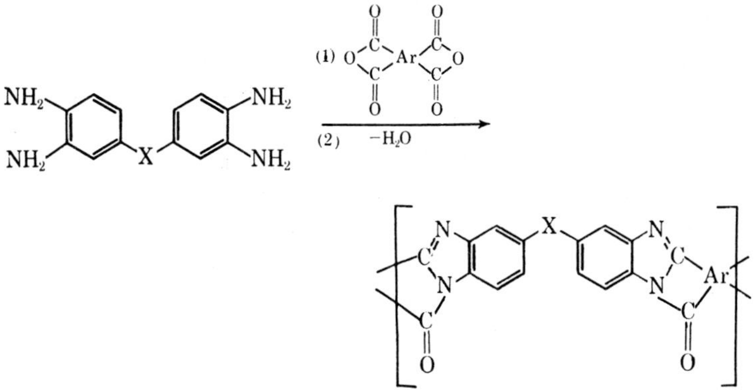

(16)

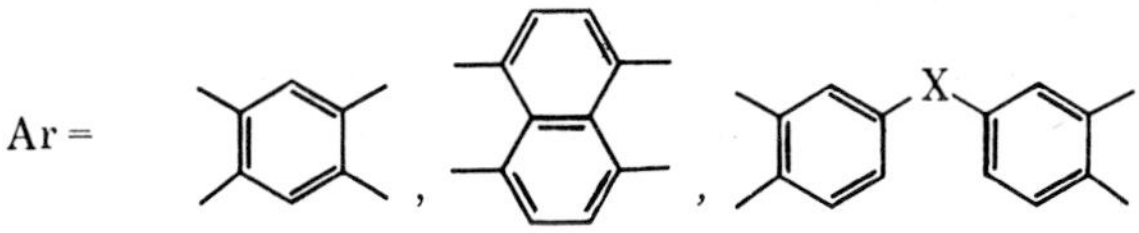

Ar =

X = zero, —O—, —S—, —SO_2— etc.

B. Properties of Wholly Aromatic Polyimides

Very little has been reported concerning wholly aromatic polyimides derived from dianhydrides other than pyromellitic dianhydride, and a large part of what has been reported on the polypyromellitimides concerns the one derived from bis(4-aminophenyl)ether, i.e., poly-*N*,*N*′-(*p*,*p*′-oxydiphenylene) pyromellitimide, **VIII**. This polypyromellitimide

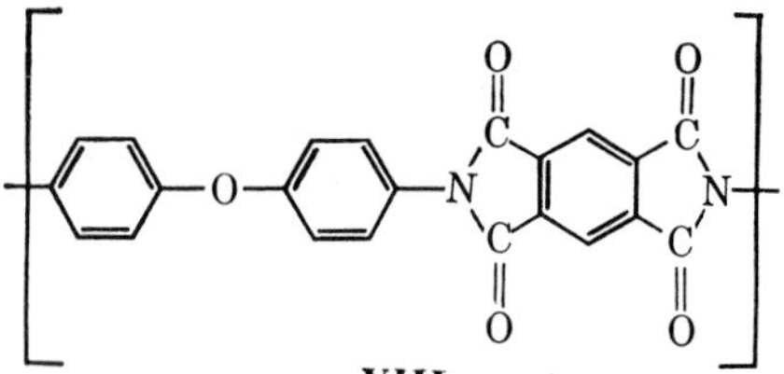

VIII

forms the basis of several commercially available products, including Kapton film (known as H-film while in the development stage). The polypyromellitimide of bis(4-aminophenyl) ether (H-film) has been studied quite extensively, and much of the property data given here has been obtained on that material. Moreover, the only fiber which has received serious attention (3) (see Section II-C) is also believed to be composed of this same polymer (4).

Much of the information reported on the thermal, mechanical, and electrical properties of polyimides has been obtained on films, particularly on films of the polypyromellitimide of bis(4-aminophenyl) ether. Experience showed in the case of aromatic polyamides (previous chapter) that many valid projections concerning fiber properties could be made from data obtained on film. There is good evidence from the meager polyimide fiber data (Section II-C) that this will also prove to be true in the case of polyimides, especially when allowances are made for differences in thermal properties due to the differences in the surface-to-volume ratio of film versus fiber. Consequently, properties obtained on films are given in some detail in this section.

1. Thermal Properties

Wholly aromatic polyimides, unlike wholly aromatic polyamides, show remarkably little variation in properties with changes in structure, as can be seen in the case of the polypyromellitimides in Table I. This is not to say, however, that molecular engineering is not of considerable importance in obtaining polyimides with optimum properties for a given application. A number of polypyromellitimides such as those derived from *m*- and *p*-phenylenediamine and bis(4-aminophenyl) ether show no evidence of softening below their zero strength temperatures (7) 750–800°C (Table I). Nevertheless, gross changes of structure do lead to products which will soften. For example, incorporation of the highly flexible ether linkage in both the diamine and dianhydride yields

TABLE I. Properties of Polypyromellitimides[a]

No.	Diamine component	Solubility	Crystallinity	Zero temp.,[b] °C	Thermal stability in air[c] 275°C	300°C
1	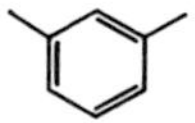	Amorphous, conc. H_2SO_4; crystalline, insol.	Crystallizable	900	1 yr.	> 1 mo.
2		Amorphous, conc. H_2SO_4; crystalline, insol.	Crystallizes readily	900	1 yr.	
3	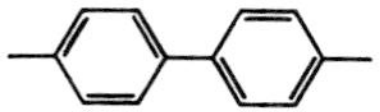	Fuming HNO_3	Highly crystalline	>900	—	1 mo.
4	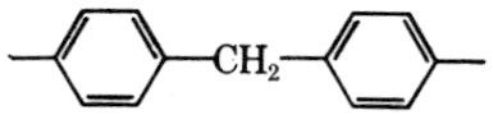 CH_2	Conc. H_2SO_4	Slightly crystalline	900		7–10 da.
5	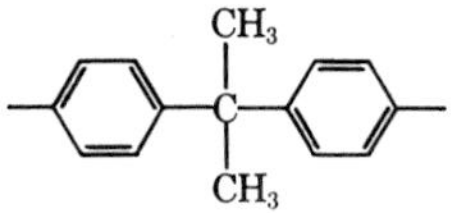 CH_3–C–CH_3	Conc. H_2SO_4	Crystallizable with difficulty	580		15–20 da.
6	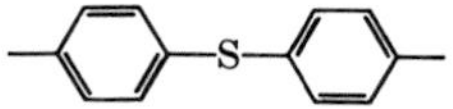 S	Fuming HNO_3	Crystallizable	800	10–12 mo. (est.)	6 wk.
7	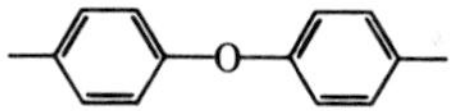 O	Fuming HNO_3	Crystallizable	850	>1 yr.	> 1 mo.
8	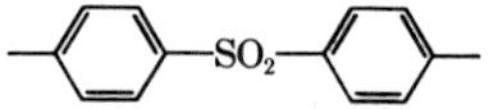 SO_2	Conc. H_2SO_4	—	—	—	> 1 mo.
9	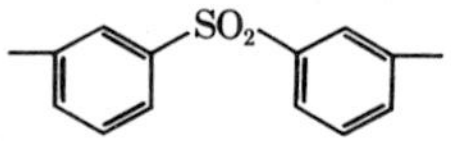 SO_2	Conc. H_2SO_4	—	—	—	> 1 mo.

[a] Sroog et al. (7). [b] "That temperature at which a film supports a load of 20 lbs/in.^{2} of film cross-sectional area for 5 ± 0.5 sec. The test is carried out by placing the sample in contact with a heated bar previously applied, and determining the length of time required for failure. This is carried out at various temperatures until the zero strength temperature is determined" (25). [c] As measured by retention of film creasability.

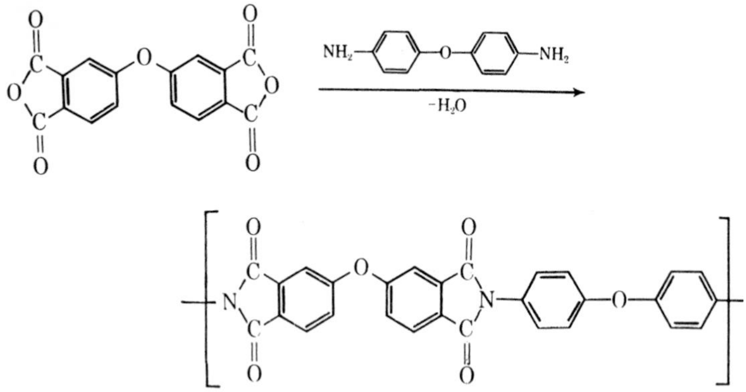

$$\xrightarrow[-H_2O]{NH_2-C_6H_4-O-C_6H_4-NH_2} \qquad (17)$$

IX

a thermoplastic polymer which can be shaped while molten (28). Most of the polyimides based on 3,3′,4,4′-benzophenone tetracarboxylic dianhydride have softening characteristics between the extremes (22,44) exhibited by the polypyromellitimides and **IX**.

Some wholly aromatic polyimides which do not melt in the conventional sense (2) do, however, exhibit an incipient melt transition (9,10) in the range of 550–570°C; the onset of severe weight loss for the polyimides upon gradual heating of the polymers in an inert atmosphere is also about 570°C (7,9,10) (Fig. 1). Further, 570°C is the temperature at which a typical polyimide, the polypyromellitimide of bis(4-amino-

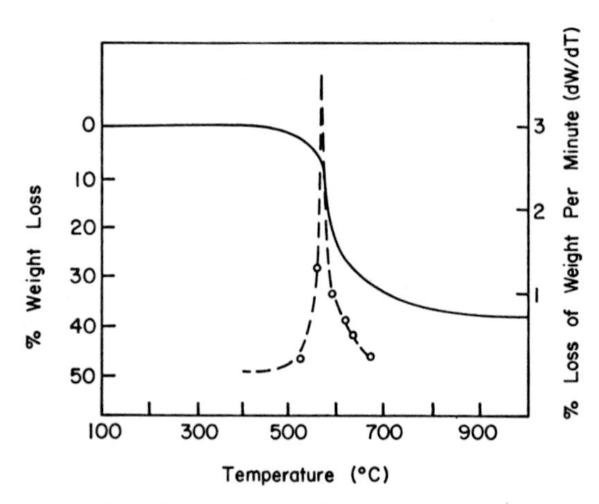

Fig. 1. Thermogravimetric curves for the polypyromellitimide of bis(4-aminophenyl) ether:(——)the weight loss in helium at a heating rate of 3°C/min. (from Sroog et al. (7)); (— — —) the corresponding differential weight loss curve (previous chapter, Section II-B).

phenyl) ether shows a maximum in its rate of decomposition upon heating at a moderate rate (Fig. 1).

Resistance to thermal degradation is undoubtedly the most outstanding property of polyimides, and, accordingly, the thermal stability of these polymers has been studied extensively (6–8,61–68). Sroog et al. (7) reported that the polypyromellitimides derived from *m*-phenylenediamine, benzidine, and bis(4-aminophenyl) ether lost only 1–1.5% of their original weight in a helium atmosphere upon heating to 500°C at a rate of 3°C/min. The isothermal weight loss of the polypyromellitimide of bis(4-aminophenyl) ether in a helium atmosphere was only 1.5% after 15 hr at 450°C, and 7% after 15 hr at 500°C; weight loss in vacuum likewise was only slight.

While the thermal stability of polyimides in air (thermooxidative stability) is greater than that of most thermally stable polymers, it is nevertheless much poorer than in inert atmospheres or in vacuum. For example, the polypyromellitimide of bis(4-aminophenyl) ether lost less than 3% in weight after 12 hr at 450°C in helium, but it lost this much weight in less than an hour in air at the same temperature. After 12 hr in air the weight loss was 40%, in extreme contrast to the 3% weight loss in helium.

Of more significance than the weight loss at extreme temperatures as a measure of thermal stability is the retention of film toughness (as measured by retention of creasability) after heat-aging in air (Table I). The thermal stability of H-film in air as measured by a related test—the retention of film flexibility—was found (7) to be 400°C after 1 day; 300°C after 1 month; 257°C after 1 year; 250°C after 10 years (extrapolated). The thermal stability of wholly aromatic polyimides is discussed further in the following section on fibers (Section II-C).

Ordered heterocycle–imide copolymers (9,10) (Table II) offer a balance of physical properties not observed for the simple wholly aromatic polyimides, but with some sacrifice in thermal stability in those cases where the rupture of the heterocyclic ring occurs at a temperature lower than that causing rupture of the imide system.

The use of amide or ester linkages in the backbone of a wholly aromatic polyimide leads to polymers of both lower softening and decomposition temperatures than found for simple wholly aromatic polyimides; in fact, some polyester-imides (17a) have discrete melting points. Resistance to thermal aging is much poorer in the case of the polyamide–imides. In many respects, aromatic polyimide–esters and aromatic polyimide-amides behave more like aromatic polyamides and aromatic polyesters for uses where thermal stability is the property of prime consideration; the degree of thermal stability in these polymers is really more

TABLE II. Thermal Properties of Ordered Heterocycle–Imide Copolymers[a]

No.	Polymer	Melt transition, T, °C[b]	Decomposition T, °C[c]
1		525[d]	550
2		530	510
3		565[d]	550
4		450[e]	510

[a] From Preston and Black (10).
[b] Endothermic transition observed by differential thermal analysis (DTA) in nitrogen (rate = 10°C/min.).
[c] Decomposition temperature observed by thermogravimetric analysis (TGA) in nitrogen (rate = 4°C/min).
[d] Sample was a film which was hot-drawn at 350°C and again at 425°C prior to testing.
[e] The softening point of the film on a hot surface in air was 350°C.

a function of the thermal stability of the aromatic amide and ester linkages than of the imide linkage. Although the thermal stability of the polyamide-imides is not as good as that for the pure polyimides, the laminating properties are claimed to be superior (45).

2. Solubility

Wholly aromatic polyimides are insoluble in organic solvents. Fuming nitric acid is apparently a general solvent for polyimides (7); many are also soluble in concentrated sulfuric acid (7). Unfortunately, both of these acids degrade the polymers, severely limiting their usefulness except for viscosity determinations. Inorganic salts such as antimony and arsenic trichlorides are also solvents (3,69), but the information is too limited to gauge their usefulness for purposes of fabrication; their usefulness in viscosity determinations, however, has been established (3). Polyimide-esters (obtained from the reaction product of ethylene glycol bis-trimellitic anhydride and various diisocyanates) are soluble in polar organic solvents (49).

That the polyimides are soluble at all tends to confirm the linear nature of these materials, and to refute the suggestion made that polypyromellitimides are branched and crosslinked (70).

3. Mechanical Properties

Wholly aromatic polyimides have useful mechanical properties over an exceptionally wide range of temperatures; for film of the polypyromellitimide of bis(4-aminophenyl) ether this range is stated to be from −269° to more than 800°C (7). Film of this polyimide has been shown by conventional tensile testing to have measurable tensile strength up to

TABLE III. Tensile Properties of H-Film[a]

Tensile strength, psi	
4°K	Flexible
25°C	25,000
200°C	17,000
300°C	10,000
500°C	4,000
Elongation, %	
25°C	70
200°C	90
300°C	120
500°C	60
Tensile modulus, psi	
25°C	400,000
200°C	260,000
300°C	200,000
500°C	40,000

[a] Data of Tatum and co-workers, cited by Sroog et al. (7).

temperatures of 500°C (7) (Table III); both tensile strength and tensile modulus, however, tend to fall off at an increasing rate beyond 300°C.

Although shear modulus studies indicate neither a glass transition temperature (T_g) nor a softening range for film of the polypyromellitimide of bis(4-aminophenyl) ether at temperatures up to 500°C, measurement of the electrical dissipation factor at 1 kC does indicate a definite glass transition temperature (385°C) (71). In considerable contrast to this polypyromellitimide, the polybenzophenone imides of bis(4-aminophenyl) ether and *m*-phenylenediamine have shear modulus T_g's of 355 and 340°C, respectively (71). (Values approximately 50°C higher were obtained on samples annealed at 250°C for 20 hr in vacuum.) The data clearly indicate that the carbonyl group of the benzophenone dianhydride introduces flexibility into the polymer chain. The difference between electrical and mechanical T_g values can probably be ascribed to differences in the nature of the test methods used—the electrical measurements reflecting very small and rapid responses, the mechanical measurements reflecting low-frequency bulk responses (71).

4. *Electrical Properties*

Wholly aromatic polyimides have an outstandingly high dielectric strength, a high volume resistivity and a low dissipation factor (Table IV) (7,61,72); moreover, the dielectric strength is essentially the same

TABLE IV. Electrical Properties of Polypyromellitimide Films (1–2 mil)[a]

Temperature, °C	Dielectric constant, 1000 cps	Dissipation factor, 1000 cps	Volume resistivity, 23°C, 50% R.H., ohm-cm	Dielectric strength, V/mil
23	3.1–3.7(3.5)[b]	0.0013–0.002 (0.002)[b]	10^{17}-5 × 10^{18} (10^{18})[b]	4550–6900 (7000)[b]
150	2.9–3.1	0.C06–0.0014	>10^{15}	—
200	2.8–3.2	0.0005–0.0010	10^{14}-10^{15}	4600–5900

[a] From Sroog et al. (7).
[b] For H film; from Heacock and Berr (61).

over the range 23–200°C. Even after heat-aging at 300°C for 8 weeks, an 80% retention of original dielectric strength is shown by film of the polypyromellitimide of bis(4-aminophenyl) ether; the volume resistivity actually increases after a short heat-aging period, then stays at a high level on further heat-aging.

Films of polyimides for motors and transformers, and coatings for magnet wire are finding wide commercial use. In general, polyimides appear to have better potential in electrical insulation applications than do aromatic polyamides (compare Section IV-C-b), especially at greatly elevated temperatures. The electrical properties of the polyamide-imides (Section II-A-4) however, are claimed to be excellent (44,45).

5. Crystallinity, Density, Moisture Regain, and Color

Although the wholly aromatic polyimides are much alike with regard to their thermal properties, considerable differences are found in their color and their tendency to crystallize. All the polyimides are colored materials. The color can be correlated with the diamine component (7): polypyromellitimides of bis(4-aminophenyl) ether, bis(4-aminophenyl) sulfide, and bis(4-aminophenyl) sulfone are, respectively, yellow, deep red, and nearly colorless. The color of the polyimides greatly restricts the number of colors to which these polymers can be dyed.

Many polyimides can be crystallized readily. The pyromellitimide of *p*-phenylenediamine is crystalline as prepared (7), but high-temperature annealing appears to be required to crystallize polyimides derived from less symmetrical diamines such as *m*-phenylenediamine. Hot-drawing of films of ordered heterocycle-imide copolymers was found to induce good orientation and moderate crystallinity (10), as is shown by the x-ray diffractogram of the oriented film of one such polymer (Fig. 2).

The densities of films of six different aromatic polypyromellitimides were found to vary over a range of only 0.02 g/cc, 1.41–1.43 g/cc (7).

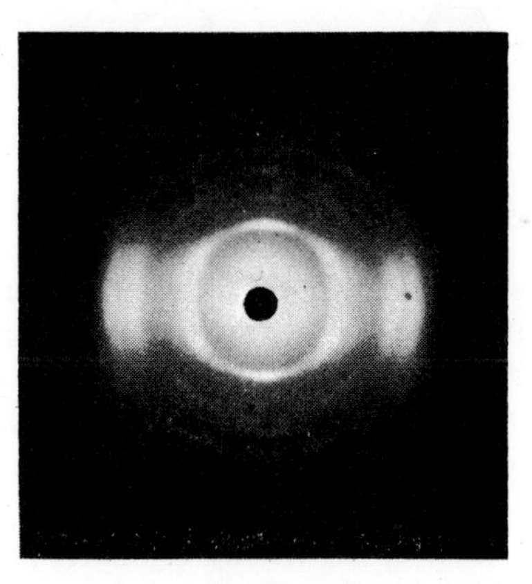

Fig. 2. X-ray diffractogram of an ordered oxadiazole–imide copolymer (hot-drawn film) (10).

This range of density is even narrower than observed for fibers of wholly aromatic polyamides, 1.35 to 1.40 g/cc (previous chapter, Section IV-C), and is all the more striking considering the variation in the structure of the diamine used: *p*- and *m*-phenylenediamine, bis(4-aminophenyl) ether, and bis(*p*-aminophenyl) sulfone (which contains the tetrahedral sulfone group). The slight variations in density reported cannot be correlated with structure. An explanation can be advanced which in part accounts for the narrow range of densities observed, namely, that in each polyimide the aromatic rings of the polymer molecules tend to pack in parallel layers. Evidence supporting this has been obtained by Ikeda (73) in an x-ray diffraction study of unstretched film of the polypyromellitimide of bis(4-aminophenyl) ether (made indirectly by solution casting of the precursor polyamic acid). Ikeda observed that such a film shows no preferential organization when viewed perpendicular to the plane of the film, but that the film viewed edge-on (i.e., parallel to the plane of the film) shows that there is a preferential ordering of the polymer parallel to the plane of the film. Presumably, the aromatic rings tend to lie in planes parallel to the plane of the film. It would not be unexpected for the planes to be about the same distance apart for each of the polymers. This of course could not account completely for the narrow density range; it would also be required that the packing of the molecules in these planes be relatively little affected by the degree of straightness of the repeating unit of the polymer chain; compare **X** and **XI**.

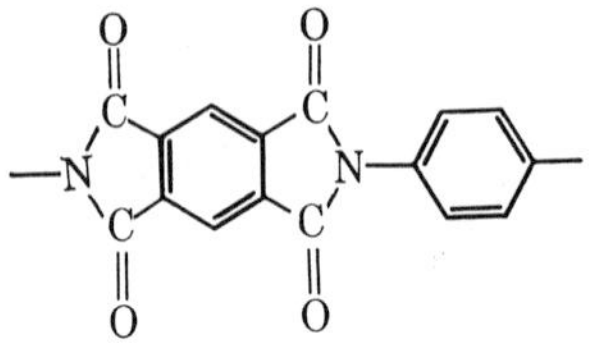

X 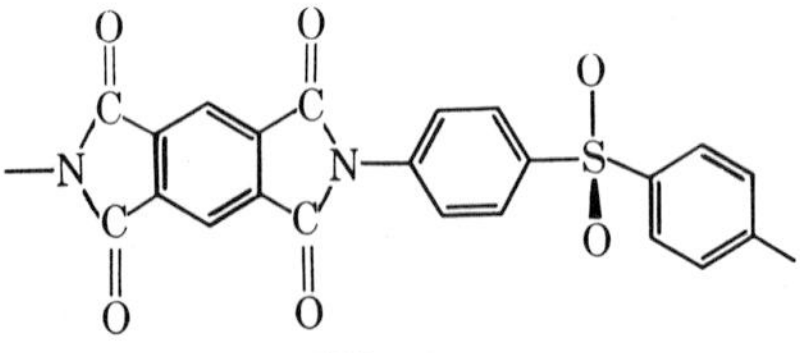 **XI**

The slight differences in density which result from substantial variations in structure are consistent with the earlier observations that such variation in the structures of polyimides result in relatively small differences in thermal properties. That the wholly aromatic polyimides have higher densities than those of the wholly aromatic polyamides is also consistent with the greater thermal stability of the wholly aromatic polyimides. Orientation of the wholly aromatic polyimides can be expected to result in a small increase in the density, as has been found for the wholly aromatic polyamides. For fiber from the polypyromellitimide of bis(4-aminophenyl) ether, this increase has been observed: the density of the fiber was 1.45 (71a) versus 1.42 g/cc for film (7).

The moisture regain (70°F, 65% RH) for fiber of the polypyromellitimide of bis(4-aminophenyl) ether has been found to be 1.7%, and for film of the same polymer, 1.4% (71a). These values, although considerably lower than those of wholly aromatic polyamides, ~5% (previous chapter, Section IV-A), are appreciably higher than that of polyethylene terephthalate, 0.6%.

6. Resistance to Change by Chemical Agents, UV Light, and Ionizing Radiation

Pyromellitimides exhibit rather good resistance to degradation by chemical agents. Hydrolytic resistance of these polymers is fair to good depending on whether acidic or basic conditions are employed (3). The quantitative determination of chemical resistance of a polyimide in the form of fiber is shown in Table V; it seems reasonable to expect that a film, because of a smaller ratio of surface to volume, would show even better resistance to attack by chemicals. The hydrolytic stability of the polyimides in boiling water is poor to outstanding depending on the structure. Films of pyromellitimides derived from *m*- and *p*-phenylenediamine, for example, are embrittled after a week or less in boiling water, whereas films of those polypyromellitimides derived from bis(4-aminophenyl) ether and bis(4-aminophenyl) sulfide retained toughness after a year and after three months, respectively (7).

TABLE V. Chemical Resistance of a Polyimide Fiber at 100°C[a]

Chemical comp.	Concentration, %	Time, hr	% Loss of tenacity
Acids			
Sulfuric	10	260	52
Hydrochloric	10	260	71
Hydrofluoric	10	150	36
Bases			
Sodium hydroxide	0.4	4	57
Miscellaneous			
Water	100	1400	4 (0.25% shrinkage)
Sodium hypochlorite	0.5	150	37
Dimethylacetamide at boil (166°C)	100		0 (2% shrinkage)

[a] From Irwin and Sweeney (3).

Polyimides are susceptible to degradation by ultraviolet light, but possibly to a lesser degree than polyamides; nevertheless, if used in direct sunlight polyimide fibers, films, or coatings probably would require the addition of light stabilizers (74a).

The resistance of aromatic polyimides to degradation by high-energy radiation is indeed outstanding (7). The degradative effect of exposure of the polypyromellitimide of bis(4-aminophenyl)methane to over

TABLE VI. Effect of Radiation on Polypyromellitimide Films[a]

Polymer film	Exposure, Van de Graaff, 2 MeV electrons: Thickness, mils	Number passes	Dose, Mrad.	Remarks
Polyimide from bis(4-aminophenyl)methane	2.0	8,000	10,000	Retains toughness, good electrical properties
Polyethylene terephthalate	2.0–3.0	200	240	Creasable
	2.0–3.0	500	600	Brittle, yellow.
	3.0			Yellow, brittle.
Polystyrene	1.2	500	600	Yellow, extremely brittle
Polyethylene (branched)	6–10	200	240	Very weak sticky gum

Polymer film	Thermal neutron degradation: Thickness, mils	Exposure, days	Temperature, °C	Flux, 10^{13} neutrons/cm^2/sec	Remarks
Polyimide from bis(4-aminophenyl) ether	2–2.7	40	50–75	0.4	Slightly darkened, brittle in spots
		40	175	0.5	Darkened, tough
		80	175	0.5	Darkened, brittle
Polyethylene terephthalate	3.0	10	50–75	0.4	Failed
	3.0	20	175	0.5	Yellow, brittle
Polystyrene	1.2	10	50–75	0.4	Yellow, very brittle
Polyethylene (branched)	3.0	10	50–75	0.4	Sticky, rubbery
	3.0	40	50–75	0.4	Brown varnish

[a] From work of Sroog et al. (7).

10,000 megarads in a Van de Graaff generator is considerably less than that for polyethylene terephthalate or polystyrene after only 600 megarads (Table VI). The resistance of the polypyromellitimide of bis(4-aminophenyl) ether to thermal neutrons in comparison with polyethylene terephthalate, polystyrene, and polyethylene is shown in Table VI.

7. *Behavior on Ignition and Pyrolysis*

Fibers and films of wholly aromatic polyimides burn only when in direct contact with an open flame; i.e., they are self-extinguishing. Studies of the gaseous pyrolytic decomposition products of the polypyromellitimide of bis(4-aminophenyl) ether under vacuum indicate that the composition of the gaseous by-products under constant vacuum (67) differs from that found when the system is closed off after evacuation but before pyrolysis (61). The principal products in both experiments, however, are carbon dioxide and carbon monoxide (61,67). Some solid and liquid components also found include amines, phenols, and phthalimides. The residue obtained upon vacuum pyrolysis of the film at temperatures from 620–850°C is reported to be semiconducting (67).

C. Fibers and Films of Aromatic Polyimides

Few polyimide fibers have been spun, and very little has been reported concerning their properties, especially at elevated temperatures and after heat-aging. Despite this, the published information on fibers, assessed in the light of the thermal, electrical, and mechanical properties of polyimide films, indicates that there is a considerable potential area of usefulness for polyimide fibers in very harsh environments. Resistance of a polyimide fiber to hydrolysis has been discussed in Section II-B.

1. *Spinning and Fiber Tensile Properties*

Polyimide fibers have been spun from solutions of their polyamic-acid precursors by both dry (74) and wet (75) spinning techniques. The dry spinning process would appear to be the preferred process, at least for the polypyromellitimide of bis(4-aminophenyl) ether (74); this process, however, may be limited to those polymers which are nonbrittle during the transition from polyamic-acid to polyimide (see Section II-A). In the dry spinning process, fibers were prepared by spinning a solution of the polyamic-acid into a gaseous medium at a temperature below 65°C, and then converting the fiber to polyimide at temperatures above 200°C. Wet spinning was accomplished by spinning a solution of a polyamic-acid (containing an amine base such as pyridine as a dehydration catalyst) into a bath of acetic anhydride at room temperature and collecting and drying the fibers. The best wet-spun fibers were obtained using high draw ratios during spinning; fiber properties were improved by heating (i.e., annealing) at elevated temperatures.

Tensile properties for some of the best examples of the few polyimide fibers reported to date are given in Tables VII and VIII. Tenacities have been low or only moderately high for wet-spun fibers, and elongations have been medium to low. Although the initial tensile moduli of wholly aromatic polyimide fibers are high compared with several conventional fibers, they are low compared with those of aromatic polyamide fibers despite the seemingly comparable rigidity of the two types of aromatic polymers due to the presence of aromatic rings in each. The inability of the polyimides to have intermolecular hydrogen bonding undoubtedly accounts in part for the lower initial tensile moduli compared with those of aromatic polyamides (previous chapter, Section IV-C).

TABLE VII. Tensile Properties of Polypyromellitimide Fibers

No.	Diamine	Inherent viscosity[a]	Spinning method	Denier	$T/E/M_i$[b]	Ref.
1	*m*-Phenylene	1.94	wet	—	1.3/45/30	25
				—	2.2/22/43[c]	
2	bis(4-Aminophenyl) ether	1.13	wet	3.6	4.5/8.4/65	25
		2.03	dry	3.4	5.6/17/56	74
3	4,4′-Diaminodiphenyl methane	1.40	wet	—	3.4/26/65[d]	25
4	bis(4-Aminophenyl) sulfide	1.20	wet	—	2.2/39/29	25
		1.63	dry	—	5.7/14.5/53	74

[a] A portion of the viscous solution of the polyamic-acid was diluted with dimethylacetamide to 0.5%, and the inherent viscosity determined at 30°C.
[b] $T/E/M_i$ = tenacity in grams per denier, elongation in percent, initial modulus in grams per denier.
[c] The improved properties given were produced by increasing the rate of takeup from 32 fpm (1.7 draw ratio) to 70 fpm (2.2 draw ratio).
[d] The tensile properties of the corresponding polyamic-acid fiber were reported to be 1.1/6.5/44 (11).

2. *Thermal Stability of Fibers*

The data available on wholly aromatic polyimide fibers, as in the case of polyimide films, reflect the fact that these fibers have been developed

TABLE VIII. Tensile Properties of a Polypyromellitimide Fiber[a]

Tensile properties at 21°C

Tenacity	6.9 g/den
% Elongation	13.0
Initial Modulus	72.0
Work-to-break	0.36 g-cm/den-cm
Denier	3.3 den/fil.
Loop Tenacity	5.8 g/den

Tenacity at elevated temperatures

Temp.	Tenacity, g/den
RT	6.9
100°C	5.5
200°C	4.3
300°C	3.0

Shrinkage in dry air

Temp.	%
300°C	0.0
400°C	~2.0

Tensile strength after heat-aging in air at elevated temperatures

Time, hr	Tenacity, g/den 283°C	333°C	400°C
0	6.9	6.9	6.9
10	—	—	1.0
250	—	3.3	—
500	3.4	1.0	—
800	3.3	—	—
1000	1.0	—	—

[a] From work of Irwin and Sweeny (3).

chiefly for those applications where resistance to heat is important. Other properties, such as high resistance to ionizing radiation and high dielectric strength, are undoubtedly also of great importance.

The tensile properties of one wholly aromatic polypyromellitimide fiber tested under a variety of conditions were recently reported (3,4). The properties of this fiber provide ample evidence of the potential importance of polyimide fibers. The fiber had a moderate degree of orientation and was moderately crystalline; the data are given in Table VIII, and a discussion follows.

a. Tensile Properties at Elevated Temperatures. This fiber (Table VIII) retained tenacity at elevated temperature better than aromatic polyamide fibers in general (Tables XV and XVII); see also previous chapter, Section IV. Although tensile properties above 300°C were not obtained in this study (3), tenacity and modulus were estimated to fall to zero at about 560°C. Unfortunately, elongation and initial modulus data for this fiber as a function of temperature were not reported.

b. Tensile Properties After Prolonged Aging at Elevated Temperatures. The significance of long-term heat-aging of fibers was discussed in the previous chapter, Sections II and IV-C. The half-life of the tenacity of this polypyromellitimide fiber (Table VIII) after heat-aging at 283, 333, and 400°C in air was, respectively, 750, 280, and 2.5 hr. Since loss of elongation upon heat-aging is equally critical as loss of tenacity (as shown by the fact that in the case of aromatic polyamides loss of elongation upon heat-aging proceeds at least as rapidly as the loss in tenacity), it is unfortunate that no data were reported concerning the effect of heat-aging on the elongation of this fiber. Some indication of what might be expected is revealed, however, by the fact that the rate of loss of elongation and impact resistance for heat-aged H-film has been shown (61) to be greater than the rate of loss of tensile strength.

III. ALIPHATIC-AROMATIC POLYIMIDES

Aliphatic-aromatic polyimides have been almost completely ignored as potential fiber-forming materials, and fiber of only one polymer of this type has been reported (75). Several reasons can be cited for this situation: aliphatic-aromatic polyimides probably have little to offer in properties over those of more conventional materials; they are not easily synthesized (this appears to be true even in the case in which the recently developed low-temperature solution polymerization procedures are used); and the emphasis in research in the field of aromatic polymers has been directed toward obtaining the most thermally stable fibers or films possible, resulting in greater attention to research on the wholly aromatic polyimides.

The primary intended use of the aliphatic-aromatic polyimides appears to be for molding resins and possibly for hot-pressed films. No commercial use, however, appears to have been made of any of these materials.

As a consequence of the quite limited information reported on aliphatic-aromatic polyimides, it is not possible to generalize as broadly here as in the case of the wholly aromatic polyimides. To a greater extent, then, than was done in the section on wholly aromatic polyimides, examples are used to provide the information considered most pertinent for an appreciation of both the synthetic techniques used for preparing polyimides of this class and the properties of these aliphatic-aromatic polyimides.

A. Syntheses of Aliphatic-Aromatic Polyimides

Both melt and low-temperature solution polycondensation have been used to prepare aliphatic-aromatic polyimides. Sroog (2), in a review of polyimides, has pointed out that the early work on aliphatic–aromatic polyimides was concerned only with those polyimides which are meltable and can be shaped from the melt. Use of solution polymerization techniques for obtaining these polyimides indirectly via soluble polyamide-acid precursors is a quite recent development.

1. Melt Polymerization

The early syntheses of aliphatic–aromatic polyimides were based on fusion of salts of aliphatic diamines and aromatic tetraacids or derivatives of tetraacids such as the diacid/diesters (1,75–77). The following scheme illustrates variations of the melt method.

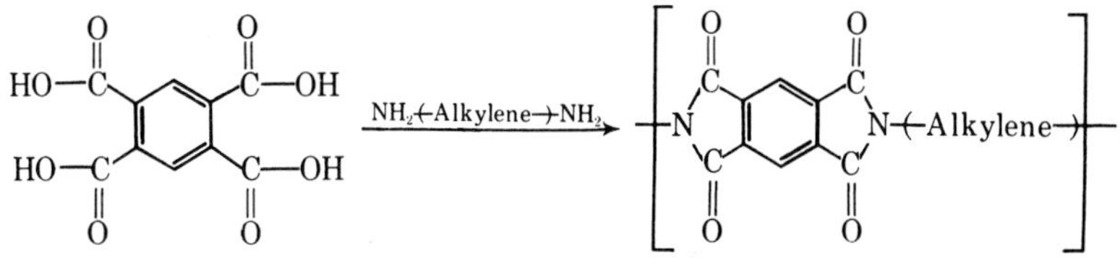

$$\text{(HOOC)}_2\text{C}_6\text{H}_2\text{(COOH)}_2 \xrightarrow{\text{NH}_2\text{-(Alkylene)-NH}_2} \left[\text{-N} \langle (\text{CO})_2 \text{C}_6\text{H}_2 (\text{CO})_2 \rangle \text{N-(Alkylene)-} \right] \quad (18)$$

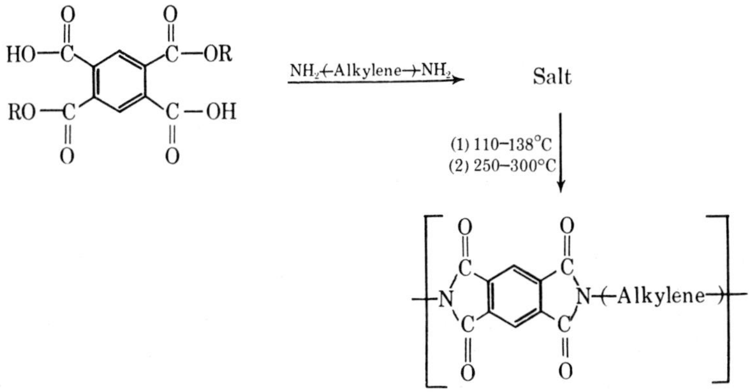

$$\text{HOOC(ROOC)C}_6\text{H}_2\text{(COOR)COOH} \xrightarrow{\text{NH}_2\text{-(Alkylene)-NH}_2} \text{Salt} \xrightarrow[(2)\ 250\text{–}300^\circ\text{C}]{(1)\ 110\text{–}138^\circ\text{C}} \left[\text{-N} \langle (\text{CO})_2 \text{C}_6\text{H}_2 (\text{CO})_2 \rangle \text{N-(Alkylene)-} \right] \quad (19)$$

Polymers of high molecular weight can be prepared by the fusion method; inherent viscosities up to 1.7 (0.5% solution in *m*-cresol) have been reported (1). In order to obtain such high-molecular-weight polymer by the above and related procedures (75–77), it is necessary that the resultant polymer be meltable. Consequently, when the polyimide is based on pyromellitic dianhydride, only straight-chain aliphatic diamines containing nine carbons or more, or seven when branched (76), can be utilized for preparing high-molecular-weight polymer. Polypyromellitimides derived from diamines having very long chains, such as 2,11-diaminododecane and 2,17-diaminoeicosadecane, have melting points below 300°C (2); the polypyromellitimide of 4,4-dimethylheptamethylenediamine (a branched diamine) has a melting point of 320°C. Polypyromellitimides from diamines containing fewer than seven carbon atoms in the chain degrade at or below their melting points; the polyimide from hexamethylenediamine is borderline in this respect (2).

Polypyromellitimides derived from diamines containing both aliphatic segments and arylene rings have also been reported (7,75). If the aliphatic linkage is short, as in **I**, or in **II** and **III** where $n \leqq 2$, the melting point of the derived polyimide is quite high, and consequently some of these polymers cannot be prepared by melt condensation. As the length of the aliphatic segments is increased, the melting point decreases. Thus, for diamine **III** when $n = 4$ the derived polypyromellitimide has a stick temperature of only 260°C and a compression molding temperature of 310°C (75). A cold-drawable melt-spun filament of this polyimide was also reported, but no fiber properties were given (75).

$NH_2-C_6H_4-C(CH_3)_2-C_6H_4-NH_2$

I

$NH_2-C_6H_4-(CH_2)_n-C_6H_4-NH_2$

II

$NH_2-(CH_2)-C(CH_3)_2-C_6H_4-C(CH_3)_2-(CH_2)-NH_2$

III

Inclusion of aliphatic or heteroatomic units in the dianhydride also leads to polyimides having lower melting or softening points. For example, polyimides derived from dianhydrides (**IV**) based on 2,2-bis(3,4-dicarboxyphenyl)propane or bis(3,4-dicarboxyphenyl) ether reacted with aliphatic diamines have considerably lower softening points than the corresponding polypyromellitimides. The polyimide based on bis-(3,4-dicarboxyphenyl) ether and hexamethylenediamine melts at 325°C (77), i.e., in the same range as the polypyromellitimide derived

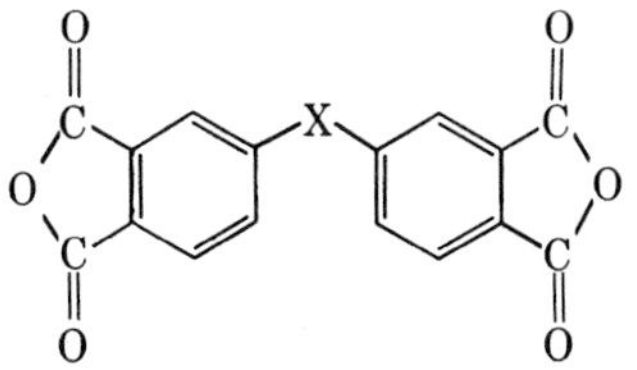

IV

$$X = -O-, \; -\overset{CH_3}{\underset{CH_3}{C}}-$$

from nonamethylenediamine (1), a diamine which is both an odd-carbon and longer chain diamine than hexamethylenediamine.

2. Preparation via a Soluble Polyamic-Acid Precursor

A more recent development has been the preparation of soluble aliphatic polyamic-acid precursors to polyimides via low-temperature solution polycondensation of aromatic dianhydrides and aliphatic diamines in solvents such as dimethylacetamide. (See previous chapter, Section II-A for a general discussion of low-temperature solution polycondensation, and Section II of this chapter for a discussion of how this technique has been applied to polyimides in particular.) Although it has been little

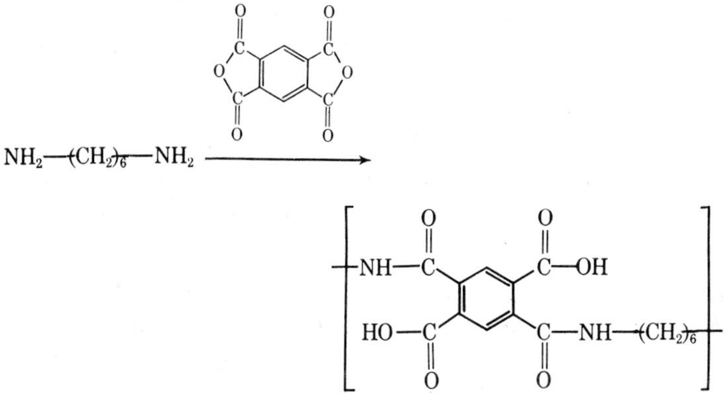

$$NH_2-(CH_2)_6-NH_2 \longrightarrow \left[-NH-\overset{O}{\overset{\|}{C}}-C_6H_2(COOH)_2-\overset{O}{\overset{\|}{C}}-NH-(CH_2)_6-\right] \quad (20)$$

used so far, this approach to the preparation of aliphatic-aromatic polyimides is presumably a general one. Nevertheless, it appears that the solution polycondensation does not go as smoothly with aliphatic diamines as with aromatic diamines. It is seen by inspection of one patent (11), which gives examples of polymerizations of pyromellitic dianhydride with several different aliphatic diamines, that in the case of each aliphatic diamine the condensation resulted first in a slush which later "dissolved." The polymerization of hexamethylenediamine with pyromellitic dianhydride was typical: a white saltlike slush formed after the first few minutes of reaction; this slush gradually dissolved upon further rapid agitation yielding a clear solution of the desired polyamic acid. A clear, tough film was cast from this polyamic-acid solution (11). Such a film can in turn be converted into a tough flexible polyimide film (2).

B. Properties of Aliphatic-Aromatic Polyimides

Information on the properties of aliphatic–aromatic polyimides is meager; no systematic study of any property of polymers of this type has been reported. Not unexpectedly, more data have been obtained on their thermal properties, particularly on thermal stabiltiy, than on other properties.

1. Thermal Properties

It is primarily with respect to thermal properties, particularly resistance to heat-aging in air or thermooxidative stability, that the incorporation of aliphatic segments into aromatic polyimides has its greatest effect.

a. Thermogravimetry. In the form of powders, polyimides derived from aliphatic diamines begin to lose weight at 200–300°C even in inert atmospheres, whereas aromatic polyimides show less than 1.5% weight loss upon heating to 500°C (2). Even the one aliphatic carbon in the backbone of the polypyromellitimides derived from such diamines as bis(4-aminophenyl)methane and 2,2-bis(4-aminophenyl)propane has a detrimental effect with regard to thermal stability as determined by the degree of weight loss at elevated temperatures (7).

b. Stability to Heat-Aging in Air (Thermooxidative Stability). The stability of aliphatic–aromatic polyimides upon heat-aging in air is very poor compared with that of wholly aromatic polyimides. At 175°C the heat-aging stability of films of the polypyromellitimides of nonamethylenediamine, 4,4-dimethylheptamethylenediamine, and 3-methylheptamethylenediamine was reported to be in the order of one day as measured by retention of film creasability (1). As in the case of weight loss at elevated temperatures, even a single aliphatic carbon in the polymer chain results in a marked lowering of thermal stability. Thus, films of the polypyromellitimides of bis(4-aminophenyl)methane and of 2,2-

bis(4-aminophenyl)propane remained creasable for only 7–10 days and 15–20 days, respectively, after heating at 300°C in air, whereas wholly aromatic polypyromellitimides retained their creasability for more than a month in the same test (7).

c. Glass Transition Temperatures. The glass transition temperatures (T_g's) for aliphatic-aromatic polyimides are much lower than those of the wholly aromatic polyimides. T_g values for the polypyromellitimides of nonamethylenediamine, 4,4-dimethylheptamethylenediamine, and 3-methylheptamethylenediamine range from 110–135°C (1). (Compare T_g's of wholly aromatic polyimides, Section II-B.) Heat distortion temperatures are also considerably lower than those of wholly aromatic polyimides. For example, the polyimide from tetramethylenediamine and 2,2-bis(3,4-dicarboxyphenyl)propane has a heat distortion temperature of only 177°C (77), compared with a temperature greater than 300°C for the polypyromellitimide of bis(4-aminophenyl) ether (7).

2. *Crystallinity and Density*

Very little has been reported with regard to crystallinity of aliphatic–aromatic polyimides. This, however, is not surprising in view of the very little work on orientation of these polymers, a treatment which frequently has been found to transform aromatic polymers from the amorphous to the crystalline state. Although a film of the polypyromellitimide of *p*-phenylene-bis(1,1-dimethyl-5-aminopentane) has been found to be crystalline, the crystallinity was of low order; the crystallinity was increased, however, to high order by annealing (75). (This aliphatic–aromatic polyimide is the same one from which fiber has been spun.)

Densities for only a few aliphatic–aromatic polyimides have been reported. These range from 1.30 to 1.36 (7), and indicate that, in general, densities for aliphatic-aromatic polyimides will be considerably lower than those for wholly aromatic polyimides (see Section II-B).

3. *Solubility*

Aliphatic–aromatic polyimides, unlike wholly aromatic polyimides, can be dissolved in organic solvents such as *m*-cresol to permit solution characterization (77). Presumably, the solvents for aromatic polyimides, such as concentrated sulfuric or fuming nitric acids (7), antimony and arsenic trichlorides (69), or a mixture of these salts (3,69), are solvents for aliphatic-aromatic polyimides.

4. Mechanical Properties

Almost nothing has been reported about the mechanical properties of the aliphatic–aromatic polyimides. Although a fiber was prepared by melt spinning the polypyromellitimide of *p*-phenylene-bis(1,1-dimethyl-5-aminopentane), no tensile properties were reported. The fiber, however, was cold-drawable (75), indicating strongly that the polyimide was not crosslinked. The cold-drawability of this fiber, when considered with the fact that this same polymer can be made highly crystalline by annealing, suggests that one could reasonably expect to prepare fibers with good tensile properties from this as well as certain other aliphatic–aromatic polyimides.

The tenacity and elongation have been reported for a film of the polyimide derived from tetramethylenediamine and the dianhydride of 2,2-bis(3,4-dicarboxyphenyl)propane (77): tenacity 14,000 psi; elongation 10%. Both the tenacity and elongation were considerably lower than the tenacity (24,000 psi) and elongation (65%) reported for a wholly aromatic polyimide, the polypyromellitimide of bis(4-aminophenyl) ether (61). These differences, however, may only reflect a presumably more perfect nature of the solution-cast film of the wholly aromatic polyimide; film of the aliphatic–aromatic polyimide was prepared by hot-pressing (77).

REFERENCES

1. W. M. Edwards and I. M. Robinson, U.S. Pat. 2,710,853 (1955) (to du Pont).
2. C. E. Sroog, in *International Symposium on Macromolecular Chemistry, Prague 1965* [*J. Polymer Sci. C,* **16** (2)], O. Wichterle and B. Sedláček, Chairmen, Interscience, New York, 1966, p. 1191.
3. R. S. Irwin and W. Sweeney, in *High Temperature Resistant Fibers* [*J. Polymer Sci. C,* **19**], A. H. Frazer, Ed., Interscience, New York, 1967, p. 41.
4. Anon., *Chem. Eng.,* **73** (4), 90 (1966).
5. P. W. Morgan, *Condensation Polymers: by Interfacial and Solution Methods,* Interscience, New York, 1965.
6. J. I. Jones, F. W. Ochynski, and F. A. Rackley, *Chem. Ind. (London),* **1962,** 1686.
7. C. E. Sroog, A. L. Endrey, S. V. Ambramo, C. E. Berr, W. M. Edwards, and K. L. Oliver, *J. Polymer Sci.,* **A3,** 1373 (1965).
8. G. M. Bower and L. W. Frost, *J. Polymer Sci. A,* **1,** 3135 (1963).
9. J. Preston and W B. Black, *J. Polymer Sci. B,* **3,** 845 (1965).
10. J. Preston and W. B. Black, *J. Polymer Sci. A-1,* **5,** 2429 (1967); see also *ACS Polymer Preprints,* **6** (2), 757 (1965) and Belg. Pat. 650,774 (1965).
11. W. M. Edwards, U.S. Pat. 3,179,614 (1965) (to du Pont).
12. A. L. Endrey, U.S. Pat. 3,179,630 (1965) (to du Pont).
13. A. L. Endrey, U.S. Pat. 3,179,631 (1965) (to du Pont).
14. W. R. Hendrix, U.S. Pat. 3,179,632 (1965) (to du Pont).

15. A. L. Endrey, U.S. Pat. 3,179,633 (1965) (to du Pont).
16. W. M. Edwards, U.S. Pat. 3,179,634 (1965) (to du Pont).
17. F. F. Holub, U.S. Pat. 3,277,043 (1966) (to General Electric).
17a. D. F. Loncrini, *J. Polymer Sci. A-1*, **4**, 1531 (1966).
17b. J. A. Kreuz, A. L. Endrey, F. P. Gary, C. E. Sroog, *J. Polymer Sci. A-1*, **4**, 2607 (1966).
18. M. L. Wallach, *ACS Polymer Preprints*, **6**(1), 53 (1965).
19. L. W. Frost and I. Kesse, *J. Appl. Polymer Sci.*, **8**, 1039 (1964).
20. M. L. Bender, Y. L. Chow, and F. Chloupek, *J. Am. Chem. Soc.*, **80**, 5380 (1958).
21. R. J. W. Reynolds and J. D. Seddon, *Preprints IUPAC Intern. Symp. Macromol. Chem. Tokyo-Kyoto, 1966*, V-1.
22. E. Lavin, A. H. Markhart, and R. E. Kass, U.S. Pat. 3,190,856 (1965) (to Shawinigan Resins Corp.).
22a. Brit. Pat. 942,025 (1963) (to Shawinigan Resins Corp.).
23. Fr. Pat. 1,404,741 (1965) (to Minnesota Mining and Mfg.).
24. W. G. Gall, U.S. Pat. 3,264,250 (1966) (to du Pont).
25. Brit. Pat. 903,271 (1962) (to du Pont).
26. W. Wrasidlo, P. M. Hergenrother, and H. H. Levine, *ACS Polymer Preprints*, **5**(1), 141 (1964).
27. W. E. Tatum, U.S. Pat. 3,261,811 (1966) (to du Pont).
28. Brit. Pat. 941,158 (1966) (to du Pont).
29. Dutch Pat. 6,414,424 (1965) (to du Pont).
30. Belg. Pat. 654,849 (1965) (to du Pont).
31. Belg. Pat. 654,850 (1965) (to du Pont).
32. Belg. Pat. 656,047 (1965) (to du Pont).
33. Belg. Pat. 656,048 (1965) (to du Pont).
34. Belg. Pat. 656,049 (1965) (to du Pont).
35. Belg. Pat. 656,054 (1965) (to du Pont).
36. Belg. Pat. 649,355 (1964) (to du Pont).
37. M. T. Bogert and R. R. Renshaw, *J. Am. Chem. Soc.*, **30**, 1135 (1908).
38. J. Brandt, *J. Prakt. Chemie*, **7**, 163 (1959).
39. J. I. Jones, paper presented at *Symp. New Aromatic Polymers, Polytechnic Institute of Brooklyn, New York*, April 27, 1963.
40. Jap. Pat. 4587/66 (1966) (to Teijin Co.).
41. T. Kurosaki and P. R. Young, *Preprints IUPAC Intern. Symp. Macromol. Chem., Tokyo–Kyoto, 1966*, V-5.
42. J. S. Rodia, U.S. Pat. 3,247,165 (1966) (to 3M).
43. C. W. Stevens, U.S. Pat. 3,049,518 (1962) (to du Pont).
44. L. W. Frost and G. M. Bower, U.S. Pat. 3,179,635 (1965) (to Westinghouse).
45. J. H. Freeman and E. J. Traynor, *SPE Trans.*, 216 (July, 1962).
46. E. Lavin, A. H. Markhart, and J. O. Santer, U.S. Pat. 3,260,691 (1966) (to Monsanto).
47. J. R. Stephens, Can. Pat. 756,179 (1967) (to Standard Oil); Fr. Pat. 1,386,617 (1965) and Brit. Pat. 1,056,564 (1967).
48. Belg. Pat. 631,373 (1965) (to General Electric).
49. Fr. Pat. 1,441,930 (1966) (to Farbenfabriken Bayer Akt.).
50. D. F. Loncrini, U.S. Pat. 3,182,073 (1965) (to General Electric).
51. Fr. Pat. 1,371,474 (1964) (to Chemische Werke Witten G.m.b.H.).
52. D. F. Loncrini, W. L. Walton, and R. B. Hughes, *J. Polymer Sci. A-1*, **4**, 440 (1966). D. F. Loncrini, U. S. Pat. 3,360,502 (1967) (to General Electric).
53. T. Unishi, *J. Polymer Sci. B*, **3**, 679 (1965).

54. Y. Imai, K. Uno, and Y. Iwakura, *J. Makromol. Chem.*, **94,** 114 (1966).
55. D. C. Blomstrom, U.S. Pat. 3,207,728 (1965) (to du Pont).
55a. S. S. Hirsch, *ACS Preprints*, **8** (2), 1155 (1967).
56. J. E. McIntyre, U.S. Pat. 3,264,270 (1966) (to ICI); Brit. Pat. 985,237 (1965).
57. F. Dawans and C. S. Marvel, *J. Polymer Sci. A*, **3,** 3549 (1965).
58. J. G. Colson, R. H. Michel, and R. M. Paufler, *J. Polymer Sci. A-1*, **4,** 59 (1966); Belg. Pat. 658,494 (1965) (to du Pont).
59. V. L. Bell and G. F. Pezdirtz, *J. Polymer Sci. B*, **3,** 977 (1965); V. L. Bell and G. F. Pezdirtz, *ACS Polymer Preprints*, **6** (2), 747 (1965).
60. R. L. Van Deusen, *J. Polymer Sci. B*, **4,** 211 (1966).
61. J. F. Heacock and C. E. Berr, *SPE Trans.*, 105 (April, 1965).
62. J. H. Freeman, L. W. Frost, G. M. Bower, and E. J. Traynor, *SPE Trans.*, 75 (April, 1965).
63. L. C. Scala and W. M Hickam, *J. Appl. Polymer Sci.*, **9,** 245 (1965).
64. J. Chiu, *J. Polymer Sci. C*, **8,** 27 (1965).
65. S. Nishizaki and A. Fukami, *Kogyo Kagaku Zasshi*, **66,** 382 (1963).
66. S. Nishizaki and A. Fukami, *Kogyo Kagaku Zasshi*, **67**(3), 474 (1964); *Chem. Abs.*, **61,** 16181 (1964).
67. S. D. Bruck, *ACS Polymer Preprints*, **5**(1), 148 (1964).
68. S. D. Bruck, *Polymer*, **6,** 319 (1965).
69. H. A. Szymajski, W. Collins, and A. Bluemle, *J. Polymer Sci. B*, **3,** 81 (1965).
70. P. H. Hermans and J. W. Streef, *Makromol. Chem.*, **74,** 133 (1964).
71. S. L. Cooper, A. D. Mair, and A. V. Tobolsky, *Textile Res. J.*, **35**(12), 1110 (1965).
71a. J. Preston and W. B. Black, data from Chemstrand Research Center, Inc.
72. L. E. Amborski, *I&EC Product Research and Development*, **2,** 189 (1963).
73. R. M. Ikeda, *J. Polymer Sci. B*, **4,** 353 (1966).
74. Brit. Pat. 1,038,738 (1966) (to du Pont); Dutch Pat. 6,504,004 (1964) and Fr. Pat. 1,432,038 (1966).
74a. N. W. Todd and F. A. Wolff, *Mater. Design Eng.*, **60**(2), 86 (1964).
75. W. M. Edwards and I. M. Robinson, U.S. Pat. 2,900,369 (1959) (to du Pont).
76. W. M. Edwards and I. M. Robinson, U.S. Pat. 2,880,230 (1959) (to du Pont).
77. W. F. Gresham and M. A. Naylor, Jr., U.S. Pat. 2,731,447 (1956) (to du Pont).

Synthetic Polypeptides

D. G. H. Ballard

Petrochemical and Polymer Laboratory, Imperial Chemical Industries Ltd., Cheshire, England

CONTENTS

I. INTRODUCTION

The naturally occurring polymers of α-amino acids include some of the most sophisticated materials that are known to man. One group of these polymers, the silks, has attracted the attention of organic chemists for many years, and it is probably correct to state that the synthetic fiber industry grew out of this interest; rayon and nylon were both at one time considered to be substitutes for silk—a state of affairs which fortunately no longer applies.

Synthetic polypeptides are important for two reasons: they have played a vital role in the development of our knowledge of the structure of proteins, both in the solid state and in solution, and they are also of interest as fiber-forming polymers in their own right. Some of the synthetic polypeptides which have been prepared, despite their chemical simplicity, have physical properties similar to those found in commercial and wild silks. In general, however, these fibers have a combination of properties which are characteristic of the polymers themselves.

Polypeptides are polymers of α-amino acids:

$$NHR_2CH_2COOH \quad \text{(I)}$$

and have the structure

$$B—(NR_2 \cdot CHR_2 \cdot CO)_n—A \quad \text{(II)}$$

in which the degree of polymerization n can be as large as several thousand. The end groups A and B are determined by the methods of preparation, but B is generally a hydrogen atom. Although these polymers may be considered polyamides, they are more closely related to the naturally occurring proteins, such as the silks and the keratins of wool and hair.

The development of our knowledge of these substances dates from the classical work of Hofmeister (1) and Fisher (2), who established the peptide bond as an important structural feature in proteins and initiated the work on the stepwise methods of synthesis of polypeptides. The important development in fiber-forming polypeptides, however, began with the publication of a paper by Woodward and Schramm (3) in 1947 which reawakened interest in the use of Leuchs anhydrides as derivatives of α-amino acids suitable for preparing high-molecular-weight polypeptides.

II. PREPARATION OF SYNTHETIC POLYPEPTIDES

A. Polymerization of α-Amino Acids and Their Esters and of Peptide Esters

Methods have been described for the synthesis of polypeptides from α-amino acids, α-amino acid esters, 2,4-diketopiperazines, and tripeptide esters using condensation reactions. A critical review of the usefulness of these intermediates for the preparation of high-molecular-weight polymers has been given by Ballard (4) and by Bamford, Elliott, and Hanby (5). For all practical purposes these methods are more useful for the preparation of polyglycines (II, $R_1 = R_2 = H$) and are of little use as a general method of synthesis. The objections to these methods of synthesis are that they proceed very slowly and are usually accompanied by the formation of cyclic peptides and diketopiperazines. Preparation of polypeptides from tripeptide esters is of more general utility, but reaction rates are still very slow and the formation of large cyclic peptides is not precluded. The molecular weights of the polyglycines prepared using these methods are still far short of the film- and fiber-forming stage even under the most favorable circumstances.

Stepwise methods of synthesis for small peptides have been developed considerably in recent years but have been little used to prepare high-molecular-weight polymers. These methods are the only available means by which polypeptides with known α-amino acid sequences can be prepared. The N-carbothiophenyl derivatives of α-amino acids (III) have been used to prepare high-molecular-weight polypeptides (6). These derivatives decompose when heated in an inert solvent, with elimination of thiophenol forming a polymer in accordance with the equations

$$\underset{\text{(III)}}{C_6H_5SCONHCHR\cdot COOH} \rightarrow C_6H_5SH + OCN\cdot CHR\cdot COOH$$

$$n\cdot OCN\cdot CHR\cdot COOH \rightarrow H(NH\cdot CHRCO)_nOH + nCO_2 \qquad (1)$$

This method of synthesis has been modified by Go et al. (7,8) to the synthesis of polypeptides containing blocks of amino acid residues in a known sequence. There is conflicting evidence, however, that molecular weights obtained were sufficiently high to give fiber-forming polymers.

B. Polypeptides from N-Carboxy-α-amino Acid Anhydrides

The polymerization of N-carboxy-α-amino acid anhydrides (NCA's) (IV) is the only general method available for the synthesis of polypeptides of high molecular weight.

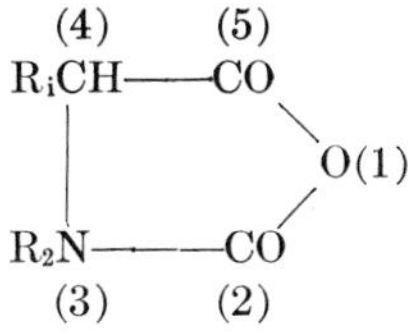

```
  (4)      (5)
R1CH------CO
 |          \
 |           O(1)                (IV)
 |          /
R2N-------CO
  (3)      (2)
```

Similar derivatives can also be used for the synthesis of polyimino acids such as polysarcosine (II, $R_1 = H$ $R_2 =$ methyl) and polyproline (V):

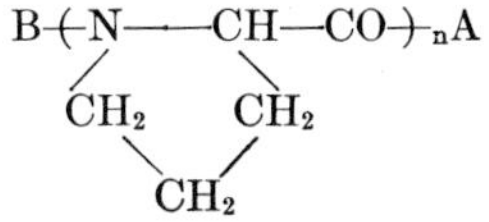

```
B-(N-----CH---CO-)nA
  /       \
CH2       CH2                   (V)
   \     /
     CH2
```

High-molecular-weight polypeptides have been produced from optically active as well as racemic amino acids and include polymers of glycine, alanine, cistene, γ-benzyl, ethyl, and methyl esters of L-glutamic acids, proline, sarcosine, etc.

1. Leuchs Synthesis of N-Carboxy-α-amino Acid Anhydrides

The preparation of NCA's was first described by Leuchs (9–11). In this synthesis the α-amino acid is reacted with methyl chloroformate at 0°C in the presence of aqueous alkali to give the carbomethoxy derivative. This is subsequently isolated by precipitating with mineral acid. Reaction of the carbomethoxy derivative with excess thionylchloride at 60° gives the NCA in good yield:

$$R_2NHCHR_1COOH + CH_3O\cdot CO\cdot Cl \rightarrow CH_3O\cdot CONR_2CHR_1COOH$$

$$CH_3O\cdot CO\cdot NR_2CHR_1COOH + SOCl_2 \rightarrow CH_3O\cdot CO\cdot NR_2CHR_1CO\cdot Cl + SO_2 + HCl \quad (2)$$

$$CH_3O\cdot CO\cdot NR_2CHR_1CO\cdot Cl \rightarrow \begin{array}{l} R_1CH\text{—}CO \\ \quad | \qquad\quad \diagdown \\ \quad | \qquad\qquad O + MeCl \\ \quad | \qquad\quad \diagup \\ R_2H\text{—}CO \end{array}$$

The initial product of the reaction of thionyl chloride with the *N*-carbomethoxy-α-amino acid is the *N*-carbomethoxy-α-amino acid chloride. This is unstable and readily undergoes ring closure to give the NCA. Considerable care is needed if the formation of significant quantities of by-products is to be avoided. The latter are halogen-containing materials and probably result from reaction of the NCA with thionyl chloride.

To obtain good yields and a pure product using Leuchs synthesis, a pure, dry starting material is essential. Unfortunately, the carbomethoxy derivatives of α-amino acids are waxy solids and some, for example, *N*-carbomethoxy sarcosine, only crystallize with difficulty. Bergmann and Zervas (12) have modified the original synthesis by employing carbobenzyloxy derivatives which are easier to purify and frequently react to give a cleaner product. Furthermore, thionyl chloride can be replaced with phosphorus pentachloride in certain preparations with significant improvements in yield and purity of the NCA.

The NCA's obtained by this method contain chloride and colored impurities. They can be purified by recrystallizing from organic solvents such as carbon tetrachloride, ethyl acetate, chloroform, benzene, or toluene, or sublimed *in vacuo* (13).

If α-amino acids containing additional functional groups—for example, amino, hydroxyl, or carboxyl, as in L-lysine, L-serine, and L-glutamic acid, then it is necessary that these should be protected. Methods of doing this have been summarized by Katchalski (14).

Leuchs synthesis have been widely used for preparation of small quantities of NCA (40–100 g) but it is not suitable for the preparation of larger batches (a kilogram or more). In this preparation it is necessary to strike a balance between heating the reaction mixture for a sufficient length of time to convert the carbomethoxy-α-amino acid chloride to the NCA and allowing the latter to remain in contact with the thionyl chloride too long, leading to the formation of substantial quantities of by-products. Moreover, it is not uncommon in small-scale preparations of this type for premature polymerization to occur during recrystallization. The frequency with which this happens with large-scale preparations renders this synthetic route to the NCA's extremely difficult to scale up.

The yield of crude NCA obtained using the Leuchs synthetic method varies considerably, but it is never quantitative even under the most favorable circumstances. Yields of 80–90% have been obtained for the conversion of α-amino acids into the carbomethoxy derivative in the case of glycine, sarcosine, L-leucine, DL-phenylalanine, L-alanine, *O*-methoxy serine, etc., and similar yields have been recorded for the carbobenzyloxy derivatives. The yields obtained for the conversion of the carbomethoxy or carbobenzyloxy derivative into the impure NCA is generally no better than 70–80%. Purification of the crude NCA to give polymerizable material can reduce this yield considerably.

2. *Direct Synthesis of the N-Carboxy-α-amino Acid Anhydrides*

Fuchs (15) was the first to report the preparation of an NCA by the phosgenation of an α-amino acid. In a short note he described the preparation of *N*-phenylglycine NCA by the reaction of *N*-phenyl glycine with phosgene in an aqueous alkaline solution. The NCA was precipitated from the reaction medium during the preparation. Fuchs considered that the reactions occurring were as follows:

$$C_6H_5NHCH_2{\cdot}COOH + COCl_2 \rightarrow \underset{\displaystyle CO{\cdot}Cl}{C_6H_5\underset{|}{N}}{\cdot}CH_2{\cdot}COOH + HCl$$

$$\underset{\displaystyle CO{\cdot}Cl}{C_6H_5\underset{|}{N}}{\cdot}CH_2{\cdot}COOH \rightarrow C_6H_5N{-}CH_2{-}CO\ (\text{ring: } N{-}CO{-}O{-}CO) + HCl \qquad (3)$$

N-phenylglycine NCA is probably the only member of this class of compounds which could be prepared in water. The majority of NCA's reacted vigorously in an aqueous alkaline medium to produce mainly the salt of the amino acid and low-molecular-weight polypeptides.

Fuchs' success in preparing *N*-phenylglycine NCA was due to its very low solubility in aqueous solution and its singularly low reactivity. *N*-phenylglycine is the least reactive member of this class of α-amino acid derivatives and can be recrystallized from water unchanged. Unfortunately, because of its inert character, it cannot be polymerized by any of the methods known at present.

In order to extend the reaction to the preparation of other NCA's it was necessary to replace water by a medium which was unreactive toward the NCA. This was done by Baird, Parry, and Robinson (16) at I.C.I., using the solvents dioxane, ethyl acetate, and tetrahydrofuran as media for the preparation of the NCA's of glycine, DL-phenylalanine, valine, and other amino acids. This was followed by contributions from Levy (17), Bailey (18), Farthing (19), and Farthing and Reynolds (20) in which the synthesis of the NCA's of glycine, DL-phenylalanine, α-amino isobutyric acid and L-leucine were described. The method adopted by these authors was to suspend the α-amino acid in the organic solvent—dioxan was preferred in most cases—and pass phosgene into the solvent at 40–60° until the reaction was complete. In practice, reaction times were lengthy, depending on the α-amino acid used, and unreacted material frequently remained after 24 hr of this treatment. The quantity of phosgene used was consequently many times greater than the stoichiometric requirements, and the amount of impurities present in the final product increased with the reaction time. These impurities are probably substances of the type (VI) and (VII), since

R·CH·CO·Cl	R·CH·CO·Cl	$CH_2\cdot CONHC_6H_5$
|	|	|
NH·CO·Cl	NCO	$NH\cdot CONHC_6H_5$
(VI)	(VII)	(VIII)

Baird, Parry, and Robinson (16) were able to isolate the analide (VIII) from the impurities obtained by reacting glycine with phosgene. These impurities seriously affect the polymerization of the NCA's and must be removed.

The phosgenation of α-amino acids in organic solvents is a heterogeneous reaction, and consequently the particle size of the reacting α-amino acid is critical (21). By ball-milling the α-amino acid in the organic solvent until the particle size of the suspension is reduced to 5–10 μ, and working under dilute conditions, reaction can be effected in less than 30 min, and only a slight excess of the stoichiometric amount of phosgene is required. The preferred solvents for carrying out the phosgenation in this way were ethyl acetate and dioxane. These gave stable suspensions of γ-methyl-L-glutamate and D-alanine which phosgenated smoothly. In solvents such as acetone, dimethylformamide, and acetic anhydride reaction occurs rapidly but the product obtained was not the NCA. In solvents such as dichloroethane, toluene, and acetonitrile, suspensions were unstable and the reaction was not controllable.

Impurities of the type (VI) and (VII) probably result from the attack of a molecule of phosgene on the intermediate α-amino acid *N*-carbonyl chloride. Reducing the concentration of phosgene in the reaction mixture would therefore be expected to lead to reduction in the amount of impurities formed. By carefully controlling the rate of feed of α-amino acid suspension and phosgene to the reactor, the reaction can be carried out so that the phosgene concentration is practically zero throughout the run. This technique gives a product containing less than 1 g-mol. % of titratable chlorine in the crude NCA. A further point of interest is that it was found that the hydrogen chloride produced in the reaction inhibited the reaction of additional α-amino acid. This difficulty could be avoided by working at high dilution (1 g α-amino acid per 20 g solvent) when the inhibition was slight. However, preparation of the NCA at these low concentrations is inconvenient if kilogram quantities of material are required. It is possible to increase the concentration of the NCA in the final reaction mixture by carrying out the phosgenation in a refluxing solvent. With this system the hydrogen chloride is expelled rapidly from the reaction mixture with a corresponding increase in the rate of phosgenation. Using a special reactor with controlled rates of feed of phosgene and α-amino acid suspension the losses of phosgene can be kept at a low level.

The effect of temperature on the phosgenation of α-amino acids is complex. Baird, Parry, and Robinson (15) demonstrated that the phosgenation at elevated temperatures (above 70°) could lead to the exclusive formation of products of the type (VI) and (VII). Studies on the phosgenation of γ-methyl-L-glutamate have shown that there is an optimum temperature at which the phosgenation can be carried out; above and below this temperature the chloride impurities in the final product are high. The optimum temperature of reaction depends on the solvent, and somewhat higher temperatures may be used with ethyl acetate.

α-Amino acids with short side chains such as glycine and L-alanine reacted slower than the long-chain homologs such as γ-methyl-1-glutamate γ-benzyl-L-glutamate. Sarcosine and L-proline react rapidly in dioxane even in the underground state. These α-amino acids are slightly soluble in this solvent, and the reaction is probably therefore not heterogeneous.

Traces of water tertiary bases or aldehydes which may be present in the α-amino acid from a preceding stage can seriously affect the rate of phosgenation and the purity of the resulting product. Tertiary bases, for example, increase the rate of phosgenation but lead to a product containing a high amount of acid chloride impurities which are difficult to remove.

3. Purification of N-Carboxy-α-amino Acid Anhydrides

In order to prepare high-molecular-weight polypeptides suitable for making textile fibers the NCA's obtained from the phosgenation of α-amino acids must be purified. The impurities present have not been isolated and identified with certainty, but it has been found that there is a relationship between quality of the NCA's and amount of titratable chlorine present (21,22). There is a definite relationship between the amount of chlorine present in the NCA and the degree of polymerization obtained for a given initiator concentration. This is shown in Fig. 1, where it is seen that with a chloride content of 0.67 g-mol. % the preparation of polymers with an intrinsic viscosity greater than 17 base mol.$^{-1}$ l. is not possible irrespective of the initiator concentration; this is too low for fiber-forming purposes. It would be preferable to have no impurities present at all, but practical considerations preclude this. Studies of the polymerization of γ-methyl-L-glutamate and L-alanine

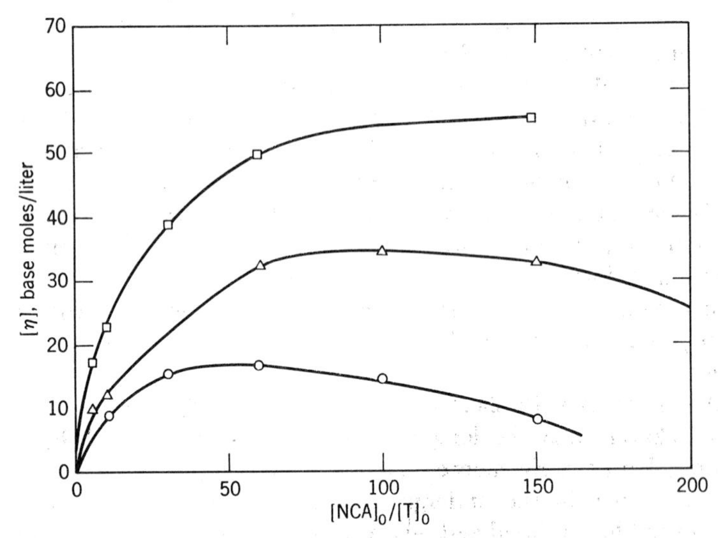

Fig. 1. Polymerization of γ-methyl-L-glutamate NCA at 20°C initiated by tri-n-butylamine (T) in methylene chloride and dioxane (9:1 v/v). Initial NCA concentration 0.538 mole/liter; amount of chloride impurity present in NCA, 0.67 (○), 0.03 (△) and 0.0 (□) g-mol. %.

NCA's in methylene chloride and nitrobenzene has shown that as much as 0.05 g-mol. % of titratable chloride may be present, and high-molecular-weight polymers with good fiber properties can still be obtained (23). Even when the phosgenation is carried out under the most favorable conditions it is difficult to keep the impurity formed down to this low level. Purification procedures are therefore necessary.

Recrystallization of the NCA from a suitable solvent is the recommended method for purifying NCA'S, and a summary of the procedures used by various workers in the field has been given (5). In many of these references no comment is made as to the effectiveness of the purification procedure in removing chloride impurities. It is frequently difficult to find a solvent which is inert and in which the NCA and impurities have markedly different solubility characteristics. With the more difficult cases several recrystallizations are required with the inherent risk that premature polymerization will occur. The instability of the majority of NCA's in solution makes it difficult to take advantage of countercurrent procedures for purifying organic solids. Mother liquors cannot be stored for reuse, and repeated heating and cooling of these leads to decomposition of the NCA.

An improvement on conventional crystallization procedures takes advantage of the fact that *N,N*-dimethylformamide preferentially complexes with hydrogen chloride and acid chlorides (25). Addition of this substance to benzene, ethyl acetate, and methylene chloride increases the solubility of the chloride-containing impurities in these solvents. Provided the impurity is present only to the extent of 1 or 2 mol. %, it is frequently possible to remove the chloride impurities completely with only one recrystallization. *N,N*-Dimethylformamide has the facility of increasing the solubility of the NCA markedly in most solvents, and if good yields of purified products are to be obtained the amount used must be limited to 5–10% w/v.

For the purification of L-proline NCA, Randall (26) has developed a method of purification which involves treating a solution of the impure NCA in ether with a tertiary base. The amount added is exactly equivalent to the amount of titratable chlorine present. In this case the tertiary base hydrochloride precipitates from solution and can be filtered off.

4. *Polymerization of N-Carboxy-α-amino Acid Anhydrides*

NCA's are crystalline solids which decompose on melting to give low-molecular-weight polymers and other products. They react readily with water, primary and secondary amines, and solutions of inorganic salts. They can be stored as dry solids for prolonged periods at −70°C, but at ambient temperatures some decomposition occurs over a period of days. In general, it is preferable to polymerize the NCA's immediately after preparation. Polymerizations are always carried out in solutions in organic solvents which are unreactive toward the NCA's.

Some of the commonly used solvents include nitrobenzene, chloroform, methylene chloride, *N,N*-dimethylformamide, dimethylsulfoxide, ethyl acetate, dioxane, etc. NCA's of amino acids with long side chains such as γ-methyl-, ethyl-, or benzyl-L-glutamate dissolve in a wide range of solvents, and frequently their polymers are also soluble in these solvents. NCA's of amino acids which have short side chains—for example, those derived from glycine or L-alanine, are only soluble in highly polar solvents such as *N,N*-dimethylformamide, nitrobenzene, etc., and the polymers formed from these NCA's are not soluble in these solvents. Polyglycine and poly-L-alanine are soluble in solvents such as dichloroacetic acid or trichloracetic acid; polymerizations cannot be carried out in these solvents, however. It is therefore necessary to polymerize glycine and L-alanine NCA's in a solvent in which the polymer separates during the polymerization. Heterogeneous polymerizations of this type can be quite successful, and high-molecular-weight polymers of L-alanine have been obtained by this method. Occasionally, it is possible to carry out the polymerization in mixed solvents, one of which is a solvent for the polymer and the other for the NCA. An example of this is the polymerization of γ-methyl-L-glutamate NCA which is preferably carried out in a mixture of ethyl acetate and methylene chloride. The mixed solvent gives the necessary combinations of properties for homogeneous polymerization (27).

The literature records a wide variety of substances which might be used as initiators for the polymerization of NCA's, and there are many reports of preparations being carried out in which no recognizable initiator was used. These latter polymerizations rely on the presence of traces of impurities in the NCA and solvent to initiate the polymerization. Polymerizations carried out under these conditions are erratic, and molecular weights are not reproducible. It is now recognized that there are two distinct classes of initiators for the polymerization of NCA's; the first is characterized by primary and secondary organic bases which will initiate the polymerization of all NCA's, but the rates are slow and it is not always possible to obtain high-molecular-weight polymers. The second class includes strong base initiators such as sodium methoxide, sodium hydroxide, and tertiary amines such as tri-*n*-butylamine. These initiators will polymerize NCA's which have an unsubstituted NH group. Solutions of inorganic salts in organic solvents—

for example, lithium chloride or lithium perchlorate in DMF (24), sodium iodide in acetone or alkali metal salts of weak organic acids in DMF—will also polymerize NCA's, but these are not generally used.

Primary and secondary bases react with NCA's to give initially the amino acid amide (IX) which in the presence of an excess of NCA reacts further to give a polymer (X):

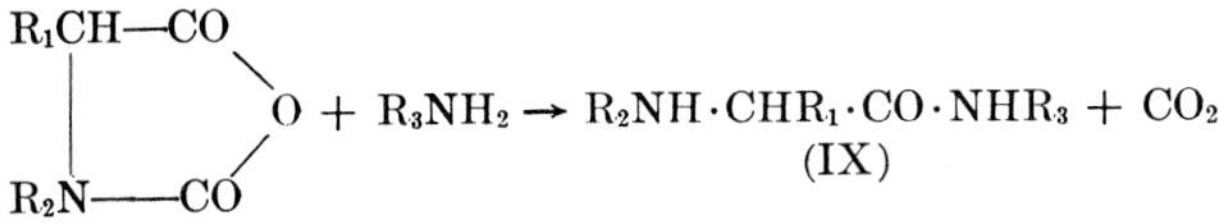

$$\begin{array}{l} R_1CH\text{—}CO \\ \quad|\qquad\quad\diagdown \\ \quad|\qquad\qquad O \\ \quad|\qquad\quad\diagup \\ R_2N\text{——}CO \end{array} + R_3NH_2 \rightarrow \underset{\text{(IX)}}{R_2NH\cdot CHR_1\cdot CO\cdot NHR_3} + CO_2 \qquad (4a)$$

$$\begin{array}{l} R_3CH\text{—}CO \\ \quad|\qquad\quad\diagdown \\ \quad|\qquad\qquad O \\ \quad|\qquad\quad\diagup \\ R_2N\text{——}CO \end{array} + H(R_2N\cdot CHR_1\cdot CO)NHR_3 \rightarrow H(R_2N\cdot CHR_1\cdot CO)_2NHR_3 + CO_2 \qquad (4b)$$

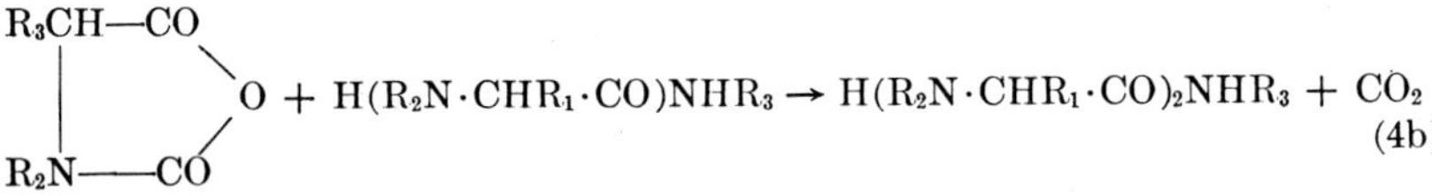

or in general

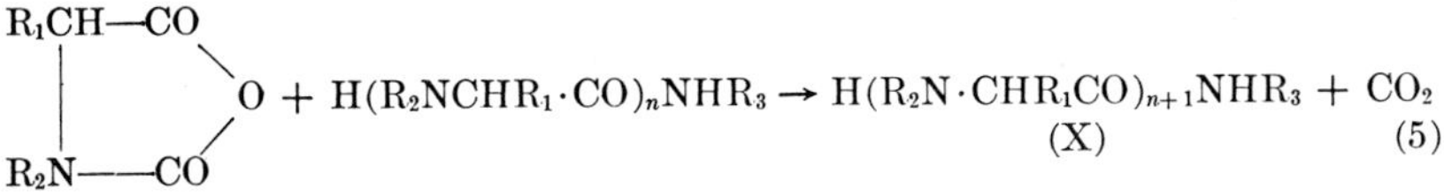

$$\begin{array}{l} R_1CH\text{—}CO \\ \quad|\qquad\quad\diagdown \\ \quad|\qquad\qquad O \\ \quad|\qquad\quad\diagup \\ R_2N\text{——}CO \end{array} + H(R_2NCHR_1\cdot CO)_nNHR_3 \rightarrow \underset{\text{(X)}}{H(R_2N\cdot CHR_1CO)_{n+1}NHR_3} + CO_2 \qquad (5)$$

Waley and Watson (13) carried out the first kinetic study on the homogeneous polymerization of NCA's, and later this work was extended by Ballard and Bamford (28,29), who studied the homogeneous polymerization of sarcosine, DL-leucine, DL-phenylalamine, and γ-benzyl-L-glutamate NCA's. It was established that the reaction proceeds by addition of the base to the carbonyl group (5) in structure (IV) leading to the formation of the intermediate (XI).

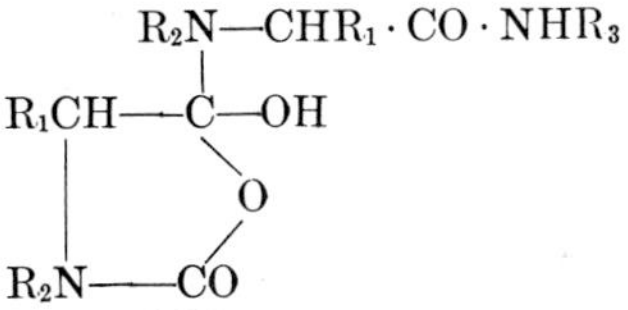

$$\begin{array}{l} \qquad\qquad R_2N\text{—}CHR_1\cdot CO\cdot NHR_3 \\ \qquad\qquad\quad | \\ R_1CH\text{——}C\text{—}OH \\ \quad|\qquad\qquad\diagdown \\ \quad|\qquad\qquad\quad O \\ \quad|\qquad\qquad\diagup \\ R_2N\text{——}CO \end{array}$$

(XI)

The decomposition of (XI) is catalyzed by traces of carbamic acids present in the reaction mixture, or it can decompose spontaneously. These reactions are, however, only of kinetic significance in the case of the polymerization of sarcosine NCA; with DL-phenylalanine, DL-leucine, and γ-benzyl-L-glutamate NCA's the kinetics are fairly represented by the equation

$$d[CO_2]/dt = -d[NCA]/dt = k_1[NCA][X_n]_0 \qquad (6)$$

where [NCA] is the concentration of NCA in solution, $[X_n]$ is the total concentration of base molecules, and $n > 3$ or 4. The velocity constant k_1 corresponds to the reaction of the base with the NCA; subsequent reactions involving intermediate (XI) are too fast to be kinetically significant. The velocity constants, energies of activation, and frequency factors for the propagation reaction (5) are given in Table I, The significance of these results for the preparation of polypeptides lies in the low values of energies of activation and frequency factors observed for DL-phenylalanine and DL-leucine NCA's, and although accurate values are not available for the polymerization of L-alanine it likewise has a low activation energy and frequency factor. Polymerization of these NCA's are members of the class of " slow reactions" in the solution. For example, in the polymerization of DL-phenylalanine NCA at 25° at a

TABLE I. Values of Normal Propagation Coefficients ($mole^{-1}$ l. sec^{-1}) × 100 and the Corresponding Activation Energies and Frequency Factors

	DL-Leucine NCA		DL-Phenylalanine NCA,	γ-Benzyl L-glutamate NCA,
Temperature, °C	Nitrobenzene	o-Nitroanisole	nitrobenzene	nitrobenzene
15°C	—	—	—	2.25
25	—	2.38	1.56	7.04
25.2	4.17	—	—	—
45	8.72	5.83	3.5	—
E (K cal/mole)	6.95	8.5	7.6	20.2
A, ($mole^{-1}$·1.sec^{-1})	5.0×10^3	3.8×10^4	6.0×10^3	3.9×10^{13}

constant NCA concentration of 1.00 mole/liter the maximum degree of polymerization achievable in an hour is $1.56 \times 10^{-2} \times 1.00 \times 3600 = 56$; increasing the temperature by 20° only increases this figure to 126. Using conditions where the propagation reaction (5) predominates, the number-average degree of polymerization obtained is given by the relation

$$\bar{P}_n = [NCA]_0/[X]_0$$

where $[NCA]_0$ and $[X]_0$ represent the initial NCA and initiator concentrations respectively. In the absence of any termination reactions $[X]_0$ should remain unchanged throughout the polymerization process. It is evident from this simple relationship that if polymers with degrees of polymerization in the fiber-forming region are required the process will be slow because of the very low base concentration necessary. Polymerization of this type requires several days to go to the point where a reasonable conversion of NCA to polymer has been obtained. Under these conditions side reactions may intervene which result in the loss of base groups (30).

```
                R·CH—CO          R·CH—CO·OH
                 |      \            |
R—NH2 +          |       O →     NH—CONHR
                 |      /
                NH—CO                              (7)
```

Reactions of the type (7) have a much higher energy of activation than the polymerization process, and because of this they become more evident at higher temperatures. Also, NCA's can decompose spontaneously in solution. This is an exceedingly slow process at ambient temperatures, but decomposition increases markedly with increase in temperature and is measurable over two or three days at 90°C in the case of DL-phenylalanine NCA. For these reasons it is usually preferable to work at temperatures well below room temperature, about 0°C, for example, rather than to increase the temperature. This prolongs the polymerization process, but higher molecular weights are usually obtained.

It has been mentioned that for many polypeptides no known solvents are available which are suitable for carrying out the polymerization homogeneously. It is therefore necessary to polymerize the NCA in a medium from which the polymer precipitates. The effect of this on the overall rate of polymerization has been studied by Ballard and Bamford (31), and typical rate curves are shown in Fig. 2 for the polymerization of sarcosine and L-alanine NCA's in benzene and nitrobenzene respectively initiated with *n*-hexylamine. Each curve consists of four portions. The initial steep portion *AB* corresponds to the reaction of *n*-hexylamine with the anhydride; the base is stronger than the basic derivative subsequently produced, and hence reacts faster (28). From *B* to *C* log $[NCA]/[NCA]_0$ is approximately linear with *t;* at *C* the slope of the plot begins to increase but eventually a second nearly linear portion is observed extending to *D*. As far as can be ascertained visually the system becomes heterogeneous just before the point *C* is reached. Between *C* and *D* the polymer is dispersed, but after *D* coagulation to a more compact precipitant occurs and a progressive decrease in rate is observed. The ultimate rate of polymerization in the heterogeneous system may not be very different from that observed under homogeneous conditions *B* to *C*. Since all the base groups are precipitated with the polymer, polymerization can only continue in the precipitated gel. The rate of increase observed on precipitation (*C* to *D*) is probably due to the absorption of anhydride from solution by the gel particles, giving a much higher concentration in the neighborhood of the basic end-groups.

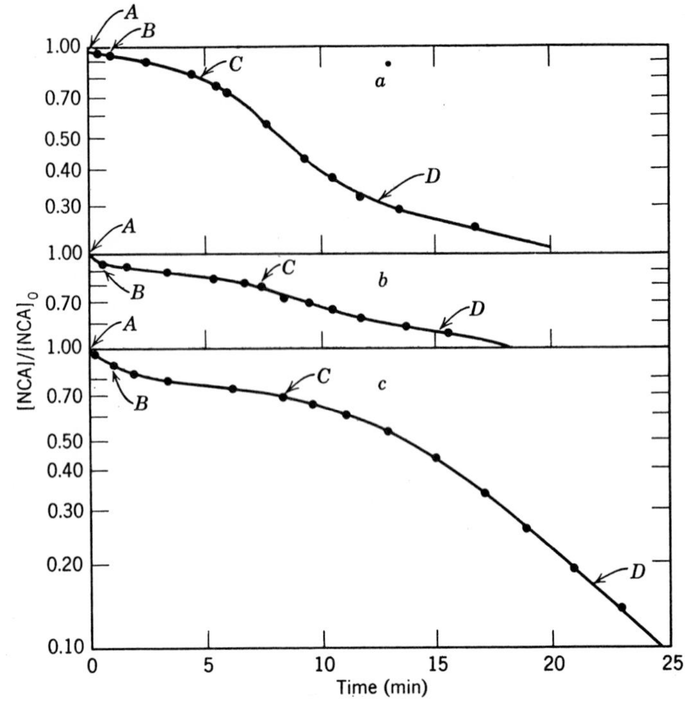

Fig. 2. Heterogeneous polymerization of NCA's. (*a*, *b*) Reaction of sarcosine NCA with *n*-hexylamine in benzene at 25°C: $[NCA]_0 = 0.100$ mole/liter; $[X]_0 =$ (*a*) 5.3×10^{-3}, (*b*) 2.6×10^{-3} mole/liter, (*c*) Reaction of L-alanine NCA with *n*-hexylamine in nitrobenzene at 25°C. $[NCA]_0 = 0.102$ mole/liter; $[X]_0 = 10^{-2}$ mole/liter. From Ballard and Bamford (31).

Reaction in the compact gel is governed by the rate of diffusion of anhydride and the accessibility of the base groups. It is important therefore to choose an inert solvent which swells the polymer. This does not present any serious difficulties in the case of the NCA's with hydrocarbon side chains, but no solvent is known which will swell polyglycine sufficiently to maintain a reasonable rate of polymerization.

It will be observed in Table I that the energy of activation and frequency factor for the polymerization of γ-benzyl-L-glutamate NCA in nitrobenzene is significantly greater than that for the other two NCA's given in the table. One would expect, therefore, to be able to carry out the polymerization of γ-benzyl-L-glutamate NCA at high temperatures to some advantage. In practice, however, primary base initiation is seldom used for preparing high-molecular-weight polymers of the esters of L-glutamic acid; tertiary bases or strong base initiation is preferred. These initiators polymerize NCA's in a fundamentally different way from that described above, and can be used for the polymerization of NCA's which have bulky side chains.

Tertiary organic bases initiate the polymerization of NCA's which have an unsubstituted nitrogen atom—for example, those derived from DL-phenylalanine and γ-methyl, ethyl, or benzyl esters of L-glutamic acid. These polymerization processes are characterized by a higher rate of polymerization and a high degree of polymerization in the resulting polymer. Polymers can be prepared with much higher molecular weights than are possible using other methods of initiation. For example, in nitrobenzene at 25°C DL-phenylalanine NCA ($[NCA]_0$ = 1.04 moles/liter) can be polymerized, using tri-*n*-butylamine as initiator (concentration = 0.023 mole/liter), to a degree of polymerization of 320 in 30 min, and with γ-methyl-L-glutamate NCA a degree of polymerization of two or three thousand has been achieved, with a reaction time of several hours. There has been some discussion in the literature about the mechanism of the polymerization of NCA's using tertiary bases, and in earlier reports it was suggested that traces of water and amino acids present in the NCA's were in fact the true initiators, the reaction being catalyzed by the tertiary bases. It has now been established that traces of water and amino acids could not be responsible for the higher rates and the higher molecular weights obtained with tertiary bases for the simple reason that traces of water with primary and secondary amines give slow rates of polymerization and low-molecular-weight polymers (32). A further point of discussion in the literature has been whether NCA's which were N-substituted—for example, those derived from sarcosine and proline—could be polymerized using tertiary based initiators. With very pure NCA's, solvent, and initiator the rates of polymerization

$$\mathrm{T} + \begin{matrix}\mathrm{R\cdot CH{-}CO} \\ | \qquad\quad \backslash \\ | \qquad\quad \mathrm{O} \\ | \qquad\quad / \\ \mathrm{NH{-}CO}\end{matrix} \rightleftharpoons \left[\begin{matrix}\mathrm{R\cdot CH{-}CO} \\ | \qquad\quad \backslash \\ | \qquad\quad \mathrm{O} \\ | \qquad\quad / \\ \mathrm{N{-}CO}\end{matrix}\right]^{\ominus} + \mathrm{TH^+}$$

(XII)

$$\mathrm{XII} + \begin{matrix}\mathrm{R\cdot CH{-}CO} \\ | \qquad \backslash \\ | \qquad \mathrm{O} \\ | \qquad / \\ \mathrm{NH{-}CO}\end{matrix} \rightarrow \left[\begin{matrix}\mathrm{R\cdot CH{-}CO} \\ | \qquad \mathrm{O} \\ \mathrm{N{-}CO} \\ | \\ \mathrm{R\cdot CH{-}C} \\ | \qquad \mathrm{O} \\ \mathrm{NH{-}CO}\end{matrix}\right] \xrightarrow{\mathrm{TH^+}} \begin{matrix}\mathrm{R\cdot CH{-}CO} \\ | \qquad \mathrm{O} \\ \mathrm{N{-}CO} \\ | \\ \mathrm{RCH{-}CO} \\ | \\ \mathrm{NH_2}\end{matrix} + \mathrm{CO} \tag{8}$$

(XIII) (XIV)

of these NCA's with tertiary bases is extremely slow if they react at all (33). Moreover, high-molecular-weight polymers are not produced. The following mechanism has been proposed (34–36) for the polymerization of NCA's initiated by tertiary bases.

The NH group of the NCA molecule is partially acidic, and in the presence of a strong base the proton is readily removed, giving rise to the species (XII). This reacts with further NCA to give an unstable intermediate (XIII), which subsequently decarboxylates to give the difunctional compound (XIV). The reactions given in (8) may be described as the initiation step. Polymer is produced by the polymerization of (XIV) or similar species by reactions analogous to

$$\underset{}{\mathrm{R{-}CH{-}N{-}(CO\cdot CHRNH)_nH}}\ (\text{ring: CO–O–CO}) + \underset{(\mathrm{XV})}{\mathrm{R{-}CH{-}N{-}(CO\cdot CH\cdot R\cdot NH)_mH}}\ (\text{ring: CO–O–CO}) \rightarrow$$

$$\mathrm{R\cdot CH{-}N(CO\cdot CHRNH)H_{n+m+1}}\ (\text{ring: CO–O–CO}) + CO_2 \qquad (9)$$

(n(or m) $\geqslant$ 1) in which propagation proceeds by reaction of the NCA fragment of (XIV) with the NH_2 group of a similar molecular-producing polymeric species of the type (XV) which can undergo similar reactions. Reactions of this type would lead rapidly to high-molecular-weight polymers. A more important polymerization process is probably

$$(\mathrm{XII}) + \mathrm{R\cdot CH{-}C{-}(CO\cdot CHRNH)_nH}\ (\text{ring: CO–O–CO}) \xrightarrow{\mathrm{TH^+}}$$

$$\mathrm{R\cdot CH{-}C(CO\cdot CHR\cdot NH)_{n+1}H} \ (\text{ring: CO–O–CO}) + CO_2 + \mathrm{T} \qquad (10)$$

in which propagation occurs by reaction of the negative nitrogen atom of (XII) with the carbonyl group (5) of the NCA fragment of (XIV) and (XV). Finally, polymerization can proceed by reaction of the basic NH_2 group of (XIV) and (XV) with the NCA molecule. This is a relatively slow process, however.

Species analogous to (XIV) have been isolated (33), and the existence of (XIV) and (XV) can be deduced from the formation of hydantoin-3-

acetic acid (XVI) and cyclic hexaglycine in the tertiary base polymerization of glycine NCA (32).

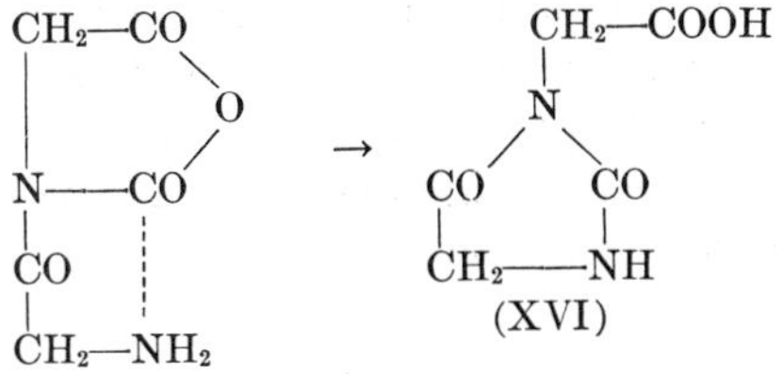

```
CH2—CO                       CH2—COOH
|      \                        |
|       O                       N
|      /            →         /   \
N——CO                      CO     CO          (11)
|    :                      |      |
CO   :                     CH2————NH
|    :                        (XVI)
CH2—NH2
```

The formation of hydantoin acetic acids is most marked with the NCA's derived from amino acids having short nonpolar side chains such as glycine and alanine. Tertiary base initiators have been most successfully applied to the synthesis of polypeptides of γ-benzyl, ethyl, and methyl-L-glutamates, DL-phenylalanine, etc.—in general, those NCA's having large (or polar) side chains.

The relationship between molecular weight and tertiary base concentration is complex and must be established experimentally for each combination of NCA, base, and solvent. The types of curve obtained are shown in Fig. 1. Initially the molecular weight increases with decreasing base concentration but eventually becomes almost independent of this quantity. At very low base concentrations the molecular weight decreases with decreasing base concentration. Experimental conditions represented by this region of the curve produce acidic reaction mixtures due probably to the formation of hydantoin-3-acetic derivatives. Rates of polymerization are also reduced.

The molecular weight distribution of polypeptides produced by primary base initiation are of the Poisson type (28,37,38), that is, the number average and weight average molecular weights are nearly the same. Tertiary base initiators would be expected to produce polymers with a broad distribution of molecular weights. Very little data are available on this subject, however.

Sodium methoxide (22) salts of weak organic acids (29) and solutions of inorganic salts in dimethylformamide have been used to initiate polymerization of NCA's. In the author's opinion, they offer very little advantage over the tertiary base initiators and, as recently shown, strong bases, such as sodium methoxide, can lead to unwanted side effects (39).

III. CONFIGURATION OF POLYPEPTIDE CHAINS IN THE SOLID STATE AND IN SOLUTION

Polypeptides can assume two extreme types of chain configuration which are determined by the arrangements of hydrogen bonds formed between peptide groups in the molecules. It is possible for the long-chain molecule to fold itself in such a way that all the hydrogen bonds between peptide groups occur intramolecularly. Alternatively, the polypeptide chain can be fully extended in a zigzag conformation with hydrogen bonds formed between chains. Polypeptides in these two forms differ in their solubility characteristics, and as fibers and films, in their physical and mechanical properties.

A. Conformations Involving Intrachain Hydrogen Bonding

Folds involving intrachain hydrogen bonding in polypeptides and proteins have been the subject of considerable discussion and study; for a detailed account of this work the reader is referred to one of the reviews on this subject (5).

Pauling, Corey, and Branson (40) in 1951 considered the folding of a polypeptide chain using bond dimensions and angles obtained from structural studies of crystals of small molecules. In these structures the peptide bond is planar, due to resonance stabilization, giving the C—N bond partial double bond character (41), and the vector from the nitrogen atom to the hydrogen-bonded oxygen atom lies not more than 30° from the NH-direction. Furthermore, if it is assumed that all residues are crystallographically equivalent, then the most reasonable repetitive structural form is a helix. Helical structures had been proposed prior to this by Huggins (42), Bragg, Kendrew, and Perutz (43), and others, but the important feature in the structures proposed by Pauling and Corey was that an integral number of residues per turn was not essential. Crystallographic studies of the structure of synthetic polypeptides has revealed that of the several helical forms described by Pauling, Corey, and Branson the α-helix (Fig. 3) is the most important. It has been established from studies of oriented films of poly-γ-methyl-L-glutamate (42,44–46), poly-γ-benzyl-glutamate (5,47), oriented fibers of poly-D-alanine (48,49), and others, and would appear to be independent of the flexibility of the side chain R.

In the α-helix, the α-amino acid residues lie in a spiral of pitch 5.4 Å, and consecutive residues have an axial translation of about 1.5 Å; the ratio of these two quantities gives the number of residues per turn of the helix, which is 3.6. The diameter of the helix is 15.3 Å. The structure nearly repeats at 18 residues (5 turns) and can be made to do so by slight changes in assumed bond angles. Repetition of the structure also occurs after 11, 18, 47 .... ($11n + 18m$) residues, where n and m are integers. It may be considered to consist of a series of 13-membered rings closed by hydrogen bonds. It is evident that a molecule with

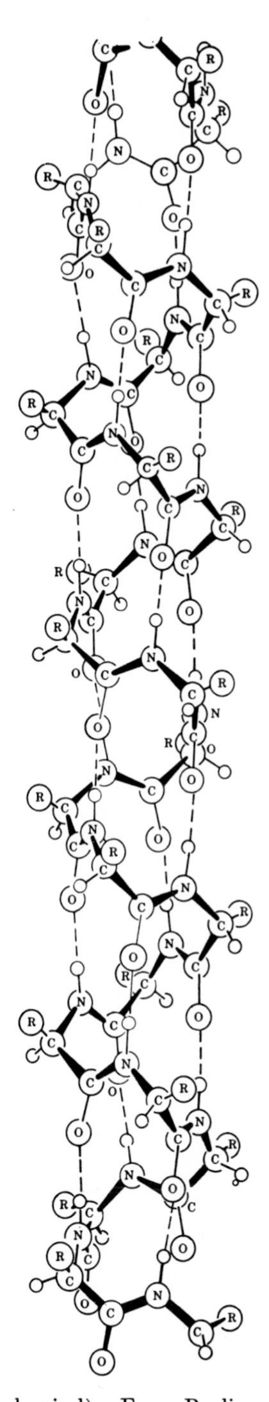

Fig. 3. The α-helix (left-hand spiral). From Pauling, Corey, and Branson (40).

such a well-defined structure could not be formed readily from racemic mixtures of residues. In the case of the α-form of poly-L-alanine it has been established (50) that the α-helix has a right-handed screw sense, implying that the α-form of poly-D-alanine will have a helix of the opposite screw sense. Studies of solution of poly-β benzyl L-aspartate on the other hand ($R_1 = CH_2{\cdot}COOO\ CH_2C_6H_5$) (51) suggest that the α-helix of this polypeptide has a left-handed screw sense. Where there is no asymmetric α-carbon atom, for example, in polyglycine, the left- and right-handed helices are mirror images.

The most stable configurations of polypeptide chain are those in which the planarity of the peptide bond is preserved; coiling up of a polypeptide chain can take place only by rotation around the single bonds of the α-carbon atom. In the α-helix the carbonyl group is *trans* with respect to the NH group, as it is in simple molecules containing amide groups. These are the conditions for minimum energy in the structure. The size and nature of the side chains is, however, not taken into account, and the conditions of minimum energy could well be altered by interaction between these in the same or different molecules. This is probably of relevance in the solid state or in concentrated solutions of α-polypeptides, where any strong interaction between side chains and peptide groups could lead to a less perfect helical form.

In addition to the α-helix, Pauling, Corey, and Branson have described a helix consisting of 17-membered rings closed by hydrogen bonds which satisfy the conditions. This helix has a diameter appreciably greater than the α-helix. Other helices have also been described which fulfill the conditions less well, but no synthetic polypeptides are known which conform to these structures. Poly-L-proline in which the NH group is substituted exists in a helical form (52). The amide group in this structure has a *trans* form, it is planar, and the chains have a repeat distance of 9.36 Å along the fiber axis. This is an example in which the helix is stabilized by the repulsion between side chains.

B. Conformations Involving Interchain Hydrogen Bonding

The dimensions of a fully extended polypeptide chain have been given by Corey and Pauling (53) and the diagram from their paper is reproduced in Fig. 4. In this form the chain has a twofold screw axis and a repeat distance of 7.23 Å. There is no difficulty in finding acceptable configurations for extended polypeptide chains, and arrangements in which the chains are parallel or antiparallel have been discussed (54). In general structures in which the hydrogen bonds are linear are preferred. The antiparallel pleated sheet (Fig. 5) seems to be closest to the

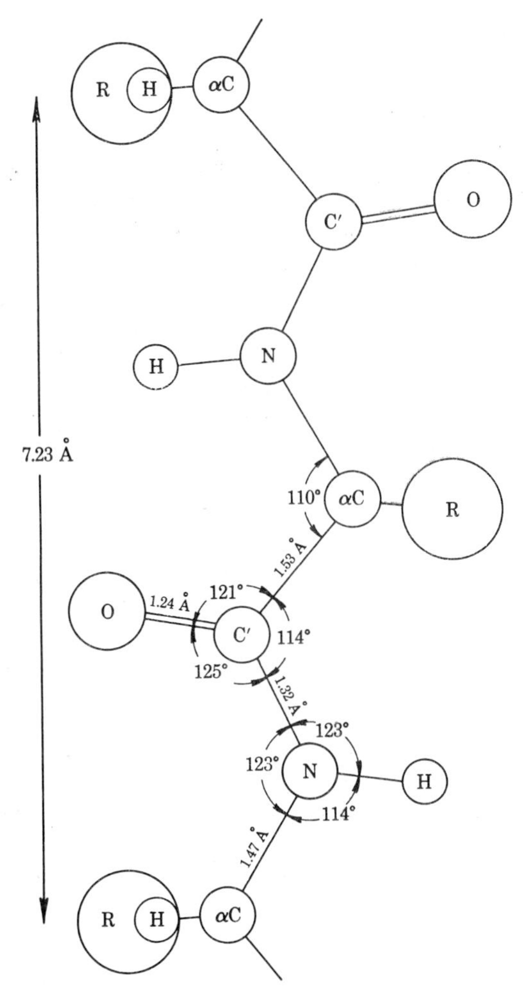

Fig. 4. Fully extended polypeptide chain. From Pauling and Corey (53).

structures of those polypeptides which have been examined. In this form the chain is contracted to permit linear hydrogen bonds to be formed, giving a repeat distance of 7.00 Å (the structure with parallel chains would have a repeat distance of 6.5 Å); this compares with the repeat distances found in polyglycine I (7.0 Å) β-poly-L-alanine (6.88 Å), and β-poly-γ-methyl-L-glutamate (6.83 Å). These are also close to the values found in Bombyx and Tussak silks. It is to be expected that slight variations of the repeat distance from the value for polyglycine would result from interactions between side chains. The latter are arranged above and below the plane of the polypeptide sheet, and the dis-

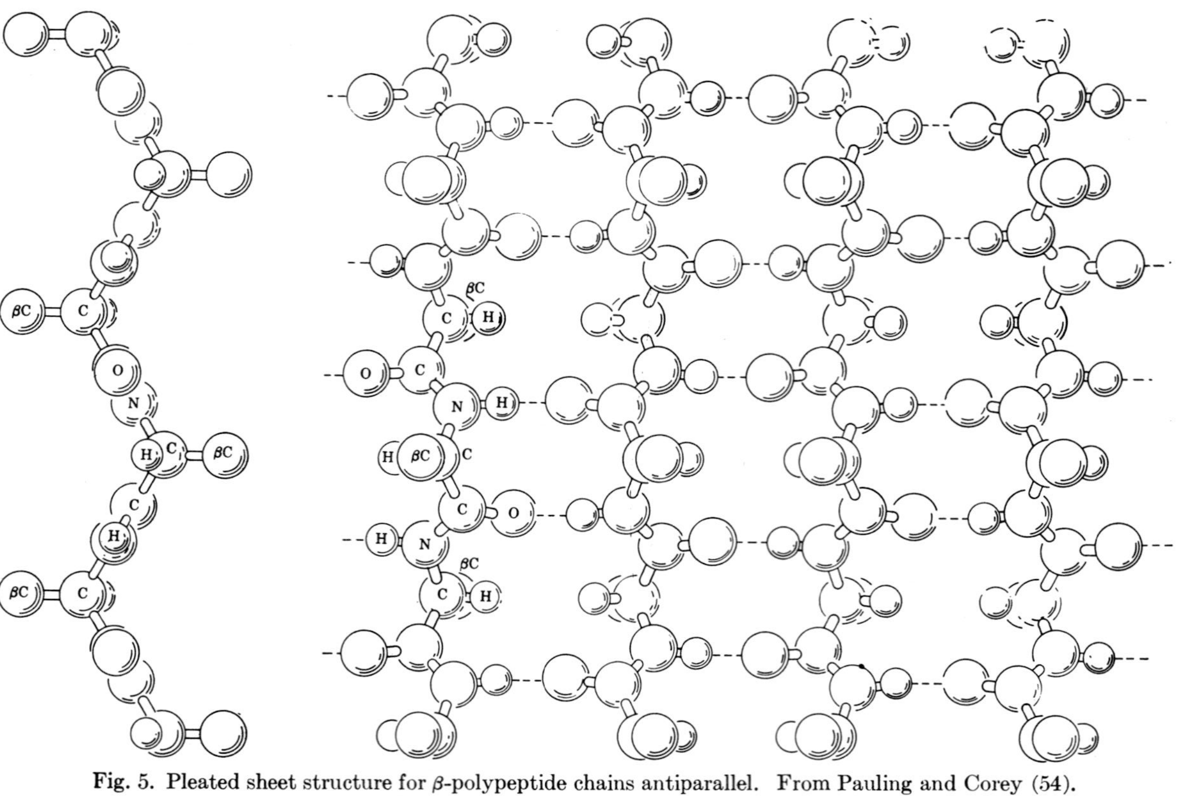

Fig. 5. Pleated sheet structure for β-polypeptide chains antiparallel. From Pauling and Corey (54).

tance between the sheets would be expected to vary with the bulkiness of the side chains. With natural silks, for example, which have a similar basic structure, this distance ranges from 9.3 Å to 15.6 Å, depending on the side chains present (55).

Polyglycine can exist in a second form in which interchain hydrogen bonds are found. This is a three-dimensional structure (56) and is unique to polyglycine.

C. Configurations of Polypeptide Chains in Solution

Doty, Bradbury, and Holtzer (57) computed the radius of gyration (R_g) from light-scattering data for samples of poly-γ-benzyl-L-glutamate in chloroform–formamide solution at 25°C. The results are given in Table II, where it is seen that R_g is proportional to the first power of the

TABLE II. Poly-γ-benzyl-L-glutamate in Chloroform–Formamide at 25°C. Dependence of Radius of Gyration on Molecular Weight

Doty, Bradbury, and Holtzer (57)			
Mol. wt.	R_g, Å	$R_g/M \times 10^3$	R_g/M
262,000	528	2.02	1.03
208,000	408	1.96	0.89
130,000	263	2.02	0.73

molecular weight. This is very good evidence that the molecule is a rigid rod; for all randomly coiled molecules R_g varies as $M^{0.5}$ to $M^{0.6}$. The length of the rod per monomer unit deduced from this data is 1.51 Å; this agrees well with the value quoted for the α-helix.

A study of the viscosity–molecular weight relationship of poly-γ-benzyl-L-glutamate in dimethylformamide clearly agrees with the expected behavior for rodlike molecules (57). That is, log $[\eta]$ changes only approximately linearly with log M, and the exponent (α) in the equation

$$[\eta] = K \cdot M^{\alpha} \tag{12}$$

should be close to 1.8. The value found by Doty et al. was 1.75, and the diameter of the equivalent cylindrical rod computed from this value was 14.9 Å, which compares with 15.3 Å for the α-helix. Viscosity measurements of solutions of poly-γ-benzyl-L-glutamate in dichloroacetic acid, however, showed that log $[\eta]$ was accurately linear with log M, and the value of α in Eq. 12 was 0.87. For flexible linear molecules the Flory-Krigbaum theory predicts that α should lie between 0.5 and 0.8.

These results indicate that in this solvent, therefore, poly-γ-benzyl-L-glutamate is a random coil, but the chain is somewhat stiff.

Information as to the configuration of polypeptide chains in solution can also be obtained from studies of the dispersion of optical rotation of these solutions. According to Moffitt (58,59) the residue rotation in vacuum $[R_{vac}]$, should be given by

$$R_{vac} = a_0 \lambda^2_0/(\lambda^2 - \lambda_0) + b_0 \lambda_0^4/(\lambda^2 - \lambda_0^2)^2 \qquad (13)$$

where a_0 is a constant which may be expected to vary considerably with the nature of the side chain of the polypeptide and the solvent, while b_0 and λ_0 should be intrinsic properties of the helical skeleton, provided the interactions of the chromophores in the side chains can be neglected. Poly-γ-benzyl-L-glutamate and poly-L-glutamic acid have $\lambda_0 = 2120 \pm 50$ Å and b_0 in the range -580 to $-660°$ (60), whereas other polypeptides containing a predominance of L-amino acids have b_0 between -450 and $-700°$. Measurements of the optical rotation of solid films of α-poly-L-alanine have yielded values of -475 for b_0 (61). Although it is now believed that the original calculations of Moffitt are based on an assumption which is not justified theoretically (62), the predictions it makes about the optical rotary dispersion of the α-helix seems to agree basically with experiment. Solutions of poly-β-benzyl aspartate in chloroform give a value of $b_0 = +631$, suggesting a left-hand screw sense for this polypeptide (51). Subsequent studies of copolymers of γ-benzyl-L-glutamate with β-benzyl-L-aspartate and with β-benzyl-D-aspartate have confirmed this (63,64).

In highly polar solvents such as dichloroacetic acid and trifluoroacetic acid b_0 is small or zero. In these solvents polypeptides exist as a random coil.

Measurements of optical rotary dispersion can be used to study conformation changes occurring in the spinning of polypeptides. Poly-γ-methyl-L-glutamate prepared in chloroform, methylene chloride, or mixtures of these solvents with dioxane have been shown, from optical rotary dispersion studies, to exist in the α-form. The fibers obtained from these solutions by spinning into acetone in the unstretched state are also α-polypeptides. Solutions of poly-γ-methyl-L-glutamate in trifluoroacetic acid, however, have values of b_0 of $+64$, indicating that the polymer in this solvent exists as a random coil. It is to be expected, therefore, that the fibers obtained by spinning into acetone would be predominantly β-polypeptides. It was found, however, from infrared studies of the unstretched fibers that the polymers were still predominantly α-polypeptides. Measurements of optical rotary dispersion of solutions of the polypeptide in acetone–trifluoroacetic acid mixtures showed that at concentrations of acetone just sufficient to cause precipitation, the polymer existed in the α-form (65). From the geometry of the spinning system and the rates of extrusion and windup it was estimated that the $\beta \rightarrow \alpha$ transformation occurred in 10^{-2} to 10^{-3} sec.

D. Configurational Changes Induced in Polypeptides in the Solid State. The $\alpha \rightarrow \beta$ Transformation

Synthetic polypeptide fibers obtained by spinning in the unstretched state are predominantly in the α-form. In this state they are amorphous and are readily soluble or swollen by organic solvents and have poor mechanical properties. On stretching, they undergo a complicated series of transformations which can give rise to a fiber with a high degree of crystallinity in the α- or β-form or mixtures of these two species can be obtained. It is possible to distinguish between the α- and β-forms of synthetic polypeptides in the solid state using x-ray diffraction studies and polarized infrared radiation. A detailed description of these techniques has been given elsewhere (5). They have been used in the study of the stretching of α-poly-L-alanine (66), but probably the most detailed study has been on poly-γ-methyl-L-glutamate.

PMLG fibers have an extensibility in the cold wet state of 100–150%, but in steam this increased to 300% or more. Stretching in steam to moderate extensions orients the α-polymer without producing a significant quantity of β material. At an extensibility of 100% the maximum amount of oriented α material is produced. The infrared spectra of these fibers is shown in Fig. 6. A fiber which is predominantly in the α-configuration is characterized by a pronounced peak in the region of 4870 cm^{-1} with electric vector perpendicular to the fiber axis. The corresponding x-ray photograph is shown in Fig. 7*c*, which is typical for an α-polypeptide. If the sample is annealed the very interesting x-ray photograph shown in Fig. 7*d* is obtained corresponding to a highly crystalline α-PMLG. Conversion to the β-form can be accomplished in two distinct ways by cold-stretching or by stretching in steam to almost the breaking point. The latter gives a fiber with a very high β-content in which the infrared spectra shows characteristic peaks, at 4520 and 4870 cm^{-1} with the electric vector parallel to the fiber axis; this is shown in Fig. 6*c*, and the corresponding x-ray photograph in Fig. 7*b*. It is possible to stop the steam stretching process at 100% and then restretch the fiber 200% in steam. In this process the transformation involves the formation of a highly oriented α-form, which is then subsequently converted to a predominantly β-fiber. The cold-stretching process appears to lead directly to a predominantly β-fiber. The use of both x-ray and infrared techniques is of special value, since the latter indicates the amounts of α or β polypeptide in the amorphous and crystalline regions, whereas the former gives this information for the

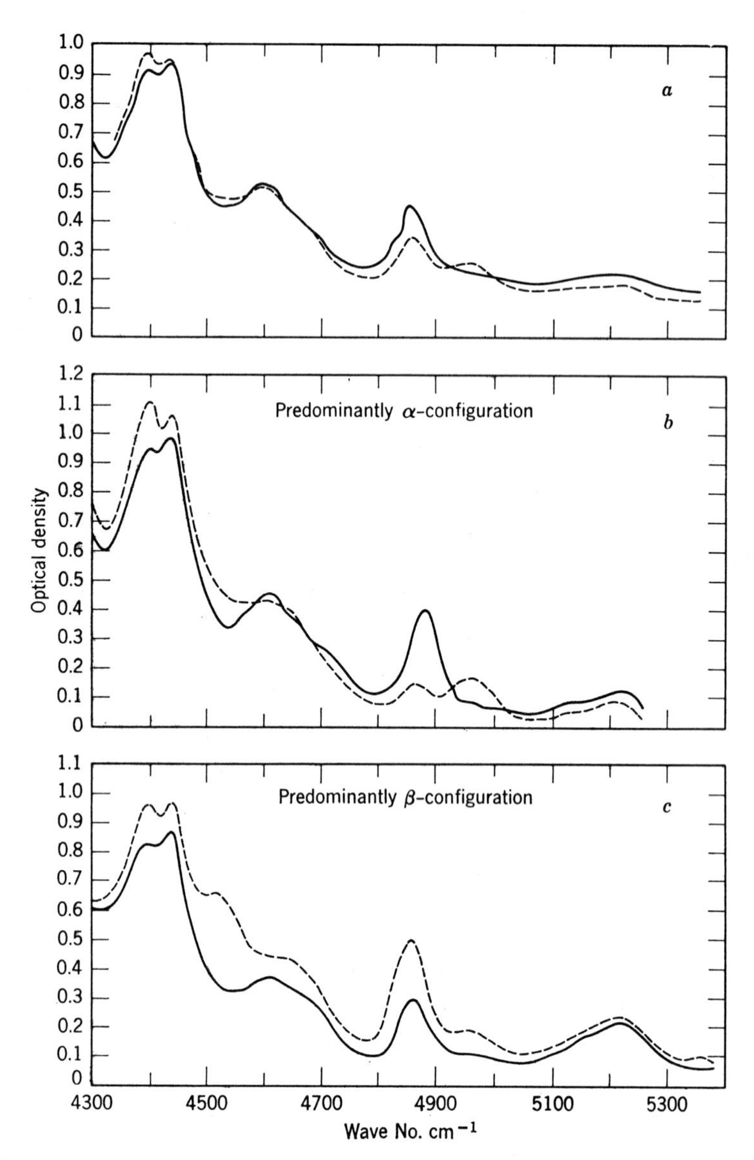

Fig. 6. Infrared spectra of poly-γ-methyl-L-glutamate fibers:(- - -)electric vector parallel to the fiber axis; (——) electric vector perpendicular to the fiber axis; (*a*) unstretched fiber, (*b*) steam-stretched 100%, (*c*) steam-stretched 300%.

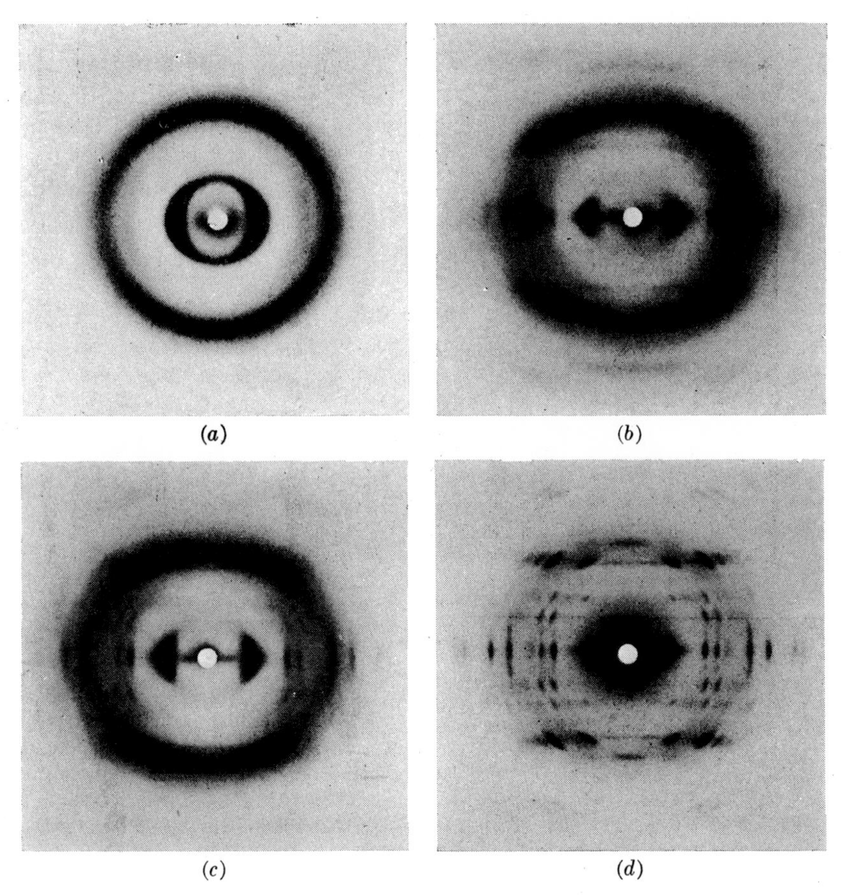

(*a*) (*b*) (*c*) (*d*)

Fig. 7. X-ray photographs of poly-γ-methyl-L-glutamate fibers Cu$K\alpha$ radiation. D = 4 cm, flat photograph: (*a*) unstretched fibers, (*b*) steam-stretched 300%, (*c*) steam-stretched 100%, (*d*) steam-stretched 100% followed by heating *in vacuo* at 140° for 4 hr.

crystalline regions only. Unfortunately, the measurement of the exact amounts is not possible as yet.

IV. SPHERULITES AND LIQUID CRYSTALS IN POLYPEPTIDES

When a solution of poly-γ-benzyl-L-glutamate is allowed to evaporate slowly and is observed with a microscope with crossed polars, birefringent material is seen to be present (67). On standing for several days, spherulites several millimeters in diameter are observed in this bire-

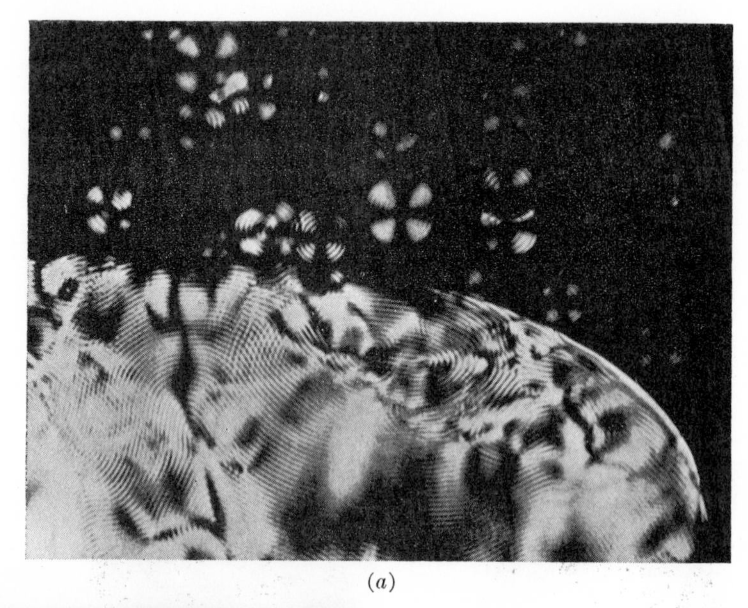

(*a*)

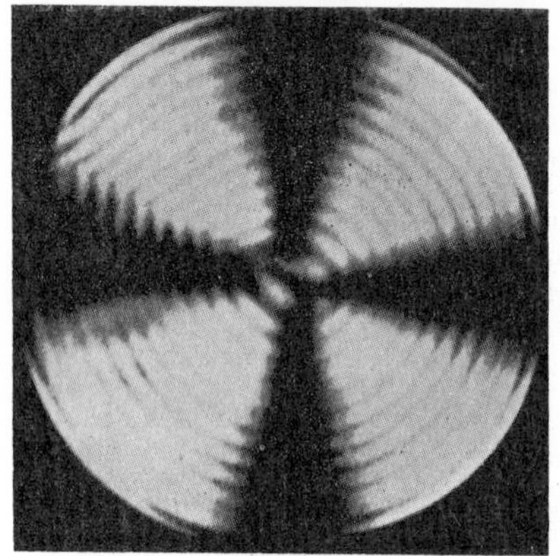

(*b*)

Fig. 8. Spherulite formation in polypeptides; (*a*) two-phase solution of poly-γ-benzyl-L-glutamate in dioxane viewed between crossed polars, ×49; (*b*) spherulite viewed through crossed polars ×154. From Robinson (68). (*c*) Unstretched poly-γ-methyl-L-glutamate fiber viewed between crossed polars ×400.

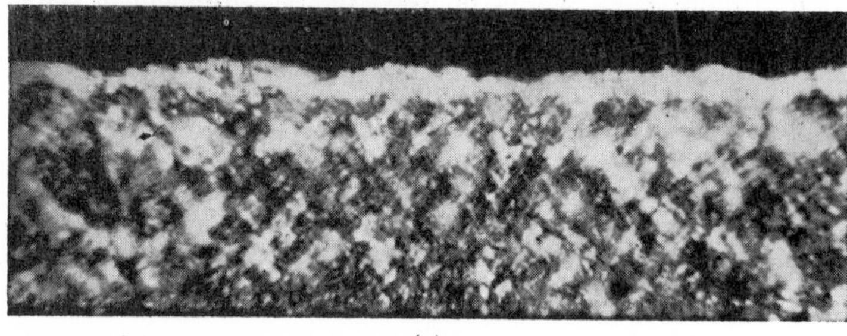

(*c*)

fringent material. Robinson (68) has studied this phenomenon in detail, and a typical photograph from his paper is shown in Fig. 8*a*. Similar observations have been made with poly-γ-methyl-L-glutamate in dichloroacetic acid and poly-DL-leucine in the same solvent. Figure 8*b* gives a photograph of a polypeptide spherulite in detail. They would appear to be two-dimensional particles with a layer structure. The layers do not form closed surfaces but appear as spirals with a fault along one radius (Fig. 8*b*).

Spherulites have been observed in a number of polymers—for example, polyethylene, polypropylene, Terelene, etc. Their formation is usually associated with the crystallization of these polymers, and x-ray diffraction studies and density measurements show a high degree of crystallinity in fibers and films containing spherulites. Undrawn polypeptide fibers when viewed with a polarizing microscope also show the presence of particles resembling spherulites (Fig. 8*c*), but x-ray examination of these fibers shows that they are amorphous (Fig. 7*a*). On drawing, these spherulites disappear, giving a fiber which is birefringent parallel to its axis.

In addition to spherulites, other paracrystalline bodies have been observed in solutions of polypeptides which are similar to cholesteric liquid crystals (69). They are usually associated with spectacular colored effects when viewed with polarized light.

Spherulite formation occurs as a result of the orientation of polypeptide molecules in some preferred geometrical pattern, giving structural units comparable in size with the wavelength of light. They are probably not associated with the rodlike character of the α-helix, although the optical effects observed are related to the high optical activity of the medium.

V. SYNTHETIC POLYPEPTIDES AS TEXTILE FIBERS

Very few polypeptides have been prepared in sufficient quantity to study them in detail as fibers. The reasons for this are as follows: (*1*) the availability and cost of optically active amino acids; (*2*) difficulties in preparing the NCA in a pure state and in good yield; (*3*) intractability of most polypeptides. The majority are only soluble in a restricted range of solvents and are infusible. It is necessary, therefore, either to spin from strong acid solutions, or to use polypeptides with large side chains, some of which are soluble in organic solvents in the α-form.

At the time of writing only two systems have been developed completely to the point where any evaluation of the polymer as a fiber has been possible. Both these developments occurred at Courtaulds Ltd, England. The first of these was the synthesis of poly-L- or D-alanine and the second the synthesis of poly-γ-methyl-L-glutamate. The following is a summary of what is known about some of the polypeptides derived from the more readily available amino acids.

A. Polyglycine

Glycine is an amino acid without an asymmetric α-carbon atom. For this reason it can be produced synthetically and is potentially very cheap.

It cannot be polymerized using catalysts of the tertiary base type. These initiators invariably produce a mixture consisting of low-molecular weight polymers, cyclic peptides, and considerable quantities of hydantoin-3-acetic acid (32). Primary and secondary bases react slowly even in solvents of high dielectric strength such as nitrobenzene. By carrying out the polymerization at 0° and under conditions where the carbon dioxide is continuously removed from the reaction mixture, degrees of polymerization of 300–400 have been obtained.

Films of this polymer can be cast from trifluoracetic acid by precipitating with another solvent. Those obtained by this procedure are interesting as films but of very little interest as fibers.

B. Copolymers of Glycine and L-Alanine

Glycine and L-alanine can be copolymerized by the methods described above for glycine. A copolymer consisting of 46% glycine and 54% L-alanine with a molecular weight of 20,000 was found to be closely similar to *Anaphe Maloneyi* silk in its behavior. A 12% solution in trifluoracetic acid when diluted with ten times its volume with water gives a stable solution. If this solution is subjected to any form of shear, however, the polymer is immediately deposited. This can be brought about by stirring the solution vigorously or passing it through a capillary or jet. The natural silk behaves in an identical way. A spinning system based on this unusual behavior has been demonstrated. The polymer was spun merely by extruding it from a jet with no need for evaporation or precipitation. The x-ray photograph of the β-fiber is very similar to Anaphe silk.

C. Poly-L-alanine

This polymer was first studied in 1953 (70). It was prepared by polymerizing the NCA in nitrobenzene using a primary base initiator.

The polymer separates as a gel during the polymerization, which takes about a week. It is freed from the solvent by washing with ether, dried, and dissolved in dichloracetic acid. It can be spun by extruding into water, methanol, etc. The fibers can be cold-drawn or steam-stretched. As a single filament it has been obtained with strengths of 2.5–4.0 g/den at 20–35% extension.

D. Poly-γ-methyl-L-glutamate

This polymer is obtained from L-glutamic acid, which is produced in Japan and the United States on a total scale of about 35,000 tons/annum. This amino acid is very cheap and available in quantity. The half ester can be prepared in good yield by conventional methods, and phosgenation procedures have been developed to give pure NCA in high yields (21). It can be polymerized in mixed solvents to give homogeneous filterable solutions of the polymer in a few hours. These can be directly spun by wet or dry techniques (27). Fibers can be converted to the insoluble β-form by stretching in steam or water.

This fiber has been produced in sufficient quantity to carry out textile evaluation. As a fabric it is similar to silk in some of its characteristics but cannot be dyed on the silk system for obvious reasons. On the other hand it is naturally white, does not yellow, and is thermally much more stable. It is not swollen or dissolved by organic solvents: it is dissolved completely, however, by strong aqueous alkalis and trifluoracetic acids.

E. Some Miscellaneous Polypeptides

Attempts have been made to synthesize polypeptides from α-amino isobutyric acid, which, like glycine, does not have an asymmetric α-carbon atom. All attempts to obtain high-molecular-weight polymers have failed, however (71).

Polymers of the higher esters of L-glutamic acids such as γ-benzyl L-glutamate do not make good fibers. Spinning systems can be developed for these, but fibers do not toughen on drawing and consequently tend to be rather weak.

Copolymers of L-leucine and DL-phenylalanine have been reported in the patent literature as film- and fiber-forming substances. Copolymers of this type are generally poorly crystalline and as a consequence make rather weak films and fibers. The naturally occurring silks are copolymers of α-amino acids, but structural studies on these materials have shown they consist of blocks of glycine and alanine interspaced with short peptides derived from other amino acids. Random copolymers of all L- or all D-residues have been synthesized, but no information is available about the mechanical properties of these polymers as fibers.

REFERENCES

1. F. Hofmeister, *Ergeb. Physiol. Biol. Chem. Exp. Pharmakol.*, **1**, 759 (1902).
2. E. Fisher, *Ber.*, **34**, 433 (1901).
3. R. B. Woodward and C. H. Schramm, *J. Am. Chem. Soc.*, **69**, 1551 (1947).
4. D. G. H. Ballard, Thesis, "The polymerization of *N*-carboxy α-amino acid anhydrides," University of London (1955).
5. C. H. Bamford, A. Elliott, and W. E. Hanby, *Synthetic Polypeptides*, Academic Press, New York, 1956.
6. J. Naguchi and T. Hyakawa, *J. Am. Chem. Soc.*, **76**, 2846 (1954).
7. Y. Go, J. Naguchi, M. Asai, and T. Hyakawa, *J. Chem. High Polymers Japan*, **13**, 171 (1956).
8. Y. Go, J. Naguchi, M. Asai, and T. Hyakawa, *J. Polymer Sci.*, **21**, 147 (1956).
9. H. Leuchs, *Ber.*, **39**, 857 (1906).
10. H. Leuchs and W. Manasse, *Ber.*, **40**, 3235 (1907).
11. H. Leuchs and W. Geiger, *Ber.*, **41**, 1721 (1908).
12. M. Bergmann and L. Zervas, *Ber.*, **65**, 1192 (1932).
13. S. G. Waley and J. Watson, *Proc. Roy. Soc. London, Ser. A.*, **199**, 499 (1949).
14. E. Katchalski, "Poly-α-amino Acids," in *Advances in Protein Chemistry*, Vol. VII, Academic Press, New York, 1952.
15. F. Fuchs, *Ber.*, **55**, 2943 (1922).
16. W. Baird, E. G. Parry, and S. Robinson, Brit. Pat. 646,033 (1947).
17. A. L. Levy, *Nature*, **165**, 152 (1950).
18. J. L. Bailey, *J. Chem. Soc.*, **1950**, 3461.
19. A. C. Farthing, *J. Chem. Soc.*, **1950**, 3213.
21. A. C. Farthing and R. J. W. Reynolds, *Nature*, **165**, 649 (1950).
21. D. G. H. Ballard, Brit. Pat. 854,139 (1958).
22. M. Idelson and E. R. Blout, *J. Am. Chem. Soc.*, **79**, 3948 (1957).
23. D. G. H. Ballard, Brit. Pat. 854,140.
24. D. G. H. Ballard, C. H. Bamford, and F. J. Weymouth, *Proc. Roy. Soc. London, Ser. A*, **227**, 155 (1955).
25. D. G. H. Ballard, Brit. Pat. Appl. 4734 (1959).
26. A. A. Randall, Unpublished data.
27. D. G. H. Ballard, Brit. Pat. 864,692.
28. D. G. H. Ballard and C. H. Bamford, *Proc. Roy. Soc. London, Ser. A*, **223**, 495 (1954).
29. D. G. H. Ballard and C. H. Bamford, *Chem. Soc. London Spec. Publ.*, **2**, 26 (1955).
30. M. Sela and A. Berger, *J. Am. Chem. Soc.*, **75**, 6350 (1953); *Ibid.*, **77**, 1893 (1955).
31. D. G. H. Ballard and C. H. Bamford, *J. Chem. Soc.*, **1959**, 1039.
32. D. G. H. Ballard, C. H. Bamford, and F. J. Weymouth, *Nature*, **174**, 173 (1954).
33. C. H. Bamford, H. Block, and A. C. P. Pugh, *J. Chem. Soc.*, **1961**, 2057.
34. D. G. H. Ballard and C. H. Bamford, *J. Chem. Soc.*, **1956**, 381.

35. C. H. Bamford and H. Block, *J. Chem. Soc.*, **1962,** 4989.
36. M. Goodman and J. Huchinson, *J. Am. Chem. Soc.*, **87,** 3524 (1964).
37. J. H. Fessler and A. G. Ogston, *Trans. Faraday Soc.*, **40,** 667 (1951).
38. M. T. Pope, T. J. Weakley, and R. J. P. Williams, *J. Chem. Soc.*, **1959,** 3442.
39. M. Goodman, *Biopolymers,* **1,** 500 (1963).
40. L. Pauling, R. B. Corey, and H. R. Branson, *Proc. Natl. Acad. Sci. U.S.*, **37,** 205 (1951).
41. L. Pauling, *The Nature of the Chemical Bond,* Cornell University Press, Ithaca, New York, 1940.
42. M. L. Huggins, *Chem. Rev.*, **32,** 195 (1943).
43. W. L. Bragg, J. C. Kendrew, and H. F. Perutz, *Proc. Roy. Soc. London, Ser. A*, **203,** 321 (1950).
44. W. Cochran, F. H. C. Crick, and V. Vand, *Acta Cryst.*, 381 (1952).
45. L. Pauling and R. B. Corey, *Proc. Natl. Acad. Sci. U.S.*, **37,** 238 (1951); **37,** 241 (1951).
46. C. H. Bamford, W. E. Hanby, and F. Happey, *Proc. Roy. Soc. London, Ser. A*, **205,** 30 (1951).
47. M. F. Perutz, *Nature,* **167,** 1053 (1951).
48. C. H. Bamford, L. Brown, A. Elliott, W. E. Hanby, and I. F. Trotter, *Nature,* **173,** 27 (1954).
49. L. Brown and I. F. Trotter, *Trans. Faraday Soc.*, **52,** 537 (1956).
50. A. Elliott and B. R. Malcolm, *Proc. Roy. Soc. London, Ser. A*, **249,** 30 (1959).
51. E. R. Blout and R. H. Karlson, *J. Am. Chem. Soc.*, **80,** 1259 (1958); corrections: *Ibid.*, 6701.
52. P. M. Cowan and S. McGavin, *Nature,* **176,** 501 (1955).
53. L. Pauling and R. B. Corey, *Proc. Roy. Soc. London, Ser. B*, **141,** 10 (1953).
54. L. Pauling and R. B. Corey, *Proc. Natl. Acad. Sci., U.S.*, **37,** 729 (1951); **39,** 247 (1953).
55. J. O. Warwicker, *J. Mol. Biol.*, **2,** 350 (1960).
56. F. H. Crick and A. Rich, *Nature,* **176,** 780 (1955).
57. P. Doty, J. H. Bradbury, and A. M. Holtzer, *J. Am. Chem. Soc.*, **78,** 947 (1956).
58. W. Moffitt, *J. Chem. Phys.*, **25,** 467 (1956).
59. W. Moffitt, *Proc. Natl. Acad. Sci. U.S.*, **42,** 736 (1956).
60. W. Moffitt and J. T. Young, *Proc. Natl. Acad. Sci. U.S.*, **43,** 723 (1956).
61. A. Elliot, W. E. Hanby, and B. R. Malcolm, *Disc. Faraday Soc.*, **25,** 167 (1958).
62. W. Moffitt, D. D. Fitts, and J. G. Kirkwood, *Proc. Natl. Acad. Sci. U.S.*, **43,** 723 (1957).
63. R. H. Karlson, K. S. Norland, G. D. Fasman, and E. R. Blout, *J. Am. Chem. Soc.*, **82,** 2268 (1960).
64. E. M. Bradbury, A. R. Downie, A. Elliott, and W. E. Hanby, *Proc. Roy. Soc. London, Ser. A*, **259,** 110 (1960).
65. A. R. Downie, unpublished data.
66. C. H. Bamford, L. Brown, A. Elliott, W. E Hanby, and I. F. Trotter, *Proc. Roy. Soc. London, Ser. B*, **141,** 49 (1953).
67. A. Elliott and E. J. Ambrose, *Discussions Faraday Soc.*, **9,** 246 (1950).
68. C. Robinson, *Trans. Faraday Soc.*, **52,** 571 (1956).
69. H. L. de Vries, *Acta Cryst.*, **4,** 219 (1951).
70. C. H. Bamford, L. Brown, A. Elliott, W. E. Hanby, and I. F. Trotter, *Nature,* **171,** 1149 (1953).
71. D. G. H. Ballard and C. H. Bamford, *J. Chem. Soc.* **1958,** 355.

Higher Nylons

J. Chambion
Rhodiaceta, Lyon, France

CONTENTS

I. INTRODUCTION

Ever since the beginning of the development of the polyamides, while nylon 66 and Perlon have been produced industrially in large quantities, many other polyamides have been synthesized and evaluated in the laboratory. The "higher homologs" of these two leaders in the field, that is the "higher nylons," are of interest for the following reasons:

1. Their preparation involves a wide range of chemical processes, some only recently discovered, which have been industrially developed for use with natural or new synthetic raw materials.

2. The study of the evolution of their physical and chemical properties as their hydrocarbon chains lengthen in a homologous series has widened our knowledge of these phenomena, thus allowing the field of practical application of the polyamides to be yet further extended.

In general we will be studying the *long-chain aliphatic polyamides* (greater than C_6) without side chains, produced either from diacids and diamines (e.g., nylon 610) or from amino acids or lactams (nylon 11, nylon 12). The influence of side chains on the properties will be indicated where relevant.

As will be shown in more detail later, only a few of these many polymers have found an outlet in the *synthetic textiles* industry. Two of the most striking examples are polyamide 610, used in the bristle industry, and polyamide 11, made in France, Italy, and Brazil under the Rilsan label, in the form of continuous filament and fiber. Nylons 7 and 9, made in Russia under the names Enant and Pelargon, respectively, might also be mentioned. Finally, in Japan the Nihon Ozone Co. (1) is said to study polyamide 69, and a polyurea based on nonamethylenediamine (2,3), in other words nylon 91, is made by Toyo Koatsu Industries under the name Urylon.

In the field of plastics, on the other hand, nylons 610, 11, and 12 have found great possibilities, as have nylons 8 and 1010, although to a lesser degree.

II. INTERMEDIATE PRODUCTS FOR HIGHER NYLONS

The preparation of the monomers of higher nylons depends on a wide range of chemical reactions, as the raw materials may either be natural products from which useful intermediates have to be synthesized, or they may simply be the basic materials of organic or petrochemistry.

In practice, in both cases, after some phases specific to the particular raw material used, the final syntheses are fairly general:

1. Lactams are prepared, principally, from cyclic ketones by oximation and Beckmann's rearrangement, by variations of the reaction described for caprolactam.

2. Diamines are prepared by the nitrilation, then hydrogenation, of the corresponding diacids, by the process known for hexamethylenediamine.

The purification of these monomers is also carried out by standard methods, e.g., (4):

1. Amino acids are purified by recrystallization in water, and under pressure if necessary for higher terms.

2. Lactams are distilled under vacuum if they are primary terms, but higher homologs have to be recrystallized in a solvent. Thus, lauryllactam is recrystallized in cyclohexane.

3. Diamines can be vacuum distilled.

Table I shows the melting or boiling points of the monomers of a few of the higher nylons.

Finally, salts are obtained from the purified diacids and diamines in solution in water or after precipitation in methanol, as is the case for nylon 66.

A. Monomers Produced from Natural Materials

Vegetable products in particular are raw materials with high carbon condensation, and their longest chains can be broken at their weak points, such as double ethylene bonds, so as to isolate desirable monomers.

1. Castor Oil

Ricinoleic acid, $CH_3(CH_2)_5CHOHCH_2CH{=}CH(CH_2)_7COOH$, in its triglyceride, forms the principal constituent of castor oil, and possesses a C_{18} chain; it is the best raw material for the production of nylon 11 and the higher nylons based on sebacic acid.

1. We will first describe the preparation of 11-aminoundecanoic acid, which is produced industrially as the monomer for Rilsan (5). The synthesis of this amino acid passes through the following stages:

(*a*) Methanolysis of the castor oil into methyl ricinoleate, which facilitates the cracking that follows.

(*b*) Pyrolysis of the methyl ricinoleate obtained into methyl undecylenate, by instantaneous vaporization at 550°C, in the presence of water to eliminate the undesirable dehydration into methyl linoleate (6). Enanthal is formed as a by-product.

(*c*) Hydrolysis of the undecylenate ester.

TABLE I
Melting and Boiling Points of the Monomers for Higher Nylons

Number of carbon atoms	Lactam		Amino acid	
	Name	mp, °C	Name	mp, °C
4	Butyrolactam or pyrrolidone	24.5		
5	Valerolactam or piperidone	39–40	5-Amino valeric	157–158
6	Caprolactam	69	6-Aminocaproic	200–206
7	Oenantholactam	25	7-Aminoenanthic	187–195
8	Capryllactam	71–72	8-Aminocaprylic	194
9	Pelargolactam	—	9-Aminopelargonic	185–188
10	Caprinolactam	128–135	10-Aminocapric	185–188
11	Undecanolactam	155	11-Aminoundecanoic	187–191
12	Lauryllactam	153–154	12-Aminolauric	183–184
13			13-Aminotridecanoic	177–178
22			22-Aminobehenic	145

(*d*) Production of 11-aminoundecanoic acid by the reaction of dry HBr and air on a solution of undecylenic acid in a mixture of benzene and toluene (7), flowing in opposite directions in a Raschig column at −10°C. The difficulty of this resides in the undesirability of the formation of the bromine derivative in the 10 position which, according to Markownikow's hypothesis, should happen most often, unless the reaction is carried out in the presence of molecular oxygen; the reaction conditions given above produce the largest quantities of bromine derivative in the 11 position.

(*e*) Finally, treatment with aqueous ammonia at about 20°C; the ammonium salt is soluble, while the 11-aminoundecanoic acid precipitates, once formed by ammonolysis.

2. Castor oil is also the raw material for the industrial production of C_{10} sebacic acid by alkaline scission of the ricinoleic acid resulting from the saponification of the fat (8):

$$CH_3(CH_2)_5CHOHCH_2CH{=}CH(CH_2)_7COOH + 2H_2O \xrightarrow{HONa}$$

$$HOOC(CH_2)_8COOH + CH_3(CH_2)_5CHOHCH_3 + H_2$$

One by-product of this reaction is therefore 2-octanol or caprylic alcohol. For example (9), when the castor oil is slowly poured into a bath of caustic soda at 245°C, 2-octanol is given off and condensed, hydrogen and water are given off, and the water is recycled. At the end of the

Diacid		Diamine			
Name	mp, °C	Name	mp, °C	bp, °C/ 760 mm Hg	bp, °C/ reduced pressure
Succinic	182	Tetramethylenediamine	27–28	158–159	
Glutaric	97.5	Pentamethylenediamine	9	178–180	
Adipic	153	Hexamethylenediamine	41	204	
Pimelic	103–106	Heptamethylenediamine	28–29	223–225	
Suberic	140	Octamethylenediamine	50–52	240–241	
Azelaic	106	Nonamethylenediamine	37	258–259	
Sebacic	134.5	Decamethylenediamine	61–64	—	140/
Undecanedioic	—	Undecamethylenediamine	43–44	—	12 mm
Dodecanedioic	126.5	Dodecamethylenediamine	66–68	—	134.5/ 11.5 mm
Brassylic	112–114	Tridecamethylenediamine	—	—	118–119/ 0.4 mm

operation, the bath is acidified, and sebacic acid is precipitated. The amount of acid produced is about 40% of the weight of castor oil used. Various purification methods are available, depending on the degree of purity required.

Sebacic acid is produced industrially in the USA by Harchem, a division of Wallace & Tiernan, and by Hardesty; in England it is made by a joint subsidiary of Geigy and Hardesty.

3. It must also be mentioned that the oxidation of castor oil by nitric acid (10) gives a mixture of azelaic and suberic acids, the production of the latter being improved by use of dilute acid and a slow oxidation. The methyl esters of these two acids may be separated by fractional distillation.

2. Olein

Oleic acid, the most common of the unsaturated fatty acids, is the raw material for the industrial production of azelaic acid produced by the American firm Emery and by its Dutch subsidiary in Gouda since 1955.

Oxidation by ozone of oleic acid, followed by a further oxidation, gives a good yield of azelaic acid (C_9) and pelargonic acid (C_9 monoacid) (11):

$$CH_3(CH_2)_7CH{=}CH(CH_2)_7COOH \xrightarrow{O_3 + O_2} CH_3(CH_2)_7COOH + HOOC(CH_2)_7COOH$$

Potassium permanganate is also used as the oxidizing agent: the first stage, in a dilute alkaline solution, gives hydroxy acids which are reoxidized in an acid medium, to give pelargonic and azelaic acids.

If the second oxidation is carried out in an alkaline medium, the result is a mixture of oxalic, octanoic, and suberic (C_8) acids.

3. *Furfural*

Furfural is present in large quantities in the form of pentosans in many vegetable wastes: oat hulls, corn cobs, etc. It has been studied extensively as a potential source of various chemicals, particularly in Germany, America, and elsewhere during World War II. It may be used in the synthesis of adiponitrile, adipic acid, and caprolactam, using several possible routes (12).

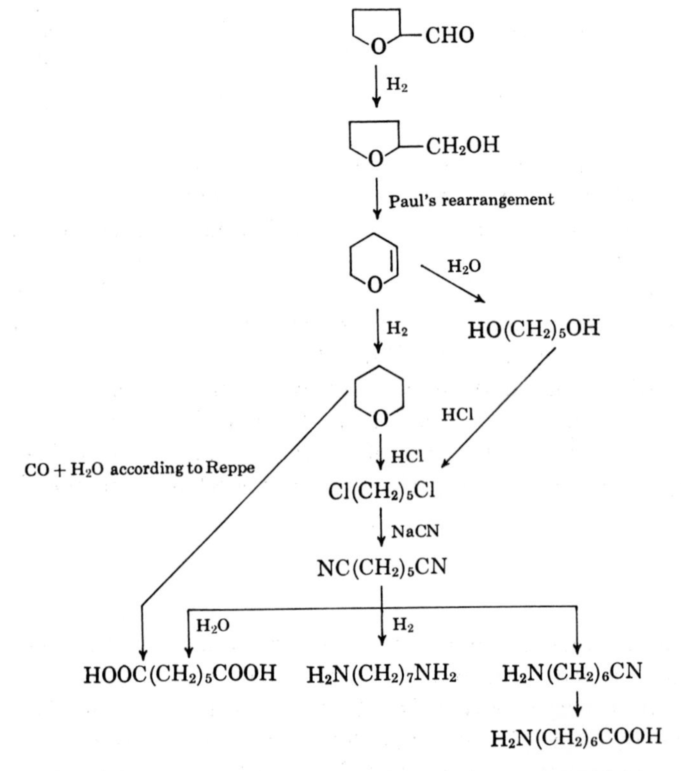

Fig. 1. Monomers for higher nylons from furfural.

Tetrahydrofurfuryl alcohol, obtained by the catalytic hydrogenation of furfural, is the base of condensation reactions leading to C_7 diamines, diacids, and amino acids. These reactions, shown schematically in Figure 1, include the following stages (12): (*1*) Paul's rearrangement, tetrahydrofurfuryl alcohol into dihydropyran (13); (*2*) hydrogenation into tetrahydropyran; (*3*) action of hydrogen chloride giving 1,5-dichloropentane; (*4*) cyaniding, which gives pimelonitrile.

However, the reaction of HCl on tetrahydropyran is awkward, and it is preferable (14) to go from dihydropyran via pentanediol, from which the dichloropentane can easily be obtained by the action of HCl.

The pimelonitrile can easily be hydrogenated into heptamethylenediamine or hydrolyzed into pimelic acid. Reppe's (15) reaction should also be mentioned: the addition of carbon monoxide and water on tetrahydropyran in the presence of nickel iodide:

$$\text{(tetrahydropyran)} + 2CO + H_2O \xrightarrow{NiI_2} HOOC(CH_2)_5COOH$$

which gives pimelic acid.

7-Aminoheptanoic acid is more difficult to obtain: 5-chlorocapronitrile can be obtained by partial cyaniding of 1,5-dichloropentane (14).

Pimelonitrile can also be semihydrogenated into aminocapronitrile, but the conversion rate is only 40%; the yield can be raised to 80% by recycling the pimelonitrile (16).

4. Other Natural Materials

Among the efforts to make use of natural materials for the production of polyamides, mention must be made of the use of phellonic acid (C_{22} hydroxy acid) extracted from cork, from which is derived aminobehenic acid (17), and the recent preparation of *nylon 1313* from brassylic acid, obtained by the ozonolysis of erucic acid, extracted from sea kale seed oil (18,19).

B. Synthetic Monomers

Although natural materials, as it has been shown, constitute one source of industrially useful raw materials for the production of the monomers of higher nylons, the considerable progress in organic and petrochemistry has offered, cheaply and in large quantities, unsaturated carbon compounds of low condensation, which can be used in many elegant syntheses of amino acids or diacids with carbon condensations greater than 6. Ethylene, acetylene, acrylonitrile, and 1,3-butadiene all lead to higher monomers such as:

7-aminoenanthic	(route to nylon 7)
9-aminopelargonic acid	(route to nylon 9)
capryllactam	(route to nylon 8)
lauryllactam	(route to nylon 12)

Some compounds, such as sebacic acid (nylons 610 and 1010) or ethyl 7-aminoheptanoate (nylon 7), can also be obtained from the synthetic intermediates of nylon 66 or 6 (adipic acid, cyclohexanone), or alternatively from aromatic carbon compounds (naphthalene) as is the case for caprinolactam (nylon 10).

1. *Telomerization of Ethylene*

This reaction, first described in the USA (20), by Hanford, has been carefully studied in the USSR by Nesmejanov (21). It consists in a limited polymerization of ethylene in the presence of carbon tetrachloride (or of phosgene), which splits and attaches itself to the ends of the chain formed. The initiator may be, for example, benzoyl peroxide, or azobisisobutyronitrile:

$$nCH_2{=}CH_2 + CCl_4 \rightarrow Cl(CH_2CH_2)_nCCl_3$$

In contrast to Hanford's (20) first experiments, performed in a stirred autoclave with water to dilute, the Soviet researchers have developed a continuous process at 120–150 kg/cm^2, without dilution (22). The reaction temperature is about 90°C and the rate of conversion of the ethylene is about 40% per pass.

Unfortunately, the result is always a mixture of tetrachloroalkanes:

$$n = 2 \quad Cl(CH_2)_4CCl_3$$
$$n = 3 \quad Cl(CH_2)_6CCl_3$$
$$n = 4 \quad Cl(CH_2)_8CCl_3$$

The choice of the proportions of the reactants, however, is capable of favoring the preferential formation of interesting derivatives. Thus, when 5 moles of ethylene is used per mole of carbon tetrachloride, a good 30% of the yield will be of C_7 chlorinated carbon compound, and 20% will be C_9 compound.

This process has also been studied in Israel by Katchalsky and Vofsi, who work with an environment of ammonia and a copper salt. Under the conditions they specify (23), the final mixture contains up to 56% C_7 compound and 25% C_9 compound with only traces of other compounds.

According to Mark and Atlas (24), the Soviet and Israeli researchers have both succeeded in obtaining a mixture of 85% C_7 compound with 15% C_9 compound, and only traces of other compounds.

The mixture of chlorinated carbon compounds may be vacuum-fractionated under a vacuum of about 10 mm of mercury.

Starting with a pure chlorinated carbon compound, amino acids with the same carbon condensation can be attained. For example, starting from 1,1,1,7-tetrachloroheptane:

1. Hydrolysis with concentrated H_2SO_4 at 90–100°C for 1 hr gives the C_7 chlorinated acid:

$$Cl(CH_2)_6CCl_3 + 2H_2O \rightarrow Cl(CH_2)_6COOH + 3HCl$$

2. By aminolysis with aqueous ammonia at 25%, under pressure and at about 100°C, the 7-chloroenanthic acid produced gives 7-aminoenanthic acid:

$$Cl(CH_2)_6COOH + 2NH_3 \rightarrow H_2N(CH_2)_6COOH + NH_4Cl$$

The aqueous solution of amino acid is cleaned of ammonium chloride by passing over ion-exchange resins.

In a similar way, 9-aminopelargonic acid is obtained from 1,1,1,9-tetrachlorononane.

3. 9-Chloropelargonic acid can also be hydrolyzed by aqueous NaOH at 140–150°C; the 9-hydroxynonanoic acid is then oxidized by HNO_3 into azelaic acid. The diacid yield is about 80% of the chloroacid.

2. Cyclooligomerization of Acetylene and 1,3-Butadiene

As early as 1940, W. Reppe of Ludwigshafen (25, p. 626; 26) was condensing acetylene into 1,5-cyclooctatetraene in solution in tetrahydrofuran at about 80–90°C, under a pressure of 5–15 kg/cm^2, in the presence of a nickel halogenide, or preferably a cyanide.

In 1947, Professor Ziegler (27) obtained a little cyclooctatetraene from butadiene, in the presence of a hydroquinone chain polymerization inhibitor. The two methods, i.e., from acetylene or from butadiene, can be used (28) in the industrial preparation of capryllactam.

The cyclooctatetraene is (29) hydrogenated into cyclooctane, then oxidized into cyclooctanone and oximated and rearranged into lactam. Alternatively, the oxime can be arrived at directly from cyclooctane by photonitrosation.

Capryllactam is produced by BASF and used in a blend with caprolactam for the production of molded parts by anionic polymerization (30).

Finally, oxidation of cyclooctanone is a route to suberic acid; this process has been used on a pilot scale by Harchem (31).

In 1956, Wilke obtained from 1,3-butadiene, with a Ziegler catalyst of the triethylaluminum and alkyl titanate types, a 90% yield of cyclododecatriene, at 40°C and at atmospheric pressure (32–34). This illustrates the selectivity of Ziegler catalysts, as the catalyst which converts ethylene into low-pressure polyethylene will also convert 1,3-butadiene into its trimer with a good yield.

Many routes can now be considered (35) for the production of lauryllactam: the cyclododecatriene may be completely hydrogenated into cyclododecane, followed by the creation of a functional group, or, on the other hand, a functional group may be attached in the 1 position to one of the double bonds.

We will only mention the route which seems best adapted. According to Wilke (36), it consists of the monoepoxidation of cyclododecatriene into epoxy-cyclododecadiene, which is then hydrogenated into epoxy-cyclododecane and isomerized into cyclododecanone (37) in the presence of MgI_2. Lauryllactam is then obtained by oximation and Beckmann's rearrangement.

These reactions have been extensively studied, especially by BASF and Hüls, and polyamide 12 is on sale in Germany and France; it is at the development stage in Japan (38).

Dodecanedioic acid can be obtained by the oxidation of cyclododecanone (31).

3. *Electrochemical Duplication of Adipic Acid* (25, pp. 743–745).

In 1943, Offe of I. G. Farben perfected the electrolytic synthesis of sebacic acid from monomethyl adipate ester. The electrolyte is a methanolic solution of acid adipate at 70°C, containing Na^+ ions; the anodes are of platinum:

$$2CH_3OOC(CH_2)_4CO_2^- \rightarrow CH_3OOC(CH_2)_8COOCH_3 + 2CO_2\uparrow + 2e$$

Dimethyl sebacate is continuously extracted with a hydrocarbon and separated and hydrolyzed in a Raschig column in the presence of sulfuric acid. The sebacic acid must be recrystallized in water. The yield is apparently of the order of 90% and the consumption of energy 4 kWh/kg of sebacate (electrical efficiency 60–70%). This process has not advanced beyond the pilot stage.

4. *Addition of Acrylonitrile on 1,3-Butadiene*

We must mention with Klare (39) the elegant Diels-Alder synthesis of pimelic acid by the following process studied by I. G. Farben (26, pp.

724–728). First, acrylonitrile is condensed on butadiene, in the form of tetrahydrobenzonitrile:

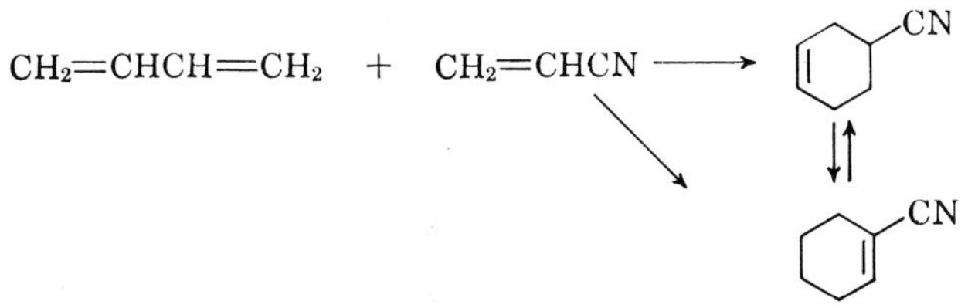

$$CH_2{=}CHCH{=}CH_2 + CH_2{=}CHCN \longrightarrow$$

Then the nitrile is saponified by 30% caustic soda at 250–260°C under pressure:

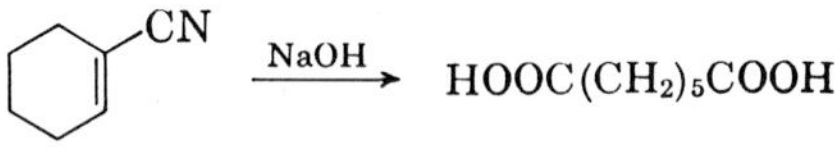

$$\xrightarrow{NaOH} HOOC(CH_2)_5COOH$$

5. Cyaniding of Omega-Halogenated Compounds

This method is frequently used to add a methylene link to a carbon chain.

Union Carbide (40) starts from caprolactone (which this firm produces by oxidation of cyclohexanone with peracetic acid), and reaches ethyl 7-aminoheptanoate via the following stages:

1. Action of anhydrous HCl at between 80 and 175°C, on caprolactone in the presence of Friedel-Crafts catalyst (41):

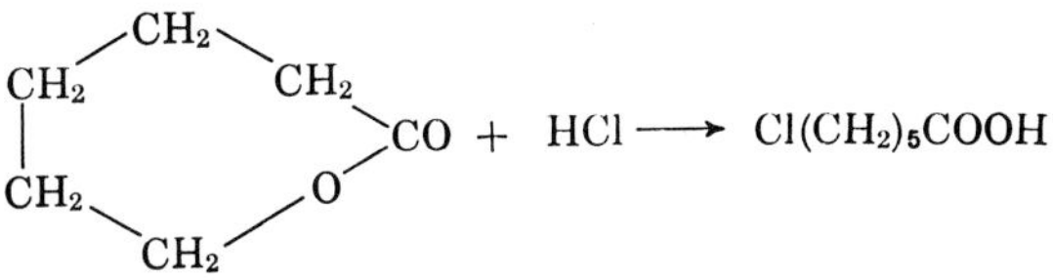

$$\text{(caprolactone: } CH_2\text{–}CH_2\text{–}CH_2\text{–}CH_2\text{–}CH_2\text{–}CO\text{–}O\text{ ring)} + HCl \longrightarrow Cl(CH_2)_5COOH$$

giving 6-chlorocaproic or 6-chlorohexanoic acid.

2. Esterification of the resulting 6-chlorohexanoic acid:

$$Cl(CH_2)_5COOH + EtOH \rightarrow Cl(CH_2)_5COOEt + H_2O$$

3. Cyaniding of the 6-chlorohexanoic acid ethyl ester (42):

$$Cl(CH_2)_5COOEt + NaCN \rightarrow NC(CH_2)_5COOEt + NaCl$$

4. Hydrogenation of 6-cyanohexanoic acid ethyl ester into ethyl 7-aminoheptanoate.

Nesmejanov (21) and his co-researchers use the same cyaniding technique to produce amino acids with an even number of carbon atoms starting from telomers:

$$Cl(CH_2)_6CCl_3$$
$$Cl(CH_2)_8CCl_3$$

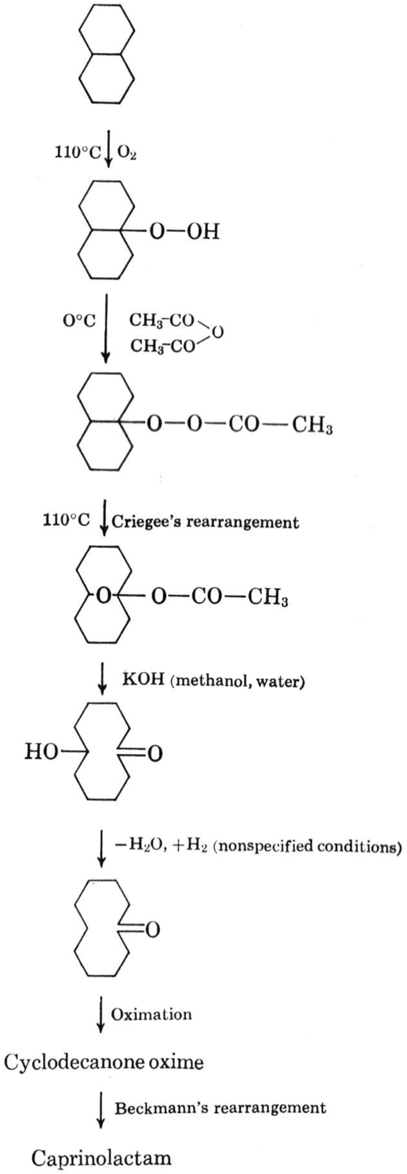

110°C $\downarrow$ O_2

—O—OH

0°C $\downarrow$ CH_3–CO>O / CH_3–CO

—O—O—CO—CH_3

110°C $\downarrow$ Criegee's rearrangement

O— O—CO—CH_3

$\downarrow$ KOH (methanol, water)

HO— =O

$\downarrow$ $-H_2O$, $+H_2$ (nonspecified conditions)

=O

$\downarrow$ Oximation

Cyclodecanone oxime

$\downarrow$ Beckmann's rearrangement

Caprinolactam

Fig. 2. Monomer caprinolactam (C_{10}) from decalin.

1. The tetrachloroalkane is hydrolyzed (see Section II-B-1) by concentrated H_2SO_4, thus:

$$Cl(CH_2)_6CCl_3 + 2H_2O \rightarrow Cl(CH_2)_6COOH + 3HC$$

2. The chlorinated acid is then cyanided in aqueous solution (for $1^1/_2$ hr, yield 63%), giving a C_8 nitrile acid, $N{\equiv}C(CH_2)_6COOH$.

3. The resulting nitrile acid may be hydrogenated in solution in aqueous NH_4OH at 25%, at 70°C on a nickel-based catalyst at a pressure of 95 kg/cm^2.

In order to obtain diacids with an even number of carbon atoms from the same telomers, it is better to start by cyaniding the tetrachloroalkane (3 hr at 100°C in solution in a monoether of ethylene glycol), and then to hydrolyze the resulting trichloronitrile.

The yields on the amounts of the corresponding tetrachloroalkane used are 80–82% for adipic acid and 72–75% for suberic acid. Yields of sebacic acid from 1,1,1,9-tetrachlorononane are not good.

We have already seen another example of this method for obtaining C_7 chains from furfural (see Section II-A-3).

6. Synthesis of Caprinolactam from Decalin

We mention the synthesis of caprinolactam (C_{10}) from decalin, reported by Müller and Pflüger (29) to show that the preparation of certain terms of the series of lactams or higher amino acids, is particularly difficult. This synthesis, shown schematically in Fig. 2, is made up of six stages, including peroxidation and rearrangement by Criegee (43, 44), which allow cyclodecanone to be reached, and caprinolactam by oximation and Beckmann's reaction.

III. PREPARATION OF THE HIGHER POLYAMIDES

A. Polycondensation of Diacid and Diamine Salts

Polyamides obtained from diacids and diamines with carbon concentration greater than 6 are usually produced by the standard process described for nylon 66: the aqueous solution is progressively concentrated, and polycondensation is carried out under a pressure of 15–20 kg/cm^2 at temperatures from 260 to 285°C. Nylons 610 and 1010 are produced industrially in this way. A large number of combinations are available by varying the choice of diacid and diamine, leading by this process to higher nylons.

Interfacial polycondensation should also be mentioned: the polymer is formed at a comparatively low temperature by reaction at the interface between the diamine dissolved in water and a chloride of the diacid dissolved in a solvent immiscible with water. Polyamide 610 lends itself well to this interesting reaction (45), which, however, has not found an industrial application in the case of aliphatic polyamides with long carbon chains.

B. Polycondensation of Amino Acids

For higher homologs of polyamide 6, the corresponding monomer amino acid can be polycondensed:

$$m\text{HOOC(CH}_2)_n\text{NH}_2 \xrightarrow{\text{heat}} \text{HO}\!\!+\!\!\text{OC(CH}_2)_n\text{NH}\!\!+_{m}\!\text{H} + (m - 1)\text{H}_2\text{O}$$

or the corresponding monomer lactam can be polymerized:

$$m\begin{bmatrix}(\text{CH}_2)_n \\ \text{CONH}\end{bmatrix} + \text{H}_2\text{O} \rightarrow \text{HO}\!\!+\!\!\text{OC(CH}_2)_n\text{NH}\!\!+_{m}\!\text{H}$$

and the difference between these reactions should be noted.

C_7 and C_9 amino acids (22), for example, are polycondensed into the polyamides 7 and 9 by the cycle described for nylon 66.

On the other hand, polyamide 11 (Rilsan) is produced industrially (46) at atmospheric pressure, in tubes in which the materials flow continuously, the time taken to pass through the tubes being of the order of 10 hr. The plant is fed with an aqueous paste of 55–60% aminoundecanoic acid and the vehicular water is quickly evaporated in the first part of the tube. In the second section, the water of polycondensation is given off, and the third part makes sure that the length of the process is sufficient to finish the polymer, which is sent directly in its molten state to the spinnerets.

11-Aminoundecanoic acid can also be polycondensed in an autoclave by the nylon 66 cycle.

The Union Carbide process (40,47,48) for the preparation of nylon 7 starts from ethyl 7-aminoheptanoate, which is heated to about 160°C with water, either under pressure or with an inert gas bubbled through it; this operation hydrolyzes the ester and gives a prepolymer which is then polycondensed at about 280°C.

Finally, we must mention the process of solid-phase polycondensation of 7-aminoheptanoic acid (49) which, by heating in the presence of magnesia or boric acid for 3 hr at 184°C, gives a polyamide 7 with sufficient viscosity for spinning.

C. Polymerization of Lactams

There are many methods of polymerizing lactams:

1. A hydrolytic process, by heating a solution or aqueous suspension of lactam, with a cycle under pressure similar to that of nylon 66.

2. A hydrolytic process at atmospheric pressure, in the presence of a little water for opening the lactam cycle, as in the "VK tube" (simplified continuous process).

These are the two processes used in the synthetic textile industry. There are also the following possibilities.

3. The anionic process, suitable for the preparation of molded parts, which consists of heating the anhydrous lactam with suitable catalysts (e.g., alkaline metals) at a temperature below the melting point of the polymer.

4. There is a variant of the anionic process (50–52) which consists of working with an inert solvent in the presence of sodium and carbon dioxide (at about 120°C). It has been studied at the Polytechnic Institute of Lodz in Poland, by Chrzczonowicz and his collaborators, for C_6, C_7, and C_8 polyamides.

5. The cationic process, carried out in an anhydrous medium in the presence of a strong acid catalyst such as H_3PO_4 or HCl, and reported in 1957 (53) by van der Want and Kruissink.

Table II lists the principal higher nylons which are at present manufactured on an industrial scale.

TABLE II. Higher Nylons Manufactured Industrially

Nylon	mp, °C	Monomer	Raw materials
6	223	Caprolactam	Phenol or toluene
7	233	(*a*) 7-Aminoheptanoic acid	Ethylene and carbon tetrachloride
		(*b*) Ethyl 7-aminoheptanoate	Caprolactone
8	200	Capryllactam	Acetylene or butadiene
9	209	9-Aminopelargonic acid	Ethylene and carbon tetrachloride
11	190	11-Aminoundecanoic acid	Castor oil
12	179	Lauryllactam	Butadiene
66	265	Salt 66	Benzene
610	208	Salt 610	Benzene and oleic acid
1010	203	Salt 1010	Oleic acid

D. Influence of the Length of the Monomer Chain on the Production of Polyamides

It is interesting to study the evolution of the conditions of polymer formation in a homologous series in terms of the number of carbon atoms in the monomer.

A very large number of publications have treated the series of the homologs of polyamide 6, whose formation depends partly on the extent to which the monomer tends to form a lactam ring, both during polycondensation from the amino acid and in the polymerization of the lactam. Despite the differences in the values published by various authors, which generally result from different experimental conditions, the following tendencies can be seen:

1. The percentage by weight of lactam in equilibrium with the polymer in the molten state, which is still present in the polymer after it has been solidified by a rapid quenching treatment, is very illustrative of the differences in the behavior of the monomers. Table III gives approximate values for 280°C.

TABLE III. Proportion by Weight of Lactam Monomer in Equilibrium with the Polyamide (Approximate values for 280°C)

Nylon	Lactam proportion, %, according to ref. 22	Lactam proportion, %, according to ref. 27
4	100	—
5	15	—
6	10	10
7	3	6–7
8	2.5	3
9	1.5	1.7
10	—	0.8
11	1.2	0.4
12	0.7	0.3

The decrease in the proportion of monomer at equilibrium as the carbon/chain lengthens is explained by the absence of tension in the five-membered 2-piperidone ring, which is thus very stable, and by the progressive appearance of tensions in the rings with more members which are thus less and less stable.

2. As the proportion of monomer at equilibrium is known, it has been possible to study the speed of formation of the polymer, in the hydrolytic polymerization of lactams for instance, in the presence of 0.5–5% water by weight and at about 210–260°C (54–56). It is known that when polymerization of caprolactam is carried out in the presence of water, there is a period of initiation, whereas in the presence of the corresponding amino acid the reaction starts immediately.

It appears that the speed of the reaction is similar for C_6, C_7, and C_8 lactams (55), and that it diminishes noticeably for longer carbon chains, which makes it necessary to raise the temperature of polymerization;

thus, caprinolactam (56) polymerizes very slowly at 257°C in the presence of 5% water; lauryllactam must be polymerized in 5 hr at 320°C (57) in the presence of the amino acid. This is a consequence of the probability that the ends of the reacting chains will meet. This probability lessens for higher lactams.

3. These two phenomena (56) may be explained with reference to the molecular configuration of the lactam monomers. The C_4 and C_5 lactams exist mainly in the *cis* form, while those with a large number of carbon atoms, C_{12} for instance, show a preference for the *trans* form. These two groups of lactams are stable. On the other hand, in the C_7 lactam, the presence of the *cis* and *trans* forms in substantially equal amounts is said to reduce the resonance of the amide group, and thus the stability of the ring.

Ogata (56) has also published a report on the heats of reaction of hydrochloric acid on the lactams, which shows the strength of their basic functions:

Nylon	$-\Delta H$, kcal/mole
4	7.64
5	6.58
6	3.15
7	1.63
8	—
9	—
10	3.70

These results confirm that the enantholactam ring would be the least stable of the series.

4. Cubbon (58) has summed up the influence of the substituents on the ease of formation of the polyamides. He comes to the conclusion that substituents reduce the ease of polymerization and increase the proportion of lactam in equilibrium with the polymer. This effect becomes less important as the carbon chain lengthens; substituents do not prevent the polymerization of lactams with a ring of C_7 and more, whereas in the case of caprolactam, bulky substituents will completely block it.

5. Finally, in the case of diacid and diamine-based polyamides, polycondensation can also be blocked by the tendency for ring formation in the first terms of the diacid (e.g., succinic acid) and diamine (e.g., ethylenediamine) series. There is thus a lower limit to the length of the carbon chains in the constituents of a salt which is to be polycondensed by the standard procedure.

In addition, linear or cyclic oligomers will always form, but in small quantities: 1% maximum in nylon 66, and less in its higher homologs.

E. Spinning of Higher Nylons

The higher nylons are more stable in the molten state than are their C_6 homologs. Their melting points are no higher (except nylon 7, m.p. 233°C), and the proportion of lactam at equilibrium in the higher homologs of nylon 6 is low. This allows these polyamides to be spun without great difficulty in plants designed for nylon 6 or 66.

IV. PROPERTIES OF HIGHER NYLONS

A. Thermal Properties

1. Melting Point

Polyamides have a strong tendency to crystallize, and even a very fast quenching treatment will not give amorphous samples. As a result, whatever the thermal history of the sample, the measured melting points are those of the crystalline portions.

The melting points of polyamides in a homologous series give the well-known zigzag curve (59,60) and as the carbon chain lengthens, they tend to the melting point of polyethylene (about 135°C).

1. Table IV and Fig. 3 give the melting points of the homologs of nylon 6, determined especially by the disappearance of the phenomenon of birefringence under the microscope (61).

According to Champetier and Aelion (60), the cohesion of the polyamides in the solid state is a result of two kinds of bonds: van der Waals

TABLE IV. Melting Points of Aliphatic Polyamides

Nylon	According to Dachs and Schwartz (28), °C	According to Pied (61), °C
4	260	—
5	—	—
6	223	217
7	233	232.5
8	200	198.5
9	209	209
10	188	192
11	190	192
12	179	179
13	—	182.5
22	—	145
Linear polyethylene	—	135

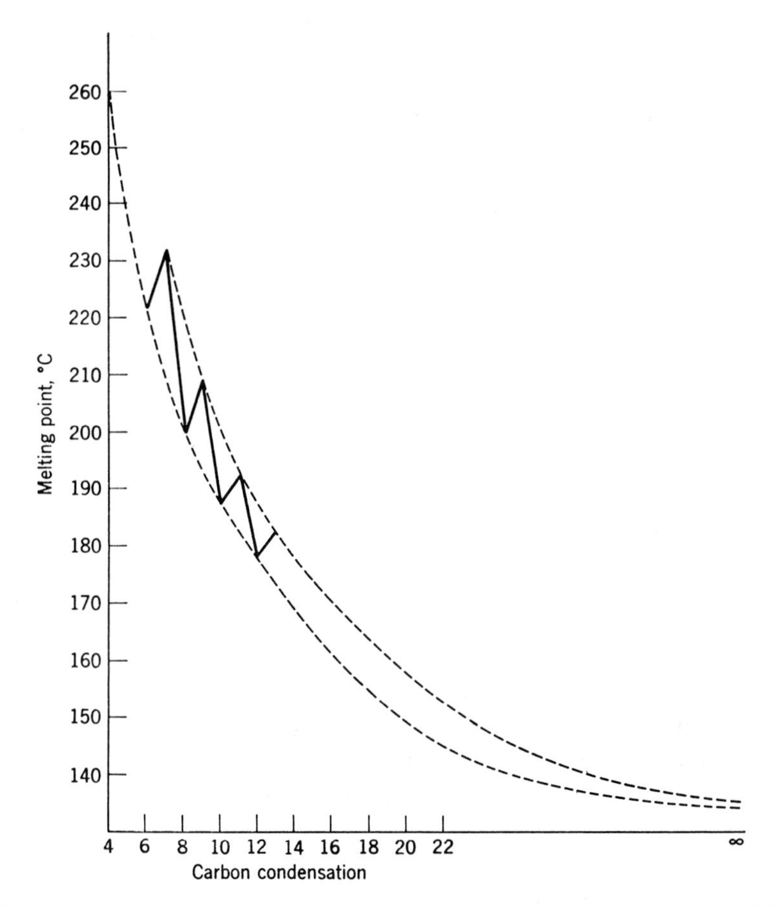

Fig. 3. Melting points of polyamides from amino acids or lactams, according to Pied (61).

forces between methylene groups and the much larger forces resulting from hydrogen bonding between amide functions. These authors therefore introduced in 1948 the notion of a "hydrogen bond index":

$$i_{\mathrm{H}} = 200/(n + 2)$$

where n is the number of methylene groups in the chain, and they showed that the melting points were an increasing linear function of this index.

To explain the lower melting point of polyamides with an odd number of methylene groups and therefore with an even number of carbon atoms, Champetier and Aelion suggested that in this case half the hydrogen bonds are abnormally weak, as a result of the greater interaction distance between the amide functions. We will see in the section on structural

TABLE V. Melting Point (°C) of Diacid- and Diamine-Based Polyamides (28)

	Diamine								
Diacid	C_2	...	C_6	C_7	C_8	C_9	C_{10}	...	C_∞
C_6			265	250	250		236		
C_7			228	214					
C_8			232	230	225				
C_9			226	201	206				
C_{10}	276		223	208	210		203		
C_{12}	261		217		202		191		
⋮									
C_{20}			189		179		171		
⋮									
C_∞[a]									135

[a] Linear polyethylene.

properties that other explanations have since been offered for this phenomenon.

2. In the case of diamine- and diacid-based polyamides (see Table V), zigzag curves are also produced when the length of the chain of one of the constituents, diacid or diamine, is varied; the higher melting points are those of the polymers with an even number of carbon atoms.

Korshak and Frunze (62) introduced the notion of an "heterochain index," which is the ratio, expressed as a percentage, of the number of amide groups to the number of methylene members (thus, nylon 66 has a heterochain index of 20%). They found an increasing linear relationship between the melting point and the heterochain index in the same series (e.g., odd diacid, even diamine). They consider that the distribution of methylene groups between the diacid and the diamine in the same series is unimportant (e.g., even diacid, even diamine), which explains why the melting points of nylons 66 and 48, for instance, are the same.

Finally, the presence of substituents on the carbon chain or the nitrogen atom lowers the melting point of polyamides.

2. Transition Point

Table VI gives the dilatometric values obtained (58) for the homologous polymers of nylon 6. The second-order transition temperatures confirm fairly well the relation reported by Beaman (63):

$$T_G/T_F \approx 0.66$$

where T_F is the melting point and T_G is the second-order transition temperature, both expressed in degrees Kelvin. Champetier and Pied (64) point out that the transition temperature, like the melting point, is a function of molecular cohesion. It is thus in any case possible to predict that the ratio of these two temperatures will remain fairly constant.

TABLE VI. Transition Temperatures of Polyamides (61)

Nylon	T_G, °K	T_F/T_G
6	—[a]	
7	62	0.66
8	51	0.68
9	51	0.67
10	43	0.67
11	46	0.68
12	37	0.68
13	41	0.69

[a] About 50°C, according to ref. 63.

More recently, Beaman (65) has published a simple method of calculating the transition temperatures of diacid- and diamine-based polyamides from the known values for neighboring polyamides.

3. *Dilatation Coefficients*

The linear and cubic dilatation coefficients of the polyamides increase with the length of the carbon chains, as is shown by the values given in Table VII.

Müller and Pflüger (29) show that, for a given polymer, the coefficient of linear dilatation decreases with the increasing crystallinity of the sample, and tends toward a limit which is the value corresponding to linear polyethylene, for an increasing length of the carbon chains.

TABLE VII. Dilatation Coefficients of the Polyamides (Averaged between 0 and 100°C) (66)

Nylons	Linear ($\times 10^{-4}$)	Cubic ($\times 10^{-4}$)
66	1.15	3.46
610	1.43	4.30
1010	1.70 (67)	4.58 (67)
6	1.35	4.04
11	1.50 (5)	
Linear polyethylene	1.60–1.80	

4. Others

The latent heat of fusion of the polyamides is of the order of 20–22 cal/g, their specific heat of the order of 0.55–0.58 cal/g/°C, and their thermal conductivity about $5–7 \times 10^{-4}$ cgs units.

B. Structural Properties

1. Hydrogen Bonds

It has already been stated in the section on the melting point that the macromolecules of polyamides are held together by hydrogen bonding at the level of the amide groups. Infrared spectrography (68,69) has shown that there are no free —NH— groups; from this it may be concluded that all the hydrogen bonds are present and have normal energy, which contradicts Champetier's hypothesis (Section IV-A-1) for polyamides with an even number of carbon atoms.

2. Crystalline Forms

The many x-ray diffraction studies that have been made up to now have suggested that the polyamides crystallize into three different forms, for which we give the most commonly accepted descriptions (70).

1. In the α form, which is the most common in nylons 66 and 6, the macromolecular chains are laid out parallel to form sheets piled one on top of the other.

In the case of polyamides from amino acids or lactams, the macromolecular chains in one sheet are parallel, but arranged alternately pointing first in one direction and then in the other (antiparallel packing). Thus the hydrogen bonds are evenly spaced and normal to the macromolecular chains. In addition, the sheets themselves are displaced with respect to each other alternately first in one direction and then in the other (monoclinic crystalline system).

When the polyamides are made from diacids and diamines, the notion of antiparallel packing disappears, and the displacement between sheets is constant and always in the same direction (triclinic crystalline system).

2. In the β form, coplanar hydrogen bonds are at an oblique angle to the axis of the molecules (triclinic crystalline system).

In the case of polyamides from amino acids, the chains are parallel and all pointing the same way (parallel packing), and there is no displacement between adjacent sheets. However, polyamides made from diamines and diacids have sheets which are displaced with respect to each other alternately one way and then the other.

3. In the γ form (71), the identity period is shorter than the repeat in the macromolecule. The macromolecular chains are not fully extended and the hydrogen bonds point in all directions (pseudohexagonal crystalline system).

Miyake (69) and Kinoshita (71) have shown that among amino acid or lactam-based polyamides: (*1*) Nylons 7, 9, 11 and their homologs are found in the α and β forms. (*2*) In the case of even polyamides, nylons 4 and 6 are found in the α and β forms, but nylon 6 can be converted to the γ form by certain treatments, such as immersion in an aqueous solution of iodine and potassium iodide (72). The stable form for nylons 8, 10, and higher is the γ form.

Vogelsong (73) confirms that the γ form is favored as the flexibility of the chains increases, that is, as the number of methylene groups increases.

As for diacid- and diamine-based nylons (66), for "even–even" polymers (66, 610, 88, etc.) both form α and form β are stable; for all other polymers the most stable form is the γ.

It thus seems that the lower melting point is linked to the presence of the γ crystalline form, supposing that all the hydrogen bonds are normal.

Another interpretation (29) has been put forward to explain the lower melting point of polyamides 6, 8, and their homologs. In the α form,

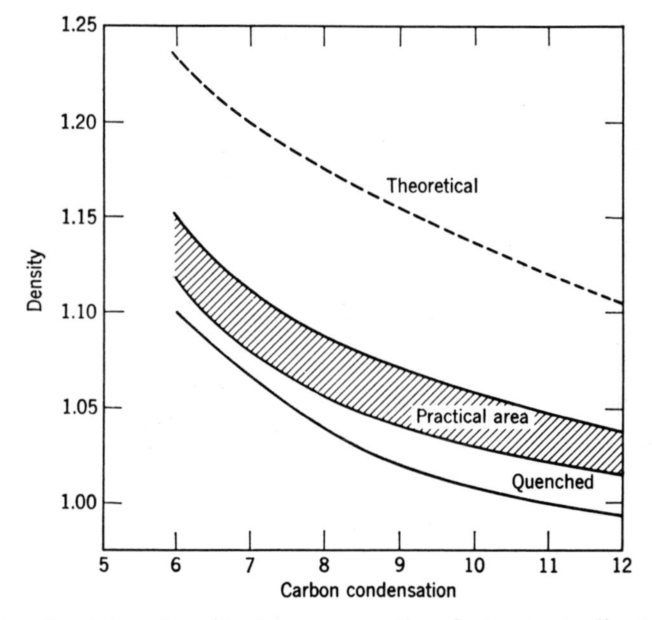

Fig. 4. Density of the polyamides from amino acids or lactams, according to Müller and Pflüger (29) (dry state, 20°C).

all the hydrogen bonds of, for instance, polyamide 6 are normal and parallel, but pointing alternately in one direction and then the other, which partially compensates the interchain cohesion forces.

3. Density

The theoretical density of the perfectly crystalline polyamide can be calculated from the dimensions of the crystalline lattice, which are well known for most of the polyamides.

The density as measured on a rapidly quenched sample gives the minimum value of the possible density. The common densities are situated in a region between these two values, as is shown by Figures 4 and 5 (29). It is already known that the degree of crystallinity can be calculated from the density of any given polyamide. It will be noticed that the densities of the homologs of nylons 6 and 66 diminish as the chain of the amino acid or the diacid lengthens. In the case of the amino acids, they tend to the density of linear polyethylene (about 0.95).

Champetier and Pied (64) have noticed that the density of polyamides 7 to 13 prepared by one of them (61) and slowly cooled (therefore quite highly crystalline) varies linearly with the number of amide groups for every 100 links in the macromolecule. They conclude that the compact-

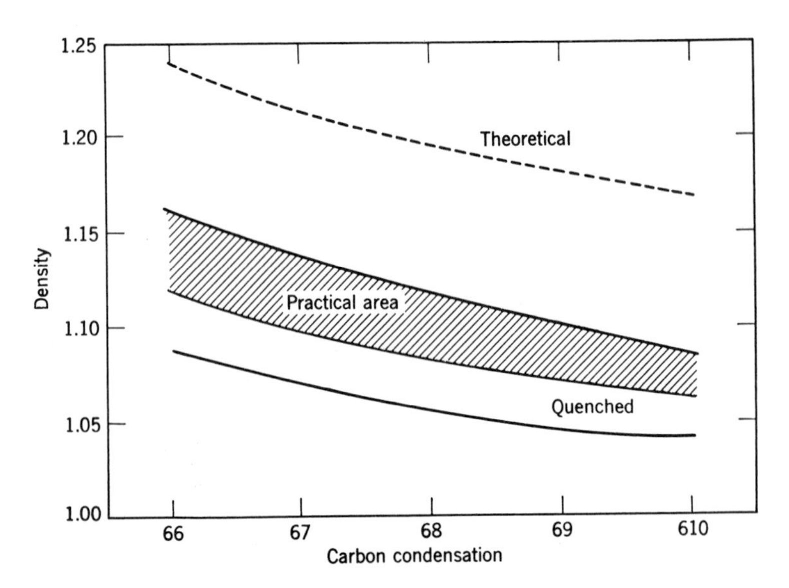

Fig. 5. Density of polyamides from hexamethylenediamine and diacids, according to Müller and Pflüger (29) (dry state, 20°C).

ness of polyamides is a function only of the frequency of the amide groups in tbe macromolecular chains.

C. Physical and Chemical Properties

1. Solubility

As might be expected, in polar solvents the solubility diminishes as the carbon chain lengthens, while in nonpolar solvents it increases (Tables VIII and IX).

TABLE VIII. Differences between the Solubilities of Homologous Higher Polyamides

Nylon	Minimum concentration (% by weight) of aqueous HCOOH necessary for solution (29)	Re-solution temperature (74)	
		In ethylene glycol	In propylene glycol
6	70%	135°C	129°C
7	—	—	—
8	85%	149°C	133°C
9	—	—	—
10	—	—	—
11	Insoluble	Insoluble	145°C
12	Insoluble	—	—

TABLE IX. Take-Up Solvent (% by Weight) at Saturation by the Higher Polyamides (29)[a]

Nylon	Methanol	Ethanol	Benzene	Toluene
6	19	17	1	1
8	17	17	4	3
9	12	12	7.5	6
11	10.5	10.5	7.5	6
12	8.5	9	8	7

[a] Measurements made on samples quickly cooled by quenching.

2. Moisture Absorption

As Table X shows, the moisture absorption at equilibrium decreases rapidly as the carbon condensation increases. It is low for all the higher nylons.

TABLE X. Moisture Absorption (% by Weight at 20°C) of Polyamides (28,29)[a]

Nylon	65% Rh	100% Rh
4	9.1	28
5	—	—
6	4.3 -4.7	9.5–11
7	2.6 -2.8	5.0
8	1.7 -1.8	3.9–4.2
9	1.45–1.5	2.5–3.3
10	1.25–1.4	1.9
11	1.2 -1.3	1.8–2.8
12	1.3	1.5–2.7
Linear polyethylene	0.01	0.01

[a] Measurements made on samples quickly cooled by quenching.

3. *Resistance to Chemical Agents*

The resistance of the polyamides to hydrolysis varies with the frequency of the amide group, which means that the higher nylons resist the action of acids and alkalis better than nylons 6 or 66 (75).

4. *Electrical Properties*

The electrical properties of the polyamides vary directly with the moisture content, as is shown by the graphs given by Müller and Pflüger (Figs. 6–8) (29). The resistivity, dielectric constant, and dielectric loss factor are nearly independent of the length of the carbon chain in the case of dry polymers, but for the wet polymers, these properties are greatly improved by lengthening the carbon chain, so that the moisture absorption decreases. Polyamides 11 and 12, for instance, have electrical properties which make them particularly suitable for insulation.

Müller and Pflüger also point out that the evolution of the dielectric constant and of the dielectric loss factor with frequency and temperature varies according to the nature of the polyamide (CONH/CH_2 ratio) and its crystallinity.

D. Mechanical Properties

The literature on most of the higher polyamides gives the values of breaking strength and extension at break for molded parts, which therefore relate to unoriented material (29). Müller and Pflüger show that flexion modulus and hardness decrease when the carbon chain lengthens.

On the other hand, it is very difficult to define perfectly comparable conditions of spinning, stretching, etc. for different polyamides in the form of yarns or of textile fibers, and it can only be said that for a given extension at break, polyamide yarns usually have comparable tenacities whatever the polyamide under consideration. Linear polyethylene fibers also have mechanical properties of the same order of magnitude.

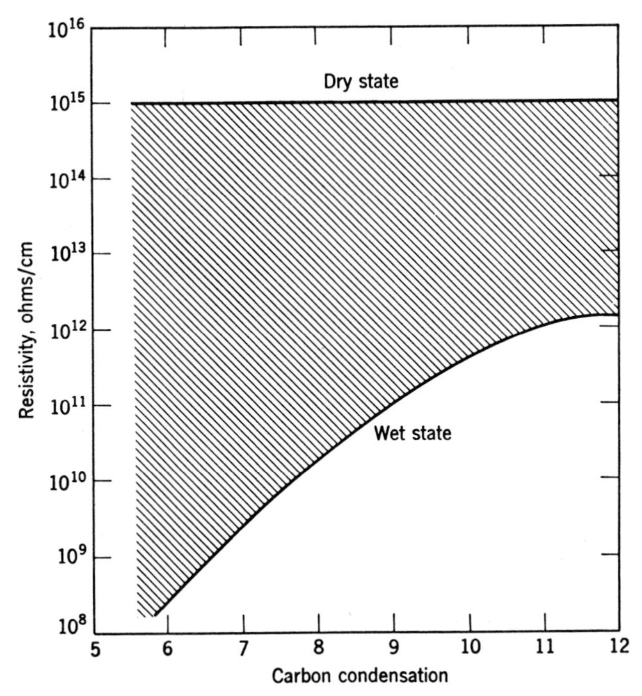

Fig. 6. Resistivity of polyamides from amino acids according to Müller and Pflüger (29), as a function of water content (20°C).

The same thing is true of the initial modulus which expresses the rigidity.

On the other hand, the loss of the mechanical properties of wet polyamide textiles is remarkable for the first terms of a series (28):

Nylon	Wet tenacity as % of dry tenacity
4	70–80
6	85–90
8	93–97
12	100
66	85–90

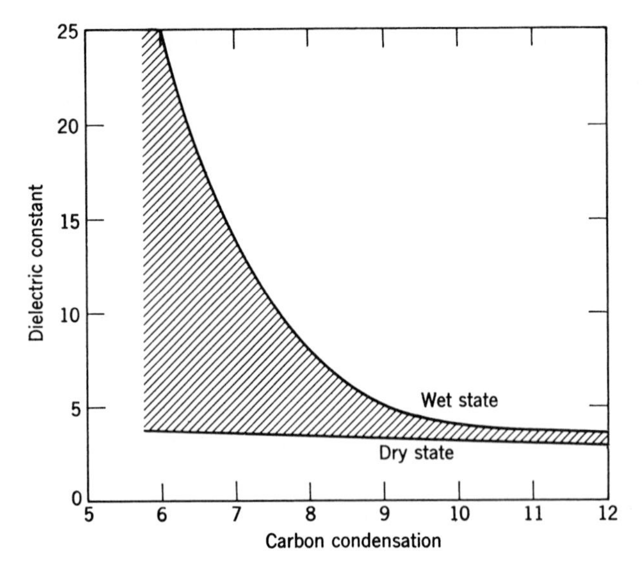

Fig. 7. Dielectric constant of polyamides from amino acids, as a function of water content (100 kc/sec, 20°C) (29).

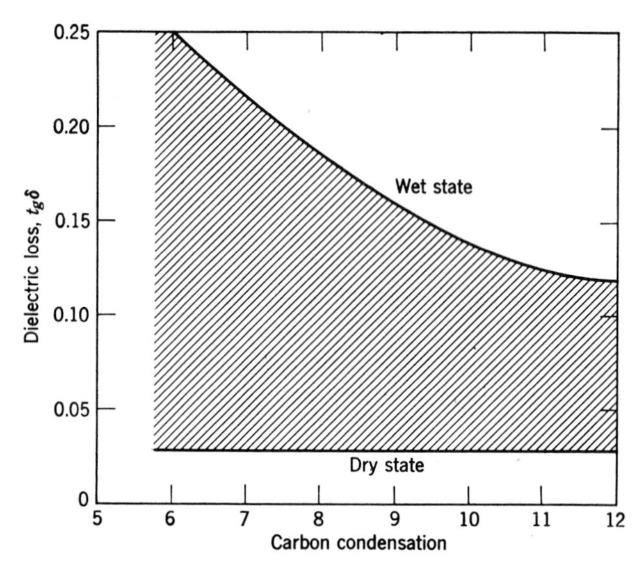

Fig. 8. Dielectric loss $t_g\delta$ of polyamides from amino acids, as a function of water content (100 kc/sec, 20°C) (29).

E. Textile Properties

The only higher nylon whose properties as a textile are well known is Rilsan (nylon 11), which offers the following differences from nylons 66 and 6 (75): Low density: 1.04 as against about 1.14; low moisture absorption, therefore small alteration in textile properties in the wet state (28); lower dyeability with acid dyestuffs (this property is clearly shown by the simultaneous dyeing in the same bath of 66 (or 6) and Rilsan yarns); and lower temperatures for the stabilization treatments, resulting from the lower melting points.

In practice, the principal advantage of Rilsan is generally accepted to be its pleasant handle, less dry, "richer," and more waxy than that of nylons 66 and 6 (as a result of its more paraffinlike character), which in wear gives a greater feeling of comfort, and makes Rilsan highly suitable for underwear and hosiery.

According to Dachs and Schwartz (28), nylon 8 is much closer to Rilsan than to nylon 6, especially by its handle; nylon 12 is very similar to Rilsan, apart from its melting point which is 10°C lower.

V. CONCLUSION

Our review of the higher nylons has shown that most of the possible routes to the intermediates have been considered and tried. We have also seen that the preparation of the polymers varies considerably, depending on the monomers used and also on the length of the carbon chains. Finally, it has been shown that the properties of all the higher nylons are well known, or at least foreseeable.

From this study we can conclude, with P. Schlack (76), the inventor of Perlon, that nylon 7 is the most interesting of the polyamides made from amino acids or lactams. Its lactam content at equilibrium is low enough to make demonomerization unnecessary, and its melting point is relatively high (233°C).

It is said that W. H. Carothers, the father of the polyamides, looked forward to the development of nylon 510, rather than nylon 66, in the series of polyamides made from diacids and diamines.

The study of C_{11} and C_{12} nylons has shown that these also have interesting properties which would justify a large production for textiles. It is therefore surprising to see that the nylons which are produced in the largest quantities are not those with the best properties. The reason is simple: the manufacturing cost is a determining factor. It is necessary to take into consideration the cost of the raw materials, the steps to the monomer, the ease of polymerization, and possibly the elimination of the monomer from the finished product.

The fact that C_6 polyamides have far and away the largest production shows the exceptional technical and economic attraction of the chemistry of benzene derivatives, and reflects the particular ease with which six-carbon-atom chains are produced.

Acknowledgment

The author wishes to thank P. Perrot and A. Raffenot (Rhodiaceta) for their assistance in the preparation of this work.

REFERENCES

1. E. P. Frieser, *Textilindustrie*, **60,** 932 (1958).
2. R. W. Moncrieff, *The Dyer*, **126,** 712 (1961).
3. M. Stratmann, *Textilindustrie*, **64,** 565 (1962).
4. R. Aelion, *Ind. Eng. Chem.*, **53,** 826 (1961).
5. M. Genas, *Angew. Chem.*), **74,** 535 (1962).
6. Organico (Wetroff et al.), French Pat. Appl. 1,120,247 (Jan. 21, 1955).
7. Organico (M. Genas and M. Kastner) French Pat. Appl. 951,932 (Aug. 7, 1947).
8. H. Jones, *Chimia*, **5,** 169 (1951).
9. American Cyanamid, French Pat. Appl. 865,006 (Feb. 8, 1939).
10. R. E. Kirk and D. F. Othmer, Eds., *Encyclopedia of Chemical Technology*, Vol. I, Interscience, New York, 1947, p. 154.
11. H. Beduneau, *Rev. Prod. Chim.*, **69,** 445 (1966).
12. K. Stickdorn, *Plaste Kautschuk*, **1,** 174 (1954).
13. R. Paul, *Bull. Soc. Chim.*, **53,** 1489 (1933).
14. O. W. Cass, *Ind. Eng. Chem.*, **40,** 216 (1948).
15. W. Reppe et al., *Ann.*, **582,** 87 (1953).
16. F. M. Mandrosova and A. A. Strepikheev, *Khim. Volokna*, **1** (No. 4), 6 (1959).
17. G. Champetier, G. Dupont, et al., *Compt. Rend.*, **245,** 542 (1957).
18. Anon., *Chem. Eng. News*, **42** (No. 48), 31 (1964).
19. W. C. Sheehan, *J. Polymer Sci. A-1*, **5,** 391 (1967).
20. R. M. Joyce, W. E. Hanford and J. Harmon, *J. Am. Chem. Soc.*, **70,** 2529 (1948).
21. A. N. Nesmejanov, A. A. Strepikheev, et al., *Chem. Tech. (Berlin)*, **9,** 139 (1957).
22. R. Ch. Freidlina and I. A. Karapetjan, *Telomerization and New Synthetic Materials*, Pergamon Press, Oxford, 1961.
23. A. Katchalsky and D. Vofsi, French Pat. Appl. 1,288,511 (May 8, 1960).
24. H. F. Mark and S. M. Atlas, *Chem. Eng.*, **68** (No. 25), 143 (1961).
25. L. H. Smith, Ed., *Synthetic Fiber Developments in Germany*, Textile Research Institute, New York, 1946.
26. W. Reppe et al., *Ann.*, **560,** 1 (1948).
27. K. Ziegler and H. Wilms, *Angew. Chem.*, **59,** 177 (1947).
28. K. Dachs and E. Schwartz, *Angew. Chem. Intern. Ed.*, **1,** 430 (1962).
29. A. Müller and R. Pflüger, *Kunststoffe*, **50,** 203 (1960).
30. BASF (K. Dachs et al.), French Pat. Appl. 1,287,073 (Apr. 12, 1960).
31. Anon., *Chem. Eng. News*, **40** (No. 18), 50 (1962).
32. Studiengesellschaft Kohle, Pat. 1,205,138, Appl. Germany (Feb. 23, 1956) and first addition no. 72.830, application Germany (Jan. 31, 1957).

33. G. Wilke, *Angew. Chem.*, **69**, 397 (1957).
34. G. Wilke, *J. Polymer Sci.*, **38**, 45 (1959).
35. W. K. Franke and K. A. Müller, *Chem. Ing. Tech.*, **36**, 960 (1964).
36. Studiengesellschaft Kohle (G. Wilke), French Pat. Appl. 1,200,860 (Apr. 26, 1957).
37. Studiengesellschaft Kohle (G. Wilke and P. W. Borner), French Pat. Appl. 1,225,184.
38. Anon., *Chem. Eng. News*, **44** (No. 27), 11 (1966).
39. H. Klare et al., *Synthetische Fasern aus.Polyamiden*, Akademie Verlag, Berlin, 1963.
40. C. F. Horn, B. T. Freure, et al., *J. Appl. Polymer Sci.*, **7**, 887 (1963).
41. Union Carbide (B. Philipp and P. S. Starcher), French Pat. Appl. 1,160,883, application USA Nov. 23, 1955.
42. Union Carbide (B. T. Freure and H. J. Decker), French Pat. Appl. 1,210, 137, application USA Sept. 6, 1957.
43. R. Criegee, *Ber.*, **77**, 22 (1944).
44. R. Criegee, *Ber.*, **77**, 722 (1944).
45. W. R. Sorenson and T. W. Campbell, *Preparative Methods of Polymer Chemistry* Interscience, New York, 1961.
46. L. Notarbartolo, *Ind. Plastiques Mod.*, **10**, 44 (1958).
47. Union Carbide (C. F. Horn), French Pat. Appl. 1,210,182, application USA Sept. 6, 1957.
48. Union Carbide (C. F. Horn), French Pat. Appl. 1,210,181, application USA Sept. 6, 1957.
49. A. V. Volokhina and G. I. Kudryavtsev, *Vysokomolekul. Soedin.*, **1**, 1724 (1959); cited in ref. 62.
50. S. Chrzczonowicz et al., *Makromol. Chem.*, **38**, 159 (1960).
51. S. Chrzczonowicz et al., *Bull. Acad. Polon. Sci.*, **10**, 173 (1962).
52. S. Chrzczonowicz et al., *Bull. Acad. Polon. Sci.*, **11**, 241 (1963).
53. G. M. van der Want and C. A. Kruissink, *J. Polymer Sci.*, **35**, 119 (1959).
54. S. M. Skuratov et al., *Dokl. Akad. Nauk. SSSR*, **95**, 591 (1954).
55. R. C. P. Cubbon, *Polymer*, **4**, 545 (1963).
56. N. Ogata, *J. Polymer Sci.*, *A*, **1**, 3151 (1963).
57. Rhone-Poulenc (P. Lafont), French Pat. Appl. 1,261,286, application France Apr. 4, 1960.
58. R. C. P. Cubbon, *Makromol. Chem.*, **80**, 44 (1964).
59. R. Hill and E. E. Walker, *J. Polymer Sci.*, **3**, 609 (1948).
60. G. Champetier and R. Aelion, *Bull. Soc. Chim. France*, **15**, 683 (1948).
61. J. P. Pied, *Ann. Chim.*, **5**, 469 (1960).
62. V. V. Korshak and T. M. Frunze, *Synthetic Heterochain Polyamides*, Israel Program for Scientific Translations, Jerusalem, 1964.
63. R. G. Beaman, *J. Polymer Sci.*, **9**, 470 (1952).
64. G. Champetier and J. P. Pied, *Makromol. Chem.*, **44**, 64 (1961).
65. R. G. Beaman, *J. Appl. Polymer Sci.*, **9**, 3949 (1965).
66. F. Ecochard, *J. Polymer Sci.*, **6**, 601 (1951).
67. Société Rhodiaceta, unpublished results.
68. D. S. Trifan and J. F. Terenzi, *J. Polymer Sci.*, **28**, 443 (1958).
69. A. Miyake, *J. Polymer Sci.*, **44**, 223 (1960).
70. D. R. Holmes, C. W. Bunn, and D. J. Smith, *J. Polymer Sci.*, **17**, 159 (1955).
71. Y. Kinoshita, *Makromol. Chem.*, **33**, 1 (1959).

72. M. Yoshida and M. Endo, *Kogyo Kagaku Zasshi*, **59**, 1074 (1956); cited in ref. 69.
73. D. C. Vogelsong, *J. Polymer Sci. A*, **1**, 1055 (1963).
74. F. R. Johnston and E. Wheadon, *J. Textile Inst. Trans.*, **55**, T 162 (1964).
75. R. Aelion, *Fibres*, **17**, 79 (1956).
76. P. Schlack, *Melliand Textilber.*, **43**, 543 (1962).

Author Index

Numbers in parentheses are reference numbers and show that an author's work is referred to although his name is not mentioned in the text. Numbers in *italics* indicate the pages on which the full references appear.

C

N

Subject Index

B

C

D

E

V

W